and the pages on which they first appear

$\cup$	union	**99**
$\cap$	intersection	**100**
(a,b) or (a,b,c)	row vector	**126**
$\begin{pmatrix} a_1 & b_1 \\ a_2 & b_2 \end{pmatrix}$	matrix	**126**
$\begin{pmatrix} a_1 & b_1 & c_1 \\ a_2 & b_2 & c_2 \end{pmatrix}$	matrix	**126**
$\overrightarrow{PQ}$	vector	**127**
$\begin{pmatrix} a \\ b \end{pmatrix}$ or $\begin{pmatrix} a \\ b \\ c \end{pmatrix}$	column vector	**127**
$\mathbf{i, j, k}$	unit vectors along the axes	**129**
$(a_1,b_1,c_1) \cdot (a_2,b_2,c_2)$	inner (scalar) product	**129**
$\mathbf{F}$	vector	**130**
$\det A = \begin{vmatrix} a_1 & b_1 \\ a_2 & b_2 \end{vmatrix}$	determinant of $\begin{pmatrix} a_1 & b_1 \\ a_2 & b_2 \end{pmatrix}$	**140**
$(a_1,b_1,c_1) \wedge (a_2,b_2,c_2)$	outer (vector) product	**147**
f	function	**169**
$f(x)$	value of a function at x	**169**
$g \circ f$	composite of g and f	**174**
$P(x)$	polynomial	**193**
$P(x)/Q(x)$	rational function	**194**
$e^x = \exp x$	exponential function	**218**
$\log x$	logarithmic function	**219**
(r,θ)	polar coordinates	**238**
$\theta^{(r)}$	radian measure of an angle	**267**
$\mathrm{Sin}\, x$	restricted sine function	**290**
$\mathrm{arc\, Sin}\, x = \mathrm{Sin}^{-1} x$	inverse sine function	**290**
$\lim\limits_{x \to a} f(x)$	limit of the value of the function f as x approaches a	**347**
$\lim\limits_{x \to \infty} f(x)$	limit of the value of the function f as x increases without bound	**354**
Σ	summation	**363**
$A_a^b = \lim\limits_{n \to \infty} \sum\limits_{i=1}^{n} f(x_i)\, \Delta x$	area under $y = f(x)$ from $x = a$ to $x = b$	**363**
$\int_a^b f(x)\, dx$	definite integral	**364**
Δx	change in x	**381**
Δf	change in f	**381**
$D_x f = f'(x)$	derivative of f	**383**
dy/dx	derivative	**383**
$\sinh \theta$	hyperbolic sine of θ	**409**

Fundamentals of Freshman Mathematics

Fundamentals of
Freshman Mathematics

C. B. Allendoerfer

PROFESSOR AND EXECUTIVE OFFICER
DEPARTMENT OF MATHEMATICS
UNIVERSITY OF WASHINGTON

C. O. Oakley

PROFESSOR AND DEPARTMENT HEAD
DEPARTMENT OF MATHEMATICS
HAVERFORD COLLEGE

McGRAW-HILL BOOK COMPANY, INC.

New York   Toronto   London   **1959**

FUNDAMENTALS OF FRESHMAN MATHEMATICS

VII
01383

Preface

It is now four years since the publication of the authors' "Principles of Mathematics" (McGraw-Hill Book Company, Inc., 1955), in whose preface we said: "This book has been written with the conviction that large parts of the standard undergraduate curriculum in mathematics are obsolete, and that it is high time that our courses take due advantage of the remarkable advances that have been made in mathematics during the past century . . . . We believe that some of the content and much of the spirit of modern mathematics can be incorporated in courses given to our beginning students. This book is designed to do just that." These remarks were in keeping with the spirit of the times, for a major modernization of mathematics teaching in high schools and colleges is now in prospect. Our present book is intended to be a further contribution to this movement. Although there is some overlap with "Principles of Mathematics," this is essentially a new book and is written for a different group of students; the spirit and general objectives, however, are the same.

In writing this book we have been greatly influenced by the publications of two important bodies of mathematicians: the Committee on the Undergraduate Mathematical Program of the Mathematical Association of America, and the Commission on Mathematics of the College Entrance Examination Board. These committees have wisely not produced any "official" syllabus but have made many valuable recommendations concerning the directions which the reform of mathematical instruction should take. We have examined all of these recommendations and adopted many of them. The book, however, represents our own ideas for a modern course of instruction and is not written to follow an outline handed down by any official body.

The purpose of this book is to bridge the gap between Intermediate Algebra and Analytic Geometry and Calculus. Since the majority of mathematics students at this level are potential scientists or engineers, we have taken pains to care for their special needs; but the book is not aimed exclusively at this group of students. It is flexibly organized so that it can be used for a variety of courses, examples of which are as follows:

(1) Twelfth-grade mathematics in high school. As such it fully meets the requirements of the College Entrance Examination Board in Elementary Functions.

(2) College Algebra. Chapters 1 to 11 form a modern treatment of material usually covered in courses bearing this title.

(3) College Algebra and Trigonometry. Chapters 1 to 13 are suitable for a combined course in these two subjects.

(4) Unified Freshman Course. The whole book provides a year course in mathematics for students who enter college with some knowledge of Intermediate Algebra and who wish to proceed to Calculus in their sophomore year.

The main differences between this book and "Principles of Mathematics" are the following:

(1) Formal logic has been omitted and is replaced by an informal discussion of the nature of abstract reasoning and mathematical proof.

(2) The theory of groups is omitted, and fields are treated informally.

(3) A review of Intermediate Algebra is included for use as may be needed. This is based upon the formal properties of real numbers (actually the axioms of a field) and differs in many details from the usual presentation.

(4) The treatment of sets is enlarged and applied as widely as possible to standard topics in the curriculum. Boolean algebra and switching circuits are omitted.

(5) Simultaneous linear equations are treated in detail.

(6) The algebra of vectors and matrices is included and applied to the solution of simultaneous linear equations. Determinants are introduced in connection with matrices.

(7) The treatment of inequalities is expanded.

(8) Aids to the graphing of relations and functions are included.

(9) Trigonometry is expanded into two chapters. The first deals with computational trigonometry and the second with analytic trigonometry.

(10) The treatment of limits and calculus is simplified and made more intuitive.

(11) Hyperbolic functions are included.

(12) Probability and statistics are omitted.

(13) In all chapters problem lists have been expanded. There are 2,725 problems in the book. The more difficult problems have been marked with asterisks (*) and can be omitted if desired. A few problems are marked "BT," which means "Booby Trap," "Use your head," "Be careful," or "Don't make a fool of yourself." Answers are given for odd-numbered problems. The even-numbered problems essentially duplicate the odd-numbered ones and can be used for review or for alternate assignments. Answers to even-numbered problems are published separately.

We are deeply indebted to the many teachers who have written to us in connection with "Principles of Mathematics" and who have told us of their experience with it. We are also grateful to many others at home and abroad with whom we have discussed these matters in private conversations. To all these people we extend our thanks and express the hope that we have dealt adequately with the suggestions that have been made.

As in the past, we hope that this book is relatively free of errors, but each author blames the other for any that may be discovered.

CARL B. ALLENDOERFER
CLETUS O. OAKLEY

Contents

x   *Contents*

CHAPTER ONE

Mathematics and Science

1.1. *Introduction*

When you became interested in the study of science or engineering, you were undoubtedly told that you would have to learn a good deal of mathematics in order to be successful in your career. The basic ideas and relationships in the physical sciences have been expressed in mathematical terms for a very long time, and in recent years the use of mathematics in the biological and social sciences has increased tremendously. As a potential scientist you are studying this book to learn some of the mathematics that you will need in your own field, but before you can appreciate the mathematics to come you need to know something of the nature of mathematics and its relationship to science. Let us, then, consider various ways in which mathematics is used by practicing scientists.

(*a*) *Substitution in Formulas.* You are surely acquainted with such formulas as

$A = \pi r^2$ for the area A of a circle of radius r, or

$s = 16t^2$ for the distance s in feet through which a body falls from rest in a time t measured in seconds.

For a specific value of r (say 2 in.) you now calculate A, and for a given time interval (say 3 sec) you calculate s. Only the simplest processes of algebra and arithmetic are needed in formulas like these,

1

but not all the formulas of science are so elementary. You have probably met formulas which are more complicated algebraic expressions, but even these do not cover all the needs of science. At the very beginning you will meet other types of functions such as the trigonometric, logarithmic, and exponential functions; and before you have gone very far you must be able to handle the symbolism of the calculus. In all these cases, there is a common idea: you are given an expression which relates one letter to a number of others. For specific values of these last letters you are asked to determine the value of the first letter by following a prescribed set of rules. To do so, you must learn the rules and develop speed and accuracy in your calculations. All of this, however, is basically mechanical and requires no real thought. Indeed, all these calculations can be performed with great ease by modern high-speed calculating machines. Since these machines are expensive and are not particularly efficient when used on simple problems, you must still learn to calculate. When you do so, however, you must remember that you are acting as a machine and not as a human being. The real reasons why a scientist must know mathematics lie, therefore, in other directions.

(*b*) *Definitions of Scientific Terms.* When you study any new subject, your first task is to learn the meanings of the special, technical terms which are introduced. This is especially important in science where words are used with very precise meanings. Since much of science is based on measurement and is therefore quantitative in character, these technical definitions are best expressed in terms of mathematics. Although you doubtless have an intuitive idea of the meaning of "the area of a circle," we cannot define this precisely without the use of the calculus. In the same way such familiar notions as "velocity" and "acceleration" remain vague until they are expressed in mathematical terms. Indeed, these basic concepts of physics cannot be defined until we have reached the final chapters of this book. After the terms of science are defined, statements about them must be made; and these generally appear as mathematical equations. Since you will, therefore, have to know mathematics in order to understand what your science teachers are saying, mathematics may well be thought of as the "language of science." If you do not understand the language, you cannot learn science.

(*c*) *Analysis of Scientific Situations.* You will often be confronted by a set of scientific statements and asked to draw a conclusion from them. In most such situations, you will need to rely upon your mathematics, and frequently you will have to do some real thinking. In algebra you have already met problems of this type and have called them "word problems" or "story problems." You will remember that they are often more difficult than routine manipulations, but success in solving these kinds of problems is of the utmost importance to a scientist. Let us consider a very familiar example of such a problem:

Illustration 1.   Mary is now four years older than John, and in 3 years her age will be twice his age. What are their ages now?
   Solution:

> Let x = John's age now $x + 3$ = John's age in 3 years
> $x + 4$ = Mary's age now $x + 7$ = Mary's age in 3 years
> Then $x + 7 = 2(x + 3)$; and finally $x = 1$.
> Therefore John is now one, and Mary is five.

If we had a large number of such problems to solve, we would have generalized the above example to read as follows:

Illustration 2.   Mary is now a years older than John, and in b years her age will be c times his age. What are their ages now?
   Solution:

> Let x = John's age now $x + b$ = John's age in b years
> $x + a$ = Mary's age now $x + a + b$ = Mary's age in b years
> Then $x + a + b = c(x + b)$; or, solving,

$$x = \frac{a + b - bc}{c - 1}$$

This is now a formula into which we can substitute to solve all age problems of this type, and you may wonder why you were asked to learn how to solve age problems when you might just as well have substituted in the formula. The answer is that you must learn how to analyze problems and not merely to substitute in formulas. Age problems like those above are actually only one type of age problems, and the kinds of scientific problems that arise are tremendous in number and diversity. You must develop your mental powers to be able to deal with these.

You, as a student, may, however, take a different view, and many engineers are especially prone to do so. You may say: "Aren't the really important problems solved in general terms, so that all that I must do is to substitute in a formula? My handbook is full of formulas, and I see no reason why I should learn how to obtain them." The answer to this depends really upon what kind of an engineer you wish to be, and is in three parts:

(1) If you are doing a particular job, such as the stress analysis of a bridge, by all means use the handbook formulas and get the

answers as rapidly as possible.   If you are a routine engineer (essentially a "slave") this will be the limit of your capabilities, and when you are in difficulty you will have to call for help.

(2) If, however, you are a better engineer, you will know the derivations of the formulas and hence will understand the assumptions that were made at the outset.   You will be able to avoid using the formulas in situations for which they were not designed, and your suspension bridges will not collapse in a moderate wind.

(3) If, finally, you are a creative engineer, who is in the forefront of progress toward new designs, you will not only be able to understand the derivations of existing formulas but you will also be able to derive new ones to fit new situations.

This book is, in spirit, dedicated to the education of creative scientists and engineers and is intended to provide them with the mathematics which they will need.   We shall insist that you learn how to calculate, but we shall also emphasize your understanding of the basic ideas and theoretical developments of the subject.

1.2. *Abstract Nature of Mathematics*

Although we have seen that mathematics is an essential tool for science, it is an entirely different kind of subject.   Science is closely tied to the physical world, but mathematics is completely abstract. Many people shudder at the thought of anything abstract and consequently may have a mental block against mathematics.   Actually, there is nothing so terrifying about the abstractness of mathematics once its true nature is understood.   In order to assist this understanding, let us now describe the essentials of a mathematical structure or theory.

As with any new subject, we begin mathematics by discussing the new, technical terms which we must introduce.   Our intuition tells us that each of these should have a definition, but sooner or later we will find that our definitions are going in circles.   To take a simple example, we may define:

> *Point:* the common part of two intersecting *lines.*
> *Line:*   the figure traced by a *point* which moves along the shortest path between two *points.*

Here we have defined *point* in terms of *line* and *line* in terms of *point,* and so we have shed no real light on the nature of either *point* or *line.*

The situation is somewhat similar to that which we would encounter if we tried to learn a foreign language, say French, by using only an ordinary French dictionary—not a French-English dictionary. We look up a particular French word and find it described in more French words and we find ourselves no further ahead. Without a knowledge of a certain amount of French, a French dictionary is useless. In mathematics we have a similar difficulty.

The only way to avoid circular definitions in mathematics, or any other subject, is to take a small number of words as *undefined*. All other mathematical words will be defined in terms of these with the understanding that our definitions may also contain common English words ("is," "and," "the," etc.) which have no special mathematical meanings. It is not easy to decide which words should be left undefined and which should be defined in terms of the undefined words. Many choices can be made, and the final decision is largely based upon consideration of simplicity and elegance.

Illustration 1. Let us suppose that *point, line*, and *between* are undefined. Then we may define:

> *Line segment:* that portion of a line contained between two given points on a line.

The words in this definition other than *point, line*, and *between* are without special meanings and thus may be used freely.

Our use of undefined words is the first phase of our abstraction of mathematics from physical reality. The penciled line on our paper and the chalk line on our blackboard are physical realities, but *line*, the undefined mathematical concept, is something quite apart from them. In geometry we make statements about a *line* (which we shall call *axioms*) which correspond to observed properties of our physical lines, but if you insist on asking: "What is a *line?*" we must give you the somewhat disturbing answer: "We don't know; it isn't defined."

Once we have built up our vocabulary from undefined words and other words defined in terms of them, we are ready to make statements about these new terms. These statements will be ordinary declarative sentences which are so precisely stated that they are either true or false. We will exclude sentences which are ambiguous or which can be called true or false only after qualifications are imposed on them.

The following are acceptable statements:

$$\text{All triangles are isosceles}$$
$$\text{If } x = 1, \text{ then } x^2 + 1 = 2$$

Our task, now, is to decide which of our statements are true and which are false. In order to give meaning to this task, we must first establish a frame of reference on which our later reasoning will be based. At the very beginning we must choose a few statements which we will call "true" by assumption; such statements are called "axioms." These axioms are statements about the technical words in our vocabulary and are completely abstract in character. They are not statements about the properties of the physical world. You must have heard that an "axiom is a self-evident truth," but axioms can be any statements at all, evident or not. Since mathematical theories can begin with any set of axioms at all, they are infinite in their variety; some of them are interesting and useful, others merely interesting, and still others only curiosities of little apparent value. The choice of a set of axioms which leads to an interesting and useful theory requires great skill and judgment, but for the most part such sets of axioms are obtained as models of the real world. We look about us, and from what we see we construct an abstract model in which our undefined words correspond to the most important objects that we have identified, and in which our axioms correspond to the basic properties of these objects. The mathematics which you will use as a scientist is entirely based on axioms which were derived in this fashion.

From our set of axioms (which we have assumed to be true) we now proceed to establish the truth or falsehood of other statements which arise. We must agree upon some rules of procedure, which we call the "Laws of Logic," and by means of these rules we seek to determine whether a given statement is true or false. We shall not dwell upon these Laws of Logic here, but if you are interested you can read about them in the References given at the end of the chapter. Except for a few tricky places which we will discuss below, you can rely upon your own good sense and previous experience in logical thinking. Whenever doubts arise, however, you must refer back to the full treatment of these logical principles.

When we have shown that the truth of a given statement follows logically from the assumed truth of our axioms, we call this statement a "theorem" and say that "we have proved it." The truth of a theorem, therefore, is relative to a given set of axioms; absolute truth has no meaning when applied to mathematical statements. The main business of a mathematician is the invention of new theorems and the construction of proofs for them. The discovery of a new theorem depends upon deep intuition and intelligent guessing, and the process of making such a discovery is very much like that of creative effort in any field. After our intuition has led us to believe that a certain statement is true, we must still prove it; and this is where our use of logical deduction comes in.

Our abstract mathematical system, then, consists of four parts:

(1) Undefined words.

(2) Defined words.

(3) Axioms; i.e., statements which are assumed to be true.

(4) Theorems; i.e., statements which are proved to be true.

Since we shall need to have a good understanding of the nature of proof, we will devote the rest of this chapter to a discussion of various problems which you will meet in mathematical proofs.

1.3. *Negations*

Whenever we make a statement about mathematics (or anything else for that matter), we mean to assert that our statement is *true*. Thus when we say:

> The square of any even number is even

we mean:

> It is *true* that the square of any even number is even

As you will see shortly, there are times in mathematics when we wish to assert that a given statement is *false*. Thus we may say:

> It is *false* that the square of 3 is even

Rather than using the awkward "It is false that . . . " every time we meet such a situation, we prefer to express the same idea in a direct way, as:

> The square of 3 is not even

This statement is called the *negation* of the statement:

> The square of 3 is even

Let us put this a little more formally. We use p to represent a given statement and *not-p* to represent its negation.

Definition: The *negation not-p* of a given statement p is a statement such that:

(*a*) If p is true, then *not-p* is false.

(*b*) If p is false, then *not-p* is true.

In many cases you can form negations easily by inserting a "not" in a convenient place, but in other cases you must be more subtle. There are general rules for taking negations which you can find in the References listed at the end of this chapter, but for our present purposes we shall rely on some examples and your own good sense.

Illustrations

   1. p: The number 3 is a perfect square.

     not-p: The number 3 is not a perfect square.

   2. p: The sum of the interior angles of a given triangle is 180°.

     not-p: The sum of the interior angles of a given triangle is not 180°.

   3. p: For all x, $x^2 - 9 = (x + 3)(x - 3)$.

     not-p: For some x, $x^2 - 9 \neq (x + 3)(x - 3)$.

   4. p: For some real x, $x^2 - 5x + 6 = 0$ (that is, $x^2 - 5x + 6 = 0$ has a real solution).

     not-p: For all real x, $x^2 - 5x + 6 \neq 0$ (that is, $x^2 - 5x + 6 = 0$ has no real solution).

Illustrations 3 and 4 are rather deceptive, and you should think them through carefully to be sure that you understand why these are the correct negations. Negations of this type are particularly important in mathematics.

PROBLEMS 1.3

   1. Choose an ordinary, nontechnical word, and build a circular chain of definitions from this word back to itself. Use a standard dictionary for your definitions. Do not put simple connections such as "the," "and," "in," "is," etc., in your chain.

   2. In any standard dictionary look up the definitions of a mathematical "point" and "line." Write these down, and explain why they are unsatisfactory for use in a logical development of geometry.

In Probs. 3 to 6 assume that *polygon*, *side* of a polygon, *angle* of a polygon, *length* of side, *equal*, and *parallel* have been previously defined. Then define:

   3. Isosceles triangle.   **4.** Parallelogram.

   5. Rectangle.   **6.** Trapezoid.

In Probs. 7 to 12, incorrect definitions of certain mathematical terms are given. Write the correct definitions.

   7. *Intersect* (for lines): Two lines are said to *intersect* if and only if they have one or more points in common.

   8. *Parallel* (for line segments): Two line segments are said to be *parallel* if and only if they do not intersect.

   9. *Equal* (for fractions): Two fractions a/b and c/d are equal if and only if $a = c$ and $b = d$.

  10. *Square root* (of a perfect square): If a is a real number, then $\sqrt{a^2} = a$.

  11. *Congruent* (for triangles): Two triangles are congruent if and only if the angles of one are equal to the corresponding angles of the other.

  12. *Concentric* (for circles): Two circles are concentric if and only if their radii are equal.

In Probs. 13 to 20 certain mathematical statements are made which omit a key phrase which you are supposed to supply. Complete each of these statements to an unambiguously clear true statement by prefixing one of the following phrases: "for all x," "for some x," "for no x."

  13. $(x - 1)(x + 1) = x^2 - 1$.   **14.** $2x + 7x = 9x$.

  15. $2x + 4 = 3x - 2$.   **16.** $4x + 2x = 6x - 3$.

17. $(x + 3)(x - 4) = x^2 - x - 12.$ **18.** $2^x = 8.$

19. $3x - x = 2x + 1.$ **20.** $(3x - 1)(x + 2) = 3x^2 + 5x - 2.$

In Probs. 21 to 30, form the negations of the given statements.

21. The base angles of a given triangle are equal.

22. Angle A is a right angle.

23. 241 is an even number.

24. The sum of the interior angles of a given square is 270°.

25. For all x, $3x + 7x = 10x.$ **26.** For all x, $x^2 + 2x + 1 = (x + 1)^2.$

27. For some x, $2x + 3 = 7.$ **28.** For some x, $x^2 - 5x + 6 = 0.$

29. For every pair of similar triangles, x_1 and x_2, x_1 is congruent to x_2.

30. For all triangles x, the sum of the interior angles of x is equal to 180°.

In Probs. 31 to 36 supply the phrase necessary to complete the statement to a true statement (as in Probs. 13 to 20), and then write the negation of your completed statement.

31. $\dfrac{x}{2} + \dfrac{x}{3} = \dfrac{x}{5}.$ **32.** $\dfrac{3x}{2} + \dfrac{3x}{5} = \dfrac{3x}{7}.$

33. $(4x + 9)(x - 1) = 5x + 4x^2 - 9.$ **34.** $(3x + 1)(3x - 1) = 9x^2 + 6x + 1.$

35. $\dfrac{16x^2 - 9}{4x - 3} = 4x + 3.$ **36.** $\dfrac{x^2 - 10x + 25}{x - 5} = x - 5.$

1.4. *Implications*

At nearly every turn in your study of mathematics, you will meet statements of the form: "If . . . , then . . . ." These are called implications; a few typical examples are:

> If a triangle is equilateral, then it is equiangular
> If $a = b$, then $a + c = b + c$
> If x is an odd integer, then $2x$ is an odd integer

For convenience in talking about implications let us write them in the standard form:

> If p, then q

where p stands for the statement that follows *if* and q for the statement that follows *then*.

Let us start from a given implication: "If p, then q"; and now suppose that we interchange the two statements, p and q. We obtain a new implication: "If q, then p," which is closely related to the given implication but which is surely different from it.

Definition: The implication: "If q, then p" is the *converse* of the implication: "If p, then q."

Slovenly thinkers and writers are likely to confuse an implication with its converse and to substitute one for the other. *To do so is a gross error*, for these two implications are quite distinct and the truth of one cannot be inferred from that of the other. Indeed, the converse of a true implication may be true or false; examples of each kind are given below.

Illustrations

    1. *Implication:* If two triangles are congruent, then they are similar.   (True)
        Converse: If two triangles are similar, then they are congruent.   (False)
    2. *Implication:* If $x = 3$, then $x + 5 = 8$.   (True)
        Converse: If $x + 5 = 8$, then $x = 3$.   (True)

Consequently, you must make very certain that you do not make errors of this type. Remember:

The truth of an implication does not imply the truth of its converse.

There are occasions, of course, where "If p, then q" and "If q, then p" are both true. In these circumstances we say that p and q are *equivalent.*

The converse of an implication is often confused with its contrapositive, which is another implication defined in the following fashion: As before, we start from a given implication, "If p, then q"; and now we do two things: (1) we take the negation of each of the statements p and q and thus obtain new statements *not-p* and *not-q*; (2) then we *interchange* the two statements "*not-p* and *not-q*." We thus obtain a new implication "If *not-q*, then *not-p*" which is called the contrapositive of the given implication.

Definition: The implication: "If *not-q*, then *not-p*" is the *contrapositive* of the implication: "If p, then q."

Illustration 3

    Implication: If $x = 3$, then $x^2 = 9$.
    Contrapositive: If $x^2 \neq 9$, then $x \neq 3$.

The big difference between the converse and the contrapositive of an implication is a result of the following law of logic:

Law of Logic.   An implication and its contrapositive are either both true or both false.

As we shall see below, contrapositives can be very helpful to us. When we find it difficult to prove that an implication is true, we can form its contrapositive. If we can prove this to be true, we have automatically established the truth of the given implication. *This remark, however, does not apply to the converse.* Hence you must distinguish most carefully between the notions of converse and contrapositive.

1.5. *Necessary and Sufficient Conditions*

Mathematicians frequently express implications in language different from that used above, and consequently you must learn to recognize implications even when they are disguised in a fashion which may seem quite confusing at first.

Consider the implication "If a polygon is a square, then it is a rectangle." This is in the standard form "If p, then q." A common alternative expression for this is: "A *sufficient* condition that a polygon be a rectangle is that it be a square," or "The fact that a polygon is a square is a *sufficient* condition that it be a rectangle." In this form note that the "If . . . then" of the original phraseology is replaced by "The fact that . . . is a sufficient condition that." Thus we see that:

"p is a sufficient condition for q" is equivalent to "If p, then q"

On the other hand, a polygon cannot be a square unless it is a rectangle. Or "In order that a polygon be a square, it is *necessary* that it be a rectangle." The usual form of this statement is "The fact that a polygon is a rectangle is a *necessary* condition that it be a square." Thus we see that:

"q is a necessary condition for p" is equivalent to "If p, then q"

Recapitulation. *The following three statements all carry the same meaning:*

> *If p, then q*
> *p is a sufficient condition for q*
> *q is a necessary condition for p*

So that you may avoid a common misunderstanding, examine the two statements:

"p is a sufficient condition for q" and "p is a necessary condition for q."

By examining the Recapitulation above you can verify that the first of these is equivalent to "If p, then q," whereas the second is equivalent to the converse "If q, then p." Hence the statement "p is a necessary condition for q" is the converse of the statement "p is a sufficient condition for q." Similarly, "p is a sufficient condition for q" is the converse of "p is a necessary condition for q." From these facts, and from our earlier observation that an implication and its converse are not in general equivalent, we can draw several conclusions:

(i) In order to obtain the converse of an implication written in "necessary and sufficient" language, replace "necessary" by "sufficient" or "sufficient" by "necessary."

(ii) A condition may be necessary and not sufficient, or it may be sufficient and not necessary.

When the propositions p and q are equivalent, both "If p, then q" and "If q, then p" are true. In this case we say that

p is a necessary and sufficient condition for q

or equally well

q is a necessary and sufficient condition for p

There is another way of expressing these same ideas. Consider the implication "If a polygon is a square, then it is a rectangle." This may also be stated: "Only if a polygon is a rectangle, is it a square." Thus we have two ways of stating the implication "If p, then q" which include the word "if":

(1) If p, then q (2) Only if q, then p

By interchanging p and q in statements (1) and (2) above we see that the converse of the above implication can be written in two ways:

(1) If q, then p (2) Only if p, then q

Note, then, that the substitution of "only if" for "if" in an implication changes the implication into its converse.

We summarize this discussion with a table, in which entries on the same horizontal line are equivalent statements. The first set of lines represents a given implication; the second set represents its converse; and the third set represents an equivalence.

if p, then q	p is sufficient for q
only if q, then p	q is necessary for p
only if p, then q	p is necessary for q
if q, then p	q is sufficient for p
q if and only if p	p is necessary and sufficient for q
p if and only if q	q is necessary and sufficient for p

PROBLEMS 1.5

In Probs. 1 to 6 state the converse and the contrapositive of the given implication.

1. If a is divisible by 3, then $2a$ is divisible by 6.
2. If the sides of a triangle are all equal, then the triangle is equiangular.
3. If a quadrilateral is a parallelogram, then its diagonals bisect each other.
4. If x does not equal zero, then x^2 is greater than zero.
5. If a is greater than b, then $a + c$ is greater than $b + c$.
6. If r is a solution of $ax = b$, then $1/r$ is a solution of $bx = a$. (Assume $a \neq 0$ and $b \neq 0$.)
7. Write the contrapositive of the converse of "If p, then q."
8. Write the converse of the contrapositive of "If p, then q."
9. Write a true implication whose converse is true.
10. Write a true implication whose converse is false.

In Probs. 11 to 16 write the given implication, using the "sufficient-condition" language.

11. If the base angles of a triangle are equal, the triangle is isosceles.
12. If two triangles are congruent, their corresponding altitudes are equal.
13. If two lines are perpendicular to the same line, they are parallel.
14. If two spherical triangles have their corresponding angles equal, they are congruent.
15. If $3x + 2 = x + 4$, then $x = 1$.
16. If $x^2 = 0$, then $x = 0$.

In Probs. 17 to 22, write the given implication, using the "necessary condition" language.

17. If a triangle is inscribed in a semicircle, then it is a right triangle.
18. If $x = 3$, then $x^2 = 9$.
19. If a body is in static equilibrium, the vector sum of all forces acting on it is zero.
20. If a body is in static equilibrium, the vector sum of the moments of all forces acting on it is zero.
21. If two forces are in equilibrium, they are equal, opposite, and collinear.
22. If three nonparallel forces are in equilibrium, their lines of action are concurrent.

In Probs. 23 to 28, write the given implication, using the phrase "only if."

23. The implication of Prob. 17.　　24. The implication of Prob. 18.
25. The implication of Prob. 19.　　26. The implication of Prob. 20.
27. The implication of Prob. 21.　　28. The implication of Prob. 22.

In Probs. 29 to 34, write the converse of the given implication, using "necessary" and then "sufficient" language. Give two answers to each problem.

29. The implication of Prob. 11.　　30. The implication of Prob. 12.
31. The implication of Prob. 13.　　32. The implication of Prob. 14.
33. The implication of Prob. 15.　　34. The implication of Prob. 16.

In Probs. 35 to 40, write the converse of the given implication, using the phrase "only if."

35. The implication of Prob. 17.　　36. The implication of Prob. 18.
37. The implication of Prob. 19.　　38. The implication of Prob. 20.
39. The implication of Prob. 21.　　40. The implication of Prob. 22.

In Probs. 41 to 44, write the given equivalence in "necessary and sufficient" language.

41. Two lines are parallel if and only if they are equidistant.
42. An integer is even if and only if it is divisible by 2.
43. Three concurrent forces are in equilibrium if and only if their vector sum is zero.
44. A lever is balanced if and only if the algebraic sum of all moments about its fulcrum is zero.
45. A man promised his girl: "I will marry you only if I get a job." He got the job and refused to marry her. She sued for breach of promise. Can she logically win her suit? Why?

1.6. *Direct Proof*

Most of the proofs you will encounter follow a familiar pattern which is called "direct proof." The simplest type of such a proof contains the following logical sequence:

Given: (1) p is true.   (Special fact of the given problem)
        (2) If p is true, then q is true.   (An axiom, definition, or previously proved theorem)
Conclusion: q is true.

In more complicated situations this sequence may be repeated several times:

Given: (1) p is true.   (Special fact of the given problem)
        (2) If p is true, then q is true.⎱ (Axioms, definitions, or
        (3) If q is true, then r is true.⎰ previously proved theo-
        (4) If r is true, then s is true. rems)
Conclusion: s is true.

Let us illustrate this method by an algebraic example.

Illustration 1.   Prove that the square of an odd number is odd.
Given: (1) x is an odd number.   (Special fact of the given problem)
        (2) If x is an odd number, then $x = 2a + 1$, where a is an integer. (Definition of odd number)
        (3) If $x = 2a + 1$, then $x^2 = 4a^2 + 4a + 1$.   (Theorem of algebra)
        (4) If $x^2 = 4a^2 + 4a + 1$, then x^2 is not divisible by 2. (Property of division)
        (5) If x^2 is not divisible by 2, then x^2 is odd.   (Definition of odd number)
Conclusion: x^2 is odd.

In constructing such proofs you will have to choose the appropriate "previously proved theorems" and arrange them in a suitable order. There is no automatic way of doing this; you must develop skill through experience and the use of your originality.

1.7. *Other Methods of Proof*

(a) *Indirect Proof.* If you have difficulty in constructing a direct proof, you can sometimes make progress by using other tactics. The method of "indirect proof" relies on the fact that, if *not-p* is false, then *p* is true. Hence, to prove that *p* is true, we attempt to show that *not-p* is false. The best way to accomplish this is to show that *not-p* is not consistent with the given statements. In other words, we add *not-p* to the list of given statements and attempt to show that this augmented list of statements leads to a contradiction. When the contradiction is reached, we know that *not-p* is not consistent with our given true statements and hence that it is false. Hence *p* is true.

To illustrate indirect proof let us consider a familiar theorem in geometry.

Illustration 1. Prove: if two lines are cut by a transversal so that a pair of alternate interior angles are equal, the lines are parallel.

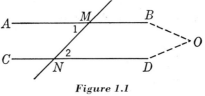

Figure 1.1

Given: $\angle 1 = \angle 2$.
Conclusion: $AB \parallel CD$.
Assume that the conclusion is false; i.e., assume that AB and CD intersect at O. Then in $\triangle MNO$ $\angle 1$ is an exterior angle and $\angle 2$ is an interior angle. But then $\angle 1$ is greater than $\angle 2$ by a previous theorem. Hence there is a contradiction with the assumption that $\angle 1 = \angle 2$. Consequently $AB \parallel CD$.

(b) *Use of the Contrapositive.* When we are trying to prove the truth of an implication "If *p*, then *q*," we can just as well prove the contrapositive "If *not-q*, then *not-p*." For we have seen that an implication and its contrapositive are equivalent. Sometimes the contrapositive is easier to prove, and then we should choose this method. Often there are great similarities between indirect proof and the proof of the contrapositive. Let us consider the theorem of Illustration 1.

Illustration 2. The contrapositive of the implication stated in Illustration 1 is: "If two lines are not parallel, then the alternate interior angles obtained by cutting these lines by a transversal are not equal."
We establish this by the precise argument used in Illustration 1. Hence the given implication is true.

(c) *Proof of Existence.* Before you spend a lot of time and money (on a high-speed computer, say) trying to solve a problem, it is a good idea to determine in advance that the problem actually does have a

solution.   You have probably never seen problems that do not have solutions, for most textbooks and teachers consider it to be bad form to ask students to do something which is impossible.   In actual practice, however, such problems may arise and it is a good idea to know how to recognize them.   A very simple example of such a problem is the following:

Find all the integers x which satisfy the equation

$$7x + 5 = 2x + 9$$

In order to reassure you that you are working on problems that do have solutions, mathematicians have developed a number of "existence theorems."   These are statements of the following form:

There exists a number x which has a given property

An important example of such a theorem is this one:

If a and b are any real numbers such that $a \neq 0$, there exists a real number x which satisfies the equation $ax + b = 0$

The best way of proving such a theorem is to exhibit a number x with the required property.   The proof of the above theorem amounts to checking that $x = -(b/a)$ satisfies the given equation.

Although there are other forms of existence proofs, a constructive proof of this kind is considered to be of greater merit, and this method is used widely in establishing the existence of solutions of various types of equations.

1.8. *Methods of Disproof*

If you have tried unsuccessfully to prove a conjectured theorem, you may well spend some time trying to disprove it.   There are two standard methods for disproving such statements.

(*a*) *Disproof by Contradiction.*   In this case we assume that the given statement is true and then proceed to derive consequences from it.   If we succeed in arriving at a consequence which contradicts a known theorem, we have shown that the given statement is false.

Illustration 1.   Disprove the statement: "The square of every odd number is even."

Of course, this immediately contradicts our previous result (Sec. 1.6, Illustration 1) that the square of every odd number is odd.   But let us disprove it from first principles.   Since every odd number can be written in the form $2a + 1$, where a is an integer, and since every even number can be written in the form $2b$, where b

is an integer, the given statement implies that:

$$(2a + 1)^2 = 2b \quad \text{for some } a \text{ and } b$$
or
$$4a^2 + 4a + 1 = 2b$$

Both sides are supposed to represent the same integer, but the left hand side *is not* divisible by 2, while the right hand side *is* divisible by 2. This is surely a contradiction, and so the given statement is false.

(*b*) *Disproof by Counterexample.* This method is effective in disproving statements of the form:

> For *all* values of x, a certain statement involving x is true

An example is the following:

> For all values of x, $x^2 + 16 = (x + 4)(x - 4)$

In order to disprove such an assertion, we proceed to find a "counterexample." In other words, we look for *one* value of x for which the statement is false; and since the statement was supposed to be true for *all* values of x, this single counterexample is the end of the matter. In the above example, $x = 0$ does the job.

Illustration 2. Disprove the statement: "The square of every odd number is even."

All that we have to do is to find a single odd number whose square is odd. Since $3^2 = 9$, we have established the disproof.

We close with this warning: Although *disproof* by counterexample is a valid procedure, theorems are not to be *proved* by verifying them in a number of special cases. Be sure that you do not confuse these two ideas.

PROBLEMS 1.8

In Probs. 1 to 18 you are given a series of mathematical statements, some of which are true and some of which are false. Prove those which are true, and disprove those which are false.

1. The sum of two even integers is odd.
2. The product of two even integers is a perfect square.
3. For all x, $2x^2 + 5x - 3 = (2x - 1)(x + 3)$.
4. For some x, $4x + 5 = 2x + 7$.
5. For some x, $3^x = 27$.   6. For all x, $2^{x+3} = 8(2^x)$.
7. The sum of the roots of: $x^2 + 7x + 12 = 0$ is equal to -7.
8. The product of the roots of: $x^2 + 9x + 18 = 0$ is equal to 18.
9. For all x, $(x + 4)^2 = x^2 + 16$.   10. For all x, $(x + 2)^3 = x^3 + 8$.
11. Two triangles are congruent if two sides and the angle opposite one of these of one triangle are equal, respectively, to the corresponding parts of the other triangle.

12. If two triangles are similar, then they have the same area.

13. If the vector sum of all the forces acting on a body is zero, then the body is in static equilibrium.

14. If the vector sum of the moments of all the forces acting on a body is zero, then the body is in static equilibrium.

15. Provided that $a \neq 0$, every equation of the form: $ax + b = c$ has a solution.

16. Provided that $a \neq b$, every equation of the form: $(x - a)(x - b) = 0$ has two distinct solutions.

17. The sum of the exterior angles of any triangle is equal to 180°.

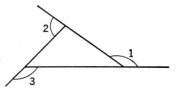

Figure 1.2

18. Any two medians of a triangle bisect each other.

19. You are given the following axiom: "One and only one line can be drawn through any two points." Prove: "Any two distinct lines meet in at most one point." HINT: Use indirect proof.

20. You are given the theorems: "(1) If $ax = 0$ and $a \neq 0$, then $x = 0$." "(2) Provided that $a \neq 0$, every equation of the form $ax + b = 0$ has a solution." Prove that every equation of this form has at most one solution. HINT: Use indirect proof.

21. You are given the theorem: "Every equation of the form $a + x = b$ has a solution." Prove that every equation of this form has at most one solution. HINT: Use indirect proof.

22. You are given the theorem: "At most one circle can be drawn through three, distinct points." Prove that two distinct circles can intersect in at most two points. HINT: Use indirect proof.

23. Give an indirect proof of the theorem: "There exist an infinite number of primes." If you are unable to do so, consult Courant and Robbins "What Is Mathematics?" page 22. This theorem is due to Euclid.

1.9. *Mathematical Models*

By this time you should have begun to understand what we mean by saying that mathematics is abstract. Mathematical proof is a process of reasoning by given rules from a set of axioms (which are assumed to be true) to a valid conclusion, which we call a "theorem." Because of the abstract character of mathematics, we cannot expect to prove anything about our physical world by purely mathematical means.

Scientists, however, spend their lives uncovering the secrets of nature, and engineers put these discoveries to work for the benefit of our society. You may quite properly wonder how an abstract subject like mathematics has become such an important tool for scientists

and engineers. The key to this matter is the concept of a "mathematical model" of nature. The first step in the study of any branch of science is that of observing nature. When enough facts have been collected, the scientist begins to organize them into some pattern. In quantitative sciences like astronomy, chemistry, and physics this pattern is expressed in terms of mathematics. The undefined terms of the abstract mathematics (points, lines, etc.) represent physical objects; refined abstract concepts (velocity, acceleration, force, etc.) are then defined to correspond to intuitive ideas which seem important to the scientist. Then mathematical equations involving these concepts are used as axioms to describe the observed behavior of nature. All of these, taken together, constitute our mathematical model. This model, of course, is only a picture of nature; it differs from nature just as a model of an aircraft differs from the real plane itself. But just as a great deal can be learned about a plane from a model which is studied in a wind tunnel, we can use our mathematical model to help us understand nature. From our axioms, we can deduce theorems, which are true only in our abstract sense. Nevertheless, if our model is well constructed, these theorems will correspond to observable properties of nature which we may well not have suspected in advance. At the very worst, these theorems are intelligent guesses about nature and serve as guides for our experimental work. At their best, when the model is a good one as is the case in most physical sciences, our mathematical results can almost be identified with physical truth. In those portions of science which you are likely to be studying along with this book, this correspondence is so close that you may not realize the difference between mathematics and nature itself. It is our hope that the study of this chapter will have helped you to appreciate this important distinction.

REFERENCES

Allendoerfer, C. B.: Deductive Methods in Mathematics, in "Insights into Modern Mathematics," pp. 65–99, National Council of Teachers of Mathematics, Washington, D.C. (1957).

Allendoerfer, C. B., and C. O. Oakley: "Principles of Mathematics," pp. 1–38, McGraw-Hill, New York (1955).

Copi, Irving M.: "Symbolic Logic," pp. 1–65, Macmillan, New York (1956).

Courant, R., and H. Robbins: "What Is Mathematics?" p. 22, Oxford, New York (1941).

Stabler, E. R.: "An Introduction to Mathematical Thought," pp. 1–119, Addison-Wesley, Reading, Mass. (1953).

Suppes, P.: "Introduction to Logic," pp. 1–19, Van Nostrand, Princeton, N.J. (1957).

Tarski, A.: "Introduction to Logic," pp. 3–140, Oxford, New York (1946).

CHAPTER TWO

The Number System

2.1. *Introduction*

Since numbers are basic ideas in mathematics, we shall devote this chapter to a discussion of the most important properties of our number system. We do not give a complete account of this subject, and you are likely to study it in more detail when you take more advanced courses in mathematics. Numerous suggestions for further reading are given at the end of the chapter.

Let us retrace briefly the development of numbers as it is usually presented in schools. As a young child you first learned to count, and thus became acquainted with the *natural numbers* 1, 2, 3, ... In your early study of arithmetic you learned how to add, subtract, multiply, and divide pairs of natural numbers. Although some divisions such as $6 \div 3 = 2$ were possible, it soon developed that new numbers had to be invented so as to give meaning to expressions like $7 \div 2$ and $3 \div 5$. To handle such situations, fractions were introduced, and the arithmetic of fractions was developed.

It should be noted that the invention of fractions was a major step in the development of mathematics. In the early days many strange practices were followed. The Babylonians considered only fractions whose denominators were 60, the Romans only those whose denominators were 12. The Egyptians insisted that the numerators must be 1, and wrote $\frac{1}{3} + \frac{1}{15}$ instead of $\frac{2}{5}$. Our modern notation dates from

20

Leonardo of Pisa (also called Fibonacci), whose great work *Liber Abaci* was published in A.D. 1202.

Later on you became acquainted with zero and negative numbers such as -7, -3, $-\frac{5}{3}$, $-4\frac{1}{5}$, etc., and you learned how to calculate with these. The entire collection consisting of the positive and negative integers zero and the positive and negative fractions is called the system of *rational numbers*. The advantage of using this system in contrast to the system of purely positive numbers is that it is possible to subtract any rational number from any rational number. With only positive numbers available, $3 - 5$, for instance, is meaningless. It is interesting to note that it took many years before negative numbers were permanently established in mathematics. Although they were used to some extent by the early Chinese, Indians, and Arabs, it was not until the beginning of the seventeenth century that mathematicians accepted negative numbers on an even footing with positive numbers.

When you were introduced to *irrational* numbers such as $\sqrt{2}$ and π, you were told that these could not be expressed as ordinary fractions. Instead, they are written as infinite decimal expansions such as 1.4142 . . . and 3.1415 . . . . The decimal expansions of the rational numbers are also infinite; for example,

$$\frac{1}{4} = 0.25000 \ \cdots$$
$$\frac{1}{3} = 0.33333 \ \cdots$$
$$2 = 2.00000 \ \cdots$$
$$\frac{1}{7} = 0.142857142857 \ \cdots$$

These, however, repeat after a certain point, whereas the irrationals do not have this property. The collection of all these, the rationals plus the irrationals, is called the system of *real* numbers. It is quite difficult to give a completely satisfactory definition of a real number, but for our present purposes the following will suffice:

Definition: A *real number* is a number which can be represented by an infinite decimal expansion.

If you wish a more subtle definition of a real number, read Courant and Robbins, "What Is Mathematics?" Chap. 2.

2.2. *Addition of Real Numbers*

Addition is defined for *pairs* of real numbers such as $2 + 3 = 5$, $-3 + 2\frac{1}{2} = -\frac{1}{2}$, etc. Indeed the sum of every pair of real numbers is defined as a third real number. We give this property the name "closure" and write the following law.

Closure Law of Addition.   The sum $a + b$ of any two real numbers is a unique real number c.

You are very familiar with the fact that the order of addition is not important. For instance, $2 + 4 = 4 + 2$, $-3 + \pi = \pi + (-3)$, etc. To describe this property, we say that addition is "commutative" and write the following law.

Commutative Law of Addition. $a + b = b + a$.

It is slightly more difficult to add three numbers such as $2 + 4 + 7$; for addition is defined for *pairs* of real numbers and not for *triples*. Normally we first add $2 + 4 = 6$, and then add $6 + 7 = 13$. But we could just as well have added $4 + 7 = 11$ and then $2 + 11 = 13$. That is, $(2 + 4) + 7 = 2 + (4 + 7)$. To describe this property, we say that addition is "associative" and write the following law.

Associative Law of Addition. $(a + b) + c = a + (b + c)$.

Actually the sum, $a + b + c$, of three real numbers needs to be defined; for originally we knew only how to add two numbers, $a + b$. Therefore we make the following definition:

Definition: $a + b + c$ is defined to be the sum $(a + b) + c$.

We now prove a theorem which illustrates the fact that the sum of three real numbers is the same regardless of the order in which the addition is performed.

Theorem 1. $a + b + c = c + b + a$.
   Proof:

$$
\begin{aligned}
a + b + c &= (a + b) + c &&\text{[Definition]}\\
&= (b + a) + c &&\text{[Commutative Law]}\\
&= c + (b + a) &&\text{[Commutative Law]}\\
&= (c + b) + a &&\text{[Associative Law]}\\
&= c + b + a &&\text{[Definition]}
\end{aligned}
$$

In a similar fashion we can define the sum of four real numbers.

Definition: $a + b + c + d$ is defined to be the sum

$$(a + b + c) + d$$

As before, the commutative and associative laws show that this addition does not depend upon the order in which the addition is carried out.

The number zero plays a special role in addition; the sum of zero and any real number a is a itself:

$$a + 0 = 0 + a = a$$

Since this leaves a identically as it was before the addition, we lay down the following definition.

Definition: The real number *zero* is called the *identity element* in the addition of real numbers. This statement is equivalent to the statement: "For any real number a, $a + 0 = 0 + a = a$."

Suppose that we have a real number a and ask the question: "Is there some other real number b such that $a + b = 0$?" If $a = 2$, then clearly $b = -2$. If $a = -3$, then $b = -(-3) = 3$. In general, $a + (-a) = (-a) + a = 0$, regardless of whether a itself is positive or negative. This leads us to the following definition.

Definition: The real number $(-a)$ is called the *additive inverse* of the real number a. This statement is equivalent to

$$a + (-a) = (-a) + a = 0$$

which can be read "The sum of a real number and its additive inverse is the additive identity."

The use of the term "inverse" may be motivated as follows: We start at 0 and add a, thus obtaining a. We now wish to retrace our steps and return to 0; hence we must add $-a$ to a. The operation of adding $-a$ undoes the operation of adding a and thus is said to be the *inverse* operation.

We must further define the *difference* of two real numbers. Of course, this is familiar when a and b are both positive and $a > b$. Other cases, however, must be treated, and we include these in the definition below. We introduce the symbol $a - b$ to denote subtraction and define it as follows.

Definition: Let a and b be two real numbers. Then by definition

$$a - b = a + (-b)$$

In other words, in order to subtract one number from another, change the sign of the number to be subtracted, and add.

You will notice that the minus sign is used in two distinct ways: (1) $-a$ denotes the additive inverse of a; (2) $a - b$ denotes the difference of a and b. This ambiguity will cause you no trouble in practice because of the above definition, which relates these two meanings.

We shall have frequent occasion to refer to the absolute value of a real number a. This is written $|a|$ and is defined as follows.

Definition: The *absolute value* $|a|$ of a real number a is the real number such that:
(1) If a is positive or zero, then $|a| = a$.
(2) If a is negative, then $|a| = -a$.

Illustration 1. $|5| = 5$; $|-6| = 6$; $|0| = 0$.

This notion of absolute value is particularly helpful when we wish to obtain rules for the addition of two *signed* numbers. Elementary arithmetic tells us how to add two positive numbers, but the sum of two negative numbers and the sum of a positive and a negative number need further discussion. The rules for the addition of signed numbers are given by the following theorem, whose proof is left to the Problems.

Theorem 2.   Let a and b be two real numbers, neither of which is zero. Then:
(1) If a and b have the same sign,

$$a + b = \begin{cases} |a| + |b| & \text{if } a \text{ and } b \text{ are both positive} \\ -(|a| + |b|) & \text{if } a \text{ and } b \text{ are both negative} \end{cases}$$

(2) If a and b have opposite signs and $|a| > |b|$,

$$a + b = \begin{cases} |a| - |b| & \text{if } a \text{ is positive} \\ -(|a| - |b|) & \text{if } a \text{ is negative} \end{cases}$$

Illustrations
2. $12 + 4 = |12| + |4| = 16$.
3. $(-12) + (-4) = -(|-12| + |-4|) = -(12 + 4) = -16$.
4. $(-12) + (4) = -(|-12| - |4|) = -(12 - 4) = -8$.
This may be justified by the following computation:

$$\begin{aligned} (-12) + (4) &= [(-8) + (-4)] + 4 \\ &= (-8) + [(-4) + 4] \\ &= (-8) + 0 = -8 \end{aligned}$$

5. $(12) + (-4) = |12| - |-4| = 12 - 4 = 8$.
This may be justified by the computation

$$12 + (-4) = (8 + 4) + (-4) = 8 + [4 + (-4)] = 8 + 0 = 8$$

2.3. *Multiplication of Real Numbers*

Now that the essential laws of addition are before us, the laws of multiplication are easy to learn; they are almost the same, with "product" written in the place of "sum."

Closure Law of Multiplication.   The product $a \times b$ of any two real numbers is a unique real number c.

Commutative Law of Multiplication. $a \times b = b \times a$.

Associative Law of Multiplication. $(a \times b) \times c = a \times (b \times c)$.

We now ask: "What is the identity element for multiplication?" It should be the number b such that, for any a, $a \times b = a$.   In other words, multiplication by b leaves a unchanged, just as in addition the addition of 0 to a leaves a unchanged.   Clearly the correct choice for the identity element is 1.

Definition: The real number 1 is called the *identity element* in the multiplication of real numbers.   This statement is equivalent to the statement: "For any real numbers a, $a \times 1 = 1 \times a = a$."

Finally we ask: "What is the inverse of a with respect to multiplication?"   The inverse b should have the property that, for any a, $a \times b = 1$ (the identity).   Compare this closely with the notion of an additive inverse above.

The correct choice for the inverse of a is $1/a$.   Here there is one rather awkward exception, namely, $a = 0$.   There is no number b such that $0 \times b = 1$.   Hence 0 has no multiplication inverse.

Definition: The real number $1/a$ $(a \neq 0)$ is called the *multiplicative inverse* of the real number a $(a \neq 0)$.   This statement is equivalent to

$$a \times \left(\frac{1}{a}\right) = \left(\frac{1}{a}\right) \times a = 1 \qquad a \neq 0$$

which can be read "The product of a real number and its multiplicative inverse is the multiplicative identity."

There is one final law; this connects multiplication and addition. You are used to writing $4(2 + 3) = (4 \times 2) + (4 \times 3)$;

$$2(x + y) = 2x + 2y$$

etc.   Or probably you did the reverse in factoring when you wrote $3x + 6y = 3(x + 2y)$.   These are illustrations of the following law.

Distributive Law. $a \times (b + c) = (a \times b) + (a \times c)$.

This law is the basis for many familiar operations.   For example, the usual way of multiplying 15×23 is

$$
\begin{array}{r}
15 \\
23 \\
\hline
45 \\
30 \\
\hline
345
\end{array}
$$

But this really amounts to the statement that

$$
\begin{aligned}
15 \times 23 &= 15 \times (20 + 3) \\
&= (15 \times 20) + (15 \times 3) \\
&= 300 + 45 \\
&= 345
\end{aligned}
$$

As a more complicated example, consider the following illustration.

Illustration 1.   Show that $(a + b)(c + d) = ac + bc + ad + bd$.

$$
\begin{aligned}
(a + b)(c + d) &= (a + b)c + (a + b)d &&\text{[Distributive Law]} \\
&= c(a + b) + d(a + b) &&\text{[Commutative Law]} \\
&= (ca + cb) + (da + db) &&\text{[Distributive Law]} \\
&= ca + cb + da + db &&\text{[Property of Addition]} \\
&= ac + bc + ad + bd &&\text{[Commutative Law]}
\end{aligned}
$$

The distributive law has a number of important consequences.   The first of these states the multiplicative property of zero.

Theorem 3.   Let a be any real number; then $a \times 0 = 0$.
Proof:
(1) $0 = 0 + 0$ [Definition, Sec. 2.2]
(2) $a \times 0 = a \times (0 + 0)$
(3) $a \times 0 = (a \times 0) + (a \times 0)$ [Distributive Law]
(4) $a \times 0 = a \times 0$ [Identity]
Subtracting (4) from (3), we obtain:
(5) $0 = a \times 0$.

A second consequence of the distributive law is the set of rules for multiplying signed numbers.   Let us look at some special cases.

Illustration 2.   Evaluate $2 \times (-3)$.
(1) $3 + (-3) = 0$
(2) $2 \times [3 + (-3)] = 0$ [Theorem 3]
(3) $(2 \times 3) + 2 \times (-3) = 0$ [Distributive Law]
(4) $6 + 2 \times (-3) = 0$
(5) $2 \times (-3) = -6$ [Definition of Additive Inverse, Sec. 2.2]

Illustration 3.   Evaluate $(-4) \times (-5)$.

  (1) $5 + (-5) = 0$

  (2) $(-4) \times [5 + (-5)] = 0$ [Theorem 3]

  (3) $(-4) \times 5 + (-4) \times (-5) = 0$ [Distributive Law]

  (4) $-20 + (-4) \times (-5) = 0$ [Illustration 2]

  (5) $(-4) \times (-5) = 20$ [Definition of Additive Inverse]

These illustrations suggest the following theorem whose proof is deferred to the problems.

Theorem 4.   Let a and b be positive real numbers.   Then:

  (1) $a \times (-b) = -(ab)$.

  (2) $(-a) \times (-b) = ab$.

Finally we wish to define division.   Just as the difference of a and b is defined to be the sum of a and the additive inverse of b, the quotient of a by b is defined to be the product of a by the multiplicative inverse of b:

Definition: Let a and b be real numbers, and let $b \neq 0$.   Then the *quotient* of a by b (written a/b) is defined to be:

$$\frac{a}{b} = a \times \left(\frac{1}{b}\right)$$

Note that division by zero is not defined.

2.4. *Formal Properties of Real Numbers*

In summary of Secs. 2.2 and 2.3, we state the following properties of the arithmetic of real numbers.   The letters a, b, c stand for arbitrary real numbers.

Addition

R1. $a + b$ is a unique real number   [Closure Law]

R2. $(a + b) + c = a + (b + c)$ [Associative Law]

R3. $a + 0 = 0 + a = a$ [Identity Law]

R4. $a + (-a) = (-a) + a = 0$ [Inverse Law]

R5. $a + b = b + a$ [Commutative Law]

Multiplication

R6. $a \times b$ is a unique real number   [Closure Law]

R7. $(a \times b) \times c = a \times (b \times c)$ [Associative Law]

R8. $a \times 1 = 1 \times a = a$ [Identity Law]

R9. $a \times \dfrac{1}{a} = \dfrac{1}{a} \times a = 1$ for $a \neq 0$ [Inverse Law]

R10. $a \times b = b \times a$ [Commutative Law]

Distributive Law

R11. $a \times (b + c) = (a \times b) + (a \times c)$

These eleven laws form the foundation of the entire subject of arithmetic. They should be carefully memorized. In more advanced mathematics these are taken to be the axioms of an abstract system called a "field." Hence we may say that the real numbers form a field.

PROBLEMS 2.4

Addition

In Probs. 1 to 4 use the commutative and associative laws to establish the truth of the given statement. Model your proofs on the one given for Theorem 1.

1. $3 + 5 + 6 = 6 + 5 + 3$.
2. $4 + 7 + 10 = 7 + 10 + 4$.
3. $a + b + c = c + a + b$.
4. $a + b + c = b + c + a$.
5. Define $a + b + c + d$.
6. Assuming that $a + b + c + d$ has been defined (Prob. 5), define $a + b + c + d + e$.
7. Find the additive inverse of each of the following:

$$2, \tfrac{1}{4}, -3, 0, -\sqrt{3}$$

8. Find the additive inverse of each of the following:

$$-1, \tfrac{2}{3}, -\pi^2, 15, \sqrt{2}$$

9. Find the absolute value of each of the following:

$$5, -1, 0, \tfrac{1}{2}, -\tfrac{3}{4}$$

10. Find the absolute value of each of the following:

$$-6, 2, \tfrac{2}{3}, 0, -\tfrac{1}{4}$$

In Probs. 11 to 16, evaluate the given expression.

11. $[3 + (2 - 4)] - [5 - (6 - 3)]$.
12. $[5 - (-3 + 6)] - [16 + (7 - 3)]$.
13. $[6 + (1 - 9)] + [2 - (4 - 3)]$.
14. $[(-15 + 3) + 7] + [-8 + (3 - 5)]$.
15. $\{[(-3 + 9) - (13 + 3)] - [-18 + 7]\} - 36$.
16. $\{[(4 - 10) - (7 - 11)] - [9 + 4]\} + 18$.

Multiplication

17. Formulate a definition for $a \times b \times c$.
18. Assuming that $a \times b \times c$ has been defined (Prob. 17), define $a \times b \times c \times d$.

In Probs. 19 to 22 use the commutative and associative laws to establish the truth of the given statement.

19. $7 \times 5 \times 2 = 5 \times 2 \times 7$.
20. $3 \times 6 \times 9 = 9 \times 6 \times 3$.
21. $a \times b \times c = c \times a \times b$.
22. $a \times b \times c = b \times a \times c$.
23. Find the multiplicative inverse of each of the following:

$$\tfrac{1}{2}, -3, -\tfrac{2}{5}, 1, 0$$

24. Find the multiplicative inverse of each of the following:

$$3, \ -\tfrac{1}{3}, \ \pi, \ \sqrt{2}, \ \tfrac{3}{4}$$

In Probs. 25 to 30 evaluate the given expression.

25. $(-3)[2(4 - 2) + 7] + 4[-3(-2 + 8) + 9]$.
26. $4[-8(5 - 2) + 3] - 3[2(3 + 7) - 43]$.
27. $2[7(-1 + 3) - 4(6 - 8)] + 4[(3 - 7)5 - (8 - 3)2]$.
28. $-5[2(6 + 5) - 3(2 - 7)] - 3[(6 - 2)8 - 15]$.
29. $3\{[-5(2 - 6) + 4(5 + 2)] - 15(1 - 2)\} - 10$.
30. $-2\{[6(8 - 3) - 5(2 + 6)] + 4(-3 + 7)\} + 8$.

Subtraction and Division

31. Does the commutative law hold for the subtraction of real numbers? *No*
32. Does the commutative law hold for the division of real numbers? *No*
33. Does the associative law hold for the subtraction of real numbers?
34. Does the associative law hold for the division of real numbers?
35. Is there an identity element for subtraction?   If so, what is it?
36. Is there an identity element for division?   If so, what is it?

Proofs

In Probs. 37 to 44 prove or disprove the given statement.   You may use R1 to R11 as given axioms.

37. $(a + b) \times c = (a \times c) + (b \times c)$.   **38.** $a + (b \times c) = (a + b) \times (a + c)$.
39. $a \div (b + c) = (a \div b) + (a \div c)$.   **40.** $(a - b) + b = a$.
41. Theorem 2, Sec. 2.2.   **42.** Theorem 4, Sec. 2.3.
43. If $a \neq 0$, $ax + b = 0$ has a unique solution.
44. To any real number a there corresponds a real number x such that $0x = a$.
45. Let "addiplication" be defined (with symbol $\odot$) as follows:

$$a \odot b = (a + b) + (a \times b)$$

Under addiplication are the real numbers closed?   Is addiplication commutative; associative?   Is there an identity; an addiplicative inverse?

2.5. *Special Properties of the Natural Numbers—Mathematical Induction*

The natural numbers 1, 2, 3, . . . are special cases of the real numbers, but they do not have all of the properties R1 to R11.   We leave it to you to verify that the natural numbers do satisfy R1, R2, R5, R6, R7, R8, R10, and R11.

Exercise A.   Choose $a = 2$, $b = 3$, $c = 5$, and for these natural numbers verify R1, R2, R5, R6, R7, R8, R10, and R11.

Let us look at the other laws.   The natural numbers cannot satisfy R3 or R4, since R3 involves zero and R4 involves negative numbers and neither zero nor the negative numbers are natural numbers.   The natural numbers cannot satisfy R9 since fractions of the form $\frac{1}{2}$, $\frac{4}{3}$, etc., are not natural numbers.

Exercise B.   Prove or disprove the statement: "For every pair of natural numbers, a and b, there is a natural number x such that $a + x = b$."
Exercise C.   Prove or disprove the statement: "For every pair of natural numbers, a and b, where $b \neq 0$, there is a natural number x such that $bx = a$."

The natural numbers, however, do have several properties which are not shared by all the real numbers.   The first of these has to do with their factorization.   We recall the following definition.

Definition: A natural number is called *prime* if and only if it has no natural numbers as factors except itself and 1.   For special reasons 1 is usually not considered prime.

Illustration 1.   2, 3, 5, 7, 11, . . . are primes, whereas 4, 6, 8, 9, 10, . . . are not primes.

In factoring a natural number like 60, we may write

$$60 = 20 \times 3$$

and then factor these factors and continue factoring until only **prime** numbers are left as factors.   Thus

$$60 = 20 \times 3 = 4 \times 5 \times 3 = 2 \times 2 \times 5 \times 3$$

This can be carried out in other ways, such as

$$60 = 15 \times 4 = 5 \times 3 \times 2 \times 2$$

Notice that these two sets of prime factors of 60 are the same except for their order.   This illustrates a general property of the natural numbers which is stated as a theorem.

Theorem 5.   Unique Factorization Theorem.   A natural number $\neq 1$ can be expressed as a product of primes in a way which is unique except for the order of the factors.

We omit the proof of this theorem.   You can find it, for instance, in Birkhoff and MacLane, "A Survey of Modern Algebra," page 20, or in Courant and Robbins, "What Is Mathematics?" page 23.

The natural numbers have an additional property which is essential for many portions of mathematics.   This property permits us to use a process called "Mathematical Induction" in proving theorems about natural numbers. To illustrate this process, suppose that we try to prove Theorem 6.

Theorem 6. The sum of the first n natural numbers:

$$1 + 2 + 3 + \cdots + n = \frac{n(n + 1)}{2}$$

Suppose that we try this formula out for $n = 1$ to see whether or not it is reasonable; we get

$$1 = \frac{1(1 + 1)}{2} = 1$$

Since this worked, try $n = 2$:

$$1 + 2 = \frac{2(2 + 1)}{2} = 3$$

This works too. Similarly we can verify the formula for any value of n. But how can we prove it in general? To do this, think of the natural numbers as represented by the rungs of an infinitely long ladder based on the ground and reaching to the sky. The bottom rung is 1, the next 2, and so on. We wish to climb this ladder to any desired rung. To do so, there are two essential steps:

    (I) We must get our foot on the bottom rung.

    (II) We must be able to climb from any rung to the next rung.

Clearly, if we can do these two things, we can climb as far as we please.

Let us imagine ourselves on the bottom rung if the theorem is true for $n = 1$. To proceed upward, we need a general process which will show us how to proceed from rung to rung. We start with

$$1 = \frac{(1)(2)}{2}$$

and add 2 to each side:

$$1 + 2 = \frac{(1)(2)}{2} + 2$$

or $$1 + 2 = \frac{(1)(2) + (2)(2)}{2}$$

$$= \frac{2(2 + 1)}{2}$$

which agrees with our formula. A similar bit of arithmetic will produce the required result for $n = 3$. But to reach $n = 100$, say, in this way would be very tedious; is there some general method of

climbing from rung to rung?   Suppose by some means we have reached
the kth rung, for k any natural number.   In other words, suppose we
have proved the theorem for $n = k$, that is,

$$1 + 2 + 3 + \cdots + k = \frac{k(k + 1)}{2}$$

Is the result true for $n = k + 1$?   To find out, add $k + 1$ to both
sides:

$$
\begin{aligned}
1 + 2 + 3 + \cdots + k + (k + 1) &= \frac{k(k + 1)}{2} + (k + 1) \\
&= \frac{k(k + 1) + 2(k + 1)}{2} \\
&= \frac{(k + 1)(k + 2)}{2}
\end{aligned}
$$

This is the required result.   The demonstration thus given permits
us to climb from any rung to the next higher rung, and thus we can
reach any desired height.   Hence the theorem is true for any n.

The intuitive process we have just described is called " Mathematical
Induction."   It must be clearly distinguished from ordinary inductive
reasoning.   For the usual type of induction amounts to the inference
of a general statement from a large number of special cases.   Such
reasoning is really just an educated guess, for no conclusion can be
reached with certainty from any number of examples.   The next
example may indeed fail to follow the proposed law.   Mathematical
induction, however, is of a different sort; it leads to firm conclusions
once the principle of it is accepted.   This principle is assumed as an
axiom about the natural numbers.

Axiom of Mathematical Induction.   If S is a set of the natural
numbers with the properties:
  (I) S contains 1,
  (II) If S contains a natural number k, then it contains the number
    $k + 1$,
then S is the set of *all* natural numbers.

To see whether a given proposed statement meets the conditions of
this axiom, we must perform two steps:
  (I) Verify the statement for $n = 1$.
  (II) Assume the statement for $n = k$, and on this basis prove it for
    $n = k + 1$.
If we can do both of these things, we then know that the statement is a
theorem, true for all n.

Illustration 1.   Prove by mathematical induction:

$$2 + 4 + 6 + \cdots + 2n = n(n + 1)$$

Solution:

(1) For $n = 1$, the formula becomes: $2 = 1(2)$, which is true.

(2) Suppose the formula to be true for $n = k$: $2 + 4 + 6 + \cdots + 2k = k(k + 1)$.

Add $2(k + 1)$ to each side. This gives

$$2 + 4 + 6 + \cdots + 2k + 2(k + 1) = k(k + 1) + 2(k + 1)$$
$$= (k + 1)(k + 2)$$

Hence the formula is true for $n = k + 1$.

(3) Therefore, by mathematical induction the formula is true for all natural numbers n.

PROBLEMS 2.5

In Probs. 1 to 14 prove the given relationship by mathematical induction.

1. $1 + 3 + 5 + \cdots + (2n - 1) = n^2$.

2. $1 + 4 + 7 + \cdots + (3n - 2) = \dfrac{n(3n - 1)}{2}$.

3. $2 + 7 + 12 + \cdots + (5n - 3) = \dfrac{n}{2}(5n - 1)$.

4. $2 + 6 + 10 + \cdots + (4n - 2) = 2n^2$.

5. $1 + 2 + 4 + 8 + \cdots + 2^{n-1} = 2^n - 1$.

6. $2 + 6 + 18 + \cdots + 2 \cdot 3^{n-1} = 3^n - 1$.

7. $1^2 + 2^2 + 3^2 + \cdots + n^2 = \dfrac{n(n + 1)(2n + 1)}{6}$.

8. $1^3 + 2^3 + 3^3 + \cdots + n^3 = \dfrac{n^2(n + 1)^2}{4}$.

9. $\dfrac{1}{1 \cdot 2} + \dfrac{1}{2 \cdot 3} + \dfrac{1}{3 \cdot 4} + \cdots + \dfrac{1}{n(n + 1)} = \dfrac{n}{n + 1}$.

10. $2 + 5 + 13 + \cdots + (2^{n-1} + 3^{n-1}) = 2^n - 1 + \frac{1}{2}(3^n - 1)$.

11. $2 + 3 \cdot 2 + 4 \cdot 2^2 + \cdots + (n + 1)(2^{n-1}) = n \cdot 2^n$.

12. $1 \cdot 4 + 2 \cdot 9 + 3 \cdot 16 + \cdots + n(n + 1)^2 = \frac{1}{12}n(n + 1)(n + 2)(3n + 5)$.

13. $a + ar + ar^2 + \cdots + ar^n = \dfrac{a(1 - r^{n+1})}{1 - r} \cdot \ r \neq 1$

14. $a + (a + d) + (a + 2d) + \cdots + [a + (n - 1)d] = \dfrac{n}{2}[2a + (n - 1)d]$.

In Probs. 15 to 18 try to establish the indicated relation by mathematical induction. Point out why the method fails. (Each relation is false.)

15. $3 + 6 + 9 + \cdots + 3n = \dfrac{3n(n + 1)}{2} + 1$.

16. $3 + 5 + 7 + \cdots + (2n + 1) = n^2 + 2$.

17. $4 + 5 + 6 + \cdots + (n + 3) = n^3 + 3$.

18. $2 + 4 + 6 + 8 + \cdots + 2n = n(n + 1) + 2$.

In Probs. 19 to 22 prove the given statement by mathematical induction.

19. $2^n \geq 1 + n$ for $n \geq 1$.   **20.** $3^n \geq 1 + 2n$ for $n \geq 1$.

21. Let $a_1 = 2$ and $a_n = 2a_{n-1}$. Then $a_n = 2^n$ for $n \geq 1$.

—**22.** Let $a_1 = 3$ and $a_n = 3a_{n-1}$. Then $a_n = 3^n$ for $n \geq 1$.

2.6. *Special Properties of Zero*

The behavior of zero is one of the more troublesome parts of the study of real numbers. It appears as the numerator or denominator of a fraction in three possible situations:

$$\frac{0}{b}, \frac{a}{0}, \frac{0}{0} \qquad \text{where } b \neq 0,\, a \neq 0$$

First let us note that the equation

$$\frac{a}{b} = c \qquad b \neq 0$$

is equivalent to the equation

$$a = b \times c$$

From this point of view $0/b = c$ is equivalent to $0 = b \times c$. Since $b \neq 0$ by hypotheses, it follows that $c = 0$. Hence

$$\frac{0}{b} = 0$$

The symbol $a/0$ $(a \neq 0)$ is quite different. The equation $a/0 = c$ is equivalent to $a = 0 \times c$. However, $0 \times c$ is equal to 0 for all values of c, and hence cannot equal a, which is not zero. Therefore

$$\frac{a}{0} \text{ is } meaningless$$

Finally, let us consider $0/0$. The equation $0/0 = c$ is equivalent to $0 = 0 \times c$. But this is satisfied for any real number c. For this reason we say that

$$\frac{0}{0} \text{ is } indeterminate$$

Do not confuse $0/0$ with a/a $(a \neq 0)$, which is equal to 1.

In summary, we note that *zero may never appear in the denominator of a fraction; but $0/a$ for $a \neq 0$ is equal to zero.*

NEVER DIVIDE BY ZERO

We meet zero in a different way when we are given that the product of two real numbers is zero; that is, $ab = 0$. In this case we have the important result:

Theorem 7.   If a and b are two real numbers such that $ab = 0$, then $a = 0$, or $b = 0$.

   Proof: If $a = 0$, the theorem is immediately verified.

   If $a \neq 0$, then $1/a$ is defined.   Then we may write:

$$(1/a)(ab) = (1/a)(0)$$

or

$$b = 0$$

which proves the theorem.

   This theorem has very many applications, especially in the solution of equations.

Illustration 1.   Solve: $x^2 - 5x + 6 = 0$.

   By factoring we find that: $(x - 2)(x - 3) = 0$.

   From Theorem 7 we see that:

Either $x - 2 = 0$ and $x = 2$

or $x - 3 = 0$ and $x = 3$

Hence 2 and 3 are roots of the given equation.

   THE PRODUCT OF TWO REAL NUMBERS IS ZERO IF AND ONLY IF AT LEAST ONE OF THE TWO FACTORS IS ZERO.

2.7. *Special Properties of the Integers*

   The integers consist of the natural numbers, zero, and the negatives of the natural numbers: . . . $-3, -2, -1, 0, 1, 2, 3, \ldots$.   Often we call these, respectively, the "positive integers," "zero," and "negative integers."   The integers are thus special cases of the real numbers, but they fail to have all the nice properties R1 to R11.   We leave it to you to verify that the integers do satisfy all of R1 to R11 except R9.

   The most important special property of the integers is given by the following theorem.

Theorem 8.   For any pair of integers, a and b, there exists a unique integer x such that $a + x = b$.

   The proof is very simple; for $x = b - a$ is certainly one such integer, and we have already seen that the solution must be unique (Prob. 21, Sec. 1.8).

   The integers, however, fail to have one desirable property.   For it is false that every equation of the form: $bx = a$ (where a and b are integers and $b \neq 0$) has an integer as a solution.   A suitable counterexample is $b = 2$, $a = 1$.   This failure leads us to consider the rational numbers, and we do so in the next section.

2.8. *Special Properties of the Rational Numbers*

A rational number is really nothing but a fraction whose numerator and denominator are both integers.   Let us give a formal definition:

Definition: A *rational number* is a real number which can be expressed in the form a/b where a and b are integers and $b \neq 0$.

As we know from the example: $\frac{1}{2} = \frac{2}{4}$, two different rational numbers may be equal.   So that we can identify such cases easily, we need the following result.

Theorem 9.   The rational numbers a/b and c/d are equal if and only if $ad = bc$.

Proof:

(1) If $a/b = c/d$, then

$$bd\left(\frac{a}{b}\right) = bd\left(\frac{c}{d}\right)$$

So
$$ad = bc$$

(2) If $ad = bc$, then

$$\frac{ad}{bd} = \frac{bc}{bd}$$

So
$$\frac{a}{b} = \frac{c}{d}$$

We can now state the following theorem, which expresses the most important and useful property of rational numbers.

Theorem 10.   Given any pair of integers a and b ($\neq 0$), there exists a rational number x such that $bx = a$.   Moreover, any two rational numbers x_1 and x_2 with this property are equal.

Proof: The existence of a solution is immediate, for $x = a/b$ has the required property.   In order to establish the second part of the theorem, we suppose that x_1 and x_2 both satisfy $bx = a$.   Then:

$$bx_1 = a$$
$$bx_2 = a$$

Subtracting, we have:

$$b(x_1 - x_2) = 0$$

or
$$x_1 - x_2 = 0 \quad \text{[Theorem 7, since } b \neq 0\text{]}$$

Finally we must remind you of the rules for adding and multiplying rational numbers. These are given by the theorems below.

Theorem 11. $$\frac{a}{b} + \frac{c}{d} = \frac{ad + bc}{bd}$$

Proof: Let $x = a/b$; then $bx = a$
      Let $y = c/d$; then $dy = c$
From these two equations we obtain:

$$bdx = ad$$
$$bdy = bc$$

Adding and using the distributive law, we get

$$bd(x + y) = ad + bc$$
So $$x + y = \frac{ad + bc}{bd}$$

Theorem 12. $(a/b) \times (c/d) = ac/bd$.

Proof: Using the notation in the proof of Theorem 11, we have again

$$bx = a$$
$$dy = c$$

Multiplying the left-hand sides and the right-hand sides separately, we have:

$$(bd)(xy) = ac$$
Therefore $$xy = \frac{ac}{bd}$$

With these concepts of addition and multiplication we can now check to see how many of R1 to R11 are satisfied by the rational numbers. As a matter of fact we find that all of these are satisfied. This means that the arithmetic of rational numbers is just like that of the real numbers. This might lead us to believe that there is no difference between the real numbers and their special case, the rational numbers. However, we shall see that real numbers such as $\sqrt{2}$ are not rational and hence that a distinction must be made.

PROBLEMS 2.8

Zero

1. What meaning is to be attached to each of the following?

$$\frac{0}{3}, \frac{3}{0}, \frac{3}{3}, \frac{0}{\frac{1}{3}}, \frac{0}{0}$$

2. What meaning is to be attached to each of the following?

$$\frac{5}{0}, \frac{5}{5}, \frac{0}{5}, \frac{0}{0}, \frac{0}{\frac{1}{5}}$$

3. For what real values of x are the following fractions meaningless?

$$\frac{3x + 2}{x + 1}, \frac{4}{x}, \frac{x + 3}{x - 1}, \frac{0}{x^2 + 2}, \frac{3}{x^2 - 6x + 8}$$

4. For what real values of x are the following fractions meaningless?

$$\frac{x}{5}, \frac{2x - 1}{x - 1}, \frac{3 + x}{x^2 + 4}, \frac{5}{x}, \frac{7}{x^2 + x - 2}$$

5. For what real values of x are the following fractions indeterminate?

$$\frac{x^2}{3x}, \frac{x - 1}{2x - 2}, \frac{2 + x^2}{3 + x^2}, \frac{0}{x}, \frac{2x - 1}{4x^2 - 1}$$

6. For what real values of x are the following fractions indeterminate?

$$\frac{x + 1}{3x + 3}, \frac{0}{x^3}, \frac{x^3}{2x^2}, \frac{1 + 3x^2}{2 + x^2}, \frac{3x + 2}{9x^2 - 4}$$

In Probs. 7 to 10, factor and solve for x.

7. $x^2 + 7x + 12 = 0$.   **8.** $x^2 - 8x + 15 = 0$.
9. $x^2 - 9 = 1$.   **10.** $x^2 - 49 = 1$.

Integers

11. Verify that R1 to R8 and R10 to R11 are satisfied when:

$$a = 3 \qquad b = 2 \qquad c = -4$$

12. Verify that R1 to R8 and R10 to R11 are satisfied when:

$$a = 2 \qquad b = -3 \qquad c = 5$$

13. Show by a counterexample that the integers do not satisfy R9.
14. Are the integers closed under subtraction? yes
15. Are the integers closed under division? No
16. Do the integers satisfy the axiom of Induction? No

Rational Numbers

17. Verify that R1 to R11 are satisfied when:

$$a = 2 \qquad b = \tfrac{1}{2} \qquad c = -3$$

18. Verify that R1 to R11 are satisfied when:

$$a = \tfrac{1}{2} \qquad b = -2 \qquad c = 4$$

19. Show that the natural numbers are special cases of the rationals.
20. Show that the integers are special cases of the rationals.

21. Prove: For any pair of rational numbers a and b, there exists a rational number x such that $a + x = b$. Moreover, any two rationals x_1 and x_2 with this property are equal.
22. Prove: For any three rational numbers a, b, and c, where $a \neq 0$, there exists a rational number x such that $ax + b = c$. Moreover, any two rationals x_1 and x_2 with this property are equal.
23. Prove: For any two rational numbers a/b and c/d, the quotient $\dfrac{a/b}{c/d} = \dfrac{ad}{bc}$.

    HINT: Consider $(c/d)x = a/b$.
24. Prove: The two rational numbers: $(-a)/b$ and $-(a/b)$ are equal. HINT: Show that $a/b + (-a)/b = 0$ and $a/b + [-(a/b)] = 0$.

2.9. *Decimal Expansions*

By carrying out the ordinary process of division, any rational number can be represented as a decimal. Some representations "terminate" after a finite number of steps; i.e., all later terms in the expansion are zero. For example,

$$\tfrac{1}{2} = 0.5000 \ldots$$
$$\tfrac{1}{4} = 0.2500 \ldots$$

But other expansions never terminate, such as

$$\tfrac{1}{3} = 0.3333 \ldots$$
$$1\tfrac{1}{7} = 1.142857142857 \ldots$$

By experimenting you may assure yourself that in each expansion the digits after a certain point repeat themselves in certain groups like (0), (3), and (142857) above. This is always true for rational numbers.

It is awkward to express numbers in this form since we cannot be sure what the . . . at the end really mean. To clear up this ambiguity, we place a bar over the set of numbers which is to be repeated indefinitely. In this notation we write

$$\tfrac{1}{2} = 0.5\overline{0}$$
$$\tfrac{1}{4} = 0.25\overline{0}$$
$$\tfrac{1}{3} = 0.\overline{3}$$
$$1\tfrac{1}{7} = 1.\overline{142857}$$

It is also true that any repeating decimal expansion of this type represents a rational number. We state this as Theorem 13.

Theorem 13. Every repeating decimal expansion is a rational number. Before giving the general proof, we give several illustrations.

Illustration 1.   Prove that $a = 3.\overline{3}$ is a rational number.

  Solution: If we multiply by 10, we merely shift the decimal point; thus

$$10a = 33.\overline{3} = 30 + a$$

Hence
$$9a = 30$$
$$a = \tfrac{30}{9} = 3\tfrac{1}{3}$$

Illustration 2.   Now consider the harder case where $b = 25.\overline{12}$.

  Solution:
$$b = 25.\overline{12}$$
$$100b = 2512.\overline{12}$$

Subtracting, we find

$$99b = 2{,}487$$
$$b = \frac{2{,}487}{99} = \frac{829}{33} = 25\frac{4}{33}$$

Illustration 3.   Finally consider $c = 2.3\overline{12}$.

  Solution: The change here is that the repeating part begins one place to the right of the decimal point.   We can correct this easily by writing

$$10c = 23.\overline{12}$$

and then proceeding as in Illustration 2.

To prove the general theorem, suppose that

$$c = a_0 . a_1 \cdots a_k \overline{b_1 \cdots b_p}$$

where the a's and b's represent digits in the expansion of c.   Using the idea of Illustration 3, we write

$$d = 10^k c = a_0 a_1 \cdots a_k . \overline{b_1 \cdots b_p}$$

Then
$$10^{\,p} d = a_0 a_1 \cdots a_k b_1 \cdots b_p . \overline{b_1 \cdots b_p}$$
$$(10^{\,p} d) - d = (a_0 a_1 \cdots a_k b_1 \cdots b_p - a_0 a_1 \cdots a_k)$$

Solving, we find that d is rational and that therefore c is rational.

2.10. *Some Irrational Numbers*

We have seen that the set of rational numbers is identical with the set of repeating decimals.   However, we may perfectly well conceive of a nonrepeating decimal.   This might be constructed in infinite time by a man throwing a 10-sided die who records the results of his throws in sequence.   Thus he might obtain the number (nonrepeating)

$$0.352917843926025 \cdots$$

Such a number is not rational but is included among the reals; and thus the reals include irrationals as well as rationals.

Perhaps this example is farfetched, and therefore we consider the very practical question of solving the equation $x^2 = 2$. The value of x is equal to the length of the hypotenuse of a right triangle whose legs are each 1. We now wish to show that $x = \sqrt{2}$ is not rational. We prove this by a sequence of theorems, in which a is assumed to be an integer.

Theorem 14. If a^2 is divisible by 2, then a is divisible by 2.

Proof: Every integer a can be written in one of the two forms:

$$a = \begin{cases} 2n & \text{where } n \text{ is an integer} \\ 2n + 1 \end{cases}$$

Hence
$$a^2 = \begin{cases} 4n^2 \\ 4n^2 + 4n + 1 \end{cases}$$

Since a^2 is divisible by 2, according to the hypothesis, a^2 must equal $4n^2$. Hence $a = 2n$, and a is divisible by 2.

Theorem 15. $\sqrt{2}$ is not a rational number.

Proof: (By contradiction.) Suppose p/q is a rational number in lowest terms, that is, p and q have no common factor. Suppose also that $p^2/q^2 = 2$, or that $p^2 = 2q^2$.

Then p^2 is divisible by 2, and thus p is divisible by 2 (Theorem 14). Write $p = 2r$, where r is an integer. Then $4r^2 = 2q^2$, or $2r^2 = q^2$. Hence q^2 is divisible by 2, and thus q is divisible by 2 (Theorem 14). Hence p and q have a common factor contrary to our assumption. This proves the theorem.

PROBLEMS 2.10

In Probs. 1 to 6 find decimal expansions for the given rational numbers.

1. $\frac{3}{7}$.   **2.** $\frac{1}{6}$.   **3.** $\frac{2}{9}$.
4. $\frac{5}{8}$.   **5.** $2\frac{8}{9}$.   **6.** $7\frac{1}{11}$.

In Probs. 7 to 12 find expressions of the form a/b for the given decimal expansions.

7. $0.\overline{7}$.   **8.** $5.3\overline{6}$.   **9.** $17.\overline{18}$.
10. $6.5\overline{81}$.   **11.** $3.81\overline{26}$.   **12.** $14.3\overline{214}$.

13. Prove that the decimal expansion of any rational number is repeating. HINT: Try dividing, and see what happens.

14. When a/b is expressed as a repeating decimal, what is the maximum length of the period? HINT: Try dividing, and see what happens.

15. State and prove the converse of Theorem 14.

16. Prove that $\sqrt{3}$ is irrational. HINT: First prove the analogue of Theorem 14: "If a^2 divisible by 3, then a is divisible by 3." To do so, note that every integer can be written in one of the forms:

$$a = \begin{cases} 3n \\ 3n + 1 \\ 3n + 2 \end{cases} \quad \text{where } n \text{ is an integer}$$

Hence

$$a^2 = \begin{cases} 9n^2 \\ 9n^2 + 6n + 1 \\ 9n^2 + 12n + 4 \end{cases}$$

Since a^2 is divisible by 3, according to the hypothesis, a^2 must equal $9n^2$, etc.

17. Prove that $\sqrt{5}$ is irrational.
18. Where does the method of Probs. 16 and 17 fail when we try to prove $\sqrt{4}$ to be irrational?
19. Prove that $1 + \sqrt{2}$ is irrational.   HINT: Suppose that $1 + \sqrt{2} = a/b$.   Then $\sqrt{2} = a/b - 1 = (a - b)/b$.   Why is this impossible?
20. Prove that $2 - \sqrt{3}$ is irrational.

2.11. *Geometric Representation of Real Numbers*

In the connection between arithmetic and geometry, the representation of real numbers as points on a line is most important. You are probably familiar with this idea, which is illustrated in Fig. 2.1. In

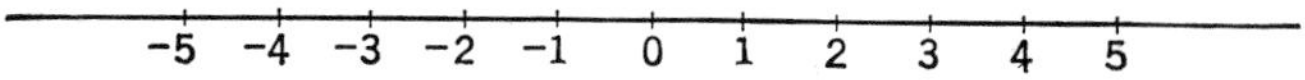

Figure 2.1

order to obtain this representation, we start with the points 0 and 1 chosen at random, except that 0 is to the left of 1. The segment [0,1] is said to have length 1 by definition of "length." It is now assumed that this segment can be slid along the line without altering its length. Doing this step by step, we locate the other integers, so that the length of the segment between any two successive integers is still equal to 1. The location of $1/b$ (where b is a natural number) is found by dividing [0,1] into b equal parts by the usual geometric construction. Then by sliding the segment [0, $1/b$] along the line we locate the points a/b. The location of the irrational numbers is more complicated, and we pass over this point. Their approximate positions, however, can be obtained from the first few decimals in their decimal expansions.

The most important fact about this representation is *that every point corresponds to one and only one real number and that every real number corresponds to one and only one point.* We cannot prove this fact here and consequently must take it as an assumption. Its proof depends upon a careful definition of a real number and upon a detailed discussion of the properties of a line; and for this you must wait until you study more advanced mathematics.

This representation has another important property, namely, it preserves *order*. Before we can state this precisely, we must define a notion of order for real numbers and a similar notion for points on a line. Let us start with real numbers.

Definition: We say that a is greater than b (written $a > b$) if $a - b$ is *positive*. Similarly a is less than b (written $a < b$) if $a - b$ is *negative*.

The symbols $\geq$ and $\leq$ mean, respectively, "greater than or equal to" and "less than or equal to." It is easy to see that, for any pair of real numbers, one and only one of the following relations is true:

$$a < b \qquad a = b \qquad a > b$$

We shall study the properties of these inequalities in some detail in Chap. 7.

For a line, we introduce order by means of the notion "beyond." First of all we place an arrow on one end of the line and thus define a "positive direction" on the line as the direction toward the arrow. We now call this line a "directed line." It is customary to direct horizontal lines to the *right* and vertical lines *upward*. Then we define "beyond" as follows.

Definition: A point P is *beyond* a point Q on a directed line if the segment (or vector) from Q to P points in the given positive direction. If P is beyond Q, we write $P > Q$.

Let us now return to our assumption about real numbers and points on the line and describe how this preserves order. Let P_a be the point corresponding to the real number a and P_b to b. Then our correspondence is such that:

$$P_a > P_b \qquad \textit{if and only if } a > b$$

In summary, we have defined a correspondence between real numbers and points on a line which is 1-to-1 and which preserves *order*. The number associated with a point is called its "coordinate," and we can use coordinates to identify points. Thus, the point whose coordinate is the number a will henceforth be written as the point a and not as P_a, as was done above. This use of coordinates is the foundation of the application of real numbers to geometry and to geometrical representations of nature.

By means of coordinates we can now define the length of an arbitrary segment whose end points are a and b. The notation for such a segment is $[a,b]$.

Definition: The *length* of the segment $[a,b]$ is the real number $|b - a|$.

2.12. *The Use of Real Numbers in the Plane*

We shall now use the correspondence of the last section to set up a relationship between ordered pairs of real numbers and points in the plane. This is based upon an idea of René Descartes (1596–1650). Since ordered pairs will turn up in several other places in this book, let us say what they are.

Definition: An *ordered pair* (x,y) of real numbers is a pair in which x is the first element and in which y is the second element. Because of the ordering (x,y) is to be distinguished from (y,x).

First, we construct two perpendicular lines in the plane (Fig. 2.2) which we call the X-axis and the Y-axis. Their point of intersection is called the origin O. We put the X-axis into an exact correspondence with the real numbers by placing zero at O, the positive reals to the right of O and the negative reals to its left. We do the same for the Y-axis, putting the positive reals above O and the negative reals below O. We remind ourselves of these conventions by putting arrows on the right end of the X-axis and the upper end of the Y-axis. These lines divide the plane into four regions called "quadrants" which are numbered I, II, III, and IV in Fig. 2.2.

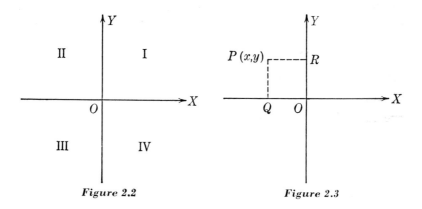

Figure 2.2   Figure 2.3

Using this scheme, we can now associate an ordered pair of real numbers (x,y) with each point P of the plane. Let P be a point on the X-axis. It corresponds to a real number x on this axis. We associate with P the ordered pair $(x,0)$. Now let P be a point on the Y-axis. Similarly we associate the ordered pair $(0,y)$ with it. When P is not on either axis, draw PQ perpendicular to the X-axis and PR perpendicular to the Y-axis (Fig. 2.3). Suppose that Q corresponds to the real number x on the X-axis and that R corresponds to the real number y on the Y-axis. Then we associate the ordered pair (x,y) with P.

By this process we find an ordered pair (x,y) which corresponds to each P in the plane. It is also evident that every pair (x,y) determines a point in the plane, for suppose (x,y) is given. These locate points Q and R (Fig. 2.3). Draw PQ and PR as perpendiculars to the X-axis and the Y-axis at Q and R, respectively. These lines intersect at P, which is the desired point.

Thus we have established a correspondence between the points of the plane and the ordered pairs (x,y).

Definition: The real numbers x and y in the ordered pair (x,y) are called the *coordinates* of the point P. Sometimes x is called the *x-coordinate,* or the *abscissa;* and y is called the *y-coordinate,* or the *ordinate.*

We often identify the point P with its pair of coordinates and speak of the "point (x,y)." By using this identification, we can convert geometric statements about points into algebraic statements about numbers and can convert geometric reasoning into algebraic manipulation. The methods of algebra are usually simpler than those of geometry, and therefore the algebraic approach is now the common one. The detailed elaboration of this method is called "analytic geometry," which is discussed in Chap. 14.

2.13. *Lengths of Segments; Units on the Axes*

Suppose that P_1 and P_2 lie on a line parallel to the X-axis. Then we may write their coordinates as $P_1(x_1,a)$ and $P_2(x_2,a)$ (Fig. 2.4). We wish to have an expression for the length of P_1P_2. Draw P_1R and P_2S perpendicular to the X-axis. Then R has coordinates $(x_1,0)$ and S has coordinates $(x_2,0)$. Moreover, the lengths P_1P_2 and RS are equal, since opposite sides of a rectangle are equal.

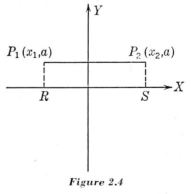

Figure 2.4

From Sec. 2.11 we know that the length $RS = |x_2 - x_1|$. Hence $P_1P_2 = |x_2 - x_1|$. This gives us Theorem 16.

Theorem 16.   The length of the segment between $P_1(x_1,a)$ and $P_2(x_2,a)$ is given by $P_1P_2 = |x_2 - x_1|$.

A similar proof gives Theorem 17.

Theorem 17.   The length of the segment between $Q_1(a,y_1)$ and $Q_2(a,y_2)$ is given by $Q_1Q_2 = |y_2 - y_1|$.

We have said nothing about the relation of distance on the X-axis to that on the Y-axis, and we prefer not to make any rigid requirements about this at present.   Indeed, it is often useful to use different scales of measurement on the two axes.   Unequal scales are used for a variety of reasons of which the following are the most common:

(1) The range of values to be plotted on the Y-axis is much greater (or smaller) than the range to be plotted on the X-axis.   In this case we must contract (or expand) the scale on the Y-axis in order to get a graph on a reasonably shaped piece of paper.

Illustration 1.   Suppose that we are plotting $y = x^{10}$ for x in the range 0 to 2. Then y lies in the range 0 to 1,024.   In this case it would be extremely awkward to use equal scales on the two axes.

(2) In applications to science the physical significance of the numbers on the two axes may be very different.   In such cases the physical units of measurement (such as time, distance, velocity, etc.) are not comparable; and suitable scales on the two axes should be chosen independently.

Illustration 2.   In order to illustrate the motion of a particle, it is customary to plot the distance traveled on the vertical axis and the corresponding time on the horizontal axis.   The units of measurement are *feet* and *seconds*, respectively, and it would be absurd to equate feet and seconds.   Hence separate, convenient scales are used on the two axes.

In geometry, however, it is necessary to plot distance on each of the axes and to use the same scale on each.   When we do this, it is meaningful to speak of the lengths of segments on slanting lines and we shall develop a formula for this in Sec. 12.2.   The notion of slant distance, however, is quite meaningless in cases (1) and (2) above, and we shall avoid mention of it until we begin our study of geometry.

PROBLEMS 2.13

1. Use the symbol $>$ to represent the correct inequality between each of the following pairs of numbers:
   1 and 4; -2 and 6; 3 and -5; -3 and -7; -4 and 0
2. Use the symbol $<$ to represent the correct inequality between each of the following pairs of numbers:
   7 and -8; -5 and -6; 5 and 2; -5 and 8; 0 and 3

3. Write a set of inequalities expressing the fact that c lies inside the segment $[a,b]$, where $a < b$.

4. Write a set of inequalities expressing the fact that c lies outside the segment $[a,b]$, where $a < b$.

5. Find the lengths of the following segments:
   $[15,2]$, $[-6,5]$, $[3,-2]$, $[-8,-3]$, $[25,-13]$

6. Find the lengths of the following segments:
   $[11,-6]$, $[-13,5]$, $[6,8]$, $[-22,0]$, $[-14,-20]$

7. Find the lengths of the segments joining the following pairs of points:
   $(1,2)$ and $(5,2)$; $(-3,-4)$ and $(-3,-6)$; $(-3,1)$ and $(6,1)$; $(4,4)$ and $(4,-5)$; $(0,0)$ and $(0,6)$

8. Find the lengths of the segments joining the following pairs of points:
   $(3,6)$ and $(3,-9)$; $(2,-4)$ and $(6,-4)$; $(5,5)$ and $(12,5)$; $(3,0)$ and $(0,0)$; $(-5,-8)$ and $(-5,-16)$

9. What signs do the coordinates of points in quadrant I have; quadrant III?

10. What signs do the coordinates of points in quadrant II have; quadrant IV?

11. State the quadrant in which each of the following points lies:
    $(1,-3)$, $(2,6)$, $(-4,-5)$, $(-8,10)$, $(-3,6)$

12. State the quadrant in which each of the following points lies:
    $(-7,-5)$, $(18,-3)$, $(-5,8)$, $(1,1)$, $(7,-3)$

Transformation of Coordinates

If we are given a coordinate system on a line in terms of numbers x, we can define a new coordinate system x' by giving a relationship between x and x'. This relabels the points with new numbers and is called a "transformation of coordinates." The following problems give some important illustrations of these.

In Probs. 13 to 16, we take $x' = a + x$. This transformation is called a "translation."

13. Prove that a translation leaves the lengths of segments unchanged. HINT: Prove that $x'_2 - x'_1 = x_2 - x_1$.

14. Prove: If the coordinate of any *one* point is left unchanged by a translation, then the coordinates of all points are unchanged. HINT: Prove that $a = 0$.

15. Express as a translation the relationship between absolute temperature K (degrees Kelvin) and centigrade temperature C.

16. Express as a translation the relationship between the distance s of a rocket from the center of the earth and its height h above the surface of the earth.

In Probs. 17 to 20, we take $x' = ax$, where $a > 0$. This transformation is called a "dilation."

17. Prove that a dilation multiplies the lengths of segments by a.

18. Prove that, if the coordinate of any *one* point (other than $x = x' = 0$) is left unchanged by a dilation, then the coordinates of all points are unchanged.

19. Express the relationship between feet F and inches I as a dilation.

20. Express the relationship between seconds S and hours H as a dilation.

In Probs. 21 to 24 we take $x' = ax + b$, where $a > 0$. This transformation is called a "linear transformation."

21. Prove that a linear transformation multiplies the lengths of segments by a.

22. Prove that a linear transformation with $a \neq 1$ leaves the coordinate of just one point unchanged. Find this point.

23. Express the relationship between degrees Fahrenheit F and degrees centigrade C as a linear transformation. What temperature is the same in both systems?

24. Express the relationship between degrees Fahrenheit F and degrees Kelvin K as a linear transformation. What temperature is the same in both systems?

Problems 25 to 28 refer to linear transformations and require a knowledge of simultaneous equations.

25. Find the linear transformation which relabels the point $x = 1$ with $x' = 5$ and $x = 2$ with $x' = 7$.

26. Given that 0°C corresponds to 32°F and 100°C corresponds to 212°F, derive the linear transformation which expresses F in terms of C.

27. In one grading system 60 is passing and 100 perfect. In a second grading system 70 is passing and 100 is perfect. Find a linear transformation between these two grading systems which takes passing into passing and perfect into perfect. What grade remains unchanged?

28. Let x_1, x_1' and x_2, x_2' be the corresponding labels for two points in the x and x' coordinate systems, respectively. Assume $x_2 > x_1$ and $x_2' > x_1'$. Then find a linear transformation between these coordinate systems. What point has the same coordinates in both systems?

29. Prove that the linear transformation $x' = ax + b$ with $a > 0$ preserves the order relationship; i.e., if $x_1 > x_2$, then $x_1' > x_2'$.

30. Prove that the linear transformation $x' = ax + b$ with $a < 0$ reverses the order relationship; i.e., if $x_1 > x_2$, then $x_1' < x_2'$.

2.14. *Complex Numbers*

There are, unfortunately, many problems that cannot be solved by the use of real numbers alone. For instance, we are unable to solve $x^2 = -1$. You have doubtless heard of the "number" i which has the property $i^2 = -1$. Because such numbers seemed so far away from reality to mathematicians of the past century, i was called an "imaginary" number and expressions of the form $a + bi$ were called "complex" numbers. Our purpose in this section is to develop the theory of these numbers in a logical and nonimaginary fashion.

Definitions:

Complex Number: A *complex number* is an ordered pair of real numbers (a,b).

Real Number (new definition): A *real number* is a complex number of the form $(a,0)$. The real number $(a,0)$ is also called the *real part* of the complex number (a,b).

Pure Imaginary Number: A *pure imaginary number* is a complex number of the form $(0,b)$. The pure imaginary $(0,b)$ is also called the *imaginary part* of the complex number (a,b).

The arithmetic of complex numbers is given by the following basic definitions:

Definitions:

Equality: Two complex numbers are said to be *equal* if and only if $a = c$ and $b = d$.

Addition: $(a,b) + (c,d) = (a + c, b + d)$.

Multiplication: $(a,b) \times (c,d) = (ac - bd, bc + ad)$.

When we called $(a,0)$ a *real number* above, we no doubt worried you, for we now have two expressions for a real number, namely, a and the pair $(a,0)$. We shall identify these two symbols and justify this by showing that they follow identical rules for addition and multiplication. From the definitions above we conclude that:

Addition: $(a,0) + (c,0) = (a + c, 0)$, which corresponds exactly to:

$$a + c = (a + c)$$

Multiplication: $(a,0) \times (c,0) = (ac,0)$, which corresponds exactly to:

$$a \times c = ac$$

The complex numbers $(a,0)$ are therefore nothing new; they are our old friends the real numbers a in a different notation. The pure imaginaries $(0,b)$, however, *are* something new. Their arithmetic, as derived from the definitions, is given by the rules:

Addition: $(0,b) + (0,d) = (0, b + d)$.

Multiplication: $(0,b) \times (0,d) = (-bd,0)$.

The important fact to note is that the *product of two pure imaginaries is a real number.*

The pure imaginary $(0,1)$ is of special importance, and we call it i for short. (Electrical engineers usually call it j since i is used to represent current.) We see that $(0,1) \times (0,1) = (0,1)^2 = (-1,0)$, or that

$$i^2 = -1$$

If we interpret the equation $x^2 = -1$ in terms of complex numbers to read:

$$(x,y)^2 = (-1,0)$$

it follows that $(x,y) = (0,1)$ is a solution and that $(x,y) = (0,-1)$ is another solution. Therefore, our introduction of complex numbers permits us to solve equations of this type, which had no solution in terms of real numbers. This is the justification for the introduction of complex numbers.

Since we will need to use complex numbers in solving considerably more complicated equations, we need to work out the full details of their arithmetic. In particular we can show that they form a *field*, i.e., that they have the properties R1 to R11 of Sec. 2.4. To do this in terms of ordered pairs is straightforward but tedious, and so we introduce a new notation for complex numbers which simplifies numerical work. In preparation for this we note the following identities:

$$(0,b) = (b,0) \times (0,1)$$
$$(a,b) = (a,0) + (b,0) \times (0,1)$$

Exercise A.   Verify the above identities.

Our new notation is given in terms of the old by the table below:

	Old (a,b) notation	New $a + bi$ notation
Real numbers	$(a,0)$	a
Unit imaginary	$(0,1)$	i
Pure imaginaries	$(0,b)$	bi
Complex numbers	(a,b)	$a + bi$

By translating from the old notation to the new notation, we obtain the following rules for equality, addition, and multiplication:

Equality: $a + bi = c + di$ if and only if $a = c$ and $b = d$.

Addition: $(a + bi) + (c + di) = (a + c) + (b + d)i.$

Multiplication: $(a + bi) \times (c + di) = (ac - bd) + (bc + ad)i.$

The advantage of the new notation is that we can apply the ordinary rules of algebra to $a + bi$ and obtain correct results provided that we replace i^2 with -1 wherever it occurs.

Exercise B.   By ordinary algebra multiply $(a + bi)(c + di)$ and obtain $ac + i(bc + ad) + i^2(bd)$. Replace i^2 with -1, and obtain our formula for multiplication.

Illustrations

   1. $(3 + 6i) + (2 - 3i) = 5 + 3i$.
   2. $(7 + 5i) - (1 + 2i) = 6 + 3i$.
   3. $(5 + 7i)(3 + 4i) = 15 + 41i + 28i^2 = (15 - 28) + 41i = -13 + 41i$.
   4. $(2 - 3i)(-1 + 4i) = -2 + 11i - 12i^2 = (-2 + 12) + 11i = 10 + 11i$.

We also must consider division. We wish to express $1/(a + bi)$ as a complex number. This is best approached through the use of the conjugate complex number $a - bi$.

Definition: The complex numbers $a + bi$ and $a - bi$ are called *conjugates*.

We write:

$$\frac{1}{a + bi} = \left(\frac{1}{a + bi}\right)\left(\frac{a - bi}{a - bi}\right) = \frac{a - bi}{a^2 + b^2} = \frac{a}{a^2 + b^2} + \frac{-b}{a^2 + b^2}i$$

which is the required complex number equal to $1/(a + bi)$. By an extension of this method we can evaluate general quotients $(a + bi)/(c + di)$:

$$\frac{a + bi}{c + di} = \left(\frac{a + bi}{c + di}\right)\left(\frac{c - di}{c - di}\right) = \frac{(ac + bd) + (bc - ad)i}{c^2 + d^2}$$

Hence we have the rule for division:

Division. In order to form the quotient $(a + bi)/(c + di)$, multiply numerator and denominator by the conjugate complex number $c - di$, and simplify the result.

Illustration 5

$$\frac{4 + i}{2 - 3i} = \frac{4 + i}{2 - 3i} \times \frac{2 + 3i}{2 + 3i} = \frac{(4 + i)(2 + 3i)}{(2 - 3i)(2 + 3i)} = \frac{5 + 14i}{13}$$

We could write this answer as $\frac{5}{13} + \frac{14}{13}i$, but this is an unnecessary refinement.

Finally, let us solve some equations involving complex numbers. The general method is suggested by the illustration below:

Illustration 6. Solve: $(x + yi)(2 - 3i) = 4 + i$. We could do this by writing $x + yi = (4 + i)/(2 - 3i)$ and evaluating the quotient on the right. But let us use another method. If we multiply out the left-hand side, we get:

$$(2x + 3y) + (-3x + 2y)i = 4 + i$$

From our definition of the equality of two complex numbers, the *real parts* of both sides must be equal, and similarly the *imaginary* parts must be equal. Hence:

$$2x + 3y = 4$$
$$-3x + 2y = 1$$

We can solve these simultaneous equations and obtain: $x = \frac{5}{13}$ and $y = \frac{14}{13}$. Note that x and y are real.

This method of equating real and imaginary parts is of great importance in the application of complex numbers to engineering, and you should be certain that you understand it.

There are a number of other important properties of complex numbers that need to be discussed. Since these depend upon a knowledge of trigonometry, we defer their treatment to Chap. 13.

PROBLEMS 2.14

In Probs. 1 to 14 find the sum or difference of the given complex numbers.

1. $(6 + 3i) + (5 - 2i)$.   **2.** $(-16 + 2i) + (7 + i)$.
3. $(20 - 7i) - (15 + 8i)$.   **4.** $(-13 + 8i) - (12 + 6i)$.
5. $(9 + 5i) + (-11 - 18i)$.   **6.** $(12 - 10i) + (-8 + 3i)$.
7. $-(3 - i) + (6 + 2i)$.   **8.** $-(-32 + 4i) + (12 - 5i)$.
9. $-(5 + 2i) - (-7 + 3i)$.   **10.** $-(-6 + 4i) - (8 - i)$.
11. $5 - (3 - 4i)$.   **12.** $(7 - 5i) + 8$.
13. $(4 + 8i) - 5i$.   **14.** $(11 - 6i) + 9i$.

In Probs. 15 to 30 find the product of the given complex numbers.

15. $(2 + 5i)(-3 + 6i)$.   **16.** $(3 - 8i)(2 + i)$.
17. $(9 + i)(6 - 4i)$.   **18.** $(8 + 4i)(5 + 3i)$.
19. $(\sqrt{2} + i)(\sqrt{2} - i)$.   **20.** $(\sqrt{3} - i)(\sqrt{3} + i)$.
21. $(5 + 8i)(5 - 8i)$.   **22.** $(7 - 6i)(7 + 6i)$.
23. $5(6 - 3i)$.   **24.** $4(-7 + 5i)$.
25. $(3i)(2 + 6i)$.   **26.** $(-4i)(-7 + 3i)$.
27. $(2i)(8i)$.   **28.** $(3i)(-4i)$.
29. i^3.   **30.** i^4.

In Probs. 31 to 40 find the quotient of the given complex numbers.

31. $(4 + 3i)/(2 + 5i)$.   **32.** $(3 + 5i)/(1 + 2i)$.
33. $(7 + 6i)/(3 - 4i)$.   **34.** $(4 + 7i)/(2 - 3i)$.
35. $(-6 + 3i)/(-1 + 2i)$.   **36.** $(-5 + 6i)/(-3 - 4i)$.
37. $3i/(4 + 7i)$.   **38.** $5i/(3 - 5i)$.
39. $(2 + 6i)/(4i)$.   **40.** $(3 - 6i)/2i$.

In Probs. 41 to 46 solve for x and y by equating real and imaginary parts.

41. $(x + iy)(2 - 5i) = 1 + 5i$.   **42.** $(x + iy)(5 + 2i) = 2 + 3i$.
43. $(x + iy)(-4 + i) = -9 + 7i$.   **44.** $(x + iy)(i + 1) = 2i + 3$.
45. $(x + iy)(3i) = 6$.   **46.** $(x + iy)(-2i) = 5i$.

In Probs. 47 to 52 show that the given complex number satisfies the given equation.

47. $2 + 3i$; $x^2 - 4x + 13 = 0$.   **48.** $2 - 3i$; $x^2 - 4x + 13 = 0$.
49. $4 + 2i$; $x^2 + (-6 + 3i)x + (18 - 16i) = 0$.
50. $2 - 5i$; $x^2 + (-6 + 3i)x + (18 - 16i) = 0$.
51. $5 + 3i$; $x^2 - (6 + 4i)x + (2 + 8i) = 0$.
52. $1 + i$; $x^2 - (6 + 4i)x + (2 + 8i) = 0$.
53. Verify that R1 to R11 are satisfied when $a = 2 + 4i$, $b = -1 + i$, and $c = 3 + 2i$.
54. What is the additive inverse of $a + bi$?   What is the multiplicative inverse of $a + bi$?
55. Discuss the possibility of inequalities between two complex numbers; i.e., does $a + bi < c + di$ have a meaning?   If so, what?   Can the complex numbers be ordered along a line like the real numbers?

2.15. *Solutions of Other Algebraic Equations*

Since we have extended our number system by considering progressively more and more complicated equations, it is reasonable to suppose that we may be led to "supercomplex" numbers in an effort to solve equations of the form:

$$ax^n + bx^{n-1} + \cdots + cx + d = 0 \qquad a \neq 0$$

where $a, b, \ldots, c, d$ are complex numbers. As a matter of fact no new types of numbers need to be introduced for this purpose. This is a consequence of the so-called "Fundamental Theorem of Algebra":

Theorem 18. The equation above with complex coefficients always has a complex number $x = u + iv$ as a solution.

The proof of this theorem is beyond the scope of this book.

Since we do not have to invent any new numbers to solve this equation, we say that the set of complex numbers is *algebraically closed*. As a consequence we end our development of the number system at this point. It should be remarked, however, that for other purposes mathematicians have developed systems of "hypercomplex" numbers, two of which are called "quaternions" and "Cayley Numbers." We do not discuss these here.

2.16. *Classification of Numbers*

The following chart shows the various types of numbers and their relationships.

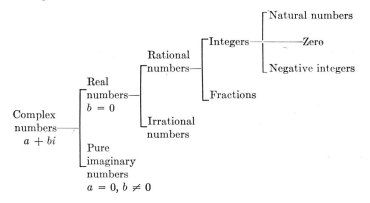

REFERENCES

Birkhoff, Garrett, and Saunders MacLane: "A Survey of Modern Algebra," Chaps. 1, 2, and 3, Macmillan, New York (1941).

Courant, Richard, and Herbert Robbins: "What Is Mathematics?" Chaps. 1 and 2, Oxford, New York (1941).

Dantzig, Tobias: "Number, the Language of Science," Macmillan, New York (1930).

Lieber, L. R.: "Infinity," pp. 87–203, Rinehart, New York (1953).

Weiss, M. J.: "Higher Algebra for the Undergraduate," Chaps. 1 and 2, Wiley, New York (1949).

Whitehead, A. N., "An Introduction to Mathematics," Chaps. 5–8, Holt, New York (1911).

Also consult the following articles in the *American Mathematical Monthly:*

Allen, E. S.: Definitions of Imaginary and Complex Numbers, vol. 29, p. 301 (1922).

Bell, E. T.: On Proofs by Mathematical Induction, vol. 27, p. 413 (1920).

Boyer, C. B.: An Early Reference to Division by Zero, vol. 50, p. 487 (1943).

Cajori, Florian: Historical Note on the Graphic Representation of Imaginaries before the Time of Wessel, vol. 19, p. 167 (1912).

Raynor, G. E.: Mathematical Induction, vol. 33, p. 376 (1926).

CHAPTER THREE

Polynomials

3.1. *Algebraic Expressions*

In this chapter and in the following two chapters we present a review of some of the most important notions in elementary algebra. These deal with the properties of *algebraic expressions*. In order to form such an expression, we start with a finite collection of numbers and letters (which represent arbitrary numbers). Then we combine these in a finite number of steps through the processes of addition, subtraction, multiplication, division, and extraction of roots. The end result is an algebraic expression. The following are examples of such expressions:

$$2a + \frac{3}{b^2} \qquad \frac{6x + 5x^2}{2 - 3x} \qquad \sqrt{3r + 5s^2}$$

For the present we shall restrict ourselves to the operation of addition, subtraction, and multiplication; and we call the resulting algebraic expressions *polynomials*. A polynomial is the sum of a finite number of *terms*, each of which is the product of a finite collection of numbers and letters. A term may also include a negative sign, corresponding to a -1 contained in this product. In writing the expressions for these terms we write, as usual, a^2 for $a \times a$; b^3 for $b \times b \times b$; etc. You should note that the only exponents which occur on letters are *positive integers;* fractional and negative exponents are excluded. The numbers involved, however, may be any real or complex numbers. Examples of polynomials are:

$$4x^3 - 2x^2 + x - 1 \quad \tfrac{1}{2}a + 3bc; \; 5xy^2 - \tfrac{1}{3}yz + \sqrt{2} \quad (3 + 2i)x^2 - 6i$$

Polynomials, such as $8x^2y^6$, which contain only one term are called *monomials;* those with two terms, such as $4a^2 - 7bc$, are called *binomials;* and those with three terms, such as $7a^2 + 4ab + 3b^2$, are called *trinomials.* No special names are given to polynomials with more than three terms.

In writing a term it is customary to multiply together all the numbers involved and to put this product in front. This number is called the *numerical coefficient* of the term. Similarly, all factors involving the same letter are brought together and are written as this letter with a suitable exponent. Thus we write:

$$2 \times a \times 4 \times b \times a \times b \times b \quad \text{as } 8a^2b^3$$

Two terms which differ only in their numerical coefficient are called *like terms.* For instance, $4x^2y^3$ and $6x^2y^3$ are like terms, but $3xy^2$ and $7x^2y$ are *not* like terms; similarly $4x^2$ and $3a^2$ are *not* like terms. In writing a polynomial it is customary to combine like terms by the use of the distributive law; for example:

$$4x^2y^3 + 6x^2y^3 = 10x^2y^3$$

As a result a polynomial will be expressed as a finite sum of unlike terms, each of which either is a number or consists of a numerical coefficient multiplied by the product of a finite number of distinct letters, each of which carries an exponent which is a positive integer.

Exercise A.   Which of the following expressions are polynomials?

(1) $3x^2 - x + \tfrac{1}{2}$.

(2) $x^3 + \dfrac{1}{x} + 3$.

(3) $\sqrt{2x} + 4x^2$.

(4) $2\sqrt{x} + 5x^2 - 2$.

(5) $\dfrac{3}{2x^2 - x + 6}$.

3.2. *Addition of Polynomials*

The procedure for adding polynomials is a direct consequence of the commutative and associative laws for addition and of the distributive law (R2, R5, R11, Sec. 2.4). Let us illustrate by adding:

$$(5x^2y + x - 3xy^2 + 2) + (-2x + 3y + 7xy^2 - 5)$$

The first step is to use the commutative and associative laws to group like terms together. In the above example we obtain:

$$(5x^2y) + (x - 2x) + (-3xy^2 + 7xy^2) + (3y) + (2 - 5)$$

Then we use the distributive law to combine the like terms. In our example we have the final result:

$$5x^2y - x + 4xy^2 + 3y - 3$$

The process of addition can be conveniently carried out by arranging the work in columns, where each column contains like terms. In the above example we write:

$$\begin{array}{c}
5x^2y + x - 3xy^2 + 2 \\
- 2x + 7xy^2 - 5 + 3y\\
\hline
5x^2y - x + 4xy^2 - 3 + 3y
\end{array}$$

This arrangement of the work is particularly helpful when three or more polynomials are to be added.

In order to subtract two polynomials, we convert the problem to addition (see the definition of subtraction, Sec. 2.2) and then proceed as above. For example:

$$(4x^2 - 3xy + 2) - (5x^2 + x - 3)$$

is written as the sum

$$(4x^2 - 3xy + 2) + (-5x^2 - x + 3)$$

and equals:

$$-x^2 - 3xy - x + 5$$

PROBLEMS 3.2

Perform the indicated operations:

1. $(3a^2 + ab + c) + (2c - 4a^2 - ab)$.
2. $(5x^2 - 3y^2 + x) + (2x + 7y^2 - 3x^2)$.
3. $(-2pq + q^3 + p^2) - (2p^2 - q^3 + 4pq)$.
4. $(8r + 5s - 5r^2s^3) - (2s + 8r + 3r^2s^3)$.
5. $(15x^2y + 5xy^2 - 3xy + 2) + (5xy + x^2 - y^2)$.
6. $(8abc + 4ab^2 - 5ab + 3) + (6ab + 2ab^2 + 2b)$.
7. $(7x^3 - 5y^3 + 2xy) - (6x^3 + 4y + 3xy)$.
8. $(-3pq + 7p^2 - 5q) - (4q^2 + 2q - 3p^2)$.
9. $(2x^2 - 3y^2 + x) + (5a^2 + 2b^2 + y)$.
10. $(8r^2 + 4rs + s^2) + (3x^2 + y^2 + s^3)$.
11. $(3x^2y - 5xy^2 + 7xy) + (4x^3 + 8x^2y + 3xy^2) + (-2xy^2 + 5xy + 3)$.
12. $(-9a^3 + 15b^2 - 7a^2b) + (10a^3 + 10b^3 - 2a^2b) + (4a^2 + 9ab + b^2)$.
13. $(3x^2 - 17y^2) + (4x^2 + 9y^2) + (-3r^2 + 5s^2)$.
14. $(-2pq + 4q^2) + (5pq - 2q^2) + (a^2 + b^2)$.

15. $(7x^4 - 3a^2 + 5xy) - (2x^4 + 6a^2 - 2xy) + (3x^4 + 2a^2 + 4xy).$
16. $(2a^2 - 3b^2 + 8c^3) + (3a^2 + 5b^2 - 6c^3) - (a^2 + b^2 + c^3).$
17. $(4xy + x^2 - 3y^4) + (x^2 + y^2 - 2xy) - (x^3 - y^2 + 7xy).$
18. $(6r^2s + r^3 + 3s^5) - (2r^3 - 4s^5 + 5rs^2) + (15r^2s + 10rs^2).$
19. $[(2a^2 - 3b^2) - (4ab + b^2)] - (5a^2 + 7ab + 11b^2).$
20. $(30x^2 - 22xy + 16y^2) - [(2x^2 + 4y^3) - (15xy - 12y^2)].$

3.3. *Multiplication of Polynomials*

The procedure for the multiplication of polynomials is based upon the method of multiplying monomials, together with the repeated use of the distributive law (R11). We recall that a monomial is either a number or the product of a numerical coefficient and a collection of letters carrying positive integral exponents. The product of two monomials is, therefore, the product of all the factors of the two given monomials taken together.

Illustrations
   1. $(2x^2y)(5x^3y^4) = 10x^5y^5.$
   2. $(-5a^3bc)(4ab^2g^3) = -20a^4b^3cg^3.$

In carrying out this product we recall that

$$a^p \cdot a^q = a^{p+q}$$

for a^p is the product of p a's and a^q is the product of q a's. There are, therefore, $(p + q)$ a's in the combined product.

We now use the distributive law to reduce the problem of multiplying polynomials to that of multiplying monomials.

Illustration 3. Multiply $(a^2 + 2b)(3a^2 + 4b + 1)$. One use of the distributive law permits us to write this as:

$$a^2(3a^2 + 4b + 1) + 2b(3a^2 + 4b + 1)$$

A second application of the distributive law gives

$$(3a^4 + 4a^2b + a^2) + (6a^2b + 8b^2 + 2b) = 3a^4 + 10a^2b + a^2 + 8b^2 + 2b$$

The work can be conveniently arranged as shown below:

$$
\begin{array}{l}
3a^2 + 4b + 1 \\
\underline{a^2 + 2b} \\
3a^4 + 4a^2b + a^2 \\
\underline{ + 6a^2b + 8b^2 + 2b} \\
3a^4 + 10a^2b + a^2 + 8b^2 + 2b
\end{array}
$$

A particularly important special case is that of the product of two polynomials which involve powers of a single letter only. In this case it is convenient to arrange the order of the terms so that the exponents decrease from term to term, i.e., "according to decreasing powers." Thus we would rearrange

$$7x^2 + 21x^5 - x^3 + 2x - 1 + 5x^4$$

to read:

$$21x^5 + 5x^4 - x^3 + 7x^2 + 2x - 1$$

This will help us to keep things straight in our multiplications and later in our divisions.

Illustration 4.　Multiply:

$$
\begin{array}{r}
5x^4 - 8x^3 + x^2 + 5x - 3 \\
x^2 + 2x - 1 \\
\hline
5x^6 - 8x^5 + x^4 + 5x^3 - 3x^2 \\
+ 10x^5 - 16x^4 + 2x^3 + 10x^2 - 6x \\
- 5x^4 + 8x^3 - x^2 - 5x + 3 \\
\hline
5x^6 + 2x^5 - 20x^4 + 15x^3 + 6x^2 - 11x + 3
\end{array}
$$

PROBLEMS 3.3

Perform the indicated operations:

1. $(3a^2b^4)(-4a^4b^3)$.
2. $(-7p^2q^6)(3p^4q^7)$.
3. $(16xy^2z^3)(4x^2wy^3)$.
4. $(-8r^2s^5t)(7s^4t^6u^2)$.
5. $(3a + 5b)(2a - 6b)$.
6. $(7x - 9y)(2x - 5y)$.
7. $(8x + 3y)^2$.
8. $(-3a + 11b)^2$.
9. $(2p - q)^3$.
10. $(r + 3s)^3$.
11. $(4x + 3y)(4x - 3y)$.
12. $(6a - 7b)(6a + 7b)$.
13. $(5x^4 - 3x^3 + x^2 - x + 1)(2x^2 + 3x + 4)$.
14. $(4x^3 + 7x^2 - x + 3)(3x^3 - 2x + 2)$.
15. $(3x^2 + x^3 - 7x^4 + 5)(x + 9x^2)$.
16. $(5x + x^4 - 2x^3 + 1)(x + 4 + 2x^2)$.
17. $(4a^4 - 9ab^2 + b^3)(7a^3 - b^2 + 3)$.
18. $(r^3 + 7r^2s^2 + s^4)(s^2 - 3s + 9)$.
19. $(8x^4 - 5x^3y + 9x^2y^2 + 3xy^3 - y^4)(2x^2 - xy + y^2)$.
20. $(7a^4 + 4a^3b - 5a^2b^2 + 2ab^3 - b^4)(a^2 + 2ab - b^2)$.

3.4. *Binomial Theorem*

By direct multiplication, as in the last section, we can easily establish the following formulas:

$$
\begin{aligned}
(a + b)^2 &= a^2 + 2ab + b^2 \\
(a + b)^3 &= a^3 + 3a^2b + 3ab^2 + b^3 \\
(a + b)^4 &= a^4 + 4a^3b + 6a^2b^2 + 4ab^3 + b^4 \\
(a + b)^5 &= a^5 + 5a^4b + 10a^3b^2 + 10a^2b^3 + 5ab^4 + b^5
\end{aligned}
$$

The coefficients in these products have a pattern which is illustrated by the following scheme, known as *Pascal's Triangle*.

$$(a + b)^0 \qquad\qquad 1$$
$$(a + b)^1 \qquad\qquad 1 \quad 1$$
$$(a + b)^2 \qquad\qquad 1 \quad 2 \quad 1$$
$$(a + b)^3 \qquad\qquad 1 \quad 3 \quad 3 \quad 1$$
$$(a + b)^4 \qquad\qquad 1 \quad 4 \quad 6 \quad 4 \quad 1$$
$$(a + b)^5 \qquad\qquad 1 \quad 5 \quad 10 \quad 10 \quad 5 \quad 1$$
$$\cdot\ \cdot\ \cdot \qquad\qquad \cdot\ \cdot\ \cdot$$

In this array each horizontal line begins and ends with a 1, and each other entry is the sum of the two numbers to its left and right in the horizontal row above.

Exercise A. By direct multiplication verify the above formulas for $(a + b)^2$, $(a + b)^3$, $(a + b)^4$, $(a + b)^5$.

Exercise B. From Pascal's Triangle determine the coefficients of the terms in the expansion of $(a + b)^6$, and verify your result by direct multiplication. (*Ans.:* 1, 6, 15, 20, 15, 6, 1.)

Whenever we discover a pattern like this, we suspect that there must be some general way of describing it and so we are led to ask whether there is some general formula for $(a + b)^n$, where n is any positive integer. There is indeed such a formula, known as the *Binomial Formula*, and we shall now proceed to develop it. By way of preparation we must introduce some new notations.

Definition: The symbol $n!$ (for n a positive integer), read "*n factorial*," stands for the product

$$n! = 1 \times 2 \times 3 \times \cdots \times n$$

Further, $0!$ is defined to be 1. Factorials are not defined for negative integers or for other real numbers.

Exercise C. Compute $2!$, $3!$, $4!$, $5!$, $6!$.

Exercise D. Show that $n!/n = (n - 1)!$.

Exercise E. Compute: $7!/3!$; $n!/(n - 1)!$; $n!(n - 2)$; $n!/r!$, where $r < n$.

Definition: The symbol $\binom{n}{r}$, where n and r are integers ≥ 0 and $n \geq r$, is defined to be

$$\binom{n}{r} = \frac{n!}{(n - r)!\,r!}$$

These symbols are called *binomial coefficients*.

Exercise F. Show that:

$$\binom{4}{2} = 6 \qquad \binom{6}{4} = 15 \qquad \binom{5}{3} = 10 \qquad \binom{4}{4} = 1 \qquad \binom{5}{1} = 5$$

Exercise G.   From the definition show that

$$\binom{n}{r} = \binom{n}{n-r}$$

The connection between these symbols and the expression for $(a + b)^n$ is easily seen from the fact that Pascal's Triangle now can be written in the form:

$(a + b)^0$	
$(a + b)^1$	
$(a + b)^2$	
$(a + b)^3$	
$(a + b)^4$	
$(a + b)^5$	
. . .	. . .

Exercise H.   Verify that this representation of Pascal's Triangle agrees with the one given earlier in this section.

We have now given you a broad hint regarding the nature of the Binomial Formula. Can you guess the correct expression for it? Cover up the next few lines of this page, and write down your guess. Please do not peek until you have written it down, for intelligent guessing is a most important part of the process of mathematical discovery, and you need practice in doing it. Now you can look, and we hope that you have written something like the following:

Theorem 1.   Binomial Theorem.   Let n be a positive integer. Then

$$(a + b)^n = a^n + \binom{n}{1} a^{n-1}b + \binom{n}{2} a^{n-2}b^2 + \cdots$$
$$+ \binom{n}{n-2} a^2b^{n-2} + \binom{n}{n-1} ab^{n-1} + b^n$$

Or, in the expansion of $(a + b)^n$, the coefficient of $a^{n-r}b^r$ is $\binom{n}{r}$.

Proof: Since this theorem is to be proved for all values of n, a reasonable approach is to try mathematical induction. The formula is trivially verified for $n = 1$, and indeed we have verified it for $n = 1, 2, 3, 4, 5$. We, therefore, assume it to be true for $n = k$ and show that this implies its truth for $n = k + 1$. To do so, we wish to show that the coefficient of $a^{k+1-r}b^r$ in the expansion of $(a + b)^{k+1}$ is $\binom{k + 1}{r}$. We write

$$(a + b)^k = a^k + \cdots + \binom{k}{r - 1} a^{k+1-r}b^{r-1} + \binom{k}{r} a^{k-r}b^r + \cdots + b^k$$

Then $(a + b)^{k+1}$ is given by the product:

$$a^k + \cdots + \binom{k}{r - 1} a^{k+1-r}b^{r-1} + \binom{k}{r} a^{k-r}b^r + \cdots + b^k$$

$$a + b$$

$$a^{k+1} + \cdots + \binom{k}{r - 1} a^{k+2-r}b^{r-1} + \binom{k}{r} a^{k+1-r}b^r + \cdots + ab^k$$

$$a^k b + \cdots \qquad\qquad + \binom{k}{r - 1} a^{k+1-r}b^r + \binom{k}{r} a^{k-r}b^{r+1}$$

$$+ \cdots + b^{k+1}$$

$$a^{k+1} + \cdots \qquad\qquad + \left[\binom{k}{r} + \binom{k}{r - 1} \right] a^{k+1-r}b^r + \cdots + b^{k+1}$$

Therefore the coefficient of $a^{k+1-r}b^r$ is $\binom{k}{r} + \binom{k}{r - 1}$. We must now simplify this.

$$\binom{k}{r} + \binom{k}{r - 1} = \frac{k!}{r!(k - r)!} + \frac{k!}{(r - 1)!(k - r + 1)!}$$

$$= \frac{k!(k - r + 1) + k!r}{r!(k - r + 1)!}$$

$$= \frac{k!(k + 1)}{r!(k + 1 - r)!} = \frac{(k + 1)!}{r!(k + 1 - r)!} = \binom{k + 1}{r}$$

Therefore, the formula is verified for $n = k + 1$, and by the axiom of induction (Sec. 2.5) the theorem is proved.

Exercise I. Relate the last computation in the proof above to the method of constructing Pascal's Triangle.

The Binomial Theorem permits us to write down rather quickly the expansions of powers of binomials which are tedious to compute by repeated multiplication.

Illustrations

1. Expand $(2x + 5y)^3$.

$$(2x + 5y)^3 = (2x)^3 + 3(2x)^2(5y) + 3(2x)(5y)^2 + (5y)^3$$
$$= 8x^3 + 60x^2y + 150xy^2 + 125y^3$$

2. Expand $(3x - 2y)^4$.

$$(3x - 2y)^4 = (3x)^4 + 4(3x)^3(-2y) + 6(3x)^2(-2y)^2 + 4(3x)(-2y)^3 + (-2y)^4$$
$$= 81x^4 - 216x^3y + 216x^2y^2 - 96xy^3 + 16y^4$$

3. Compute the term involving x^4y^3 in the expansion of $(3x - 5y)^7$. This term will involve $(3x)^4(-5y)^3$ with an appropriate coefficient. The theorem tells us that this coefficient is $\binom{7}{3} = 35$. So the term is

$$35(3x)^4(-5y)^3 = -354{,}375x^4y^3$$

PROBLEMS 3.4

1. Compute: $\binom{5}{2}$; $\binom{7}{4}$; $\binom{6}{3}$; $\binom{4}{0}$; $\binom{3}{1}$.

2. Compute: $\binom{4}{3}$; $\binom{5}{0}$; $\binom{7}{5}$; $\binom{6}{2}$; $\binom{8}{3}$.

In Probs. 3 to 6 verify the given formulas by direct computation.

3. $\binom{6}{2} + \binom{6}{3} = \binom{7}{3}$.   4. $\binom{5}{3} + \binom{5}{4} = \binom{6}{4}$.

5. $1 + \binom{4}{1} + \binom{4}{2} + \binom{4}{3} + \binom{4}{4} = 2^4$.

6. $1 + \binom{5}{1} + \binom{5}{2} + \binom{5}{3} + \binom{5}{4} + \binom{5}{5} = 2^5$.

In Probs. 7 to 16 expand by the Binomial Theorem.

7. $(x + 2y)^5$.   8. $(3a + b)^4$.
9. $(2r - s)^6$.   10. $(3p - 4q)^4$.
11. $(\frac{1}{2}x + y)^6$.   12. $(x + \frac{1}{3}y)^6$.
13. $(3/x + x^2)^3$.   14. $(x^2 - 2/x)^4$.
15. $(1.01)^5 = (1 + 0.01)^5$.   16. $(1.98)^4 = (2 - 0.02)^4$.

In Probs. 17 to 22 find the coefficient of the given term in the given expansion.

17. a^9b^4 in $(a + b)^{13}$.   18. r^4s^5 in $(2r + 3s)^9$.
19. x^2y^5 in $(2x - 3y)^7$.   20. p^3q^3 in $(4p - 5q)^6$.
21. x^6y^3 in $(x^2 + y^3)^4$.   22. x^4 in $(x^2 + 1/x)^5$.
23. Write $(x + y + z)^3 = [x + (y + z)]^3$, and expand through repeated use of the binomial theorem.
24. Write $(x + y - z)^3 = [(x + y) - z]^3$, and expand through repeated use of the binomial theorem.

25. In the Binomial Formula put $a = 1$ and $b = 1$, and then prove that $2^n =$
$$1 + \binom{n}{1} + \binom{n}{2} + \cdots + \binom{n}{n-2} + \binom{n}{n-1} + \binom{n}{n}.$$

3.5. *Division of Polynomials*

In this section we shall restrict ourselves to polynomials which involve only a single letter, and we shall assume them to be arranged in descending powers of that letter. Examples of such polynomials are:

$$15x^5 + 8x^3 - 4x^2 + x + 7 \qquad 8a^4 + \tfrac{1}{2}a^3 - a^2 + 2a + 5$$

The highest exponent which appears is called the *degree* of the polynomial. The degrees of the two examples above are 5 and 4, respectively. We shall denote such polynomials by the symbols $P(x)$, $Q(x)$, $D(x)$, etc., where the letter in the parentheses indicates the letter of the polynomial and P, Q, R, etc., are names to represent different polynomials of this type.

Suppose that we have two polynomials $P(x)$ of degree n and $D(x)$ of degree r, where $n \geq r$. We wish to consider what happens when we divide $P(x)$ by $D(x)$. This process of division needs a definition, but we shall postpone giving this until the method is clear. We illustrate by an example:

Illustration 1. Divide $6x^4 + 7x^3 + 12x^2 + 10x + 1$ by $2x^2 + x + 4$.

$$
\begin{array}{r}
3x^2 + 2x - 1 \\
\hline
2x^2 + x + 4\,\overline{)\,6x^4 + 7x^3 + 12x^2 + 10x + 1} \\
6x^4 + 3x^3 + 12x^2 \\
\hline
4x^3 + 0x^2 + 10x + 1 \\
4x^3 + 2x^2 + 8x \\
\hline
-\ 2x^2 + 2x + 1 \\
-\ 2x^2 - x - 4 \\
\hline
3x + 5
\end{array}
$$

We have a quotient of $3x^2 + 2x - 1$ and a remainder of $3x + 5$.

The process of division as illustrated above is straightforward and should already be familiar to you. Let us suppose that we have carried through the division

$$D(x)\overline{)P(x)}$$

and obtained a *quotient* $Q(x)$ and a *remainder* $R(x)$. $D(x)$ is called the *divisor*, and $P(x)$ is called the *dividend*. There are several points worthy of mention:

(1) The division continues step by step until a remainder is reached whose *degree is less than the degree of the divisor.*

(2) When the remainder is zero, the division is said to be *exact.*

(3) By reversing the steps of the computation we can show that

$$P(x) = D(x) \cdot Q(x) + R(x)$$

for all values of x.

This leads us to the following statement:

The Division Algorithm. Let $P(x)$ and $D(x)$ be polynomials of degrees n and r, respectively, where $n \geq r$. Then there exist polynomials $Q(x)$, called the quotient, and $R(x)$, called the remainder, such that:

(1) $P(x) = D(x) \cdot Q(x) + R(x)$ for all x.

(2) The degree of $R(x)$ is less than the degree of $D(x)$.

The proof of this algorithm can be obtained by a generalization of the process shown in Illustration 1 or by more sophisticated means. Since either of these is too complicated to explain in detail here, we shall omit the proof.

In the problems below, follow the method of the illustration. You may run into trouble if a term is missing from the dividend or the divisor as in:

$$4x^3 + 2x^2 - 3$$

which has no term in x. It will help you to keep matters straight if you will supply the missing term (or terms) with zero coefficients and write the above as:

$$4x^3 + 2x^2 + 0x - 3$$

PROBLEMS 3.5

In Probs. 1 to 20 obtain the quotient and remainder, and check your result by substituting back in the equation $P(x) = D(x) \cdot Q(x) + R(x)$.

Dividend	*Divisor*
1. $6x^3 + x^2 + x + 2$	$3x + 2$
2. $6x^3 - 5x^2 - 8x + 3$	$2x - 3$
3. $4x^3 + 17x^2 - 10x + 31$	$x + 5$
4. $10x^3 - x^2 - 16x + 4$	$2x - 1$
5. $5x^4 + 6x^3 - 3x - 5$	$x^2 + x + 1$
6. $4x^4 - 2x^3 + 3x^2 + 4x - 1$	$4x^2 + 2x - 3$
7. $6x^5 + x^3 + 8x^2 + 7$	$2x^2 + 1$
8. $4x^5 + 30x^3 + 14x - 1$	$4x^3 + 2x - 3$
9. $10x^5 - 3x^4 - x^3 + 3$	$5x^3 + x^2 - 1$
10. $3x^5 + 2x^4 - 7x^3 + 2x$	$x^3 + 1$

	Dividend	*Divisor*

11. $9x^3 + x + 14x^5 + 1 - 10x^4 - 9x^2$ $1 + 2x^2$

12. $2x^3 - 26x^2 - 24x - 3x^4 + 12x^5 + 20$ $4 - 3x^2$

13. $x^4 - 1$ $x^2 - 1$

14. $x^6 - 1$ $x^3 - 1$

15. $x^6 - 1$ $x^2 + 1$

16. $x^5 - 1$ $x^2 + 1$

17. $x^6 - y^6$ $x - y$

18. $x^8 - y^8$ $x + y$

19. $\frac{2}{3}x^3 - 3x^2 - 5x + 1$ $2x + 3$

20. $(2 - i)x^3 + (6 - 4i)x^2 + (4 - i)x - (3 + 9i)$ $x + (3 - i)$

21. If $P(x)$ is of degree n and $D(x)$ of degree r and if $r > n$, show that the division algorithm is satisfied trivially with $Q(x) = 0$ and $R(x) = P(x)$.

3.6. Factoring

In factoring we seek to undo the process of multiplication. We are given a polynomial and are asked to discover how it can be expressed as a product of other polynomials, called its factors. You will find factoring important when you are asked to simplify algebraic fractions or to solve certain types of equations.

Definition: If a polynomial $P(x)$ is the product of r polynomials $Q_1(x)$, . . . , $Q_r(x)$, that is, if

$$P(x) = Q_1(x) \cdot Q_2(x) \cdot \cdot \cdot \cdot \cdot Q_r(x)$$

then $Q_1(x)$, . . . , $Q_r(x)$ are called *factors* of $P(x)$.

Exercise A. If $Q(x)$ is a factor of $P(x)$, show that the quotient of $P(x)$ by $Q(x)$ involves no remainder, i.e., that the division is exact.

The problem of factoring a general polynomial can be a quite complicated affair. As we shall see in Chap. 10, it is equivalent to the problem of finding all the roots of a polynomial equation, and this is by no means an elementary topic. We have a more limited objective here, namely, to factor certain simple polynomials by methods which are elementary and straightforward. Although these methods are not adequate to factor a general polynomial, they are very useful when they do apply. Hence they are worth mastering.

(a) *Removal of a Common Factor.* When all the terms of the given polynomial have a factor in common, this expression may be factored out by use of the distributive law in reverse. These common factors should be removed before other methods of factoring are employed.

Illustration 1

(a) $2x^3 + 6x^2 - 10 = 2(x^3 + 3x^2 - 5)$.

(b) $x^4 - x^2 = x^2(x^2 - 1)$.

(c) $ac + bc + ad + bd = (ac + bc) + (ad + bd) = c(a + b) + d(a + b) = (c + d)(a + b)$.

(b) *Trinomials with Integral Coefficients.* We consider here trinomials of the form

$$ax^2 + bx + c$$

where a, b, and c are integers. We seek to write this as the product of two linear polynomials with integral coefficients, i.e.,

$$ax^2 + bx + c = (px + q)(rx + s)$$

where p, q, r, and s are integers. This factorization is not always possible, but our method produces the required factors whenever they exist.

Let us first consider the simpler situation where $a = 1$. Then p and r must also equal 1, and we write:

$$x^2 + bx + c = (x + q)(x + s)$$

Multiplying out the right-hand side, we find:

$$x^2 + bx + c = x^2 + (q + s)x + qs$$

Thus, we are looking for two integers, q and s, such that

$$q + s = b \qquad qs = c$$

To find these, we factor c into all possible pairs (q,s) such that $qs = c$. Then we examine these pairs (q,s) to determine whether or not in any of them $q + s = b$. If we find such a pair, we have solved the problem; otherwise there are no factors of the prescribed form. The details of the method are best shown by illustrations.

Illustration 2

(a) Factor $x^2 + 5x + 6$.

The integral pairs of factors of 6 are:

$$(1,6), (2,3), (-1,-6), (-2,-3)$$

We exclude the last two immediately since the sum of two negative integers cannot be $+5$. Examining the other two in turn, we find that $(2,3)$ is a solution since $2 + 3 = 5$. Therefore,

$$x^2 + 5x + 6 = (x + 2)(x + 3)$$

(b) Factor $x^2 - 6x + 8$.

The integral pairs of factors of 8 are:

$$(1,8), \ (2,4) \ (-1,-8), \ (-2,-4)$$

We exclude the first two immediately since the middle coefficient, -6, is negative. We find that $(-2,-4)$ is a solution since $(-2) + (-4) = -6$. Therefore

$$x^2 - 6x + 8 = (x - 2)(x - 4)$$

(c) Factor $x^2 + 3x - 10$.

The integral pairs of factors of -10 are:

$$(1,-10), \ (-1,10), \ (2,-5), \ (5,-2)$$

Examining these in turn, we find that $(5,-2)$ is a solution since $5 + (-2) = 3$. Therefore

$$x^2 + 3x - 10 = (x + 5)(x - 2).$$

(d) Factor $x^2 + 3x + 4$.

The integral pairs of factors of 4 are

$$(1,4), \ (2,2), \ (-1,-4), \ (-2,-2)$$

None of these is a solution, and hence there are no factors of the prescribed form.

In the case of the general trinomial, we write:

$$ax^2 + bx + c = (px + q)(rx + s)$$
$$= prx^2 + (ps + qr)x + qs$$

Therefore, $a = pr$, $b = ps + qr$, $c = qs$. The method is similar to the special case above, but here we have more possibilities. We find the pairs (p,r) which factor a and the pairs (q,s) which factor c. Then we examine each pair (p,r) in connection with each pair (q,s) to see whether or not for any of these combinations: $ps + qr = b$. If so, we have a solution; otherwise, there are no factors of this form.

The number of possibilities will be reduced if we always take $a > 0$. This can always be arranged by removing the common factor, -1, if a is initially negative. Moreover, we can assume that p and r are both positive without losing any possible solutions; we must, however, allow q and s to take all appropriate positive and negative signs.

Illustration 3. Factor $8x^2 + 2x - 15$.

The pairs of factors of 8 are: $(1,8)$ and $(2,4)$. The pairs of factors of -15 are: $(1,-15), \ (-1,15), \ (3,-5), \ (5,-3), \ (-15,1), \ (15,-1), \ (-5,3), \ (-3,5)$. In this case it is necessary to write the numbers in each pair in the two possible orders in order to cover all cases.

Now write one of the first pairs and one of the second pairs as shown below:

$$(1,8)(1,-15)$$

Multiply the two outside numbers, 1 and -15, and add to this the product of the two inside numbers, 8 and 1. This gives $(1)(-15) + (8)(1) = -7$. This should equal the coefficient of x, namely, 2. Since it does not, these two pairs do not give a solution. Try each combination of a first pair and a second pair. Among these we find that the solution is

$$(2,4)(3,-5)$$

for $(2)(-5) + (4)(3) = 2$. Hence

$$8x^2 + 2x - 15 = (2x + 3)(4x - 5).$$

(c) *Difference of Two Squares.* We consider expressions of the form:

$$x^2 - a^2$$

where a^2 is a positive real number. An elementary calculation shows that

$$x^2 - a^2 = (x + a)(x - a)$$

Hence, the factors may be written down at sight.

Illustration 4
- (a) $x^2 - 9 = (x + 3)(x - 3)$.
- (b) $16x^2 - 25 = (4x + 5)(4x - 5)$.
- (c) $25x^4 - 36y^6 = (5x^2 + 6y^3)(5x^2 - 6y^3)$.
- (d) $(3x + 5)^2 - (2x - 1)^2 = [(3x + 5) + (2x - 1)][(3x + 5) - (2x - 1)] = (5x + 4)(x + 6)$.
- (e) $x^2 - 2 = (x + \sqrt{2})(x - \sqrt{2})$.

This method may be extended to cover expressions of the form:

$$x^2 + a^2$$

For
$$x^2 + a^2 = x^2 - (ia)^2$$
$$= (x + ia)(x - ia)$$

Illustration 5
- (a) $4x^2 + 9 = (2x + 3i)(2x - 3i)$.
- (b) $x^2 + 3 = (x + i\sqrt{3})(x - i\sqrt{3})$.

(d) *Sum and Difference of Two Cubes.* We rely upon the two formulas:

$$x^3 + a^3 = (x + a)(x^2 - ax + a^2)$$
$$x^3 - a^3 = (x - a)(x^2 + ax + a^2)$$

which require no further explanation.

(e) *Combinations of the Above Methods.* It is often possible to factor complicated looking expressions by using two or more of these methods in turn.

Illustration 6   Factor:

$$4x^2 + 24x + 32 - 16y^2 + 16y$$
$$= 4x^2 + 24x + 36 - 16y^2 + 16y - 4$$
$$= 4[(x^2 + 6x + 9) - (4y^2 - 4y + 1)]$$
$$= 4[(x + 3)^2 - (2y - 1)^2]$$
$$= 4[(x + 3 + 2y - 1)(x + 3 - 2y + 1)]$$
$$= 4(x + 2y + 2)(x - 2y + 4)$$

PROBLEMS 3.6

In Probs. 1 to 56 factor the given expression if possible.

1. $xy + 2x + 3y + 6$.

2. $xy + 20 + 4x + 5y$.

3. $x^3 + x^2 + x + 1$.

4. $cy - dy + 5xy$.

5. $sx + sy + vx + vy$.

6. $xy + xz + uy + uz$.

7. $x^2 + 2x - 8$.

8. $x^2 - 3x - 4$.

9. $x^2 - 14x + 40$.

10. $x^2 + 11x + 24$.

11. $36 - 15x + x^2$.

12. $18 - 11x + x^2$.

13. $y^2 - 23xy + 42x^2$.

14. $a^2 - 15ab + 36b^2$.

15. $x^2 + 7x + 14$.

16. $x^2 - 3x - 5$.

17. $3x^2 + 5x + 2$.

18. $2x^2 + 7x + 5$.

19. $3x^2 + 5x - 2$.

20. $2x^2 - 21x + 10$.

21. $2x^2 - 5x + 3$.

22. $7x^2 - 22x + 3$.

23. $5x^2 - 11xy + 2y^2$.

24. $2x^2 - 7xy + 3y^2$.

25. $10x^2 + 9x - 36$.

26. $12x^2 + 2x - 80$.

27. $32x^2 + 48x - 54$.

28. $24x^2 + 22x - 35$.

29. $6x^2 - 29x - 120$.

30. $12x^2 - 32x + 21$.

31. $3x^2 + 14x + 16$.

32. $14x^2 + 69x + 27$.

33. $25x^2 - 16$.

34. $9x^2 - 144$.

35. $x^2 - 5$.

36. $x^2 - 11$.

37. $4x^2 + 9$.

38. $9x^2 + 16$.

39. $(x + 5)^2 - (x - 1)^2$.

40. $(x + 2)^2 - (x - 7)^2$.

41. $x^4 - y^4$.

42. $x^8 - y^8$.

43. $x^2 - 4x - y^2 + 6y - 5 = (x^2 - 4x + 4) - (y^2 - 6y + 9)$.

44. $x^2 + 6x - y^2 + 12y - 27 = (x^2 + 6x + 9) - (y^2 - 12y + 36)$.

45. $8x^3 - y^3$.

46. $64x^3 - 1$.

47. $x^3 + 125$.

48. $x^3 + 1{,}000$.

49. $(a^2 - 4b^2)x^2 + 2ax + 1$.

50. $(2h - h^2)x^2 + 2x + 1$.

51. $x^4 + 2x^2 + 9 = (x^4 + 6x^2 + 9) - 4x^2$.

52. $x^4 + 3x^2 + 4 = (x^4 + 4x^2 + 4) - x^2$.

53. $9x^3 + 2x^2y + 4xy^2$.

54. $27 - 3y^2$.

55. $2x^2 + 2x + 42$.

56. $48 + 3x^2 + 24x$.

57. Show that $x - y$ is a factor of $x^n - y^n$, where n is an integer ≥ 1.   HINT: Use mathematical induction and the identity: $x^{n+1} - y^{n+1} = x(x^n - y^n) + y^n(x - y)$.

58. Show that $x + y$ is a factor of $x^{2n} - y^{2n}$, where n is an integer ≥ 1.   HINT: Use method of Prob. 57.

CHAPTER FOUR

Algebraic Fractions

4.1. *Introduction*

An algebraic fraction is the quotient of two algebraic expressions.
Examples of these are:

$$(a)\ \frac{3x^2 + 4a}{x + 1} \qquad (b)\ \frac{\sqrt{x^3 - 1} + 4x}{\sqrt[3]{x + 7}} \qquad (c)\ \frac{1/x^2 + \sqrt{3}\,x}{2/(x + 5)}$$

We recall that the letters in these expressions stand for arbitrary numbers. In the most general circumstances these numbers are complex,
but in particular situations it may be specified that they are real or
rational. This leads to two important remarks:

(1) The algebra of fractions can be derived from properties R1 to
R11 of Sec. 2.4.

(2) It is understood that we cannot assign values to any letter which
makes any denominator equal to zero. Thus in example (a) above
we exclude $x = -1$; in example (b) we exclude $x = -7$; in example (c)
we exclude $x = 0$ and $x = -5$. It is tedious to state these exclusions
each time that we write a fraction, and so you will have to supply this
information yourself and to take necessary precautions.

Throughout this chapter we shall restrict ourselves to fractions
whose numerators and denominators are either polynomials or quotients of polynomials. We do this for simplicity of exposition, and

not because the theory is restricted to such cases.   Fractions containing radicals will be treated in Chap. 5.

4.2. *Simplification of Fractions*

Since fractions are troublesome enough in any case, we wish to be able to simplify any fraction that turns up as much as possible before putting it back into some further calculation.   The most important way of doing this is nothing more than the familiar "reducing to lowest terms."   In spite of the simplicity of this method, its misuse is a source of frequent errors on the part of careless students—so read this section carefully.

Basic Principle.   The method depends upon the familiar relation:

$$\frac{ka}{kb} = \frac{a}{b} \qquad \text{for } k \neq 0$$

In other words: If we divide the numerator and denominator of a given fraction by the same quantity (not zero) the result is a fraction equal to the given one.

In order to apply this principle to algebraic fractions, we factor the numerator and denominator, look for common factors, and divide top and bottom by any factor which is common to both.

Illustration 1

(a) $\dfrac{x^2 - 5x + 6}{x^2 - 4x + 3} = \dfrac{(x - 3)(x - 2)}{(x - 3)(x - 1)} = \dfrac{x - 2}{x - 1}$.

(b) $\dfrac{4x^2 + 7x}{x^2} = \dfrac{x(4x + 7)}{x(x)} = \dfrac{4x + 7}{x}$.

(c) $\dfrac{x^2 + 4x + 4}{x^2 + 4x + 3} = \dfrac{(x + 2)(x + 2)}{(x + 1)(x + 3)}$, which does not simplify since the numerator

and denominator have no common factor.

The matter of excluded values of x raises the question of what we mean by the equality of two fractions.   In Illustration 1a, the fraction on the left is defined for all values of x except $x = 1$ and $x = 3$; on the other hand, the fraction on the right is defined for all values of x except $x = 1$.   A strict use of equality between these two would lead us to the following nonsensical relation when we put $x = 3$:

$$\frac{0}{0} = \text{nonsense} = \frac{3 - 2}{3 - 1} = \frac{1}{2}$$

In order to avoid such difficulties, let us define equality of algebraic fractions as follows:

Definition: *Two algebraic fractions* involving the letter x are *equal* if and only if they have the same numerical values when x is put equal to any number for which both fractions are defined.

Common Errors. Some of the mistakes which students make are based upon the following erroneous relation:

$$\frac{k+a}{k+b} = \frac{a}{b} \qquad FALSE$$

In other words, it is incorrect to simplify a fraction by subtracting the same quantity from numerator and denominator!

Illustration 2

(a) $\dfrac{x^2 + 4x + 4}{x^2 + 4x + 3}$ does not equal $\dfrac{4}{3}$. See Illustration 1c.

(b) $\dfrac{2x + 3}{2x + 1}$ does not equal $\dfrac{3}{1} = 3$.

Exercise A. Disprove the statements: $\dfrac{x^2 + 4x + 4}{x^2 + 4x + 3} = \dfrac{4}{3}$ and $\dfrac{2x + 3}{2x + 1} = 3$ by finding suitable counterexamples.

Other errors are caused by failure to remember the distributive law. These are based upon the following erroneous relation:

$$\frac{k+a}{k} = a \qquad FALSE$$

The trouble here is that k has not been treated as a factor of the numerator. Proceeding correctly, we can write, however:

$$\frac{k+a}{k} = \frac{k\left(1 + \dfrac{a}{k}\right)}{k} = 1 + \frac{a}{k} \qquad TRUE$$

Another approach to this is the following:

$$\frac{k+a}{k} = \frac{1}{k}(k+a)$$

Now apply the distributive law, which gives:

$$\frac{1}{k}(k+a) = \frac{1}{k}(k) + \frac{1}{k}(a) = 1 + \frac{a}{k} \qquad TRUE$$

Illustration 3

(a) $\dfrac{5x + 7}{5x}$ is not equal to 7 but does equal $1 + \dfrac{7}{5x}$.

(b) $\dfrac{(x + 3)^2 + x - 2}{x + 3}$ is not equal to $(x + 3) + x - 2$ but does equal $x + 3 + \dfrac{x - 2}{x + 3}$.

Exercise B.   Disprove the statements: $\dfrac{5x + 7}{5x} = 7$ and $\dfrac{(x + 3)^2 + x - 2}{x + 3} = (x + 3) + x - 2$ by finding suitable counterexamples.

In the problems which follow, some fractions will simplify, and others will not.   In your zeal to effect a simplification do not commit either of the common errors illustrated above.

PROBLEMS 4.2

In Probs. 1 to 20 simplify where possible.

1. $\dfrac{x^2 - 4}{x^2 + 4x + 4}$.

2. $\dfrac{x^2 + 6x + 9}{x^2 - 9}$.

3. $\dfrac{x^2 + 7x + 12}{x^2 + 7x + 10}$.

4. $\dfrac{x^2 - 6x + 8}{x^2 - 9x + 8}$.

5. $\dfrac{x^2 + 3x}{x + 2}$.

6. $\dfrac{x^2 + 5x}{x}$.

7. $\dfrac{3x^2 + 5x - 2}{2x^2 + 7x + 6}$.

8. $\dfrac{2x^2 + 11x + 15}{x^2 - x - 12}$.

9. $\dfrac{4x^2 - 9}{2x^2 + 11x - 21}$.

10. $\dfrac{x^2 + 5x + 6}{x + 5}$.

11. $\dfrac{ac + bc + ad + bd}{3a + 3b - ay - by}$.

12. $\dfrac{y^2 + 3zy + 2z^2}{ay - by + az - bz}$.

13. $\dfrac{x^3 - y^3}{x^2 - y^2}$.

14. $\dfrac{x^3 + y^3}{x^2 + y^2}$.

15. $\dfrac{a^4 + b^4}{a^2 + b^2}$.

16. $\dfrac{4a^2x^2 - 25x^2}{2ax + 5x}$.

17. $\dfrac{a^2x^3 + 6ax^3 + 9x^3}{a^2x - 9x}$.

18. $\dfrac{a^4 - b^4}{a^2 - b^2}$.

19. $\dfrac{x^3 + 7x^2 + 12x}{x - 1}$.

20. $\dfrac{ax^2 + 12ax + 20a}{y + 10}$.

In Probs. 21 to 26 find counterexamples which disprove the given statements.

21. $\dfrac{4x + 5}{4x} = 5$.

22. $\dfrac{7x - 10}{7x} = -10$.

23. $\dfrac{13x + x^2}{13x + x} = x$.

24. $\dfrac{12x + 6}{12x - 3} = -2$.

25. $\dfrac{3x}{2} + \dfrac{4x}{3} = \dfrac{7x}{5}$.

26. $\dfrac{2x}{8} - \dfrac{5x}{3} = \dfrac{-3x}{5}$.

4.3. *Addition*

The addition of fractions is a straightforward application of the formula below, which we derived in Sec. 2.8:

$$\frac{a}{b} + \frac{c}{d} = \frac{ad + bc}{bd}$$

When the fraction on the right is obtained, it should then be simplified as much as possible.

Illustration 1

(a) $\dfrac{2x - 1}{x + 3} + \dfrac{x^2}{3x - 1} = \dfrac{(2x - 1)(3x - 1) + (x + 3)x^2}{(x + 3)(3x - 1)}$

$$= \frac{x^3 + 9x^2 - 5x + 1}{3x^2 + 8x - 3}$$

(b) $\dfrac{x}{x + 3} + \dfrac{5x^2}{x^2 - 9} = \dfrac{x(x^2 - 9) + (x + 3)(5x^2)}{(x + 3)(x^2 - 9)}$

$$= \frac{6x^3 + 15x^2 - 9x}{(x + 3)(x^2 - 9)}$$

$$= \frac{3x(2x - 1)(x + 3)}{(x + 3)(x^2 - 9)}$$

$$= \frac{3x(2x - 1)}{x^2 - 9}$$

Although the above process always gives the correct result, it may involve unnecessary complexities. These occur because the process leads to a denominator which is not necessarily the *least common denominator* (L.C.D.). You have doubtless met the notion of a least common denominator in arithmetic. When you added

$$\frac{4}{9} + \frac{7}{12}$$

you learned to write:

$$\frac{4}{9} + \frac{7}{12} = \frac{16}{36} + \frac{21}{36} = \frac{37}{36}$$

and you avoided the use of $9 \times 12 = 108$ as a denominator. In arithmetic the least common denominator is the smallest number which contains the given denominators as factors. We found it above by first factoring $9 = 3^2$ and $12 = 2^2 \times 3$ into prime factors. Then we formed a number (the L.C.D.) by multiplying together the several distinct factors we had found (namely, 2 and 3), each raised to the larger of the two powers to which it was raised in the given two numbers. Thus the L.C.D. of $\frac{4}{9}$ and $\frac{7}{12}$ is $3^2 \times 2^2 = 36$.

In algebra we would like to follow the same procedure, but here we run into difficulties of both a theoretical and a practical nature. Our factoring of 9 and 12 above was into *prime* factors, but we can give no definition of what is meant by a prime factor of a general algebraic expression. Even with numbers we get into difficulty in factoring when we leave the domain of integers; for $6 = 2 \times 3$ and also

$$6 = (1 - \sqrt{-5}) \times (1 + \sqrt{-5})$$

and the unique factorization theorem (Sec. 2.5) fails to hold. When, in particular, our denominators are polynomials, it is possible to define prime factors; but then we may well have practical difficulty in finding these factors. Therefore, there may in fact be no L.C.D., or we may be unable to find one even when it exists. The point to remember is that the use of the L.C.D. is a great convenience when it can be found easily but that the method of the L.C.D. cannot be applied universally. The use of the L.C.D. is not, therefore, a fixed requirement of the addition process, but it should be used wherever possible. In most of the problems below its use is recommended.

Illustration 2

(a) $\dfrac{3x + 4}{x^2 - 16} + \dfrac{x - 3}{x^2 + 8x + 16}$.

We write $x^2 - 16 = (x + 4)(x - 4)$ and $x^2 + 8x + 16 = (x + 4)(x + 4)$. Hence we form the L.C.D., which is $(x + 4)^2(x - 4)$. Then:

$$
\begin{aligned}
\frac{3x + 4}{x^2 - 16} + \frac{x - 3}{x^2 + 8x + 16} &= \frac{3x + 4}{(x + 4)(x - 4)} + \frac{x - 3}{(x + 4)^2} \\
&= \frac{(3x + 4)(x + 4)}{(x + 4)^2(x - 4)} + \frac{(x - 3)(x - 4)}{(x + 4)^2(x - 4)} \\
&= \frac{4x^2 + 9x + 28}{(x + 4)^2(x - 4)}
\end{aligned}
$$

Since this fraction does not simplify, it is the final answer.

(b) $\dfrac{x}{x + 3} + \dfrac{5x^2}{x^2 - 9}$ (see Illustration 1b).

The L.C.D. is $x^2 - 9$. Hence we write:

$$\frac{x(x - 3)}{x^2 - 9} + \frac{5x^2}{x^2 - 9} = \frac{6x^2 - 3x}{x^2 - 9} = \frac{3x(2x - 1)}{x^2 - 9}$$

(c) $\dfrac{x}{x^2 - 2x + 5} + \dfrac{3}{x - 1}$.

In this case our procedure breaks down, for we do not know how to factor $x^2 - 2x + 5$. So we forget about the L.C.D. and write:

$$\frac{x}{x^2 - 2x + 5} + \frac{3}{x - 1} = \frac{(x^2 - x) + 3(x^2 - 2x + 5)}{(x^2 - 2x + 5)(x - 1)}$$

$$= \frac{4x^2 - 7x + 15}{(x^2 - 2x + 5)(x - 1)}$$

(d) $\dfrac{x}{x^2 - 2x + 5} + \dfrac{3}{x - 1 + 2i}.$

As in Illustration 2c, the only thing you can do is to write:

$$\frac{x}{x^2 - 2x + 5} + \frac{3}{x - 1 + 2i} = \frac{(x^2 - x + 2ix) + (3x^2 - 6x + 15)}{(x^2 - 2x + 5)(x - 1 + 2i)}$$

$$= \frac{4x^2 - 7x + 2ix + 15}{(x^2 - 2x + 5)(x - 1 + 2i)}$$

Actually, however, a little more knowledge will give you a better result. If you had been clever, you might have noted that

$$x^2 - 2x + 5 = (x - 1 + 2i)(x - 1 - 2i)$$

So you could have written

$$\frac{x}{x^2 - 2x + 5} + \frac{3}{x - 1 + 2i} = \frac{x + 3(x - 1 - 2i)}{x^2 - 2x + 5}$$

$$= \frac{4x - 6i - 3}{x^2 - 2x + 5}$$

This is a better answer than that given above, but it was obtained by methods which you are not likely to have thought of. We shall not discuss these methods here, but this illustration should be a sufficient hint for a good student.

PROBLEMS 4.3

Carry out the indicated operations.

1. $\dfrac{2}{x - 1} + \dfrac{5}{x + 1}.$

2. $\dfrac{3}{4 - x} + \dfrac{2}{5 - x}.$

3. $\dfrac{6}{2r - s} + \dfrac{2}{s - 2r}.$

4. $\dfrac{7}{2x + 4y} + \dfrac{3}{x + 2y}.$

5. $\dfrac{4}{a} - \dfrac{3}{a - b}.$

6. $\dfrac{7}{x + 3} - \dfrac{9}{x + 1}.$

7. $\dfrac{2}{xy + y^2} + \dfrac{3}{x^2 + xy}.$

8. $\dfrac{x}{x + y} + \dfrac{y}{x^2 - y^2}.$

9. $\dfrac{2x}{x^2 + 3x + 2} - \dfrac{x}{x^2 - 1}.$

10. $\dfrac{x + 1}{x^2 - 5x + 6} + \dfrac{x}{x^2 - x - 6}.$

11. $\dfrac{3x}{x^2 + 4x + 4} - \dfrac{x^2}{x^2 + 2x + 1}.$

12. $\dfrac{2x}{(x - y)^2} + \dfrac{3}{x + y}.$

13. $\dfrac{x + 2}{x^2 + x + 1} + \dfrac{x}{x^2 + x + 2}.$

14. $\dfrac{x^2}{x^2 + 3x + 4} - \dfrac{x + 7}{x + 2}.$

15. $\dfrac{x}{x+2} + \dfrac{1}{x} - \dfrac{4}{x+1}.$ **16.** $1 - \dfrac{1}{a+1} + \dfrac{2}{a^2-1}.$

17. $\dfrac{5}{x^2+x-12} + \dfrac{4}{x^2-x-20} - \dfrac{3}{x^2-8x+15}.$

18. $\dfrac{2}{x^2-3x-4} - \dfrac{5}{x^2+3x+2} + \dfrac{4}{x^2-2x-8}.$

19. $\dfrac{1}{x-y} + \dfrac{y}{x^2-xy} - \dfrac{x}{(x-y)^2}.$

20. $2x + \dfrac{3x^2}{x-y} + x - y.$

4.4. Multiplication and Division

We saw in Sec. 2.8 that the multiplication of fractions follows the rule:

$$\frac{a}{b} \times \frac{c}{d} = \frac{ac}{bd}$$

Also from Prob. 23, Sec. 2.8, we know that division follows the rule:

$$\frac{a}{b} \div \frac{c}{d} = \frac{a}{b} \times \frac{d}{c} = \frac{ad}{bc}$$

These rules apply equally well to algebraic fractions. When a, b, c, and d are polynomials, it is desirable to factor them if possible so that simplifications in the final answer can be made easily. As shown in the illustrations below, it is usually convenient to make these simplifications at an early stage of the work rather than to wait to carry them out after the product has been found.

Illustration 1

(a)
$$\frac{x^2-y^2}{4y} \times \frac{2y}{x+y} = \frac{(x-y)(x+y)}{4y} \times \frac{2y}{x+y}$$
$$= \frac{(x-y)(x+y)(2y)}{4y(x+y)} = \frac{x-y}{2}$$

In the next to the last fraction we have divided numerator and denominator by $(x+y)(2y)$ in order to obtain the final result. You might just as well, however, have carried out this division at the previous stage and thus have shortened the calculation as follows:

$$\frac{x^2-y^2}{4y} \times \frac{2y}{x+y} = \frac{(x-y)(x+y)}{4y} \times \frac{2y}{x+y} = \frac{x-y}{2}$$

$$\checkmark$$

In order to keep track of our divisions, we have placed check marks above those factors that have been divided out. We have also written a 2 as the quotient of 4 by 2. Instead of using check marks many people cross out these factors and say that they have been "canceled." There is no harm in canceling if it is done with understanding, but too often it is used blindly without an appreciation of the fact that *division* is the true operation involved.

(b)
$$\frac{x^2 + 3x + 2}{x^2 - x - 2} \times \frac{x^2 + x - 2}{x^2 + 4x + 4} \div \frac{x^2 - x}{x^2 + x - 6}$$

$$= \frac{(x + 2)(x + 1)}{(x - 2)(x + 1)} \times \frac{(x + 2)(x - 1)}{(x + 2)(x + 2)} \times \frac{(x - 2)(x + 3)}{x(x - 1)} = \frac{x + 3}{x}$$

(c)
$$\frac{x^2 + 5x + 6}{x^2 - 1} \div \frac{x^2 + 1}{x + 4}$$

$$= \frac{(x + 2)(x + 3)}{(x + 1)(x - 1)} \times \frac{x + 4}{x^2 + 1} = \frac{(x + 2)(x + 3)(x + 4)}{(x + 1)(x - 1)(x^2 + 1)}$$

There are no common factors to divide out, and so no simplification is possible.

Do not expect that every problem will simplify. You will make errors if you force yourself to simplify *every* problem just because simplifications do occur in *many* problems proposed in books. Actual problems derived from nature rarely simplify, but you must know the process just in case you are lucky enough to find a problem in your work which does simplify.

PROBLEMS 4.4

Carry out the indicated operations, and simplify where possible.

1. $\dfrac{x^2 - 2x + 1}{x^2 - 1} \times \dfrac{x - 1}{2}.$

2. $\dfrac{x^2 - 4}{x^2 + x} \times \dfrac{x + 1}{x + 2}.$

3. $\dfrac{x^2 + 3x + 2}{x^2 - x - 2} \div \dfrac{x^2 + 4x + 4}{x^2 + x - 2}.$

4. $\dfrac{x^2 + 5x + 4}{x^2 - 4} \div \dfrac{x^2 - 1}{x + 2}.$

5. $\dfrac{x^2 + 4x + 4}{x^2 + 4x + 3} \times \dfrac{x^2 - 4}{(x + 1)^2}.$

6. $\dfrac{x^2 - 16}{x^2 - 9} \div \dfrac{4x^2 - 1}{x^2 - 1}.$

7. $\dfrac{x^2 + 7x + 12}{x^2 + 2x - 3} \times \dfrac{x^2 + 4x - 5}{x + 1}.$

8. $\dfrac{5x - x^2}{x^2 + 8x + 12} \times \dfrac{x^2 - 2x - 8}{x^2 - 4x - 5}.$

9. $\dfrac{6r - 2s}{3rs} \div \dfrac{9r - 3s}{7rs}.$

10. $\dfrac{xy + x}{5y} \div \dfrac{x^2y + x^2}{3y}.$

11. $\dfrac{2x^2 + x - 3}{3x^2 + 5x - 2} \times \dfrac{3x^2 + 2x - 1}{x^2 - x}.$

12. $\dfrac{4x^2 - 3x - 10}{2x^2 + 12x + 18} \times \dfrac{2x^2 + 4x - 6}{x^2 - 4x + 4}.$

13. $\dfrac{4x^2 - 12x + 9}{2x^2 - 5x + 2} \div \dfrac{9 - 4x^2}{1 - 4x^2}.$

14. $\dfrac{2x^2 - x - 10}{2x^2 - 5x - 7} \div \dfrac{2x^2 - 3x - 5}{2x^2 - 3x - 14}.$

15. $\dfrac{xy + xz}{xy - xz} \times \dfrac{y}{y + z} \times \dfrac{y - z}{y}.$

16. $\dfrac{xy^2 - x}{y - 1} \times \dfrac{x + 2}{y + 1} \times \dfrac{3}{x^2 + 2x}.$

17. $\dfrac{x^3 + y^3}{y^2} \times \dfrac{x^2}{x^2 - y^2} \div \dfrac{x^2 - xy + y^2}{x^2 + 2xy + y^2}.$

18. $\dfrac{8 - r^3}{r^2 - 4r + 4} \times \dfrac{r^2 + 3r}{4 - r^2} \div \dfrac{4r + 2r^2 + r^3}{r^2 - 3r + 2}.$

19. $\dfrac{x^2 + 9x + 18}{x^2 + 4x - 5} \times \dfrac{x^2 + x - 12}{x^2 + 3x + 2}.$

20. $\dfrac{2x^2 - 3x - 2}{x} \times \dfrac{3x^2 + 5x - 2}{x^2 + 3}.$

21. $\dfrac{p}{p + q - r} \times \dfrac{(p + q)^2 - r^2}{rp + rq + r^2}.$

22. $\dfrac{(a + 5)^2 - b^2}{a - b + 5} \times \dfrac{a^2 - ab + 5a}{(a + b)^2 - 25}.$

4.5. *Compound Fractions*

The operations of adding, subtracting, multiplying, and dividing fractions can be combined in various ways.   The only situation which calls for special comment is that of simplifying a fraction whose numerator and denominator are themselves sums of fractions.   In this case the numerator and denominator should be simplified separately, and finally the division should be performed.

Illustration 1

$$\dfrac{\dfrac{1}{x + 1} - \dfrac{1}{x - 1}}{\dfrac{1}{x + 1} + \dfrac{1}{x - 1}} = \dfrac{\dfrac{(x - 1) - (x + 1)}{(x + 1)(x - 1)}}{\dfrac{(x - 1) + (x + 1)}{(x + 1)(x - 1)}} = \dfrac{\dfrac{-2}{x^2 - 1}}{\dfrac{2x}{x^2 - 1}}$$

$$= \dfrac{-2}{x^2 - 1} \times \dfrac{x^2 - 1}{2x} = -\dfrac{1}{x}.$$

PROBLEMS 4.5

General Review of Fractions

Carry out the indicated operations, and simplify where possible.

1. $\left[\dfrac{2}{x - 3} - \dfrac{5}{x - 4} \right] \times \dfrac{2x}{3x - 7}.$

2. $\left[\dfrac{4}{x + 1} + \dfrac{3}{x - 2} \right] \times \dfrac{x + 3}{7x - 5}.$

3. $\left[\dfrac{x}{x + 3} + \dfrac{2x}{-2x + 1} \right] \div \dfrac{2x}{3x + 5}.$

4. $\left[\dfrac{x}{x + 1} - \dfrac{2}{x + 2} \right] \div \dfrac{x^4 - 4}{3}.$

5. $\dfrac{\dfrac{x}{x + y} + \dfrac{y}{x - y}}{\dfrac{x}{x - y} + \dfrac{y}{x + y}}.$

6. $\dfrac{2 + \dfrac{5a}{a + 2b}}{\dfrac{3a}{a + 2b}}.$

7. $5x - \dfrac{3}{5x - \dfrac{3}{5x}}.$

8. $2x - \dfrac{5}{2x - \dfrac{5}{2x}}.$

9. $\left[\dfrac{2x^2 + 3x - 2}{x^2 - 3x} \times \dfrac{x^2 - 5x + 6}{x^2 + 3x + 2}\right] + \left[\dfrac{4x + 3}{x} \times \dfrac{x - 6}{4x^2 + 7x + 3}\right].$

10. $\left[\dfrac{x^2 - 4}{4x^2 - 1} \times \dfrac{1 - 2x}{x + 2}\right] - \left[\dfrac{3x + 1}{2x^2 + 13x + 6} \times \dfrac{x + 6}{3x^2 + 7x + 2}\right].$

11. $\left[\dfrac{2x + 1}{x + 1} \times \dfrac{1}{x - 2}\right] + \left[\dfrac{1}{x - 2} \div \dfrac{x + 3}{x - 3}\right] - \left[\dfrac{1}{x + 1} \times \dfrac{3x + 4}{x + 3}\right].$

12. $\left[\dfrac{1}{x} \div \dfrac{x + 4}{3x - 2}\right] - \left[\dfrac{1}{x} \times \dfrac{x + 3}{x - 1}\right] + \left[\dfrac{1}{x - 1} \div \dfrac{x + 4}{2x - 1}\right].$

13. $\dfrac{\dfrac{x + 2}{4x^2 - 1}}{\dfrac{4x + 3}{2x^2 + 7x + 3}}.$

14. $\dfrac{\dfrac{x - 3}{x^2 + 6x + 5}}{\dfrac{2x + 7}{x^2 - 1}}.$

15. $\left[\dfrac{2x + 1}{x} - \dfrac{x}{2x + 1}\right] \times \left[\dfrac{5x - 1}{x} + \dfrac{x}{5x - 1}\right].$

16. $\left[\dfrac{x^2}{x + 3} + \dfrac{x + 3}{x^2}\right] \times \left[\dfrac{x}{2x + 5} - \dfrac{2x + 5}{x}\right].$

17. $\dfrac{\dfrac{x^2}{x + 3} + \dfrac{x - 1}{x + 2}}{\dfrac{2}{x - 2} - \dfrac{x^2}{x + 4}}.$

18. $\dfrac{\dfrac{x}{x - 2} + \dfrac{2x}{3x - 5}}{\dfrac{x^2}{x + 3} - \dfrac{x - 1}{x - 2}}.$

19. $\dfrac{x + 1}{x^2 + 4x + 8} - \dfrac{3x}{x + 2 + 2i}.$

20. $\dfrac{2x - 1}{x^2 + 6x + 10} + \dfrac{x + 2}{x + 3 - i}.$

CHAPTER FIVE

Exponents and Radicals

5.1. *Positive Integral Exponents*

By this time you should be well acquainted with the notation a^n, where a is any real or complex number and n is a positive integer. For the record, let us give a formal definition:

Definition: The symbol a^n (where a is any number and n is a positive integer) stands for the *product* of n factors, each equal to a.

$$a^n = \underbrace{a \times a \times \cdots \times a}_{n \text{ factors}}$$

We read a^n "the nth power of a" and call n the "exponent."

Exercise A. The product $a \times a \times \cdots \times a$ above is meaningful because of the associative law of multiplication. Explain why this is the case.

We must now examine the rules for handling these symbols. All of them are derived from properties R1 to R11 (Sec. 2.4).

Theorem 1. Let m and n be positive integers, and let a be any number. Then

$$a^m \times a^n = a^{m+n}$$

This theorem follows at once from the above definition, since each side of the equation contains $m + n$ factors each equal to a.

Exercise B. Where have we used the associative law of multiplication in the above proof?

Illustration 1

   (a) $2^5 \times 2^3 = 2^{5+3} = 2^8 = 256$.

   (b) $r^8 \times r^{15} = r^{8+15} = r^{23}$.

   (c) But note that the theorem does not apply to $2^4 \times 3^6$, which cannot be written more simply in terms of exponents.

Theorem 2. Let m and n be positive integers and let a be any number. Then

$$(a^m)^n = a^{mn}$$

The truth of this theorem is fairly evident from the definition above, for each side contains mn factors each equal to a. Nevertheless, let us give a proof using mathematical induction. We hold m fixed throughout the proof and let n assume various values.

When $n = 1$, we have $(a^m)^1 = a^{m \times 1}$, and so the first step in the induction process is fulfilled. Now assume the relation for $n = k$, that is,

$$(a^m)^k = a^{mk}$$

To prove it true for $n = k + 1$, we multiply both sides of the above equation by a^m:

$$(a^m)^k \times a^m = a^{mk} \times a^m$$

On the left we have $(a^m)^k \times (a^m)^1 = (a^m)^{k+1}$ from Theorem 1. On the right we have $a^{mk} \times a^m = a^{mk+m} = a^{m(k+1)}$ from Theorem 1. Therefore:

$$(a^m)^{k+1} = a^{m(k+1)}$$

and the second condition for induction is verified. Hence the relation is true for all positive integers n.

Exercise C. Which of R1 to R11 have we used in the above proof?

Exercise D. Find a counterexample to the following false relation, which is sometimes confused with Theorem 2:

$$(a^m)^n = a^{(m^n)}$$

Illustration 2

   (a) $(4^2)^3 = 4^6$.

   (b) $(x^4)^2 = x^8$.

   (c) $2^3 \times 4^5 = 2^3 \times (2^2)^5 = 2^3 \times 2^{10} = 2^{13}$.

Theorem 3. Let n be a positive integer, and let a and b be any numbers. Then:

$$(ab)^n = a^n \times b^n$$

Proof (by induction): The relation is certainly true for $n = 1$. Assume it for $n = k$, that is,

$$(ab)^k = a^k \times b^k$$

Then $\qquad (ab)^k \times (ab) = (a^k \times b^k)(ab).$

Simplifying both sides, we get:

$$(ab)^{k+1} = a^{k+1} \times b^{k+1}$$

and the induction is complete.

Illustration 3

(a) $(3 \times 5)^4 = 3^4 \times 5^4$.

(b) $(xy)^7 = x^7 \times y^7$.

5.2. *Negative and Zero Exponents*

In order to discuss the proper simplification of a^n/a^m, let us look at a few examples. We see at once that:

$$\frac{a^6}{a^2} = a^4 \qquad \text{and} \qquad \frac{a^5}{a^3} = a^2$$

By a simple argument we can show that in general

$$\frac{a^m}{a^n} = a^{m-n}$$

provided that $m > n$. We run into trouble, however, when we consider a^2/a^7. The above formula suggests that we should write

$$\frac{a^2}{a^7} = a^{2-7} = a^{-5}$$

At this point, however, a^{-5} is a meaningless symbol, and we must define it before we can use it. We note, however, that $a^2/a^7 = 1/a^5$ and hence are led to define $a^{-5} = 1/a^5$. In general we say:

Definition: The symbol a^{-n} (where n is a positive integer and a is a number $\neq 0$) stands for the *quotient* $1/a^n$.

We have further trouble when we consider a^5/a^5. The formula $a^m/a^n = a^{m-n}$ suggests that we write

$$\frac{a^5}{a^5} = a^{5-5} = a^0$$

But zero exponents need a definition before we can use them. The above example suggests that we put $a^0 = 1$, and in general we say:

Definition: The symbol a^0 (where a is any number $\neq 0$) is equal to 1.

Exercise A. Why must we exclude $a = 0$ in the above definition?

We can now reexamine Theorems 1, 2, and 3 of Sec. 5.1 in order to see how they generalize when the exponents are arbitrary integers (positive, negative, or zero).

Theorem 1′. Let m and n be any integers, and let a be any number $\neq 0$. Then

$$a^m \times a^n = a^{m+n}$$

To prove this, we must treat various cases separately:
(a) $m > 0, n > 0$. This is then Theorem 1 of Sec. 5.1.
(b) m arbitrary, $n = 0$. Then:

$$a^m \times a^n = a^m \times a^0 = a^m \times 1 = a^m = a^{m+0} = a^{m+n}$$

(c) $m > 0, n < 0$. Let $n = -p$, and suppose $m > p$. Then

$$a^m \times a^n = a^m \times a^{-p} = \frac{a^m}{a^p} = a^{m-p} = a^{m+n}$$

Now suppose $m < p$. Then:

$$a^m \times a^n = a^m \times a^{-p} = \frac{a^m}{a^p} = \frac{1}{a^{p-m}} = a^{m-p} = a^{m+n}$$

Finally suppose $m = p$. Then:

$$a^m \times a^n = a^m \times a^{-p} = \frac{a^m}{a^p} = 1 = a^0 = a^{m-p} = a^{m+n}$$

(d) $m < 0, n < 0$. Let $m = -p; n = -q$. Then:

$$a^m \times a^n = a^{-p} \times a^{-q} = \frac{1}{a^p} \times \frac{1}{a^q}$$

$$= \frac{1}{a^p \times a^q} = \frac{1}{a^{p+q}} = a^{-(p+q)} = a^{-p-q} = a^{m+n}$$

Theorem 2′. Let m and n be any integers, and let a be any number $\neq 0$. Then:

$$(a^m)^n = a^{mn}$$

The proof is by cases as above and is included in the Problems.

Theorem 3′. Let n be any integer, and let a and b be any numbers $\neq 0$. Then:

$$(ab)^n = a^n \times b^n$$

The proof is again by cases and is included in the Problems.

Exercise B.   Why must we exclude $a = 0$ in the statements of Theorems 1′, 2′, and 3′?

PROBLEMS 5.2

Perform the indicated operations.   Write your answers in a form which uses *positive* exponents only.

1. $5^3 \times 5^8$.

2. $7^2 \times 7^6$.

3. $3^{-2} \times 3^4 \times 3^0$.

4. $11^5 \times 11^{-4} \times 11^0$.

5. $2^4 \times 5^{-2} \times 5^6 \times 2^{-8}$.

6. $7^3 \times 13^8 \times 7^{-6} \times 13^{-5}$.

7. $(-2)^3 \times 11^4 \times 11^3 \times (-2)^4$.

8. $(3)^5 \times (-5)^4 \times (-5)^3 \times (3)^2$.

9. $\dfrac{(3^{-1})(5) + 3 + 3(5^{-1})}{(3^{-1})(5^{-1})}$.

10. $\dfrac{(2)(7^{-1}) + 1 + (2^{-1})(7)}{(2^{-1})(7^{-1})}$.

11. $\dfrac{xy^{-1} + 3 + x^{-1}y}{x^{-1}y^{-1}}$.

12. $\dfrac{x^{-1}y^{-1} + 2 + 5xy}{xy}$.

13. $\dfrac{abc^{-1} - a^{-1}b^{-1}c}{a^{-1}b^{-2}c^{-1}}$.

14. $(z + z^{-1})(z^{-1} - z^{-2})$.

15. $(3 + y^{-1})(y + 2)$.

16. $(1 + x^{-1} + x^{-2})(1 + x)$.

17. $\dfrac{x^{-1} - 1 - 6x}{x^{-1} + 2}$.

18. $\dfrac{2x^{-1} + 1 - 15x}{x^{-1} + 3}$.

19. $\dfrac{2x + 1 + 6x^{-1} + 3x^{-2}}{2x^{-1} + x^{-2}}$.

20. $\dfrac{x^4 - x^2 + 1 - x^{-2}}{x^2 + x^{-2}}$.

21. Prove: Let a and b be any numbers $(\neq 0)$ and n any integer; then $(a/b)^n = a^n/b^n$.

22. Prove Theorem 2′.   Consider the cases: $(m > 0, n > 0)$; $(m > 0, n < 0)$; $(m < 0, n > 0)$; $(m < 0, n < 0)$; $(m = 0, n$ arbitrary$)$; $(m$ arbitrary, $n = 0)$.

23. Prove Theorem 3′.   Consider the cases: $n > 0, n = 0, n < 0$.

5.3. *Fractional Exponents*

We now come to the matter of taking the square root, the cube root, and fourth root, etc., of a number.   In order to avoid some troublesome difficulties, in this section we shall assume that we are dealing with the roots of *positive real* numbers only.

Let a be a positive real number, and suppose that $b^n = a$.   Then we say that "*b* is *an* nth root of a"; we must not say "*the* nth root," for indeed there may be several of these.   For instance,

$$2^2 = 4 \qquad \text{and} \qquad (-2)^2 = 4$$

so that both 2 and (-2) are square roots of 4.   As a general principle a mathematical symbol should stand for just one mathematical object rather than for several such objects.   For this reason we use $\sqrt[n]{a}$ in a carefully defined sense as given below.

Definition: Let a be a positive real number and n a positive integer. Then the symbols $\sqrt[n]{a}$ and $a^{1/n}$ will be used interchangeably to mean that particular one of the nth roots of a which is a positive real number.

Illustration 1. $\sqrt{4} = 4^{\frac{1}{2}} = +2; \sqrt{25} = 25^{\frac{1}{2}} = +5; - \sqrt{36} = -36^{\frac{1}{2}} = -6.$ We never write $\sqrt{25} = \pm 5$.

   Exercise A.   Why is $a^{1/n}$ a desirable notation for $\sqrt[n]{a}$?   HINT: Consider a reasonable generalization of Theorem 2.

   Now that we know what we mean by $a^{1/n}$, we must extend our definition to symbols of the form $a^{p/q}$.

Definition: Let a be a positive real number, and let p and q be positive integers.   Then the symbols $(\sqrt[q]{a})^p$ and $a^{p/q}$ are used interchangeably to mean the pth power of $a^{1/q}$.   That is, $a^{p/q} = (a^{1/q})^p$.
   Another meaning for $a^{p/q}$ is derived from Theorem 4:

Theorem 4.   The symbol $a^{p/q}$ also equals $\sqrt[q]{a^p}$, that is, the positive qth root of a^p.   That is, $(a^{p/q})^q = a^p$.
   Proof: We must show that $(a^{p/q})^q = a^p$.   From the above definition we have:

$$(a^{p/q})^q = [(a^{1/q})^p]^q$$
$$= [a^{1/q}]^{pq} \qquad \text{[Theorem 2]}$$
$$= [(a^{1/q})^q]^p \qquad \text{[Theorem 2]}$$
$$= a^p \qquad \text{[Definition of } a^{1/q}\text{]}$$

Finally we extend our definition of negative exponents to our fractional exponents.

   Definition: Let a be a positive real number and p and q be positive integers.   Then

$$a^{-p/q} = \frac{1}{a^{p/q}}$$

We have now completely defined the symbol a^r when a is positive and r is any rational number.   Let us see how Theorems 1, 2, and 3 generalize to this situation.

Theorem 1″. Let a be a positive real number and r and s any rational numbers. Then

$$a^r \times a^s = a^{r+s}$$

Proof: Let $r = p/q$ and $s = u/v$, where p, q, u, and v are integers. Then we must prove that

$$a^{p/q} \times a^{u/v} = a^{(pv+qu)/qv}$$

Because of Theorem 4 this is equivalent to proving that

$$(a^{p/q} \times a^{u/v})^{qv} = a^{pv+qu}$$

However:

$$
\begin{aligned}
(a^{p/q} \times a^{u/v})^{qv} &= (a^{p/q})^{qv} \times (a^{u/v})^{qv} && \text{[Theorem 3′]} \\
&= [(a^{p/q})^q]^v \times [(a^{u/v})^v]^q && \text{[Theorem 2′]} \\
&= (a^p)^v \times (a^u)^q && \text{[Theorem 4]} \\
&= a^{pv} \times a^{qu} && \text{[Theorem 2′]} \\
&= a^{pv+qu} && \text{[Theorem 1′]}
\end{aligned}
$$

Theorem 2″. Let a be a positive real number and r and s any rational numbers. Then

$$(a^r)^s = a^{rs}$$

Theorem 3″. Let a and b be any positive real numbers and r any rational number. Then

$$(ab)^r = a^r \times b^r$$

The proofs of these theorems are similar to that of Theorem 1′ and are included in the Problems.

Exercise B. Define $0^r = 0$ where r is a *positive* rational number. Show that Theorems 1″, 2″, and 3″ can be extended to include the case where $a = 0$ and r and s are *positive* rational numbers.

5.4. *Special Problems Concerning Square Roots*

In the last section we required that a be a positive real number. Here we relax that restriction and consider two special difficulties that occur when we take square roots.

(a) *The Square Root of* a^2, *or* $\sqrt{a^2} = (a^2)^{\frac{1}{2}}$. When a is positive, Theorem 2″ tells us that $(a^2)^{\frac{1}{2}} = a$. Consider, however, $[(-3)^2]^{\frac{1}{2}}$. We have:

$$[(-3)^2]^{\frac{1}{2}} = 9^{\frac{1}{2}} = +3$$

This does not agree with Theorem 2″, and so we see that we cannot extend the validity of this theorem to cover the case where a is negative. A correct statement which includes all cases is the following:

Theorem 5. For any real number a, $(a^2)^{\frac{1}{2}} = |a|$, where $|a|$ denotes the absolute value of a.

Proof: When $a \geq 0$, Theorem 5 is a consequence of Theorem 2″. When $a < 0$, let $a = -b$, where $b > 0$. Then

$$(a^2)^{\frac{1}{2}} = [(-b)^2]^{\frac{1}{2}} = (b^2)^{\frac{1}{2}} = b = |a|$$

Illustration 1.

(a) $(-5^2)^{\frac{1}{2}} = \sqrt{(-5)^2} = +5$.

(b) $(x^2)^{\frac{1}{2}} = \sqrt{x^2} = |x|$.

(c) $(x^2 + 2x + 1)^{\frac{1}{2}} = \sqrt{x^2 + 2x + 1} = |x + 1|$.

The result of Theorem 5 can be extended at once to any even root.

Theorem 6. For any real number a and any positive integer n, $(a^{2n})^{1/(2n)} = |a|$.

Proof:
$$(a^{2n})^{1/(2n)} = [(a^2)^n]^{1/(2n)} = (a^2)^{\frac{1}{2}} = |a|$$

Exercise A. State the justification for each step in the proof of Theorem 6.

(b) *The Square Root of a Negative Number.* Let a be a positive real number, and consider $(-a)^{\frac{1}{2}}$. This needs to be defined.

Definition: For any positive real number a,

$$(-a)^{\frac{1}{2}} = i(a^{\frac{1}{2}})$$

Illustration 2

$$\sqrt{-3} = (-3)^{\frac{1}{2}} = i\sqrt{3} = i3^{\frac{1}{2}}$$

Expressions of this kind need special care, for Theorem 3 does not hold in this case. Let us consider $(-a)^{\frac{1}{2}} \times (-b)^{\frac{1}{2}}$, where a and b are both positive.

$$(-a)^{\frac{1}{2}} \times (-b)^{\frac{1}{2}} = i(a^{\frac{1}{2}}) \times i(b^{\frac{1}{2}}) = i^2 a^{\frac{1}{2}} b^{\frac{1}{2}} = -(ab)^{\frac{1}{2}}$$

The application of Theorem 3 would have given the incorrect result:

$$(-a)^{\frac{1}{2}} \times (-b)^{\frac{1}{2}} = +(ab)^{\frac{1}{2}}$$

Illustration 3

(a) $(-3)^{\frac{1}{2}} \times (-5)^{\frac{1}{2}} = i(3)^{\frac{1}{2}} \times i(5)^{\frac{1}{2}} = -15^{\frac{1}{2}}$.

(b) $\sqrt{-10} \times \sqrt{-7} = i\sqrt{10} \times i\sqrt{7} = -\sqrt{70}$.

(c) $\sqrt{13} \times \sqrt{-3} = \sqrt{13} \times i\sqrt{3} = i\sqrt{39}$.

5.5. Special Problems Concerning Odd Roots

Again let a be a positive real number, and consider $\sqrt[3]{-a}$. There is always a negative real number $-b$ such that $(-b)^3 = -a$, and we shall write $-b = \sqrt[3]{-a} = (-a)^{\frac{1}{3}}$. In general we proceed as follows:

Definition: Let a be a positive real number and p be any odd positive integer. Then the symbols $\sqrt[p]{-a}$ and $(-a)^{1/p}$ will be used interchangeably to denote the negative real number, $-b$ such that $(-b)^p = -a$.

Illustration 1

(a) $\sqrt[3]{-27} = (-27)^{\frac{1}{3}} = -3$.

(b) $\sqrt[5]{-32} = (-32)^{\frac{1}{5}} = -2$.

(c) $\sqrt[11]{-x^{11}} = -x^1 = -x$.

Remarks

(a) The notation $(-a)^{1/p}$ is used by many authors in a fashion different from that defined above. In their usage this symbol denotes a certain complex number called the "principal pth root of $-a$." We shall discuss this notion in Sec. 13.10.

(b) The symbol $(-a)^{p/q}$ for a positive and q odd can now be defined in a fashion analogous to the definition of $a^{p/q}$ in Sec. 5.3. These symbols then obey Theorems 1″, 2″, and 3″. The proofs are included in the Problems.

5.6. Unanswered Questions

Although we have discussed the meaning of the symbol a^b, where a and b are certain types of real numbers, there are still several cases which we have omitted. We call your attention to the following situations, which we shall treat later in this book:

(1) $(-a)^{p/q}$, where a is positive, p is odd, and q is even. This is included as a special case in Sec. 13.10.

(2) a^b, where a is positive and b is irrational. This is discussed in Sec. 11.2.

We must omit entirely the complicated, but fascinating story of (3) a^b, where a and b are any complex numbers. For this consult G. H. Hardy, "Pure Mathematics," pages 409 to 410, 457 to 459, Cambridge, New York, 1945.

PROBLEMS 5.6

In Probs. 1 to 10 perform the given operations. All letters appearing in the problems stand for *positive* real numbers.

1. $(2x^{\frac{1}{2}} - 3x^{-\frac{1}{2}})x^{\frac{1}{2}}.$ **2.** $(x^{\frac{1}{3}} + 5x^{-\frac{1}{3}})x^{-\frac{1}{3}}.$

3. $(x^{\frac{1}{2}} + y^{\frac{1}{4}})^2.$ **4.** $(a^{\frac{1}{3}} + b^{\frac{1}{3}})^3.$

5. $(p^{\frac{1}{2}} - q^{\frac{1}{3}})(p^{\frac{1}{2}} + q^{\frac{1}{3}}).$ **6.** $(x^{-\frac{1}{2}} + y^{\frac{1}{2}})(x^{\frac{1}{2}} + y^{\frac{1}{2}}).$

7. $\dfrac{x^2 - x^{\frac{1}{2}}}{x^{\frac{1}{3}}}.$ **8.** $\dfrac{x^2 + 2x^{-1} - x^{-\frac{1}{2}}}{x^{\frac{1}{3}}}.$

9. $\dfrac{x^{\frac{3}{3}} - x^{-\frac{5}{6}} + x^2}{x^{\frac{1}{6}}}.$ **10.** $(y^{\frac{4}{7}} + 2y^{-\frac{2}{7}} - y^{-1})(y^{\frac{2}{7}}).$

In Probs. 11 to 16 perform the given operations. Letters appearing in these problems stand for real numbers, positive or negative, or zero.

11. $(x^2 + 4x + 4)^{\frac{1}{2}}.$ **12.** $(4x^2 + 4x + 1)^{\frac{1}{2}}.$

13. $(x^2 + 2x + 1)^{\frac{1}{2}} + (x^2 - 2x + 1)^{\frac{1}{2}}.$ Give a counterexample to show that $2x$ is an incorrect answer.

14. $(x^2 + 6x + 9)^{\frac{1}{2}} - (x^2 - 6x + 9)^{\frac{1}{2}}.$ Give a counterexample to show that 6 is an incorrect answer.

15. $\dfrac{(4x^2 + 4x + 1)^{\frac{1}{2}}}{2x + 1}.$ **16.** $\dfrac{(9x^2 - 12x + 4)^{\frac{1}{2}}}{3x - 2}.$

In Probs. 17 to 30 perform the given operations:

17. $\sqrt{-7} \times \sqrt{-9}.$ **18.** $\sqrt{-16} \times \sqrt{-25}.$

19. $\sqrt{4} \times \sqrt{-16}.$ **20.** $\sqrt{9} \times \sqrt{-25}.$

21. $\sqrt[3]{-8} \times \sqrt{16}.$ **22.** $\sqrt{81} \times \sqrt[3]{-27}.$

23. $\sqrt[3]{-64} \times \sqrt[3]{125}.$ **24.** $\sqrt{-25} \times \sqrt[3]{-64}.$

25. $\sqrt{2} + \sqrt{8}.$ HINT: $\sqrt{8} = 2\sqrt{2}.$ **26.** $\sqrt{3} + \sqrt{12}.$

27. $\sqrt{5} - 2\sqrt{7}.$ **28.** $\sqrt{20} - \sqrt{5}.$

29. $\sqrt{3} + \sqrt{27} + \sqrt{-3}.$ **30.** $2\sqrt{2} - \sqrt{50} + 3\sqrt{-32}.$

31. Give a definition for $(-a)^{p/q}$, where a is a positive real number and p and q are integers with q odd.

32. Review the proofs of Theorems 4, 1″, 2″, and 3″. What changes are needed in these proofs so that these theorems apply to the symbols $(-a)^{p/q}$, where a is positive, p any integer, and q an odd integer?

5.7. *Rationalizing Denominators*

From time to time you will meet fractions containing square root in the denominator, such as:

$$\frac{1}{\sqrt{2}} \qquad \frac{2}{\sqrt{3} - \sqrt{5}} \qquad \frac{x + 5}{\sqrt{x + 1} + \sqrt{2x - 3}}$$

Let us consider problems which these present. If we wish to express $1/\sqrt{2}$ as a decimal, it is awkward to divide $1/1.414$. A simpler procedure is to write:

$$\frac{1}{\sqrt{2}} = \frac{1}{\sqrt{2}} \cdot \frac{\sqrt{2}}{\sqrt{2}} = \frac{\sqrt{2}}{2} \approx \frac{1.414}{2} = 0.707$$

In some textbooks it is required that all answers be written with rational denominators; thus $1/\sqrt{2}$ is incorrect, and $\sqrt{2}/2$ is correct. This is an absurd requirement, and we shall accept either answer as correct. The choice between them depends on how we are to use them. Consider the examples below:

Illustration 1

(a) Find $1/\sqrt{2} + 1/\sqrt{3}$. Here we find it wise to write

$$\frac{1}{\sqrt{2}} + \frac{1}{\sqrt{3}} = \frac{\sqrt{2}}{2} + \frac{\sqrt{3}}{3} = \frac{3\sqrt{2} + 2\sqrt{3}}{6}$$

(b) Find $1/\sqrt{2} \times 1/\sqrt{2}$. Here we can write

$$\frac{1}{\sqrt{2}} \times \frac{1}{\sqrt{2}} = \frac{1}{\sqrt{2} \times \sqrt{2}} = \frac{1}{2}$$

It would be silly to write:

$$\frac{1}{\sqrt{2}} \times \frac{1}{\sqrt{2}} = \frac{\sqrt{2}}{2} \times \frac{\sqrt{2}}{2} = \frac{2}{4} = \frac{1}{2}$$

Hence, leave your answer in whatever form is most convenient for later use.

When we are faced with $2/(\sqrt{3} - \sqrt{5})$, another technique is needed if we wish a rational denominator. We can rationalize this one as follows:

$$\frac{2}{\sqrt{3} - \sqrt{5}} = \frac{2}{\sqrt{3} - \sqrt{5}} \times \frac{\sqrt{3} + \sqrt{5}}{\sqrt{3} + \sqrt{5}} = \frac{2\sqrt{3} + 3\sqrt{5}}{3 - 5}$$
$$= \frac{2\sqrt{3} + 2\sqrt{5}}{-2} = -\sqrt{3} - \sqrt{5}$$

We can apply this method to various cases as shown in the examples below:

Illustration 2

(a)
$$\frac{3}{1 + \sqrt{3}} = \frac{3}{1 + \sqrt{3}} \times \frac{1 - \sqrt{3}}{1 - \sqrt{3}} = \frac{3 - 3\sqrt{3}}{1 - 3}$$

$$= -\frac{3 - 3\sqrt{3}}{2}$$

(b)
$$\frac{x + 5}{\sqrt{x + 1} + \sqrt{2x - 3}} = \frac{(x + 5)(\sqrt{x + 1} - \sqrt{2x - 3})}{(\sqrt{x + 1} + \sqrt{2x - 3})(\sqrt{x + 1} - \sqrt{2x - 3})}$$

$$= \frac{(x + 5)\sqrt{x + 1} - (x + 5)\sqrt{2x - 3}}{(x + 1) - (2x - 3)}$$

$$= \frac{(x + 5)\sqrt{x + 1} - (x + 5)\sqrt{2x - 3}}{-x + 4}$$

(c)
$$\frac{x}{1 + \sqrt{x}} + \frac{2}{\sqrt{x + 1}} = \frac{x}{1 + \sqrt{x}} \times \frac{1 - \sqrt{x}}{1 - \sqrt{x}} + \frac{2\sqrt{x + 1}}{x + 1}$$

$$= \frac{x - x\sqrt{x}}{1 - x} + \frac{2\sqrt{x + 1}}{x + 1}$$

$$= \frac{(x - x\sqrt{x})(x + 1) + 2(1 - x)\sqrt{x + 1}}{1 - x^2}$$

PROBLEMS 5.7

In Probs. 1 to 10 rationalize the denominators in the given expressions.

1. $2/\sqrt{5}$.

2. $-3/\sqrt{7}$.

3. $\dfrac{4}{\sqrt{3} - \sqrt{2}}$.

4. $\dfrac{-1}{\sqrt{5} + \sqrt{7}}$.

5. $\dfrac{3}{\sqrt{x + 1}}$.

6. $\dfrac{x^2}{\sqrt{x^2 - 1}}$.

7. $\dfrac{2x}{\sqrt{x + 2} + \sqrt{x - 1}}$.

8. $\dfrac{x^2}{\sqrt{x^2 - 1} + \sqrt{x + 3}}$.

9. $\dfrac{5}{\sqrt{2} + \sqrt{3} + \sqrt{8}}$.

10. $\dfrac{3}{\sqrt{5} + \sqrt{20} - \sqrt{3}}$.

In Probs. 11 to 18 perform the stated operations.

11. $\dfrac{1}{\sqrt{2}} \times \dfrac{1}{\sqrt{8}}$.

12. $\dfrac{1}{\sqrt{3}} \times \dfrac{1}{\sqrt{27}}$.

13. $\dfrac{1}{\sqrt{2}} + \dfrac{1}{\sqrt{5}}$.

14. $\dfrac{1}{\sqrt{3}} - \dfrac{1}{\sqrt{7}}$.

15. $\dfrac{1}{1 + \sqrt{x}} - \dfrac{1}{x}$.

16. $\dfrac{2}{\sqrt{x - 1} + 3} + \dfrac{1}{x^2}$.

17. $\dfrac{x}{1 + \sqrt{x}} \times \dfrac{3}{1 - \sqrt{x}}$.

18. $\dfrac{4}{2 + \sqrt{x + 1}} \times \dfrac{5}{2 - \sqrt{x + 1}}$.

In Probs. 19 to 24 use a table of square roots to compute the following to three decimal places.

19. $3/\sqrt{5}$.

20. $2/\sqrt{6}$.

21. $\dfrac{1}{\sqrt{5} + \sqrt{3}}$.

22. $\dfrac{4}{\sqrt{7} - \sqrt{2}}$.

23. $\dfrac{1}{\sqrt{5}} \times \dfrac{1}{\sqrt{125}}$.

24. $\dfrac{1}{\sqrt{3}} \times \dfrac{1}{\sqrt{12}}$.

CHAPTER SIX

Sets and Equations

6.1. *Sets*

In previous chapters we have referred to "sets" without saying too much about them. In this chapter we shall repair this deficiency and discuss sets in some detail. The study of sets will be particularly rewarding, for they are one of the most fundamental notions in modern mathematics.

We think of a set as a collection of objects: pencils, trees, numbers, points, etc. The individual components of the set are called its *elements*. As an example, consider the set consisting of the four boys named: John, Joe, Jerry, Jim. This set has four elements. Sets may be of any size. We may think of the set of all particles of sand on a beach; this has a finite number of elements, but this number is certainly very large. A set, however, may have infinitely many elements. An example of an infinite set is the set of all positive integers: 1, 2, 3, 4, 5, ... Indeed a set may contain no elements, in which case we call it the *empty* set, or the *null* set.

We can describe sets in this way, but *set* is a primitive notion which cannot be defined. Hence we take *set* and *element* to be undefined. The statement: "*p* is an element of a set *P* " is similarly an undefined relationship.

Examples and Notation. In the list below we give some typical examples of sets occurring in mathematics and indicate the notations appropriate for these. Note that we regularly use curly brackets { } to represent a set; but there are exceptions to this as we shall see in (8) and (9) below.

(1) $\emptyset$, the empty, or null, set containing no elements.

(2) {3}, the finite set, of which 3 is the only element. Note that this is quite different from the real number 3.

(3) {2, 7, 15, 36}, a finite set of four elements.

(4) $X = \{x \mid x$ is a real number$\}$, the set of all real numbers. This expression should be read: "The set X is the set of numbers x such that x is a real number," the vertical line standing for "such that."

(5) $X \times Y = \{(x,y) \mid x$ and y are real numbers$\}$, the set of all ordered pairs (x,y) of real numbers (see Sec. 2.12). This set is sometimes called the *Cartesian Product* of X and Y.

(6) $\{x \mid x$ is a positive integer$\}$, the infinite set of all positive integers. We shall often write this as the set {1, 2, 3, 4, 5, . . .}.

(7) $\{x \mid x$ is an even positive integer$\}$, the infinite set of all even positive integers. We shall often write this as the set {2, 4, 6, 8, 10, . . .}.

(8) $[a,b] = \{x \mid x$ is a number in the interval $[a,b]\}$. Remember that we defined $[a,b]$ to be the segment whose left end point is a and whose right end point is b, both end points being included. We shall have frequent occasion to refer to sets of this type and need a briefer notation for them. We shall, therefore, use $[a,b]$ to denote this set.

(9) $]a,b] = \{x \mid x$ is in the half-open interval $]a,b]\}$.

$[a,b[= \{x \mid x$ is in the half-open interval $[a,b[\}$.

$]a,b[= \{x \mid x$ is in the open interval $]a,b[\}$.

These sets are similar to that described in (8). The notation $]a,b]$ means the segment with end points a and b including b but not including a. Similarly in $[a,b[$ the end point a is included and b is excluded, and in $]a,b[$ both end points are excluded.

(10) $\{L \mid L$ is a line parallel to line $M\}$, the set of all lines parallel to a given line M.

There are several types of relations between sets which we shall need in the future. One of these is the notion of *identity*.

Definition: Two sets are said to be *identical* if and only if every element of each is an element of the other. When A and B are identical, we write $A = B$.

The next notion is that of a 1 to 1 correspondence between two sets. We have already met this in Sec. 2.11, where we set up a 1 to 1 correspondence between the set of ordered pairs of real numbers and the set of points in a plane. Let us take another example. Suppose that in your classroom there are 30 seats and 30 students (all present). When the students all sit down, one to a chair, they set up a correspondence between the set of students and the set of seats. Since there is one seat for each student and one student for each seat, this is called a "1 to 1 correspondence."

Definition: Two sets $A = \{a_1, a_2, \ldots\}$ and $B = \{b_1, b_2, \ldots\}$ are said to be in 1 *to* 1 *correspondence* when there exists a pairing of the a's and the b's such that each a corresponds to one and only one b and each b corresponds to one and only one a.

Illustration 1. Establish a 1 to 1 correspondence between the set of numbers $\{1, 2, \ldots, 26\}$ and the set of letters of the alphabet $\{a, b, \ldots, z\}$.
We make the pairing:

$$
\begin{array}{cccc}
1 & 2 & \cdots & 26 \\
a & b & \cdots & z
\end{array}
$$

However, there are many other possible pairings such as:

$$
\begin{array}{ccccc}
2 & 3 & \cdots & 26 & 1 \\
a & b & \cdots & y & z
\end{array}
$$

Illustration 2. Establish a 1 to 1 correspondence between the set $\{1, 2, 3, 4, 5, \ldots\}$ and the set $\{2, 4, 6, 8, 10, \ldots\}$.
Let n represent an element of $\{1, 2, 3, 4, 5, \ldots\}$. Then the pairing $n \leftrightarrow 2n$ gives the required correspondence, examples of which are:

$$
\begin{array}{ccccccc}
1 & 2 & \cdots & 50 & \cdots & 100 & \cdots \\
2 & 4 & \cdots & 100 & \cdots & 200 & \cdots
\end{array}
$$

Exercise A. Establish a 1 to 1 correspondence between the sets $\{$John, Joe, Jerry, Jim$\}$ and $\{$Mildred, Marcia, Ruth, Sandra$\}$.
Exercise B. Establish a 1 to 1 correspondence between the sets $\{1, 2, 3, 4, 5, \ldots\}$ and $\{3, 6, 9, 12, 15, \ldots\}$.

6.2. *Subsets*

The sets which we shall meet most frequently will be *subsets* of some very large set such as the set of all real numbers. When all the subsets in a given context are subsets of a fixed set of this kind, we shall call this set the *universal set*. Of course, the universal set may be different in various contexts; i.e., it may be the set of real numbers, the set of rational numbers, the set of complex numbers, the set of ordered pairs of real numbers, etc.

Definition: A set A is a subset of a set B if and only if every element of A is an element of B.
We write this relationship $A \subseteq B$, read "A is a subset of B."

Definition: A set A is a *proper subset* of B if and only if A is a subset of B and at least one element of B is not an element of A.

We write this relationship $A \subset B$, read "A is a proper subset of B." By convention, the null set $\emptyset$ is a subset of every set and is a proper subset of every set except itself.

Illustration 1

(*a*) Given the set $\{1, 2, 3\}$, its subsets are $\{1,2,3\}$, $\{1,2\}$, $\{1,3\}$, $\{2,3\}$, $\{1\}$, $\{2\}$, $\{3\}$, $\emptyset$. Its proper subsets are the above excepting for $\{1, 2, 3\}$.

(*b*) The set $\{1, 2, 3, 4, 5, \ldots\}$ is a proper subset of the set of all real numbers.

(*c*) The set $\{2, 4, 6, 8, 10, \ldots\}$ is a proper subset of the set $\{1, 2, 3, 4, 5, \ldots\}$. This illustrates the important point that an infinite proper subset A of an infinite set B may be in 1 to 1 correspondence with B. This cannot happen in the case of finite sets.

Subsets of a set A are often defined as containing those elements of A which have some property in common. If S represents the universal set consisting of all the students at your university, we may be interested in the following subsets:

$$\{s \mid s \text{ is a girl}\}$$
$$\{s \mid s \text{ is a football player}\}$$
$$\{s \mid s \text{ is a member of the } \Sigma O \Sigma \text{ fraternity}\}$$
$$\{s \mid s \text{ is a graduate student}\}$$

In mathematics these common properties are often expressed in language like the following. Here we let our universal set be X, the set of all real numbers.

$\{x \mid x > 0\}$, the set of positive real numbers

$\{x \mid x \text{ is rational}\}$, the set of rational numbers

$\{x \mid x + 3 = 0\}$, the set of real solutions of $x + 3 = 0$, namely, the set $\{-3\}$

$\{x \mid x^2 - 5x + 6 = 0\}$, the set of real solutions of $x^2 - 5x + 6 = 0$, namely, the set $\{2, 3\}$

$\{x \mid x^2 + 1 = 0\}$, the set of real solutions of $x^2 + 1 = 0$, namely, the set $\emptyset$

To complicate the situation a little, let (x,y) be an ordered pair of real numbers. Then consider the following subsets of the set of all ordered pairs, $X \times Y$, which is now our universal set:

$\{(x,y) \mid x^2 + y^2 = 1\}$, the set of pairs whose elements satisfy $x^2 + y^2 = 1$. This set corresponds to the set of points on the circle whose center is O and whose radius is 1.

$\{(x,y) \mid x > 0 \text{ and } y > 0\}$, the set of pairs both of whose elements are positive.   This set corresponds to the set of points in the first quadrant of the plane.

We shall meet many subsets of these types in later chapters of this book.

6.3. *Union and Intersection*

We have just seen that a subset can consist of those objects (points, real numbers, ordered pairs of real numbers, etc.) which have a certain property in common.   What is the situation when we have two properties to consider?   For example, let us look at the following subsets of the set of real numbers:

$$P = \{x \mid x > 0\} \qquad \text{and} \qquad I = \{x \mid x \text{ is an integer}\}$$

From these we can construct two new sets:

(1) The set of real numbers which are elements of P or of I or of both.   This is the set consisting of all positive real numbers, 0, and all negative integers.   It can be represented by Fig. 6.1.   We call this set the "union of P and I" and write it as $P \cup I$.

$$\underset{-5\ -4\ -3\ -2\ -1\ \ 0\ \ 1\ \ 2\ \ 3\ \ 4\ \ 5}{}$$

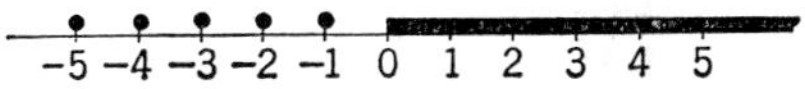

Figure 6.1

(2) The set of real numbers which are elements of both P and I. This is the set of positive integers.   We call this set the "intersection of P and I" and write it as $P \cap I$.

More generally we can define the union and intersection of any two sets without taking them to be any sort of subsets.

Definition: The *union* of X and Y, written $X \cup Y$, is the set of elements which belong to either X or Y or to both X and Y.   (See Fig. 6.2, in which $X \cup Y$ is shaded.)

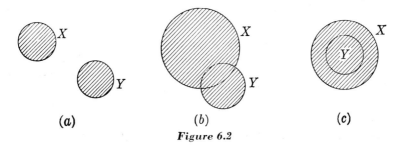

(a)   (b)   (c)

Figure 6.2

Definition: The *intersection* of X and Y, written $X \cap Y$, is the set of elements which belong to both X and Y. (See Fig. 6.3, in which $X \cap Y$ is shaded.)

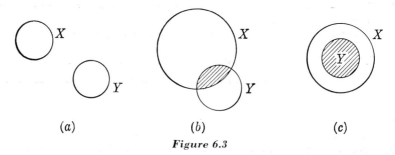

(a)   (b)   (c)

Figure 6.3

Illustration 1. Using the notation of Sec. 6.1, we find that:

(a) $[1,2] \cup [2,3] = [1,3]$.   (b) $[1,4] \cup [2,5] = [1,5]$.

(c) $[2,6] \cup [3,4] = [2,6]$.   (d) $[1,2] \cap [2,3] = \{2\}$.

(e) $[1,4] \cap [2,5] = [2,4]$.   (f) $[2,6] \cap [3,4] = [3,4]$.

(g) $]2,4[\cup [1,3] = [1,4]$.   (h) $]3,5[\cup [5,7] =]3,7]$.

(i) $]1,4[\cap]4,5] = \emptyset$.

(j) $[3,6[\cap [4,5] = [4,5]$.

(k) $\emptyset \cup A = A$.

(l) If $B \subset A$, then $B \cup A = A$, and $B \cap A = B$.

PROBLEMS 6.3

1. Which pairs of the following sets are identical?

(a) {John, Jim, Jerry}.   (b) {1, 2, 3}.

(c) {Jim, John, Jerry}.   (d) {3, 2, 1}.

(e) {a, b, c}.   (f) {1, 2, 3, 4}.

2. Which pairs of the following sets are identical?

(a) {Susan, Sarah, Sally, Sophie}.

(b) {algebra, geometry, chemistry, physics}.

(c) {1, 2, 3, 4}.

(d) {Sarah, Susan, Sophie, Sally}.

(e) {4, 2, 1, Susan}.

(f) {geometry, chemistry, algebra, physics}.

In Probs. 3 to 15 establish a 1 to 1 correspondence between the given two sets whenever this is possible.

3. The set of negative integers; the set of positive integers.

4. {2, 4, 6, 8, 10, . . .}; {3, 6, 9, 12, 15, . . .}.

5. The set of married men; the set of married women.

6. The set of Chevrolets in operation; the set of Fords in operation.

7. The set of all students in your university; the set of mathematics professors in your university.

8. The set of all French words; the set of all English words.

9. The set of positions on a baseball team; the set of players of one team as listed in their batting order.

10. The set of elective offices in your state government; the set of elected officials.

11. The set of all integers; the set of positive integers.
12. The set of real numbers in the interval [0,1]; the set of real numbers in the interval [0,2].
13.* The set of real numbers in the interval]0,1[; the set of all real numbers.
14.* The set of positive integers; the set of rational numbers. (See Courant and Robbins, "What Is Mathematics?" pages 79 to 80.)
15.* The set of positive integers; the set of real numbers. (See Courant and Robbins, "What Is Mathematics?" pages 81 to 83.)
16.* The set of all real numbers; the set of ordered pairs of real numbers.

In Probs. 17 to 22 list all the subsets of the given set. Which of these are "proper" subsets?

17. {2,6}.   18. {a, b}.
19. {3, 5, 7}.   20. {John, James, Jerry}.
21. {a, b, c, d}.   22. {1, 2, 3, 4}.
23.* Count the number of subsets in each of Probs. 17 to 22 that you have worked. Now guess a general formula for the number of subsets of a given, finite set. Prove that your guess is correct.
24. Show that, if $A \subseteq B$ and $B \subseteq A$, then B is identical with A.

In Probs. 25 to 40 find the set defined by the given operation. All sets mentioned are subsets of the set of real numbers.

25. $[3,5] \cup [4,7]$.   26. $[3,5] \cap [4,7]$.
27. $[2,10] \cap [5,8]$.   28. $[2,10] \cup [5,8]$.
29. $[1,3[\cup [2,6]$.   30. $]2,4] \cap [1,2[$.
31. $]0,3[\cap]1,4]$.   32. $]2,8] \cup [0,2]$.
33. $\{x \mid x \text{ is an integer}\} \cap \{x \mid x > 0\}$.
34. $\{x \mid x \text{ is rational}\} \cap \{x \mid x > 0\}$.
35. $\{x \mid x \text{ is rational}\} \cup \{x \mid x \text{ is irrational}\}$.
36. $\{x \mid x \text{ is an even integer}\} \cup \{x \mid x \text{ is an odd integer}\}$.
37. $\{x \mid x \text{ is rational}\} \cap \{x \mid x \text{ is irrational}\}$.
38. $\{x \mid x \text{ is positive}\} \cap \{x \mid x \text{ is negative}\}$.
39. $\{(x,y) \mid x \geq 0\} \cup \{(x,y) \mid x \leq 0\}$.
40. $\{(x,y) \mid x \geq 0\} \cap \{(x,y) \mid x \leq 0\}$.
41. Show that $\{x \mid x^2 - 7x + 12 = 0\} = \{x \mid x - 3 = 0\} \cup \{x \mid x - 4 = 0\}$.
42. Show that $\{(x,y) \mid x - 2 = 0 \text{ and } y + 3 = 0\} = \{(x,y) \mid x - 2 = 0\} \cap \{(x,y) \mid y + 3 = 0\}$. What is the geometrical interpretation?

6.4. Sets Defined by Equations

We have seen how the equation $x - 3 = 0$ can be used to define the set $\{x \mid x - 3 = 0\} = \{3\}$. Similarly

$$\{x \mid x^2 - 5x + 6 = 0\} = \{2,3\}$$

is defined by the equation $x^2 - 5x + 6 = 0$. In general any equation involving x defines a set consisting of those values of x which satisfy the equation. Hence we may speak of the "set of solutions" of an equation, or of its "solution set."

We shall have to deal with various types of equations. The simplest is $P(x) = Q(x)$, where $P(x)$ and $Q(x)$ are polynomials in x. We can also consider $F(x) = G(x)$, where $F(x)$ and $G(x)$ are general algebraic expressions, or trigonometric, exponential, or logarithmic expressions. We must be careful to specify the universal set from which x is to be chosen. In most cases in this book this is the set of real numbers. We may restrict it, say, to the set of rational numbers, or we may expand it to the set of complex numbers. In any case we must be sure that we know what universal set we are using.

Definition: Given a universal set X and an equation $F(x) = G(x)$ involving x, the set $\{x \mid F(x) = G(x)\}$ is called the *solution set* of the given equation. It consists of those x in X for which $F(x)$ and $G(x)$ have equal numerical values.

Suppose that A is the solution set of the equation $F(x) = G(x)$. We ask: "Are there other equations for which A is the solution set?" Surely the answer is "yes," for $F(x) + 2 = G(x) + 2$ is such an equation. To suggest the variety of equations which have the same solution set, we note that the following equations all have the same real x as solutions, namely, $x = -1$ and -3.

$$x^2 + 4x + 3 = 0 \qquad 3x^2 + 12x = -9 \qquad (x+3)^3(x+1)^4 = 0$$

$$\frac{x^2 + 4x + 3}{x^2 + 1} = 0 \qquad 3 + \frac{4x + 2}{x^2 + 1} = 2$$

In the usual situation we are given one of these equations and are asked to find the solution set. If we can see the solutions at once, we write them down. But more often the solution is not evident at once, and we proceed by transforming the equation into one which we can solve. You are surely familiar with this process, which we illustrate here in a simple case.

Illustration 1. Solve $5x + 4 = 3x + 8$.

Subtracting 4 from each side, we get the simpler equation:

$$5x = 3x + 4$$

Subtracting $3x$ from each side, we get

$$2x = 4$$

Dividing by 2, we get

$$x = 2$$

We must be certain, however, that each new (and simpler) equation has the same solution set as the given equation. This leads us to the notion of "equivalent equations." In Illustration 1 all four equations which appear are equivalent.

Definition: Given a fixed universal set X, two equations in x are *equivalent* if and only if they have identical sets of solutions.

The problem of solving algebraic equations thus requires us to answer the question: "What algebraic operations on an equation transform it into an equivalent equation, and what operations do not?" Operations of the first type may be used safely at any time; those of the second kind are dangerous to use and may lead to wrong answers.

Let us examine the most important kinds of operations to see how they behave.

First of all let us add (or subtract) the same expression to (or from) both sides. You doubtless recognize this as a standard operation in algebra which is not supposed to alter the solutions of an equation. This process is more complicated than appears at first sight; so let us restrict ourselves to the following simple case.

Theorem 1. Let $F(x)$ and $G(x)$ be any algebraic expressions and $P(x)$ any polynomial. Then the equations $F(x) = G(x)$ and

$$F(x) + P(x) = G(x) + P(x)$$

are equivalent: i.e.,

$$\{x \mid F(x) = G(x)\} = \{x \mid F(x) + P(x) = G(x) + P(x)\}$$

Proof: Let a be a value of x for which $F(a) = G(a)$. We see from this that $F(a) + P(a) = G(a) + P(a)$. Therefore any solution of $F(x) = G(x)$ is a solution of $F(x) + P(x) = G(x) + P(x)$. Conversely, if a is such that $F(a) + P(a) = G(a) + P(a)$, it follows by subtraction of $P(a)$ from both sides that $F(a) = G(a)$. Hence the two equations are equivalent.

Remark. It would seem reasonable to extend this theorem to permit $P(x)$ to be any algebraic expression. But here our troubles begin. Consider the equation $x = 1$. If we add $1/(x - 1)$ to both sides of this equation, we get

$$x + \frac{1}{x - 1} = 1 + \frac{1}{x - 1}$$

If we put $x = 1$ into this equation, we find that neither side of the equation is defined and hence that no equality can be claimed. Hence

$x = 1$ is not a solution of the transformed equation, and the two equations are not equivalent.

You may well insist that no one in his right mind would try to solve $x = 1$ by adding $1/(x - 1)$ to both sides, and we agree. Nevertheless, this is a valid counterexample to the false statement that the addition of an algebraic fraction to both sides of an equation transforms it into an equivalent equation. Although you will seldom get into trouble if you do carry out this dubious operation, there is never any urgent need to use it. Therefore, do not add (or subtract) algebraic fractions to (or from) both sides of an equation. For methods of solving equations involving algebraic fractions see Sec. 6.7.

Theorem 2. Let $F(x)$ and $G(x)$ be any algebraic expressions and a any number $\neq 0$. Then the equations $F(x) = G(x)$ and $aF(x) = aG(x)$ are equivalent; i.e.,

$$\{x \mid F(x) = G(x)\} = \{x \mid aF(x) = aG(x)\}$$

The proof is immediate and is included in the Problems.

Remarks

(1) Since a may be $1/b$, Theorem 2 includes division by a constant $b \neq 0$.

(2) If $a = 0$, the two equations in Theorem 2 are not necessarily equivalent, since any x for which $F(x)$ and $G(x)$ are defined is a solution of $0 \cdot F(x) = 0 \cdot G(x)$. Thus we must exclude $a = 0$ in the statement of the theorem.

When we try to extend Theorem 2 to multiplication by a polynomial $P(x)$, we run into trouble. This is expressed in the next theorem.

Theorem 3. Let $F(x)$ and $G(x)$ be any algebraic expressions and $P(x)$ any polynomial. Then the equations $F(x) = G(x)$ and

$$P(x) \cdot F(x) = P(x) \cdot G(x)$$

may not be equivalent. Indeed:

$$\{x \mid F(x) = G(x)\} \subseteq \{x \mid P(x) \cdot F(x) = P(x) \cdot G(x)\}$$

Proof: The set on the right contains all the elements of the set on the left and in addition it contains those values of x for which $P(x) = 0$. When there are values of x in our universal set for which $P(x) = 0$ and for which $F(x) \neq G(x)$, the two equations in the theorem are definitely not equivalent. In the special case, however, in which $P(x)$

has no such solutions we do get equivalence. This is why we use the word "may" in the statement of the theorem.

Illustration 2

(a) Let the given equation be $2x + 1 = 3$, whose solution set is $\{1\}$. Put $P(x) = x - 2$. Then we have:

$$(x - 2)(2x + 1) = 3(x - 2)$$

whose solution set is $\{1, 2\}$. Thus we have enlarged the solution set.

(b) Let the given equation be $\dfrac{x^2 - 3x + 2}{x - 1} = 0$. Its solution set is $\{2\}$; note that $x = 1$ is not a solution since the left side is $0/0$ when $x = 1$. If we multiply both sides by $x - 1$, we get $x^2 - 3x + 2 = 0$, whose solution set is $\{1, 2\}$. Again we have enlarged the solution set.

Theorem 4. Let $F(x)$ and $G(x)$ be any algebraic expressions and $P(x)$ any polynomial. Then the equations $F(x) = G(x)$ and

$$F(x)/P(x) = G(x)/P(x)$$

may not be equivalent. Indeed:

$$\left\{ x \mid \frac{F(x)}{P(x)} = \frac{G(x)}{P(x)} \right\} \subseteq \{x \mid F(x) = G(x)\}$$

This is in fact just a restatement of Theorem 3.

Illustration 3. Let the given equation be $x^2 + 5x + 4 = 0$, whose solution set is $\{-1, -4\}$. Put $P(x) = x + 4$. Then we have:

$$\frac{x^2 + 5x + 4}{x + 4} = 0 \qquad \text{or} \qquad x + 1 = 0$$

Its solution set is $\{-1\}$, and so we have reduced the solution set and missed a solution of the given equation.

The conclusion to be drawn from Theorems 3 and 4 is:

In attempting to solve an equation, never multiply or divide both sides by a polynomial in x, or indeed by any algebraic expression other than a number $a \neq 0$.

Theorem 5. Let $F(x)$ and $G(x)$ be any algebraic expressions. Then the equations $F(x) = G(x)$ and $[F(x)]^2 = [G(x)]^2$ may not be equivalent. Indeed:

$$\{x \mid F(x) = G(x)\} \subseteq \{x \mid [F(x)]^2 = [G(x)]^2\}$$

The proof follows from the fact that:

$$\{x \mid [F(x)]^2 = [G(x)]^2\} = \{x \mid F(x) = G(x)\} \cup \{x \mid F(x) = -G(x)\}$$

Illustration 4

(a) Let the given equation be $x + 1 = 3$, whose solution set is $\{2\}$. Squaring both sides, we get: $x^2 + 2x + 1 = 9$, which is equivalent to $x^2 + 2x - 8 = 0$. The solution set of this, however, is $\{2, -4\}$. So we have enlarged the solution set.

(b) Let the given equation be $\sqrt{x^2 + 7} = -4$. The solution set is $\emptyset$, for the left side is nonnegative for any x, and the right side is negative. Squaring both sides, we obtain: $x^2 + 7 = 16$, which is equivalent to $x^2 - 9 = 0$. This solution set is therefore $\{3, -3\}$. So we have enlarged the solution set.

The conclusion to be drawn from Theorem 5 is that the squaring of both sides of any equation may introduce extra "solutions," which are frequently called "extraneous roots." This is therefore a dubious method of procedure, but in certain situations it is the only possible approach to a problem. If we are forced to square both sides, the "solutions" finally obtained may well not be solutions of the given equation. We must, therefore, check them in this equation and must discard any that are not, in fact, solutions.

We conclude this section with a slightly different type of theorem.

Theorem 6. Let $P(x)$ be a polynomial which factors into the product $P(x) = P_1(x) \cdot P_2(x) \cdots \cdots P_r(x)$. Then:

$$\{x \mid P(x) = 0\} = \{x \mid P_1(x) = 0\} \cup \{x \mid P_2(x) = 0\} \cup \cdots$$
$$\cup \{x \mid P_r(x) = 0\}$$

Proof. If x satisfies any one of the equations $P_1(x) = 0$, $P_2(x) = 0, \ldots, P_r(x) = 0$, it is clear that $P(x) = 0$. Hence the right-hand set is a subset of the left-hand side. Conversely, suppose that x satisfies $P(x) = 0$. Then the product

$$P_1(x) \cdot P_2(x) \cdots P_r(x) = 0$$

and at least one of the factors must be zero. Hence the left-hand set is a subset of the right-hand set. Combining these results, we get a proof of the theorem.

As we have noted earlier (Sec. 2.6), this theorem is extremely useful in the solution of polynomial equations. We factor the given polynomial and then set each factor equal to zero. The union of the solution sets of the equations so obtained is the solution set of the given equation.

Illustration 5. Solve $x^2 + 12x + 32 = 0$.

Since $x^2 + 12x + 32 = (x + 8)(x + 4)$, we consider

$$x + 8 = 0 \quad \text{and} \quad x + 4 = 0$$

Since their solution sets are $\{-8\}$ and $\{-4\}$, respectively, the solution set of the given equation is

$$\{-8\} \cup \{-4\} = \{-8, -4\}$$

6.5. *Linear Equations*

These have appeared so often in earlier chapters (especially in Sec. 2.8) that we need not discuss them here. For reference let us state the following theorem, which summarizes the situation:

Theorem 7. The linear equation: $ax + b = 0$, with $a \neq 0$, has one and only one solution, namely, $x = -b/a$.

6.6. *Quadratic Equations*

The next simplest type of equation is the quadratic:

$$(1) \qquad\qquad ax^2 + bx + c = 0$$

where $a \neq 0$. The coefficients a, b, and c are, in general, complex numbers, but in various special circumstances we shall require them to be real. We have seen (Theorem 6, Sec. 6.4) that one way to solve such an equation is to factor it, and in Sec. 3.6 we learned how to factor certain expressions of the form $ax^2 + bx + c$. When we cannot write down the factors at sight in this way, we proceed by a method known as "completing the square." This depends upon the fact that

$$(2) \qquad\qquad x^2 + 2dx + d^2 = (x + d)^2$$

Since $a \neq 0$, let us write Eq. (3), which is equivalent to (1):

$$(3) \qquad\qquad x^2 + \frac{b}{a}x + \frac{c}{a} = 0 \quad \text{[Theorem 2, Sec. 6.4]}$$

If we put $d = b/2a$, the first two terms on the left side of (2) are equal to the corresponding terms in (3). In general, however, $d^2 \neq c/a$. Therefore we write (4), which is equivalent to (3):

$$(4) \qquad\qquad x^2 + \frac{b}{a}x + \left(\frac{b}{2a}\right)^2 = \left(\frac{b}{2a}\right)^2 - \frac{c}{a}$$

Now the left-hand side of (4) is of the same form as the left-hand side of (2). Thus:

$$(5) \qquad\qquad \left(x + \frac{b}{2a}\right)^2 = \frac{b^2 - 4ac}{4a^2}$$

We can solve (5) by extracting the square root of both sides. We use the fact that, if $y^2 = r$, then $y = +\sqrt{r}$ or $y = -\sqrt{r}$. Hence from (5) we find that:

$$x + \frac{b}{2a} = \frac{\sqrt{b^2 - 4ac}}{2a} \qquad \text{or} \qquad x + \frac{b}{2a} = -\frac{\sqrt{b^2 - 4ac}}{2a}$$

Therefore

$$x = \frac{-b + \sqrt{b^2 - 4ac}}{2a} \qquad \text{or} \qquad x = \frac{-b - \sqrt{b^2 - 4ac}}{2a}$$

This proves the following theorem:

Theorem 8.   The quadratic equation

$$ax^2 + bx + c = 0 \qquad a \neq 0$$

where a, b, and c are complex numbers, and where x is an element of the set of all complex numbers, has two solutions, namely:

$$x = \frac{-b \pm \sqrt{b^2 - 4ac}}{2a}$$

In other words, the set $\{x \mid ax^2 + bx + c = 0\}$ is the set

$$\left\{ \frac{-b + \sqrt{b^2 - 4ac}}{2a}, \ \frac{-b - \sqrt{b^2 - 4ac}}{2a} \right\}$$

Remarks

(1) Theorem 8 would have been false, even for real a, b, and c, if we had restricted x to belong to the set of real numbers. For $x^2 + 1 = 0$ has no real solutions.

(2) If a, b, and c are real, we may easily deduce the following properties of the solutions:

When $b^2 - 4ac$ is positive, the two solutions are real and unequal.

When $b^2 - 4ac$ is zero, the two solutions are real and equal.

When $b^2 - 4ac$ is negative, the two solutions are unequal and neither of them is real.

(3) Let r_1 and r_2 be the two roots of $ax^2 + bx + c = 0$; that is,

(6) $$r_1 = \frac{-b + \sqrt{b^2 - 4ac}}{2a} \qquad r_2 = \frac{-b - \sqrt{b^2 - 4ac}}{2a}$$

Then:

$$(7) \qquad\qquad r_1 + r_2 = -\frac{b}{a} \qquad r_1 r_2 = \frac{c}{a}$$

Exercise A. By direct calculation verify the above statements.

(4) The above formulas permit us to give a general expression for the factors of $ax^2 + bx + c$, namely:

$$(8) \qquad\qquad ax^2 + bx + c = a(x - r_1)(x - r_2)$$

where r_1 and r_2 are defined in (6) above. To prove this correct, we note that

$$a(x - r_1)(x - r_2) = ax^2 - a(r_1 + r_2)x + ar_1 r_2$$
$$= ax^2 - a\left(-\frac{b}{a}\right)x + a\left(\frac{c}{a}\right)$$
$$= ax^2 + bx + c$$

The use of formula (8) permits us to factor trinomials which could not be factored by the methods of Chap. 3. It also provides a direct approach to certain trinomials which can be factored by the methods of Chap. 3 but whose factorization by those methods is likely to be long and tedious.

Illustration 1

(a) Factor $x^2 + 2x + 5$.

$$r_1 = \frac{-2 + \sqrt{-16}}{2} = -1 + 2i$$

$$r_2 = \frac{-2 - \sqrt{-16}}{2} = -1 - 2i$$

So $x^2 + 2x + 5 = (x + 1 - 2i)(x + 1 + 2i)$.

(b) Factor $35x^2 - 11x - 72$.

$$r_1 = \frac{11 + \sqrt{10{,}201}}{70} = \frac{11 + 101}{70} = \frac{112}{70} = \frac{8}{5}$$

$$r_2 = \frac{11 - \sqrt{10{,}201}}{70} = \frac{11 - 101}{70} = -\frac{90}{70} = -\frac{9}{7}$$

So $35x^2 - 11x - 72 = 35(x - \frac{8}{5})(x + \frac{9}{7}) = (5x - 8)(7x + 9)$.

PROBLEMS 6.6

In each of Probs. 1 to 12, one of the following relations is true: $A \subset B$; $A = B$; $A \supset B$. Write the correct relation in each case. The universal set is the set of real numbers.

A

B

1. $\{x \mid 2x + 3 = x - 5\}$ $\{x \mid 3x + 4 = 2x - 4\}$
2. $\{x \mid x^2 + 3 = -2x + 2\}$ $\{x \mid x^2 + 2x = -1\}$
3. $\{x \mid (x + 3)(x - 2) = 0\}$ $\{x \mid x + 3 = 0\}$
4. $\{x \mid (x - 1)(x + 4) = 0\}$ $\{x \mid x - 1 = 0\} \cup \{x \mid x + 4 = 0\}$
5. $\{x \mid (x + 3)(x - 5) = 0\}$ $\{x \mid x + 3 = 0\} \cup \{x \mid x - 5 = 0\}$
6. $\{x \mid x + 2 = 6\}$ $\{x \mid (x + 2)^2 = 36\}$
7. $\{x \mid \sqrt{x + 7} = 3\}$ $\{x \mid x + 7 = 9\}$
8. $\{x \mid \sqrt{3x + 1} = -2\}$ $\{x \mid 3x + 1 = 4\}$
9. $\{x \mid x + 2 = 6\}$ $\{x \mid (x - 1)(x + 2) = (x - 1)6\}$
10. $\left\{ x \,\middle|\, \dfrac{x^2 - 7x + 12}{x - 3} = 0 \right\}$ $\{x \mid x^2 - 7x + 12 = 0\}$
11. $\{x \mid x^2 - 9x + 20 = 0\}$ $\left\{ x \,\middle|\, \dfrac{x^2 - 9x + 20}{x - 5} = 0 \right\}$
12. $\{x \mid 2x(x + 5) = (x + 5)\}$ $\{x \mid 2x = 1\}$

In Probs. 13 to 22 solve the quadratic equations.

13. $2x^2 - 4x + 7 = 0.$ 14. $x^2 + 10x + 2 = 0.$
15. $4x^2 + 4x + 1 = 0.$ 16. $-x^2 + 5x + k = 0.$
17. $x^2 + 4x - 5 = 0.$ 18. $18x^2 + 27x - 56 = 0.$
19. $36x^2 + 17x - 35 = 0.$ 20. $-2x^2 + 7x + b = 0.$
21. $x^2 - (4 + 2i)x + 3 + 4i = 0.$ 22. $x^2 - (2 - 2i)x - 2i = 0.$

In Probs. 23 to 28 add terms to both sides so that the left-hand side becomes a perfect square.

23. $x^2 + 3x + 1 = 0.$ 24. $x^2 - 3x + 7 = 0.$
25. $x^2 + 12x + 36 = 0.$ 26. $x^2 + 8x - 9 = 0.$
27. $4x^2 - 8x + 2 = 0.$ 28. $3x^2 - 18x - 1 = 0.$

In Probs. 29 to 34 find the sum and product of the roots without solving the equation.

29. $x^2 + 8x + 9 = 0.$ 30. $x^2 - 5x + 11 = 0.$
31. $3x^2 + 8x - 5 = 0.$ 32. $5x^2 + 9x + 14 = 0.$
33. $(1 + i)x^2 + (3 - i)x + (2 + 4i) = 0.$
34. $(2 - i)x^2 + (4 + 2i)x - (3 - 5i) = 0.$

In Probs. 35 to 40 find the value of k for which the roots of the given equation are equal.

35. $x^2 + 5x + k = 0.$ 36. $x^2 - 7x + k = 0.$
37. $2x^2 + 3x - k = 0.$ 38. $3x^2 - 4x + k = 0.$
39. $x^2 + 2kx + 4 = 0.$ 40. $x^2 - 3kx + 5 = 0.$

In Probs. 41 to 46 find a quadratic equation the sum and product of whose roots have the given values.

41. Sum 6, product 8.   42. Sum -2, product 4.
43. Sum 7, product 5.   44. Sum $\frac{1}{2}$, product $\frac{3}{4}$.
45. Sum $\frac{3}{5}$, product $\frac{2}{5}$.   46. Sum 18, product 3.

In Probs. 47 to 52 factor the given trinomial.

47. $2x^2 - 3x + 4.$ 48. $x^2 + x + 1.$
49. $x^2 + 2x + 2.$ 50. $5x^2 - x - 1.$

51. $32x^2 + 100x + 63$.   **52.** $90x^2 + 14x - 24$.

53. Prove Theorem 2, Sec. 6.4.

54. The sum of two numbers is **11**, and their product is 24. Write down the quadratic equation of which they are the solutions, and solve.

55. Find the value of k for which the sum of the solutions of the following equation is twice their product:

$$3x^2 - 4x + k = 0$$

56. Find a quadratic equation whose solutions are the reciprocals of those of

$$2x^2 + 3x + 7 = 0. \quad \text{HINT: } \frac{1}{p} + \frac{1}{q} = \frac{p+q}{pq}; \left(\frac{1}{p}\right)\left(\frac{1}{q}\right) = \frac{1}{pq}.$$

57. Find a quadratic equation whose solutions are the squares of those of $x^2 + 3x + 5 = 0$.   HINT: $p^2 + q^2 = (p+q)^2 - 2pq$; $(p^2)(q^2) = (pq)^2$.

58. Find a quadratic equation whose solutions are, respectively, the sum and product of the solutions of $x^2 - 5x + 8 = 0$.

6.7. *Equations Containing Fractions*

It is not uncommon for you to meet equations like

$$\frac{1}{x} + \frac{2}{x+1} = 3 \quad \text{or} \quad \frac{x-1}{x+4} - \frac{x+2}{x-3} = 5$$

in which algebraic fractions appear. The solution of these depends upon one important fact:

Basic Principle. Let a/c and b/c be two fractions with equal denominators, $c \neq 0$. Then $a/c = b/c$ if and only if $a = b$.

We apply this principle in the following way: First we express all the given fractions in terms of a common denominator. Then we write the equation obtained by equating the numerators of both sides and solve this equation. This gives us a tentative set of solutions, but there is still the possibility that some or all of these will make one of the denominators of the given fractions equal to zero. Such values must be discarded. It is therefore wise to check all solutions in the original equation before announcing the final answer.

Illustration 1. Solve $\dfrac{1}{x} + \dfrac{6}{x+4} = 1$.

In terms of a common denominator this becomes:

$$\frac{(x+4) + (6x)}{x(x+4)} = \frac{x(x+4)}{x(x+4)}$$

Putting the numerators equal, we obtain:

$$7x + 4 = x^2 + 4x$$

or

$$x^2 - 3x - 4 = 0$$

Hence $x = 4, -1$.

Both of these satisfy the given equation.

Illustration 2.   Solve $\dfrac{7}{x - 1} - \dfrac{6}{x^2 - 1} = 5$.

$$\frac{7(x^2 - 1) - 6(x - 1)}{(x - 1)(x^2 - 1)} = \frac{5(x - 1)(x^2 - 1)}{(x - 1)(x^2 - 1)}$$

$$7(x^2 - 1) - 6(x - 1) = 5(x - 1)(x^2 - 1)$$

or

$$(x - 1)(x - 2)(5x + 3) = 0$$

So $x = 1, 2, -\frac{3}{5}$.

If we put $x = 1$ in the original equation, we obtain $\frac{7}{0} - \frac{6}{0} = 5$, which is certainly false.   However, $x = 2$ and $x = -\frac{3}{5}$ do satisfy the original equation.   The correct solution set is therefore $\{2, -\frac{3}{5}\}$.

The above method of solution is not as elegant as it might have been, for we did not use the L.C.D.   If we had observed that $x^2 - 1$ serves as the L.C.D., we would have written:

$$\frac{7(x + 1) - 6}{x^2 - 1} = \frac{5(x^2 - 1)}{x^2 - 1}$$

$$(7x + 7) - 6 = 5x^2 - 5$$

$$5x^2 - 7x - 6 = 0$$

$$(x - 2)(5x + 3) = 0$$

$$x = 2, -\frac{3}{5}$$

In this case the incorrect solution $x = 1$ does not appear.   Hence it is advisable to use the L.C.D. whenever you can find it.   But even the consistent use of the L.C.D. will not excuse you from testing every tentative solution.   See the next illustration.

Illustration 3

$$\frac{x}{x + 2} - \frac{4}{x + 1} = \frac{-2}{x + 2}$$

Using the L.C.D. $(x + 2)(x + 1)$, we get:

$$\frac{x(x + 1) - 4(x + 2)}{(x + 2)(x + 1)} = \frac{-2(x + 1)}{(x + 2)(x + 1)}$$

Equating numerators, we find:

$$x^2 - x - 6 = 0$$

So

$$x = 3, -2$$

Testing, we observe that $x = 3$ satisfies the given equation but that $x = -2$ makes two denominators zero and hence is not a solution.   The correct solution set is therefore $\{3\}$.

6.8. *Equations Containing Radicals*

In this section we are interested in equations like:

$$\sqrt{x + 13} - \sqrt{7 - x} = 2 \quad\text{or}\quad 2\sqrt{x + 4} - x = 1$$

in which x appears under a radical. For simplicity we shall consider square roots only. The only possible method of procedure involves squaring both sides and hence is subject to the cautions expressed in Theorem 5, Sec. 6.4.

When there is only one radical in the given equation, write the equivalent equation in which the radical is on one side and all the other terms on the other side. Then squaring both sides removes the radical and leaves an equation without radicals to be solved. Since this equation is not equivalent to the given equation, all solutions must be checked in the given equation.

Illustration 1. Solve $2\sqrt{x + 4} - x = 1$.

$$2\sqrt{x + 4} = x + 1$$
$$4(x + 4) = x^2 + 2x + 1$$
$$x^2 - 2x - 15 = 0$$
$$(x - 5)(x + 3) = 0$$
$$x = 5, \ -3$$

Checking $x = 5$, we have $2\sqrt{9} - 5 = 1$, or $6 - 5 = 1$, which is true.
Checking $x = -3$, we have $2\sqrt{1} + 3 = 1$, or $2 + 3 = 1$, which is false.
The solution set of the given equation is, therefore, $\{5\}$.

When there are two radicals, the method is similar; but two squarings are required. Proceed as in the illustration below.

Illustration 2. Solve: $\sqrt{x + 13} - \sqrt{7 - x} = 2$.

$$\sqrt{x + 13} = 2 + \sqrt{7 - x}$$
$$x + 13 = 4 + 4\sqrt{7 - x} + 7 - x$$
$$2x + 2 = 4\sqrt{7 - x}$$
$$x + 1 = 2\sqrt{7 - x}$$
$$x^2 + 2x + 1 = 28 - 4x$$
$$x^2 + 6x - 27 = 0$$
$$(x - 3)(x + 9) = 0$$
$$x = 3, \ -9$$

Checking $x = 3$, we have $\sqrt{16} - \sqrt{4} = 2$, or $4 - 2 = 2$, which is true.
Checking $x = -9$, we have $\sqrt{4} - \sqrt{16} = 2$, or $2 - 4 = 2$, which is false.
Hence the correct solution set is $\{3\}$.

Illustration 3. Solve: $\sqrt{x+1} - \sqrt{x+6} = 1$.

$$\sqrt{x+1} = 1 + \sqrt{x+6}$$
$$x + 1 = 1 + 2\sqrt{x+6} + x + 6$$
$$-6 = 2\sqrt{x+6}$$
$$36 = 4(x+6)$$
$$4x = 12$$
$$x = 3$$

Testing, we find

$$\sqrt{3+1} - \sqrt{3+6} \neq 1$$

Therefore the equation has no solution.

PROBLEMS 6.8

Solve for x.

1. $\dfrac{12}{x+2} + \dfrac{8}{x} = 4$.

2. $\dfrac{6}{x-3} - \dfrac{4}{x+1} = 1$.

3. $\dfrac{7}{x+2} - \dfrac{2}{x^2-4} = 1$.

4. $\dfrac{21}{x+3} - \dfrac{7}{x^2-9} = 2$.

5. $\dfrac{2}{x} - \dfrac{6}{x+1} + \dfrac{5}{x+3} = 0$.

6. $\dfrac{2}{x} - \dfrac{9}{x-1} + \dfrac{8}{x-2} = 0$.

7. $\dfrac{3}{x+1} - \dfrac{2x-9}{x^2+1} = 0$.

8. $\dfrac{1}{x} + \dfrac{3}{x^2+2} = 0$.

9. $\dfrac{2x}{x+3} - \dfrac{4}{x-3} = \dfrac{-6}{x+3}$.

10. $-\dfrac{x}{x+1} + \dfrac{1}{x-1} = \dfrac{1}{x+1}$.

11. $\sqrt{x+5} - 4x + 13 = 0$.

12. $\sqrt{x-2} + 2x - 14 = 0$.

13. $\sqrt{x+1} + \sqrt{x+5} = 0$.

14. $\sqrt{x-3} + \sqrt{x-1} = 0$.

15. $\sqrt{x+18} - \sqrt{x+11} = 1$.

16. $\sqrt{x+3} + \sqrt{x+8} = 5$.

17. $\sqrt{3x+7} + \sqrt{2x+6} = 4$.

18. $\sqrt{4x+2} - \sqrt{6x+6} = -1$.

19. $\dfrac{1}{\sqrt{x}} - \dfrac{2}{\sqrt{x+3}} = 0$.

20. $\dfrac{x}{\sqrt{x+2}} - \dfrac{2x}{\sqrt{x+14}} = 0$.

CHAPTER SEVEN

Simultaneous Equations

and Matrices

7.1. *Linear Equations and Their Graphs*

In this chapter we shall be dealing with linear equations involving two or more unknowns. Examples of such equations are:

$$2x - 3y + 1 = 0 \qquad 3x + 4y - 5z + 7 = 0$$

For simplicity let us consider first the general linear equation in two unknowns:

$$ax + by + c = 0$$

where a, b, and c are real numbers.

A solution of this equation is an ordered pair (x,y) of real numbers which satisfy the given equation. Thus $(1,2)$ is a solution of

$$3x - 2y + 1 = 0$$

We see at once that there is not just one solution but in fact that there are infinitely many solutions. These form the "solution set"

$$\{(x,y) \mid ax + by + c = 0\}$$

This is a subset of the set $X \times Y$ of all ordered pairs of real numbers.

115

Since this is an infinite set, we cannot list all its elements, but we still need some alternative means of describing it.   The best approach is to construct its *graph*.   To form the graph of an equation we plot those points on the XY-plane whose coordinates satisfy the equation. You are probably aware of the fact that the graph of $ax + by + c = 0$ is a straight line.   We shall take this for granted here, but shall prove it in Chap. 14.   This straight line has the important properties:

(1) The coordinates (x,y) of every point on the line satisfy the equation.
(2) Every solution (x,y) of the equation gives the coordinates of a point which lies on the line.

In other words there is a 1 to 1 correspondence between

$$\{(x,y) \mid ax + by + c = 0\}$$

and the set of points lying on the graph of this equation.   Consequently, the line is an accurate way of representing the solution set of the equation.   We shall use this correspondence so often that we find it convenient to abbreviate our language and speak of "the line $ax + by + c = 0$" when we really mean "the line which is the graph of $ax + by + c = 0$."

The practical problem before us is to construct the line when we are given the equation.   The standard procedure is to find two points on the line (i.e., to find two solutions of the equation) and to draw the line through them.   Usually you are advised to find three points so that an error in computation or plotting is easily discovered.

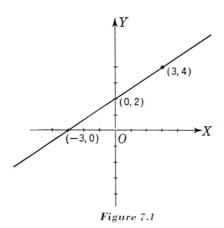

Figure 7.1

Illustration 1.   Plot the graph of $2x - 3y + 6 = 0$.   Let $x = 0$; then $y = 2$.   Let $y = 0$; then $x = -3$. So two points are $(0,2)$ and $(-3,0)$. A third point is $(3,4)$.

Notice how we found the first two points in Illustration 1. We let $x = 0$ and computed y; then we let $y = 0$ and computed x.   This gave us the two points, called the *intercepts*, at which the line crosses the axes.   It is wise to find them whenever we can.

Exercise A. What lines have both intercepts zero? What lines have just one intercept?

Two special cases are worthy of note. Any line of the form $x = a$ is parallel to the Y-axis, and any line of the form $y = b$ is parallel to the X-axis.

7.2. *The Graph of a Set of Ordered Pairs*

Now that we understand the notion of the graph of a linear equation, let us look at a more general situation. We wish to define the graph of a subset of the set of ordered pairs $X \times Y$. Let us call this subset $A = \{(x,y) \mid (x,y)$ have a given property in common$\}$. We recall that in Sec. 2.12 we established a definite 1 to 1 correspondence between the elements of $X \times Y$ [(that is, the ordered pairs (x,y)) and the set P of all points in the plane]. Let us call this correspondence C (for "coordinates") and write:

$$C: \quad X \times Y \leftrightarrow P$$

Under this correspondence there is a certain set of points $G \subseteq P$ which corresponds to our given subset A. That is:

$$C: \quad A \leftrightarrow G$$

We call G the *graph* of the set A.

Illustration 1
  (a) The graph of $\{(x,y) \mid x > 0\}$ is the right-hand half plane.
  (b) The graph of $\{(x,y) \mid y < 0\}$ is the lower half plane.
  (c) The graph of $\{(x,y) \mid x^2 + y^2 = 1\}$ is the circle of radius 1 whose center is at the origin.
  (d) The graph of $\{(x,y) \mid x^2 = 1\}$ is the pair of lines $x = 1$, $x = -1$ parallel to the Y-axis and at a distance 1 on either side of it.

In the following chapters we shall find it very helpful to use graphical techniques in studying sets of this type. When we are dealing with the graph of a subset of $X \times Y$ which is defined by an equation or an inequality, we shall speak of the "graph of the equation," or the "graph of the inequality." This is an abbreviation for the more complete description "the graph of the set $\{(x,y) \mid (x,y)$ satisfies the given equation or inequality$\}$."

7.3. *Simultaneous Linear Equations*

Here we complicate the situation a little by considering a pair of simultaneous linear equations in two unknowns. The general expression for such a pair is

(1)
$$a_1x + b_1y + c_1 = 0$$
$$a_2x + b_2y + c_2 = 0$$

By a solution of (1) we mean an ordered pair (x,y) which satisfies both equations. In set language the solution set of (1) is the set

$$\{(x,y) \mid a_1x + b_1y + c_1 = 0\} \cap \{(x,y) \mid a_2x + b_2y + c_2 = 0\}$$

Graphically, we are looking for those points which lie on each of the two given lines.

So far we have not proved that there actually exists a solution of (1) or that a solution (if it exists) is unique. We shall examine this matter presently, but let us build up some intuition by looking at the graphical situation. If we are given two lines in the plane, three possible situations may arise:

(a) They intersect.

(b) They are parallel.

(c) They are coincident; i.e., they are really the same line.

What about the solution of (1) in each of these three cases?

(a) When the lines intersect, they have a single point in common; and so there is one and only one solution of (1).

(b) When the lines are parallel, they have no points in common; and so there is no solution of (1).

(c) When the lines coincide, every point on this common line is a solution; so there are infinitely many solutions of (1).

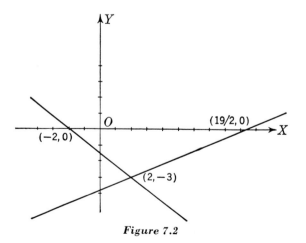

Figure 7.2

Hence (1) may have one solution, no solutions, or infinitely many solutions.   Let us see how these cases arise when we attack the problem analytically.   The method of solution is best explained by the examples below.

Illustration 1.   Solve
$$2x - 5y - 19 = 0$$
$$3x + 4y + 6 = 0 \qquad \text{(Fig. 7.2)}$$

To eliminate x, we multiply the first equation by 3 and the second by 2.   This gives us

$$6x - 15y - 57 = 0$$
$$6x + 8y + 12 = 0$$

Subtracting, we have

$$-23y - 69 = 0 \qquad \text{or} \qquad y + 3 = 0$$

This equation, combined with the first equation of the stated system, gives us the equivalent system:
$$2x - 5y - 19 = 0$$
$$y + 3 = 0$$

We solve the second equation for y and get $y = -3$.   Putting $y = -3$ in the first equation and solving for x, we have $x = 2$.   Hence the solution is the pair $(2, -3)$.

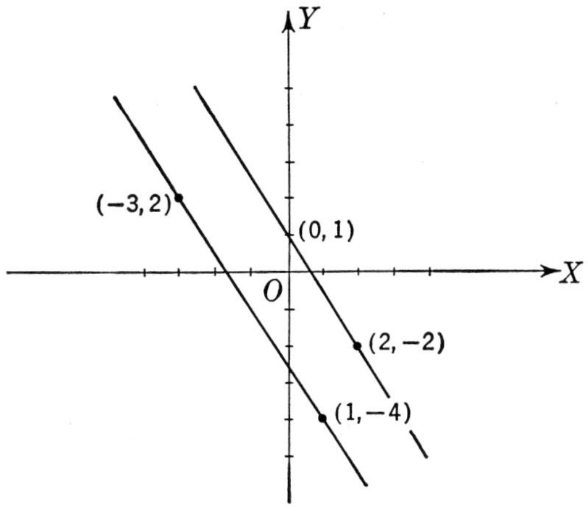

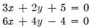

Figure 7.3

Illustration 2.   Solve
$$3x + 2y + 5 = 0$$
$$6x + 4y - 4 = 0 \qquad \text{(Fig. 7.3)}$$

Elimination of x as in Illustration 1 gives us the equivalent system:

$$3x + 2y + 5 = 0$$
$$14 = 0$$

Since the last equation is, in fact, not an equality, there can be no solution.   The lines are parallel.

Illustration 3.   Solve

$$4x - y + 3 = 0$$
$$8x - 2y + 6 = 0 \qquad (Fig. 7.4)$$

Elimination of x as above gives us the equivalent system:

$$4x - y + 3 = 0$$
$$0 = 0$$

Hence the system reduces to a single equation: i.e., the lines are coincident, and there are infinitely many solutions.

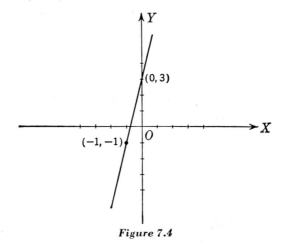

Figure 7.4

Now let us try the solution of the general case:

$$a_1x + b_1y + c_1 = 0$$
$$a_2x + b_2y + c_2 = 0$$

Let us suppose that x or y actually appears in at least one of these equations, i.e., that a_1, a_2, b_1, and b_2 are not all zero.   Suppose, then, that $a_1 \neq 0$.   Elimination of x gives us the equivalent system:

$$a_1x + b_1y + c_1 = 0$$
$$(a_1b_2 - a_2b_1)y + (a_1c_2 - a_2c_1) = 0$$

If $a_1b_2 - a_2b_1 \neq 0$, we can solve the second equation for y and obtain x as in Illustration 1.   If $a_1b_2 - a_2b_1 = 0$, there are two possibilities:

(a) $a_1c_2 - a_2c_1 \neq 0$. Then we have a contradiction, and there is no solution.

(b) $a_1c_2 - a_2c_1 = 0$. Then the system reduces to a single equation, and there are infinitely many solutions. In this case it also follows that $b_1c_2 - b_2c_1 = 0$. For we have the identity:

$$a_1(b_1c_2 - b_2c_1) = b_1(a_1c_2 - a_2c_1) - c_1(a_1b_2 - a_2b_1)$$

which becomes, under our assumptions:

$$a_1(b_1c_2 - b_2c_1) = 0 \qquad \text{with } a_1 \neq 0.$$

If, however, $b_1 \neq 0$, we may repeat this argument and obtain similar conclusions in which $-(b_1c_2 - b_2c_1)$ replaces $(a_1c_2 - a_2c_1)$ in (a) and (b) above. We summarize these results in the following theorem:

Theorem 1. The simultaneous equations

$$\begin{aligned} a_1x + b_1y + c_1 &= 0 \qquad \text{(Not all of } a_1, a_2, b_1, b_2 \text{ equal to zero)} \\ a_2x + b_2y + c_2 &= 0 \end{aligned}$$

(a) Have a unique solution if $a_1b_2 - a_2b_1 \neq 0$.
(b) Have no solution if $a_1b_2 - a_2b_1 = 0$ and at least one of $a_1c_2 - a_2c_1$ and $b_1c_2 - b_2c_1$ is not zero.
(c) Have infinitely many solutions if $a_1b_2 - a_2b_1 = 0$, $a_1c_2 - a_2c_1 = 0$, and $b_1c_2 - b_2c_1 = 0$.

Exercise A. Extend this theorem to cover the case where

$$a_1 = a_2 = b_1 = b_2 = 0.$$

7.4. *Simultaneous Linear Equations* (*Continued*)

The treatment in the previous section is entirely adequate for the solution of these equations, but it omits an idea which will help you to understand what has been going on. We explain this here. For simplicity we shall always assume that the two lines intersect at point $P(x_0, y_0)$.

When we eliminate one unknown, we multiply the first equation by some number, say k_1, and the second equation by k_2, and then we add. This gives:

$$(1) \qquad k_1(a_1x + b_1y + c_1) + k_2(a_2x + b_2y + c_2) = 0$$

For all values of k_1 and k_2 Eq. (1) is the equation of some line. Moreover this line has an important special property; namely it passes through point $P(x_0, y_0)$, the point of intersection of the two given lines. To see this, substitute (x_0, y_0) in (1); the result is zero since each parenthesis is zero by hypothesis. As k_1 and k_2 take different values, we get a family of lines all passing through P.

Theorem 2. If the lines $a_1x + b_1y + c_1 = 0$ and $a_2x + b_2y + c_2 = 0$ intersect at a point P, Eq. (1) represents a family of lines, each of which passes through P.

Let us not forget our original problem—to solve the simultaneous system (1), Sec. 7.3. The point P of intersection of the two given lines can be found equally well by solving the equations of any two other lines through P. In other words, we will get the same point P if we

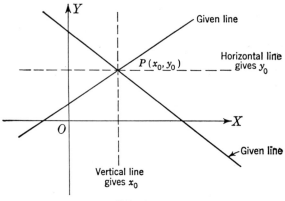

Figure 7.5

solve any pair of equations chosen from the family (1). In the terminology of Sec. 6.4, the given system of two equations is equivalent to any system of two distinct equations obtained from (1). So let us pick the simplest possible pair of equations from (1). These will correspond to the horizontal and vertical lines through P. To find the horizontal line, choose k_1 and k_2 so that the coefficient of x in (1) is zero; i.e., eliminate x. This gives the solution for y. Similarly, to find the vertical line through P, choose k_1 and k_2 so that y disappears, and solve for x. This solves the problem.

Incidentally, Eq. (1) permits us to obtain easy solutions to a number of other problems. The illustration below will give you the idea.

Illustration 1. Find the equation of the line passing through the point $(2, -1)$ and through the point of intersection of the lines $2x + y - 5 = 0$ and $x + 2y - 7 = 0$.

Using (1), we obtain the equation of the family of lines through this point of intersection:

$$k_1(2x + y - 5) + k_2(x + 2y - 7) = 0$$

We want to pick out the one passing through $(2,-1)$. So substitute $(2,-1)$ for (x,y) in the above equation. This gives

$$k_1(-2) + k_2(-7) = 0$$

Choose any k_1 and k_2 for which this is true, say $k_1 = 7$, $k_2 = -2$. This gives the required equation, namely:

$$7(2x + y - 5) + (-2)(x + 2y - 7) = 0$$
or
$$12x + 3y - 21 = 0$$

which is the answer. Observe that we never found the point $(1,3)$, which is the point of intersection of the two given lines.

7.5. *Simultaneous Linear Equations in Three Unknowns*

The method of Sec. 7.3 can be applied without substantial change to simultaneous systems of three equations in three unknowns. The general expression for such a system is:

(1)
$$a_1x + b_1y + c_1z + d_1 = 0$$
$$a_2x + b_2y + c_2z + d_2 = 0$$
$$a_3x + b_3y + c_3z + d_3 = 0$$

A solution is an ordered triple (x,y,z) which satisfies all three equations. If we wish to plot ordered triples, we need three dimensions and so we shall not draw the graphs of these equations. Their geometric interpretation, however, is helpful. It can be proved that the equation $ax + by + cz + d = 0$ corresponds to a plane in 3-space; so the system (1) represents three planes. The number of possible configurations for three planes is a little large, but here they are:

(a) The three planes intersect in a point; hence (1) has a unique solution.

(b) The three planes are mutually parallel; hence (1) has no solutions.

(c) Two planes coincide, and the third plane is parallel to this common plane; hence (1) has no solutions.

(d) All three planes coincide; hence (1) has a plane of solutions.

(e) The three planes intersect in three parallel lines; hence (1) has no solutions.

(f) Two planes are parallel, and the third intersects them in two parallel lines; hence (1) has no solutions.

(g) The three planes intersect in a common line; hence (1) has a line of solutions.

In summary, (1) may have a unique solution, a line of solutions, a plane of solutions, or no solution.

The method of solution, which handles all these cases, is best explained by the illustrations below.

Illustration 1. Solve:

$$2x - y + 3z + 9 = 0$$
$$x + 3y - z - 10 = 0$$
$$3x + y - z - 8 = 0$$

First we eliminate x between the first and second and between the first and third equations.   The result, together with the unchanged first equation, is the equivalent system:

$$2x - y + 3z + 9 = 0$$
$$7y - 5z - 29 = 0$$
$$5y - 11z - 43 = 0$$

Next eliminate y between the second and third equations.   Leaving the first two equations unchanged, we have the equivalent system:

$$2x - y + 3z + 9 = 0$$
$$7y - 5z - 29 = 0$$
$$z + 3 = 0$$

From the last equation, $z = -3$.   Putting $z = -3$ in the second equation enables us to find $y = 2$; and putting $y = 2$ and $z = -3$ in the first equation gives us $x = 1$.

Hence the solution is $(1,2,-3)$.

Illustration 2. Solve:

$$x + 2y - z + 3 = 0$$
$$2x + y + z - 1 = 0$$
$$3x + 3y + 2 = 0$$

The first elimination (of x) gives us the equivalent system:

$$x + 2y - z + 3 = 0$$
$$3y - 3z + 7 = 0$$
$$3y - 3z + 7 = 0$$

The final elimination (of y) gives the equivalent system:

$$x + 2y - z + 3 = 0$$
$$3y - 3z + 7 = 0$$
$$0 = 0$$

Thus the system really reduces to two equations, i.e., to two planes which meet in a line.   Hence there is a line of solutions.

Illustration 3. Solve

$$x - y + 2z + 1 = 0$$
$$2x - 2y + 4z + 2 = 0$$
$$3x - 3y + 6z + 3 = 0$$

The first elimination (of x) gives:

$$x - y + 2z + 1 = 0$$
$$0 = 0$$
$$0 = 0$$

Thus the system reduces to a single equation, i.e., to a single plane all of whose points are solutions. The three planes are coincident, and there is a plane of solutions.

Illustration 4. Solve

$$x + y + z - 1 = 0$$
$$2x - 3y - 2z + 4 = 0$$
$$3x - 2y - z + 2 = 0$$

The first elimination (of x) gives the system:

$$x + y + z - 1 = 0$$
$$5y + 4z - 6 = 0$$
$$5y + 4z - 5 = 0$$

The final elimination (of y) gives the system:

$$x + y + z - 1 = 0$$
$$5y + 4z - 6 = 0$$
$$- 1 = 0$$

Since the last equation is not, in fact, an equality, the system has no solution. There is no need to look further into the geometry of the case.

PROBLEMS 7.5

In Probs. 1 to 6, plot the graphs of the given equation on squared paper.

1. $3x - 4y + 12 = 0$.
2. $-5x + 2y + 10 = 0$.
3. $4x + y = 0$.
4. $3x + 8 = 0$.
5. $-2y + 5 = 0$.
6. $5x - 8y = 0$.

In Probs. 7 to 16 solve the given pair of equations algebraically. Then plot the graph of the two lines, and check your solution graphically.

7. $3x - 4y + 1 = 0$.
   $x + 2y - 3 = 0$.
8. $3x - 2y - 12 = 0$.
   $5x + 2y - 4 = 0$.
9. $4x + y - 8 = 0$.
   $8x - y - 4 = 0$.
10. $6x + y + 3 = 0$.
    $3x - 2y + 9 = 0$.
11. $x + 3y - 10 = 0$.
    $-2x + 4y = 0$.
12. $5x + 2y - 5 = 0$.
    $x - y - 8 = 0$.
13. $x + y - 4 = 0$.
    $2x + 2y - 1 = 0$.
14. $3x + 5y + 15 = 0$.
    $6x + 10y - 4 = 0$.
15. $-2x + 7y + 14 = 0$.
    $4x - 14y - 28 = 0$.
16. $3x - 2y - 1 = 0$.
    $9x - 6y - 3 = 0$.

In Probs. 17 to 26 solve the given system algebraically.

17. $2x - y + z - 3 = 0$.
    $x + 2y - z - 1 = 0$.
    $3x + y + z - 6 = 0$.
18. $7x + y - 2z + 9 = 0$.
    $-x + 2y + z - 2 = 0$.
    $5x + y - z + 5 = 0$.

19. $3x \quad\quad + z - 5 = 0.$
$\quad\quad -2y + 3z + 5 = 0.$
$\quad\quad x + y - z - 4 = 0.$

20. $4x - y + 2z + 10 = 0.$
$\quad\quad x + 3y - z + 4 = 0.$
$\quad\quad 2x \quad\quad + z + 5 = 0.$

21. $2x + 4y - z + 3 = 0.$
$\quad\quad 3x - 5y + 4z - 5 = 0.$
$\quad\quad 5x - y + 3z + 4 = 0.$

22. $-x + 3y - 5z + 8 = 0.$
$\quad\quad 4x - y + 3z + 5 = 0.$
$\quad\quad 3x + 2y - 2z + 4 = 0.$

23. $-3x + 3y + 2z - 5 = 0.$
$\quad\quad 5x - 2y + z + 6 = 0.$
$\quad\quad 2x + y + 3z + 1 = 0.$

24. $x + y \quad\quad + 2 = 0.$
$\quad\quad y + 2z - 4 = 0.$
$\quad\quad 2x + 5y + 6z - 8 = 0.$

25. $\quad\quad 2x - y + 4z + 5 = 0.$
$\quad\quad 6x - 3y + 12z + 15 = 0.$
$\quad\quad -4x + 2y - 8z - 10 = 0.$

26. $\quad\quad 3x + y - 2z - 3 = 0.$
$\quad\quad -12x - 4y + 8z + 12 = 0.$
$\quad\quad 6x + 2y - 4z - 6 = 0.$

In Probs. 27 to 32 find an equation of the line passing through the intersection of the two given lines and the given point.

27. $3x + y - 5 = 0;\ x - 2y + 3 = 0;\ (4,6).$
28. $x + y = 0;\ 2x - y + 3 = 0;\ (2,2).$
29. $4x + y - 1 = 0;\ x + 2y - 2 = 0;\ (3,5).$
30. $x + y - 2 = 0;\ -2x + 5y - 3 = 0;\ (-2,5).$
31. $x = 2;\ y = 5;\ (2,4).$
32. $x = -1;\ y = 6;\ (5,-1).$
33. Find an equation of the line through $(4,4)$ and $(2,3)$.   HINT: $x - 4 = 0$, $y - 4 = 0$ pass through $(4,4)$. Use the above method.
34. Find an equation of the line through $(-2,4)$ and $(5,1)$. See the hint for Prob. 33.
35. Find an equation of the line through (x_1,y_1) and (x_2,y_2).

7.6. *Vectors*

In this section we begin the study of a new kind of algebra in which the elements are as follows:

(1) Ordered pairs like (x,y), ordered triples like (x,y,z). We will call these vectors.

(2) Rectangular arrays like those in the coefficients of our simultaneous equations, such as

$$\begin{pmatrix} a_1 & b_1 \\ a_2 & b_2 \end{pmatrix} \quad \begin{pmatrix} a_1 & b_1 & c_1 \\ a_2 & b_2 & c_2 \end{pmatrix}$$

$$\begin{pmatrix} a_1 & b_1 & c_1 \\ a_2 & b_2 & c_2 \\ a_3 & b_3 & c_3 \end{pmatrix} \quad \begin{pmatrix} a_1 & b_1 & c_1 & d_1 \\ a_2 & b_2 & c_2 & d_2 \\ a_3 & b_3 & c_3 & d_3 \end{pmatrix}$$

We call these matrices.

Definition: A *matrix* is any rectangular (or square) array of numbers, and a *vector* is a special case of a matrix which has only one row or one column.

Let us begin by restricting ourselves to vectors. You have probably met vectors before in your study of physics, and may wonder about the connection between the vectors of physics and those defined above. In physics a vector is represented in the plane as

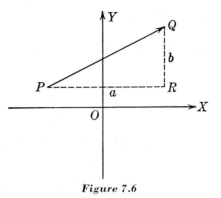

Figure 7.6

a directed distance $\overrightarrow{PQ}$ and is said to have magnitude and direction. The magnitude is represented by the length of the line segment in the plane, and the direction is given by the angle which this line makes with the horizontal and by the sense in which the arrow points. Common examples of vectors in physics are velocity, acceleration, and force.

Corresponding to the vector $\overrightarrow{PQ}$, we may draw a right triangle PQR (Fig. 7.6) with PR horizontal and QR vertical. The length of PR is the "x-component a" of $\overrightarrow{PQ}$; a is positive if $\overrightarrow{PQ}$ points to the right and is negative if $\overrightarrow{PQ}$ points to the left. Similarly RQ is the "y-component b" of $\overrightarrow{PQ}$; b is positive if $\overrightarrow{PQ}$ points up and negative if $\overrightarrow{PQ}$ points down. Clearly these components are known if the vector is known, and, conversely, a pair of components determines a vector if we know its initial point P. To simplify the discussion, we shall suppose that all of our vectors have the origin O as their initial point, so that the coordinates of their end points are equal to the components of the vectors. Then any vector is determined by the ordered pair of numbers (a,b). In the same way vectors in space have three components and are determined by a triple (a,b,c).

This gives us the connection between our vectors and the vectors of physics. You should note, however, that every physical vector can be represented by a pair or a triple, but that vectors as we have defined them do not necessarily have physical interpretations. This is a good example of a mathematical concept which has arisen as a generalization of a concrete physical object.

Notation for Vectors. We shall write our vectors as "row-vectors":

(a,b) or (a,b,c) or as "column-vectors": $\begin{pmatrix} a \\ b \end{pmatrix}$ or $\begin{pmatrix} a \\ b \\ c \end{pmatrix}$. There is no real distinction between row-vectors and column-vectors, but it will be convenient to use both notations in the applications which follow.

Addition of Vectors.   Since vectors are not numbers, the sum of two vectors is a new idea and must be defined.

Definition: The *sum of two vectors* is defined by the formulas:

$$(a,b) + (c,d) = (a + c, b + d)$$
$$(a,b,c) + (d,e,f) = (a + d, b + e, c + f)$$

In other words, to add two vectors of the same dimension, add their corresponding components. This has an important geometric interpretation, which we illustrate in the plane. In order to add $\overrightarrow{OP}$ to

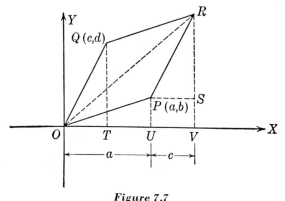

Figure 7.7

$\overrightarrow{OQ}$, we find point R, which is the fourth vertex of the parallelogram having O, P, and Q as its other vertices. Then triangle PRS is congruent to triangle OQT so that $PS = c$ and $RS = d$. Now $OU = a$, and OV is the x-component of OR. From the figure

$$OV = OU + UV$$
$$= OU + PS$$
$$= a + c$$

Similarly $RV = b + d$. Thus $\overrightarrow{OR} = \overrightarrow{OP} + \overrightarrow{OQ}$. This interpretation is the source of the graphical method for adding vectors which is used widely in physics and navigation.

Illustration 1

(a) $(1,-3,2) + (3,4,-1) = (4,1,1)$.
(b) $(5,2,-1) + (-5,-2,1) = (0,0,0)$, the "zero vector."
(c) $(-4,7,3) - (2,-1,4) = (-6,8,-1)$.
(d) $(6,4,3) - (6,4,3) = (0,0,0)$.

7.7. *Products of Vectors*

When we are speaking of vectors, we shall refer to an ordinary real number as a *scalar*. We now define the product of a scalar times a vector.

Definition: If (a,b,c) is a vector and k is a scalar, the *product* $k(a,b,c)$ is defined to be the vector (ka,kb,kc).

Illustration 1
(a) $2(1,3,-4) = (2,6,-8)$.
(b) $-1(2,1,3) = (-2,-1,-3)$.
(c) $0(a,b,c) = (0,0,0)$.

It is often useful to define three *base vectors* **i**, **j**, and **k** as follows. These are vectors of length 1 drawn along the positive directions of the three coordinate axes.

Definition: $\mathbf{i} = (1,0,0)$; $\mathbf{j} = (0,1,0)$; $\mathbf{k} = (0,0,1)$.

In terms of these any vector (a,b,c) can be written:

$$(a,b,c) = a\mathbf{i} + b\mathbf{j} + c\mathbf{k}$$

Although this notation is quite common in physics and engineering, we shall not use it regularly in this book.

Exercise A. Using the definitions of **i**, **j**, and **k**, show that (a,b,c) is correctly expressed as $a\mathbf{i} + b\mathbf{j} + c\mathbf{k}$.

The product of a vector by a vector is another concept which needs definition. There are, in fact, three kinds of products in common use; but we shall discuss only the inner (or "scalar," or "dot") product.

Definition: The *inner product* of two vectors (a_1,b_1,c_1) and (a_2,b_2,c_2) is defined to be the scalar $a_1a_2 + b_1b_2 + c_1c_2$. This product is denoted by a dot, so that

$$(a_1,b_1,c_1) \cdot (a_2,b_2,c_2) = a_1a_2 + b_1b_2 + c_1c_2$$

Illustration 2
(a) $(3,1,-2) \cdot (1,3,4) = 3 \cdot 1 + 1 \cdot 3 + (-2)(4) = -2$.
(b) $(5,2,6) \cdot (1,1,1) = 5 + 2 + 6 = 13$.
(c) $(-4,1,7) \cdot (0,0,0) = 0 + 0 + 0 = 0$.
(d) $\mathbf{i} \cdot \mathbf{j} = (1,0,0) \cdot (0,1,0) = 0 + 0 + 0 = 0$.

In terms of inner products we can define the *length* of a vector:

Definition: The *length* of a vector (a,b,c) is the square root of the inner product $(a,b,c) \cdot (a,b,c)$. That is:

$$\text{Length of } (a,b,c) = \sqrt{(a,b,c) \cdot (a,b,c)} = \sqrt{a^2 + b^2 + c^2}$$

Illustration 3

   (*a*) The length of $(3,2,4) = \sqrt{9 + 4 + 16} = \sqrt{29}$.

   (*b*) The length of $\mathbf{i} = \sqrt{1 + 0 + 0} = 1$.

   (*c*) The length of $(0,0,0) = \sqrt{0 + 0 + 0} = 0$.

The importance of the inner product in physics lies in the following geometrical interpretation, which you can understand if you have an elementary knowledge of trigonometry:

The inner product $(a_1,b_1,c_1) \cdot (a_2,b_2,c_2)$ is equal to the length of (a_1,b_1,c_1) times the length of (a_2,b_2,c_2) times the cosine of the angle between these two vectors. This statement is equivalent to the Law of Cosines for a triangle (see Sec. 12.13).

Physical concepts are frequently defined in terms of the inner product. For example, if a force $\mathbf{F} = (f_1,f_2,f_3)$ in pounds acts during a displacement $\mathbf{s} = (s_1,s_2,s_3)$ in feet, the work W which is done is defined to be:

$$W = \mathbf{F} \cdot \mathbf{s} = (f_1,f_2,f_3) \cdot (s_1,s_2,s_3) \qquad \text{ft-lb}$$

PROBLEMS 7.7

In Probs. 1 to 6 add the given vectors algebraically, and check your result graphically.

1. $(1,3) + (-2,4)$.

2. $(-2,5) + (1,3)$.

3. $(-4,1) + (2,2)$.

4. $(5,3) + (4,-2)$.

5. $(1,1) + (-2,2)$.

6. $(1,3) + (-2,-6)$.

In Probs. 7 to 12 write a vector equal to the given expression.

7. $(1,2,-1) + (-3,1,5) - (2,7,1)$.   **8.** $(0,1,3) - (4,1,-3) + (3,5,2)$.

9. $2(3,1,-1) + 3(1,1,1) - 4(-2,1,5)$.

10. $-4(1,0,2) + 2(3,2,-1) + 3(1,-2,1)$.

11. $3(2\mathbf{i} - 3\mathbf{j} + \mathbf{k}) - 4(\mathbf{i} + 2\mathbf{j} + 3\mathbf{k})$.

12. $-2(3\mathbf{i} + 5\mathbf{j} + 2\mathbf{k}) + 3(4\mathbf{i} + 2\mathbf{j} - \mathbf{k})$.

In Probs. 13 to 16 prove the given statement.

13. Addition of vectors is commutative.   **14.** Addition of vectors is associative.

15. The zero vector $(0,0,0)$ is the additive identity for vectors.

16. The vector $(-a,-b,-c)$ is the additive inverse of (a,b,c).

In Probs. 17 to 22 compute the given inner products.

17. $(1,1,3) \cdot (2,-1,4)$.   **18.** $(3,1,-2) \cdot (2,2,5)$.

19. $(1,0,2) \cdot (3,1,-2)$.   **20.** $(2,1,-3) \cdot (5,7,1)$.

21. $\mathbf{i} \cdot \mathbf{k}$.   **22.** $\mathbf{j} \cdot \mathbf{k}$.

In Probs. 23 to 30 find the length of the given vector.

23. $(2,2,1)$.   **24.** $(1,4,-2)$.

25. $(3,1,0)$.   **26.** $(-2,5,3)$.

27. $\mathbf{j}$.   **28.** $\mathbf{k}$.

29. $2\mathbf{i} + 3\mathbf{j} - 2\mathbf{k}$.   **30.** $-3\mathbf{i} + 4\mathbf{j} + \mathbf{k}$.

In Probs. 31 to 33 prove the given statement.

31. In the multiplication of a scalar times a vector the following distributive laws hold:

$$k[(a_1,b_1,c_1) + (a_2,b_2,c_2)] = k(a_1,b_1,c_1) + k(a_2,b_2,c_2)$$

and
$$(k_1 + k_2)(a,b,c) = k_1(a,b,c) + k_2(a,b,c)$$

32. The inner product is commutative.

33. For the inner product the following distributive law holds:

$$[(a_1,b_1,c_1) + (a_2,b_2,c_2)] \cdot (a_3,b_3,c_3) = (a_1,b_1,c_1) \cdot (a_3,b_3,c_3) + (a_2,b_2,c_2) \cdot (a_3,b_3,c_3)$$

7.8. *Matrices*

As we have said above, a matrix is a square or rectangular array of numbers. The numbers of which a matrix is composed are called its elements. You are already familiar with many examples of them, such as the statistical tables which compose the bulk of the "World Almanac." In mathematics, matrices first appeared as the arrays of coefficients in simultaneous linear equations. In physics they are widely used in quantum theory and appear in elementary physics as (1) the set of moments and products of inertia of a rigid body or (2) the set of pressures at a point in a viscous fluid.

Although matrices may be of any dimensions, in this book we shall deal only with those of dimensions 2×2 (that is, two rows and two columns), 2×3, 3×2, and 3×3. As special cases we have already discussed vectors, which are matrices of dimensions 2×1, 3×1, 1×2, and 1×3. We shall now develop the elementary algebra of matrices.

Definition: Two matrices are *equal* if and only if they have the same dimensions and are *identical*.

That is, for example:

$$\begin{pmatrix} a & b \\ c & d \end{pmatrix} = \begin{pmatrix} x & y \\ z & w \end{pmatrix}$$

if and only if

$$a = x \qquad b = y \qquad c = z \qquad d = w$$

The sum of two matrices is analogous to the sum of two vectors:

Definition: The *sum* of two matrices of the same dimensions is a matrix whose elements are the sums of the corresponding elements of the given matrices.

For example,

$$\begin{pmatrix} a & b \\ c & d \end{pmatrix} + \begin{pmatrix} x & y \\ z & w \end{pmatrix} = \begin{pmatrix} a + x & b + y \\ c + z & d + w \end{pmatrix}$$

Again, as for vectors, we can define the product of a scalar times a matrix.

Definition: The *product* of a scalar k times a matrix is a matrix whose elements are k times the corresponding elements of the given matrix.

For example:

$$k \begin{pmatrix} a & b \\ c & d \end{pmatrix} = \begin{pmatrix} ka & kb \\ kc & kd \end{pmatrix}$$

7.9. Products of Matrices

We now turn our attention to the product of two matrices, when this can be defined. This concept is a generalization of the inner product of two vectors.

We begin with the special case of the product of a 2×3 matrix and a 3×1 vector. This can be written in the form:

$$\begin{pmatrix} a_1 & b_1 & c_1 \\ a_2 & b_2 & c_2 \end{pmatrix} \begin{pmatrix} x \\ y \\ z \end{pmatrix}$$

Each row of the 2×3 matrix can be thought of as a three-dimensional row-vector, and we can form its inner product with the given column-vector. This gives us two scalars which we write as the elements of a 2×1 column-vector:

$$\begin{pmatrix} a_1 & b_1 & c_1 \\ a_2 & b_2 & c_2 \end{pmatrix} \begin{pmatrix} x \\ y \\ z \end{pmatrix} = \begin{pmatrix} a_1x + b_1y + c_1z \\ a_2x + b_2y + c_2z \end{pmatrix}$$

which is defined to be the desired product.

Illustration 1

(a)
$$\begin{pmatrix} 1 & -2 & 3 \\ 2 & 1 & 4 \end{pmatrix} \begin{pmatrix} 2 \\ 1 \\ 5 \end{pmatrix} = \begin{pmatrix} 15 \\ 25 \end{pmatrix}$$

(b) By analogy:
$$\begin{pmatrix} 2 & -3 \\ 1 & 4 \end{pmatrix} \begin{pmatrix} 3 \\ -2 \end{pmatrix} = \begin{pmatrix} 12 \\ -5 \end{pmatrix}$$

(c) Similarly
$$\begin{pmatrix} 4 & 1 & -2 \\ 3 & 2 & 5 \\ -1 & 2 & 1 \end{pmatrix} \begin{pmatrix} 1 \\ 3 \\ -1 \end{pmatrix} = \begin{pmatrix} 9 \\ 4 \\ 4 \end{pmatrix}$$

Definition: A matrix each of whose elements is zero is said to be *zero.*

Illustration 2. By analogy with the above:

$$\begin{pmatrix} a_1 & b_1 \\ a_2 & b_2 \end{pmatrix} \begin{pmatrix} x \\ y \end{pmatrix} = \begin{pmatrix} a_1x + b_1y \\ a_2x + b_2y \end{pmatrix}$$

and
$$\begin{pmatrix} a_1 & b_1 \\ a_2 & b_2 \end{pmatrix} \begin{pmatrix} x \\ y \end{pmatrix} + \begin{pmatrix} c_1 \\ c_2 \end{pmatrix} = \begin{pmatrix} a_1x + b_1y + c_1 \\ a_2x + b_2y + c_2 \end{pmatrix}$$

We can, therefore, write the system of simultaneous equations,

$$a_1x + b_1y + c_1 = 0$$
$$a_2x + b_2y + c_2 = 0$$

in the compact form

$$AX + C = 0$$

where $A = \begin{pmatrix} a_1 & b_1 \\ a_2 & b_2 \end{pmatrix}$ $X = \begin{pmatrix} x \\ y \end{pmatrix}$ $C = \begin{pmatrix} c_1 \\ c_2 \end{pmatrix}$ $0 = \begin{pmatrix} 0 \\ 0 \end{pmatrix}$

Exercise A. Show that the simultaneous system:

$$a_1x + b_1y + c_1z + d_1 = 0$$
$$a_2x + b_2y + c_2z + d_2 = 0$$
$$a_3x + b_3y + c_3z + d_3 = 0$$

can be written in the form:

$$AX + D = 0$$

where $A = \begin{pmatrix} a_1 & b_1 & c_1 \\ a_2 & b_2 & c_2 \\ a_3 & b_3 & c_3 \end{pmatrix}$ $X = \begin{pmatrix} x \\ y \\ z \end{pmatrix}$

$$D = \begin{pmatrix} d_1 \\ d_2 \\ d_3 \end{pmatrix}$$ $$0 = \begin{pmatrix} 0 \\ 0 \\ 0 \end{pmatrix}$$

We are now ready to define the product $AB = C$ of a $p \times q$-dimensional matrix A and a $q \times r$-dimensional matrix B. A consists of p q-dimensional row-vectors, and B consists of r q-dimensional column-vectors.   The elements of C are the inner products of the row-vectors of A times the column-vectors of B.

Definition: Let A be a $p \times q$-dimensional matrix and B a $q \times r$-dimensional matrix.   Their *product* $AB = C$ is a $p \times r$-dimensional matrix whose elements are as follows: The element in the ith row and the jth column of C is the inner product of the ith row-vector of A with the jth column-vector of B.

Illustration 3

(a) $\begin{pmatrix} 2 & -1 & 4 \\ 1 & 3 & 5 \end{pmatrix} \begin{pmatrix} 4 & 2 \\ -1 & 3 \\ 2 & 1 \end{pmatrix} = \begin{pmatrix} 17 & 5 \\ 11 & 16 \end{pmatrix}.$

(b) $(3 \quad -2) \begin{pmatrix} 2 & -1 & -2 \\ 6 & 3 & 4 \end{pmatrix} = (-6 \quad -9 \quad -14).$

(c) $\begin{pmatrix} 5 & 1 \\ -2 & 3 \end{pmatrix} \begin{pmatrix} 2 & 4 \\ -1 & 1 \end{pmatrix} = \begin{pmatrix} 9 & 21 \\ -7 & -5 \end{pmatrix}.$

Remarks

(1) The product AB is in this order: A first, B second.   The necessity for this follows from the definition in which A and B are treated differently; we multiply the *rows* of A by the *columns* of B.

(2) The product AB is defined only when the dimension of the row-vectors of A equals that of the column-vectors of B.   That is, the number of columns in A must equal the number of rows in B.

(3) When A and B are square and of the same dimension, both AB and BA are defined.   However, in general, AB does not equal BA; that is, multiplication of square matrices is *not* commutative.

Illustration 4

$$\begin{pmatrix} 2 & 1 \\ -3 & 4 \end{pmatrix} \begin{pmatrix} 1 & 3 \\ 5 & -1 \end{pmatrix} = \begin{pmatrix} 7 & 5 \\ 17 & -13 \end{pmatrix}$$

but

$$\begin{pmatrix} 1 & 3 \\ 5 & -1 \end{pmatrix} \begin{pmatrix} 2 & 1 \\ -3 & 4 \end{pmatrix} = \begin{pmatrix} -7 & 13 \\ 13 & 1 \end{pmatrix}$$

On the other hand, it can be shown that matrix multiplication *is* associative; that is, $A(BC) = (AB)C$.

PROBLEMS 7.9

In Probs. 1 to 20 find the product of the given two matrices.

1. $(-1 \quad 4 \quad 2) \begin{pmatrix} 5 \\ 1 \\ 3 \end{pmatrix}.$

2. $(2 \quad 0 \quad 3) \begin{pmatrix} 6 \\ -2 \\ 3 \end{pmatrix}.$

3. $\begin{pmatrix} 2 & 1 & 4 \\ 6 & -2 & 3 \end{pmatrix} \begin{pmatrix} 1 \\ -2 \\ 1 \end{pmatrix}.$

4. $\begin{pmatrix} -2 & 0 & 3 \\ 1 & -2 & 4 \end{pmatrix} \begin{pmatrix} 3 \\ -2 \\ 4 \end{pmatrix}.$

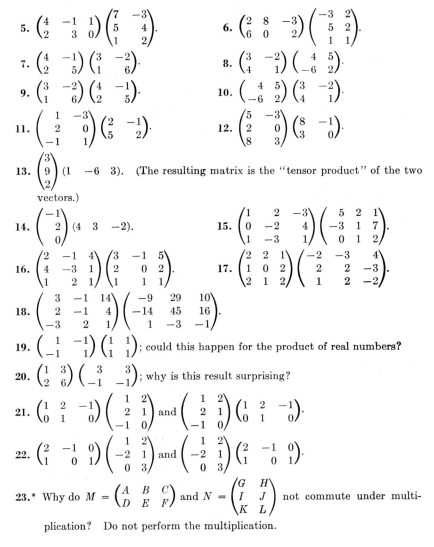

5. $\begin{pmatrix} 4 & -1 & 1 \\ 2 & 3 & 0 \end{pmatrix} \begin{pmatrix} 7 & -3 \\ 5 & 4 \\ 1 & 2 \end{pmatrix}$.

6. $\begin{pmatrix} 2 & 8 & -3 \\ 6 & 0 & 2 \end{pmatrix} \begin{pmatrix} -3 & 2 \\ 5 & 2 \\ 1 & 1 \end{pmatrix}$.

7. $\begin{pmatrix} 4 & -1 \\ 2 & 5 \end{pmatrix} \begin{pmatrix} 3 & -2 \\ 1 & 6 \end{pmatrix}$.

8. $\begin{pmatrix} 3 & -2 \\ 4 & 1 \end{pmatrix} \begin{pmatrix} 4 & 5 \\ -6 & 2 \end{pmatrix}$.

9. $\begin{pmatrix} 3 & -2 \\ 1 & 6 \end{pmatrix} \begin{pmatrix} 4 & -1 \\ 2 & 5 \end{pmatrix}$.

10. $\begin{pmatrix} 4 & 5 \\ -6 & 2 \end{pmatrix} \begin{pmatrix} 3 & -2 \\ 4 & 1 \end{pmatrix}$.

11. $\begin{pmatrix} 1 & -3 \\ 2 & 0 \\ -1 & 1 \end{pmatrix} \begin{pmatrix} 2 & -1 \\ 5 & 2 \end{pmatrix}$.

12. $\begin{pmatrix} 5 & -3 \\ 2 & 0 \\ 8 & 3 \end{pmatrix} \begin{pmatrix} 8 & -1 \\ 3 & 0 \end{pmatrix}$.

13. $\begin{pmatrix} 3 \\ 9 \\ 2 \end{pmatrix}$ (1   −6   3). (The resulting matrix is the "tensor product" of the two vectors.)

14. $\begin{pmatrix} -1 \\ 2 \\ 0 \end{pmatrix}$ (4   3   −2).

15. $\begin{pmatrix} 1 & 2 & -3 \\ 0 & -2 & 4 \\ 1 & -3 & 1 \end{pmatrix} \begin{pmatrix} 5 & 2 & 1 \\ -3 & 1 & 7 \\ 0 & 1 & 2 \end{pmatrix}$.

16. $\begin{pmatrix} 2 & -1 & 4 \\ 4 & -3 & 1 \\ 1 & 2 & 1 \end{pmatrix} \begin{pmatrix} 3 & -1 & 5 \\ 2 & 0 & 2 \\ 1 & 1 & 1 \end{pmatrix}$.

17. $\begin{pmatrix} 2 & 2 & 1 \\ 1 & 0 & 2 \\ 2 & 1 & 2 \end{pmatrix} \begin{pmatrix} -2 & -3 & 4 \\ 2 & 2 & -3 \\ 1 & 2 & -2 \end{pmatrix}$.

18. $\begin{pmatrix} 3 & -1 & 14 \\ 2 & -1 & 4 \\ -3 & 2 & 1 \end{pmatrix} \begin{pmatrix} -9 & 29 & 10 \\ -14 & 45 & 16 \\ 1 & -3 & -1 \end{pmatrix}$.

19. $\begin{pmatrix} 1 & -1 \\ -1 & 1 \end{pmatrix} \begin{pmatrix} 1 & 1 \\ 1 & 1 \end{pmatrix}$; could this happen for the product of real numbers?

20. $\begin{pmatrix} 1 & 3 \\ 2 & 6 \end{pmatrix} \begin{pmatrix} 3 & 3 \\ -1 & -1 \end{pmatrix}$; why is this result surprising?

21. $\begin{pmatrix} 1 & 2 & -1 \\ 0 & 1 & 0 \end{pmatrix} \begin{pmatrix} 1 & 2 \\ 2 & 1 \\ -1 & 0 \end{pmatrix}$ and $\begin{pmatrix} 1 & 2 \\ 2 & 1 \\ -1 & 0 \end{pmatrix} \begin{pmatrix} 1 & 2 & -1 \\ 0 & 1 & 0 \end{pmatrix}$.

22. $\begin{pmatrix} 2 & -1 & 0 \\ 1 & 0 & 1 \end{pmatrix} \begin{pmatrix} 1 & 2 \\ -2 & 1 \\ 0 & 3 \end{pmatrix}$ and $\begin{pmatrix} 1 & 2 \\ -2 & 1 \\ 0 & 3 \end{pmatrix} \begin{pmatrix} 2 & -1 & 0 \\ 1 & 0 & 1 \end{pmatrix}$.

23.* Why do $M = \begin{pmatrix} A & B & C \\ D & E & F \end{pmatrix}$ and $N = \begin{pmatrix} G & H \\ I & J \\ K & L \end{pmatrix}$ not commute under multiplication? Do not perform the multiplication.

7.10. *Inverse of a Square Matrix*

The multiplication of square matrices has many, but not all, of the properties R6 to R10 of ordinary multiplication. For instance, we have seen that it is associative, but not commutative. We now show that it has an identity element.

Theorem 3. There exists an identity for the multiplication of 3 × 3 square matrices, namely, the matrix

$$\begin{pmatrix} 1 & 0 & 0 \\ 0 & 1 & 0 \\ 0 & 0 & 1 \end{pmatrix}$$

Proof:

$$\begin{pmatrix} 1 & 0 & 0 \\ 0 & 1 & 0 \\ 0 & 0 & 1 \end{pmatrix} \begin{pmatrix} a_1 & b_1 & c_1 \\ a_2 & b_2 & c_2 \\ a_3 & b_3 & c_3 \end{pmatrix} = \begin{pmatrix} a_1 & b_1 & c_1 \\ a_2 & b_2 & c_2 \\ a_3 & b_3 & c_3 \end{pmatrix}$$

and moreover

$$\begin{pmatrix} a_1 & b_1 & c_1 \\ a_2 & b_2 & c_2 \\ a_3 & b_3 & c_3 \end{pmatrix} \begin{pmatrix} 1 & 0 & 0 \\ 0 & 1 & 0 \\ 0 & 0 & 1 \end{pmatrix} = \begin{pmatrix} a_1 & b_1 & c_1 \\ a_2 & b_2 & c_2 \\ a_3 & b_3 & c_3 \end{pmatrix}$$

Remarks

(1) For 2 × 2 matrices, the identity matrix is similarly $\begin{pmatrix} 1 & 0 \\ 0 & 1 \end{pmatrix}$.

(2) We denote these identity matrices by the common symbol I.

Finally, we ask whether there is a multiplicative inverse for square matrices. In the 2 × 2 case we are given a matrix A and are looking for a matrix, which we call A^{-1}, such that

$$A A^{-1} = I$$

If A is $\begin{pmatrix} a & b \\ c & d \end{pmatrix}$ and $A^{-1} = \begin{pmatrix} w & x \\ y & z \end{pmatrix}$, we are asked to solve the matrix equation:

$$\begin{pmatrix} a & b \\ c & d \end{pmatrix} \begin{pmatrix} w & x \\ y & z \end{pmatrix} = \begin{pmatrix} 1 & 0 \\ 0 & 1 \end{pmatrix}$$

Taking the product on the left, we have:

$$\begin{pmatrix} aw + by & ax + bz \\ cw + dy & cx + dz \end{pmatrix} = \begin{pmatrix} 1 & 0 \\ 0 & 1 \end{pmatrix}$$

From the definition of the equality of two matrices, this gives us the simultaneous system:

$$aw + by = 1$$
$$ax + bz = 0$$
$$cw + dy = 0$$
$$cx + dz = 1$$

Writing $\Delta = ad - bc$, and supposing this not to be zero, we find that the solution is:

$$w = \frac{d}{\Delta} \qquad x = -\frac{b}{\Delta} \qquad y = -\frac{c}{\Delta} \qquad z = \frac{a}{\Delta}$$

Therefore

$$A^{-1} = \frac{1}{\Delta} \begin{pmatrix} d & -b \\ -c & a \end{pmatrix}$$

As a bonus we find that

$$A^{-1}A = \frac{1}{\Delta}\begin{pmatrix} d & -b \\ -c & a \end{pmatrix}\begin{pmatrix} a & b \\ c & d \end{pmatrix} = \begin{pmatrix} 1 & 0 \\ 0 & 1 \end{pmatrix} = I$$

This gives us Theorem 4 in which $A = \begin{pmatrix} a & b \\ c & d \end{pmatrix}$.

Theorem 4.   If $ad - bc \neq 0$, the matrix A has an inverse A^{-1} such that

$$AA^{-1} = A^{-1}A = I$$

In the case of 3×3 matrices there is a similar theorem, but the computations are very tedious.   We shall approach this from a simpler point of view in the next section.

Illustration 1

(a) If $A = \begin{pmatrix} 2 & 5 \\ -1 & 4 \end{pmatrix}$, $A^{-1} = \frac{1}{13}\begin{pmatrix} 4 & -5 \\ 1 & 2 \end{pmatrix} = \begin{pmatrix} \frac{4}{13} & -\frac{5}{13} \\ \frac{1}{13} & \frac{2}{13} \end{pmatrix}$.

(b) If $A = \begin{pmatrix} 2 & -3 \\ 4 & -6 \end{pmatrix}$, A^{-1} does not exist.

A 2×2 matrix for which $ad - bc \neq 0$ is called *nonsingular;* if $ad - bc = 0$, it is *singular.*   Hence a *matrix has an inverse if and only if it is nonsingular.*

PROBLEMS 7.10

In Probs. 1 to 10 find the inverses of the given matrices when they exist.   Check your answers in the formulas $AA^{-1} = I$; $A^{-1}A = I$.

1. $\begin{pmatrix} 2 & -1 \\ 1 & 3 \end{pmatrix}$.

2. $\begin{pmatrix} 1 & 1 \\ 2 & 4 \end{pmatrix}$.

3. $\begin{pmatrix} 2 & 5 \\ 1 & 3 \end{pmatrix}$.

4. $\begin{pmatrix} 1 & 0 \\ 2 & -3 \end{pmatrix}$.

5. $\begin{pmatrix} 2 & 4 \\ -1 & -2 \end{pmatrix}$.

6. $\begin{pmatrix} 1 & 5 \\ -2 & -10 \end{pmatrix}$.

7. $\begin{pmatrix} 1 & 0 \\ 0 & 1 \end{pmatrix}$.

8. $\begin{pmatrix} 0 & 0 \\ 0 & 0 \end{pmatrix}$.

9. $\begin{pmatrix} \dfrac{1}{\sqrt{2}} & \dfrac{1}{\sqrt{2}} \\ -\dfrac{1}{\sqrt{2}} & \dfrac{1}{\sqrt{2}} \end{pmatrix}$.

10. $\begin{pmatrix} 1 & 0 \\ 1 & -1 \end{pmatrix}$.

Transformation of Coordinates (cf. Probs. 2.13)

If we are given a coordinate system in the plane in terms of the pairs (x,y), we can define a new coordinate system (x',y') by means of the *linear transformation:*

$$x' = a_1x + b_1y + c_1$$
$$y' = a_2x + b_2y + c_2$$

where we assume $a_1b_2 - a_2b_1 \neq 0$. The new pairs (x',y') serve as new labels for the points in the plane. The point O', where $x' = 0$, $y' = 0$, is the new origin, the X'-axis is the line $y' = 0$, and the Y'-axis is the line $x' = 0$. These axes, however, need not be at right angles.

A point P is called a *fixed point* if its coordinates in both systems are equal, i.e., if $x' = x$, $y' = y$ at P. If every point is a fixed point, the transformation has the equations $x' = x$, $y' = y$ and is called the *identity transformation*.

In working the problems below you will need to anticipate the following result, which will be proved in Sec. 12.2. Let s be the distance between $P_1(x_1,y_1)$ and $P_2(x_2,y_2)$. Then:

$$s^2 = (x_2 - x_1)^2 + (y_2 - y_1)^2$$

This is really nothing but the Pythagorean theorem.

In Probs. 11 to 14 we take $x' = x + a$, $y' = y + b$. This transformation is called a *translation*.

11. Prove that a translation leaves the lengths of segments unchanged.

12. Prove: if a translation has a fixed point, then it is the identity transformation.

13. Show that the correspondence $(x,y) \leftrightarrow (x',y')$ defined by a translation is 1 to 1.

14. For the translation $x' = x - 2$, $y' = y - 5$ find the new origin and sketch the new axes.

In Probs. 15 to 18 we take $x' = ax$, $y' = ay$, where $a > 0$. This transformation is called a *dilation*.

15. Prove that a dilation multiplies lengths of segments by a and areas of rectangles by a^2. Hence show that a triangle is transformed into a similar triangle.

16. Prove that the origin is a fixed point under a dilation.

17. Prove that, if a dilation has a fixed point in addition to the origin, then it is the identity transformation.

18. Show that the correspondence $(x,y) \leftrightarrow (x',y')$ defined by a dilation is 1 to 1.

In Probs. 19 to 21 we take $x' = -x$; $y' = y$. This transformation is called a *reflection* in the Y-axis.

19. Prove that a reflection leaves the lengths of segments unchanged.

20. Find the fixed points for the above reflection.

21. Prove that the correspondence $(x,y) \leftrightarrow (x',y')$ defined by a reflection is 1 to 1.

In Probs. 22 to 26 we take

$$\left.\begin{array}{l} x' = ax + by \\ y' = -bx + ay \end{array}\right\} \quad \text{where } a^2 + b^2 = 1$$

This transformation is called a *rotation*.

22. Sketch the new axes when

$$x' = \frac{1}{\sqrt{2}}x + \frac{1}{\sqrt{2}}y$$

$$y' = -\frac{1}{\sqrt{2}}x + \frac{1}{\sqrt{2}}y$$

23. Prove that a rotation leaves the lengths of segments unchanged.

24. Prove that the origin is a fixed point under a rotation.

25. Prove that, if a rotation has a fixed point other than the origin, then it is the identity transformation.

HINT: Solve

$$\left. \begin{array}{rcl} x &=& ax + by \\ y &=& -bx + ay \end{array} \right\} \quad \text{for } a \text{ and } b$$

assuming $(x,y) \neq (0,0)$.

26. Prove that the correspondence $(x,y) \leftrightarrow (x',y')$ defined by a rotation is 1 to 1.

In Probs. 27 to 34 we consider the *centered* linear transformation

$$\left. \begin{array}{rcl} x' &=& a_1x + b_1y \\ y' &=& a_2x + b_2y \end{array} \right\} \quad \text{where } a_1b_2 - a_2b_1 \neq 0$$

27. Prove that every point on the line $x + y = 0$ is a fixed point for the transformation

$$x' = 2x + y$$
$$y' = x + 2y$$

HINT: Solve

$$\left. \begin{array}{rcl} x &=& 2x + y \\ y &=& x + 2y \end{array} \right\} \quad \text{for } x \text{ and } y$$

28. Find the fixed points of the transformation

$$x' = 3x - y$$
$$y' = 2x$$

29. Prove that the origin is the only fixed point of the general centered linear transformation unless $a_1b_2 - a_2b_1 - b_2 - a_1 + 1 = 0$.

30. Solve the equations of the general centered linear transformation for (x,y) in terms of (x',y'). This is the *inverse* transformation. Compare the matrix of its coefficients with the inverse of the matrix of the coefficients of the original transformation.

31. Prove that the correspondence $(x,y) \leftrightarrow (x',y')$ defined by a centered linear transformation is 1 to 1.

32. Consider the pair of transformations:

$$\begin{array}{ll} x' = ax + by & x'' = px' + qy' \\ y' = cx + dy & y'' = rx' + sy' \end{array}$$

Find (x'',y'') in terms of (x,y). Compare the matrix of coefficients so obtained with the product

$$\begin{pmatrix} p & q \\ r & s \end{pmatrix} \begin{pmatrix} a & b \\ c & d \end{pmatrix}$$

This result motivates our definition of the product of two matrices.

33. The transformations of Prob. 32 can be written as follows in matrix notation:

$$X' = AX \qquad X'' = BX'$$

What are X, X', X'', A, and B?

Then solve Prob. 32, using matrix notation.

34. Solve Prob. 30, using matrix notation.

7.11. *Determinants*

In finding the inverse of a 2×2 matrix and in solving a system of two simultaneous equations we have run across expressions like $ad - bc$ and $a_1b_2 - a_2b_1$ in critical places. It is time we gave these a formal discussion. This brings us to determinants, which is the name given to expressions of this kind.

Definition: Let A be the 2×2 matrix $\begin{pmatrix} a_1 & b_1 \\ a_2 & b_2 \end{pmatrix}$. Then we define the expression $a_1b_2 - a_2b_1$ to be the *determinant* of A and write:

$$\det A = \begin{vmatrix} a_1 & b_1 \\ a_2 & b_2 \end{vmatrix} = a_1b_2 - a_2b_1.$$

Exercise A. Prove that the determinant of a 2×2 matrix is zero if the two columns (rows) are proportional or equal.

Remarks

(1) We use parentheses for matrices and parallel lines for the corresponding determinants.

(2) A determinant is a single number associated with a square matrix. The determinant is *not* the array; the array is the matrix.

For 3×3 matrices we define the determinant in the following fashion. Let $A = \begin{pmatrix} a_1 & b_1 & c_1 \\ a_2 & b_2 & c_2 \\ a_3 & b_3 & c_3 \end{pmatrix}$ be a given 3×3 matrix. If we strike out the row and column containing any element, we are left with a 2×2 matrix whose determinant has already been defined. This determinant is called the *minor* of the corresponding element. We list a few examples of these:

Element	Minor
a_1	$b_2c_3 - b_3c_2$
b_1	$a_2c_3 - a_3c_2$
c_2	$a_1b_3 - a_3b_1$
c_3	$a_1b_2 - a_2b_1$

We now attach an algebraic sign to each minor in the following way: Consider the corresponding element, and move it by a series of horizontal and/or vertical steps to the upper left-hand corner. The sign is $+$ if the number of steps required is even, $-$ if this number is odd. The product of the minor times this sign is called the *cofactor* of the corresponding element. The cofactor of any element will be denoted by the corresponding capital letter; for instance, the cofactor of a_1 is A_1. We list a few examples:

Element	Cofactor
a_1	$A_1 = \quad b_2c_3 - b_3c_2$
b_1	$B_1 = -(a_2c_3 - a_3c_2)$
c_2	$C_2 = -(a_1b_3 - a_3b_1)$
c_3	$C_3 = \quad a_1b_2 - a_2b_1$

To define the determinant, we now consider the first row and define

$$\det A = a_1A_1 + b_1B_1 + c_1C_1$$

We might equally well have done this for any row or column, and at first sight you would expect the results to be six different numbers. They are, in fact, all equal. There is no simple proof of this, and direct computation is too tedious; so we take it for granted.

Exercise B.   By direct computation show that

$$a_1A_1 + b_1B_1 + c_1C_1 = b_1B_1 + b_2B_2 + b_3B_3$$

Definition: The *determinant* of a 3×3 matrix is equal to the inner product of any row-vector (or column-vector) with the vector of its corresponding cofactors.

Illustration 1.   Find

$$\det \begin{pmatrix} 1 & -2 & 3 \\ 4 & 1 & -1 \\ 1 & 2 & 1 \end{pmatrix} = \begin{vmatrix} 1 & -2 & 3 \\ 4 & 1 & -1 \\ 1 & 2 & 1 \end{vmatrix}$$

Choosing the first row, the cofactors are, respectively:

$$\begin{vmatrix} 1 & -1 \\ 2 & 1 \end{vmatrix} = 3 \qquad -\begin{vmatrix} 4 & -1 \\ 1 & 1 \end{vmatrix} = -5 \qquad \begin{vmatrix} 4 & 1 \\ 1 & 2 \end{vmatrix} = 7$$

So the answer is: $(1)(3) + (-2)(-5) + (3)(7) = 34$.

As an alternative solution, choose the first column. The cofactors are, respectively:

$$\begin{vmatrix} 1 & -1 \\ 2 & 1 \end{vmatrix} = 3 \qquad -\begin{vmatrix} -2 & 3 \\ 2 & 1 \end{vmatrix} = 8 \qquad \begin{vmatrix} -2 & 3 \\ 1 & -1 \end{vmatrix} = -1$$

So the answer is: $(1)(3) + 4(8) + (1)(-1) = 34$.

The following two theorems about determinants are of great utility:

Theorem 5.   If two rows (columns) of a matrix are proportional (or equal), its determinant is zero.

The proof is immediate. First choose the third row (column) not involved in the proportionality. Then all the corresponding cofactors are zero (see Exercise A).

Theorem 6. The inner product of any row- (column-) vector and the vector of cofactors of a different row (column) is zero.
    Proof: Consider for example $a_1B_1 + a_2B_2 + a_3B_3$. This, however, is the determinant of the matrix

$$\begin{pmatrix} a_1 & c_1 & a_1 \\ a_2 & c_2 & a_2 \\ a_3 & c_3 & a_3 \end{pmatrix}$$

which is zero since two columns are equal.
    Finally we can calculate the inverse of a 3×3 matrix.

Theorem 7. Let $A = \begin{pmatrix} a_1 & b_1 & c_1 \\ a_2 & b_2 & c_2 \\ a_3 & b_3 & c_3 \end{pmatrix}$, and let $\det A = \Delta$. Then, if $\Delta \neq 0$,

$$A^{-1} = \frac{1}{\Delta}\begin{pmatrix} A_1 & A_2 & A_3 \\ B_1 & B_2 & B_3 \\ C_1 & C_2 & C_3 \end{pmatrix}$$

Proof: We must show that $AA^{-1} = A^{-1}A = I$.

$$AA^{-1} = \frac{1}{\Delta}\begin{pmatrix} a_1 & b_1 & c_1 \\ a_2 & b_2 & c_2 \\ a_3 & b_3 & c_3 \end{pmatrix}\begin{pmatrix} A_1 & A_2 & A_3 \\ B_1 & B_2 & B_3 \\ C_1 & C_2 & C_3 \end{pmatrix} = \frac{1}{\Delta}\begin{pmatrix} \Delta & 0 & 0 \\ 0 & \Delta & 0 \\ 0 & 0 & \Delta \end{pmatrix}$$

$$= \begin{pmatrix} 1 & 0 & 0 \\ 0 & 1 & 0 \\ 0 & 0 & 1 \end{pmatrix} = I$$

because of the definition of the determinant and Theorem 6. A similar proof gives $A^{-1}A = I$.
    Determinants of square matrices of higher dimension are defined inductively in a similar fashion. For a 4×4 matrix, for example, the cofactors are $\pm$ determinants of 3×3 matrices. The determinant, in an obvious notation, is defined to be $a_1A_1 + a_2A_2 + a_3A_3 + a_4A_4$. We can continue step by step to define determinants of square matrices of any size.
    We conclude by giving without proof the following theorem for any square matrices:

Theorem 8. If $AB = C$, then $(\det A) \times (\det B) = \det C$.

PROBLEMS 7.11

In Probs. 1 to 16 find the determinants of the given matrices.

1. $\begin{pmatrix} 4 & -1 \\ 2 & 5 \end{pmatrix}$.

2. $\begin{pmatrix} 3 & -2 \\ 1 & 6 \end{pmatrix}$.

3. $\begin{pmatrix} 4 & 5 \\ -6 & 2 \end{pmatrix}$.

4. $\begin{pmatrix} 2 & 3 \\ -9 & -6 \end{pmatrix}$.

5. $\begin{pmatrix} 1 & 4 \\ 2 & 8 \end{pmatrix}$.

6. $\begin{pmatrix} 7 & -2 \\ 1 & 3 \end{pmatrix}$.

7. $\begin{pmatrix} 1 & 2 & -3 \\ 0 & -2 & 4 \\ 1 & -3 & 1 \end{pmatrix}$.

8. $\begin{pmatrix} 5 & 2 & 1 \\ -3 & 1 & 7 \\ 0 & 1 & 2 \end{pmatrix}$.

9. $\begin{pmatrix} 2 & -1 & 4 \\ 4 & -3 & 1 \\ 1 & 2 & 1 \end{pmatrix}$.

10. $\begin{pmatrix} 3 & -1 & 5 \\ 2 & 0 & 2 \\ 1 & 1 & 1 \end{pmatrix}$.

11. $\begin{pmatrix} 2 & 2 & 1 \\ 1 & 0 & 2 \\ 2 & 1 & 2 \end{pmatrix}$.

12. $\begin{pmatrix} -2 & -3 & 4 \\ 2 & 2 & -3 \\ 1 & 2 & -2 \end{pmatrix}$.

13. $\begin{pmatrix} 3 & -1 & 14 \\ 2 & -1 & 4 \\ -3 & 2 & 1 \end{pmatrix}$.

14. $\begin{pmatrix} 2 & 0 & 3 \\ 1 & -2 & 4 \\ 3 & -2 & 7 \end{pmatrix}$.

15. $\begin{pmatrix} 1 & 2 & -3 \\ 4 & -1 & 7 \\ 2 & 4 & -6 \end{pmatrix}$.

16. $\begin{pmatrix} 3 & 6 & 6 \\ 1 & 0 & 2 \\ -2 & 4 & -4 \end{pmatrix}$.

In Probs. 17 to 22 find the inverse of the given matrix.

17. $\begin{pmatrix} 2 & 2 & 1 \\ 1 & 0 & 2 \\ 2 & 1 & 2 \end{pmatrix}$.

18. $\begin{pmatrix} 3 & -1 & 14 \\ 2 & -1 & 4 \\ -3 & 2 & 1 \end{pmatrix}$.

19. $\begin{pmatrix} 1 & -1 & 2 \\ 3 & 1 & 4 \\ 0 & 2 & 1 \end{pmatrix}$.

20. $\begin{pmatrix} 1 & 0 & 2 \\ 3 & 1 & 0 \\ -1 & 2 & 1 \end{pmatrix}$.

21. $\begin{pmatrix} 2 & -1 & 4 \\ 2 & 0 & 1 \\ 1 & 2 & 0 \end{pmatrix}$.

22. $\begin{pmatrix} 3 & 1 & 0 \\ 2 & 0 & 2 \\ 3 & 1 & 1 \end{pmatrix}$.

23. Use the method of this section to find the inverse of

$$\begin{pmatrix} a & b \\ c & d \end{pmatrix}$$

Show that the result agrees with the formula of Sec. 7.10

24. Prove that det $\begin{pmatrix} x & y & 1 \\ x_1 & y_1 & 1 \\ x_2 & y_2 & 1 \end{pmatrix} = 0$ is an equation of the line passing through

(x_1,y_1) and (x_2,y_2).

HINT: (1) Expand by the first row to show that the equation is linear. (2) Use Theorem 5 to show that (x_1,y_1) and (x_2,y_2) satisfy this equation.

25. Verify Theorem 8 for the product

$$\begin{pmatrix} 4 & 2 \\ 1 & 3 \end{pmatrix} \begin{pmatrix} 1 & 3 \\ -2 & 1 \end{pmatrix}$$

26. Verify Theorem 8 for the product

$$\begin{pmatrix} 2 & -1 \\ 3 & 4 \end{pmatrix} \begin{pmatrix} 5 & 2 \\ 1 & 6 \end{pmatrix}$$

27. Verify the steps in the following derivation: Let the vertices of a triangle be labeled as in the figure. The subscripts are numbered in the counterclockwise

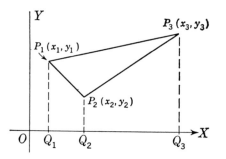

direction around the triangle. Then the areas of the triangle and the three trapezoids satisfy

$$P_1P_2P_3 = P_1P_3Q_1Q_3 - P_1P_2Q_1Q_2 - P_2P_3Q_2Q_3$$
$$= \tfrac{1}{2}[(x_3 - x_1)(y_1 + y_3) - (x_2 - x_1)(y_1 + y_2) - (x_3 - x_2)(y_2 + y_3)]$$
$$= \tfrac{1}{2}[(x_2y_3 - x_3y_2) - (x_1y_3 - x_3y_1) + (x_1y_2 - x_2y_1)]$$

Therefore,   Area of $P_1P_2P_3 = \dfrac{1}{2} \begin{vmatrix} x_1 & y_1 & 1 \\ x_2 & y_2 & 1 \\ x_3 & y_3 & 1 \end{vmatrix}$

How is this result altered if we number the vertices in the clockwise direction?

7.12. *Applications of Matrices to Simultaneous Equations*

We have seen above that the simultaneous system

$$a_1x + b_1y + d_1 = 0$$
$$a_2x + b_2y + d_2 = 0$$

can be written in the compact form

$$AX + D = 0$$

where $A = \begin{pmatrix} a_1 & b_1 \\ a_2 & b_2 \end{pmatrix}$; $D = \begin{pmatrix} d_1 \\ d_2 \end{pmatrix}$; $0 = \begin{pmatrix} 0 \\ 0 \end{pmatrix}$.

Similarly

$$a_1x + b_1y + c_1z + d_1 = 0$$
$$a_2x + b_2y + c_2z + d_2 = 0$$
$$a_3x + b_3y + c_3z + d_3 = 0$$

can be written in the form $AX + D = 0$, where

$$A = \begin{pmatrix} a_1 & b_1 & c_1 \\ a_2 & b_2 & c_2 \\ a_3 & b_3 & c_3 \end{pmatrix} \qquad D = \begin{pmatrix} d_1 \\ d_2 \\ d_3 \end{pmatrix} \qquad 0 = \begin{pmatrix} 0 \\ 0 \\ 0 \end{pmatrix}$$

This suggests that the problem of solving simultaneous equations is really that of solving the matrix equation

$$AX + D = 0$$

But this is now an easy problem for us. For $AX + D = 0$ is equivalent to

$$AX = -D$$

Multiplying both sides, on the left, by A^{-1}, we have

$$A^{-1}AX = -A^{-1}D$$

or
$$IX = -A^{-1}D$$

since $A^{-1}A = I$, or

$$X = -A^{-1}D \qquad \text{the solution}$$

A possible method of solution, therefore, is to compute A^{-1} by the method of Sec. 7.10 and then to find $-A^{-1}D$. Although this is not the best method in practice, the above formula is of considerable theoretical value. It is known as "Cramer's Rule."

Illustration 1.   Solve

$$2x + 5y - 6 = 0$$
$$x - 2y + 5 = 0$$

$$A = \begin{pmatrix} 2 & 5 \\ 1 & -2 \end{pmatrix} \qquad \det A = -9$$

$$A^{-1} = -\frac{1}{9}\begin{pmatrix} -2 & -5 \\ -1 & 2 \end{pmatrix} \qquad D = \begin{pmatrix} -6 \\ 5 \end{pmatrix}$$

$$X = -A^{-1}D = \frac{1}{9}\begin{pmatrix} -2 & -5 \\ -1 & 2 \end{pmatrix}\begin{pmatrix} -6 \\ 5 \end{pmatrix} = \frac{1}{9}\begin{pmatrix} -13 \\ 16 \end{pmatrix} = \begin{pmatrix} -\frac{13}{9} \\ \frac{16}{9} \end{pmatrix}$$

So $x = -\frac{13}{9};\ y = \frac{16}{9}$.

The problem of solving systems of linear equations is theoretically handled by Cramer's Rule, and we have a practical means for their solution in simple cases. In applied mathematics, however, one meets systems of linear equations containing 100 or more unknowns with coefficients which are 5- to 10-place decimals. The practical problem of solution is quite formidable, even on a high-speed machine. Modern research has developed elaborate techniques for tackling this problem, but improvements in these are currently under study.

Finally let us consider the following "homogeneous" system of two equations in three unknowns:

$$a_1x + b_1y + c_1z = 0$$
$$a_2x + b_2y + c_2z = 0$$

Geometrically these equations represent two planes through the origin, and so we expect to find a *line of solutions*. By the use of determinants we can express this solution in a very elegant form.

Theorem 9. The solutions of

$$a_1x + b_1y + c_1z = 0$$
$$a_2x + b_2y + c_2z = 0$$

are

$$x = k \begin{vmatrix} b_1 & c_1 \\ b_2 & c_2 \end{vmatrix} \qquad y = -k \begin{vmatrix} a_1 & c_1 \\ a_2 & c_2 \end{vmatrix} \qquad z = k \begin{vmatrix} a_1 & b_1 \\ a_2 & b_2 \end{vmatrix}$$

where k is an arbitrary scalar (provided that at least one of these is different from zero).

Proof: If we substitute these values of x, y, and z into the left-hand side of the first equation, we get:

$$k \left\{ a_1 \begin{vmatrix} b_1 & c_1 \\ b_2 & c_2 \end{vmatrix} - b_1 \begin{vmatrix} a_1 & c_1 \\ a_2 & c_2 \end{vmatrix} + c_1 \begin{vmatrix} a_1 & b_1 \\ a_2 & b_2 \end{vmatrix} \right\}$$

The expression in braces, however, is precisely the determinant of the matrix

$$\begin{pmatrix} a_1 & b_1 & c_1 \\ a_1 & b_1 & c_1 \\ a_2 & b_2 & c_2 \end{pmatrix}$$

which is zero by Theorem 5. Therefore the first equation is satisfied. A similar argument shows that the second equation is satisfied.

Illustration 1. Solve

$$3x - 2y + z = 0$$
$$x + 4y + 2z = 0$$

By Theorem 8:

$$x = k \begin{vmatrix} -2 & 1 \\ 4 & 2 \end{vmatrix} \qquad y = -k \begin{vmatrix} 3 & 1 \\ 1 & 2 \end{vmatrix} \qquad z = k \begin{vmatrix} 3 & -2 \\ 1 & 4 \end{vmatrix}$$

or $x = -8k \qquad y = -5k \qquad z = 14k$

Illustration 2.   Find the vector (x,y,z) whose inner products with each of the vectors $(4,1,-2)$ and $(2,1,3)$ are zero.

The required conditions are:

$$4x + y - 2z = 0$$
$$2x + y + 3z = 0$$

Hence $x = 5k$, $y = -16k$, $z = 2k$.   The required vector is $k(5,-16,2)$.

Illustration 2 motivates the following definition of the outer (or *vector* or *cross*) product of two vectors:

Definition: The *outer product* of the two vectors (a_1,b_1,c_1) and (a_2,b_2,c_2) is the vector

$$\left(\begin{vmatrix} b_1 & c_1 \\ b_2 & c_2 \end{vmatrix}, \ -\begin{vmatrix} a_1 & c_1 \\ a_2 & c_2 \end{vmatrix}, \ \begin{vmatrix} a_1 & b_1 \\ a_2 & b_2 \end{vmatrix} \right)$$

The notation for this product is $(a_1,b_1,c_1) \wedge (a_2,b_2,c_2)$.*

Illustration 3

$$(2,4,-3) \wedge (1,-2,6) = (18,-15,-8)$$

Remarks

(1) The inner product of $(a_1,b_1,c_1) \wedge (a_2,b_2,c_2)$ with each of its factors is zero.

(2) $(a_1,b_1,c_1) \wedge (a_2,b_2,c_2) = -(a_2,b_2,c_2) \wedge (a_1,b_1,c_1)$.   The "wedge" symbol $\wedge$ is commonly used in higher mathematics to denote "skew-commutative" multiplication, i.e., multiplication for which

$$a \wedge b = -b \wedge a$$

(3) A convenient way of expressing this product is the expansion of the following symbolic determinant by means of its first row:

$$\begin{vmatrix} \mathbf{i} & \mathbf{j} & \mathbf{k} \\ a_1 & b_1 & c_1 \\ a_2 & b_2 & c_2 \end{vmatrix}$$

Illustration 4

$$(1,-3,2) \wedge (4,1,3) = \begin{vmatrix} \mathbf{i} & \mathbf{j} & \mathbf{k} \\ 1 & -3 & 2 \\ 4 & 1 & 3 \end{vmatrix}$$
$$= -11\mathbf{i} + 5\mathbf{j} + 13\mathbf{k}$$
$$= (-11,5,13)$$

---

*The $\wedge$ symbol used here has no connection with the similar symbol which sometimes denotes *conjunction* in symbolic logic.

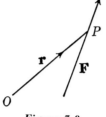

Figure 7.8

(4) Let $\mathbf{A} = (a_1, b_1, c_1)$ and $\mathbf{B} = (a_2, b_2, c_2)$. Then the length of $\mathbf{A} \wedge \mathbf{B}$ is equal to the length of $\mathbf{A}$ times the length of $\mathbf{B}$ times the absolute value of the sine of the angle between $\mathbf{A}$ and $\mathbf{B}$.

(5) Let $\mathbf{F}$ be a force acting on a body at point P; let O be a reference point and $OP = \mathbf{r}$. Then the vector moment $\mathbf{M}$ is defined to be

$$\mathbf{M} = \mathbf{r} \wedge \mathbf{F}$$

PROBLEMS 7.12

In Probs. 1 to 10 use Cramer's Rule to solve the given systems of equations.

1. $2x - y + 3 = 0$
$x + 3y - 1 = 0$ [See Prob. 1, Sec. 7.10]

2. $x + y + 6 = 0$
$2x + 4y + 5 = 0$ [See Prob. 2, Sec. 7.10]

3. $2x + 5y - 7 = 0$
$x + 3y + 3 = 0$ [See Prob. 3, Sec. 7.10]

4. $x + 1 = 0$
$2x - 3y - 4 = 0$ [See Prob. 4, Sec. 7.10]

5. $2x + 4y + 3 = 0$
$x - 2y + 7 = 0$

6. $x + 5y - 8 = 0$
$2x - y + 3 = 0$

7. $2x + 2y + z - 1 = 0$
$x + 2z + 3 = 0$ [See Prob. 17, Sec. 7.11]
$2x + y + 2z - 4 = 0$

8. $3x - y + 14z - 3 = 0$
$2x - y + 4z - 5 = 0$ [See Prob. 18, Sec. 7.11]
$-3x + 2y + z + 2 = 0$

9. $x - y + 2z + 1 = 0$
$3x + y + 4z - 2 = 0$ [See Prob. 19, Sec. 7.11]
$2y + z + 4 = 0$

10. $x + 2z + 1 = 0$
$3x + y - 3 = 0$ [See Prob. 20, Sec. 7.11]
$-x + 2y + z + 4 = 0$

In Probs. 11 to 14 solve the given system of equations.

11. $2x + 7y - z = 0.$
$x - 4y + 5z = 0.$

12. $3x - 2y + 4z = 0.$
$-x + 3z = 0.$

13. $x - 5y + 2z = 0.$
$2x + y - z = 0.$

14. $4x - y + 2z = 0.$
$x + y + z = 0.$

In Probs. 15 to 18 find the vector whose inner products with each of the two given vectors are zero.

15. $(1,1,1)$; $(2,-3,5)$.

16. $(5,2,-3)$; $(2,1,1)$.

17. $(4,-2,5)$; $(2,2,7)$.

18. $(-1,4,3)$; $(5,2,-2)$.

19. Why does the method of Theorem 9 fail for the system:

$$2x + y \ - 3z = 0$$
$$4x + 2y - 6z = 0$$

20. Why does the method of Theorem 9 fail for the system:

$$3w + 2x - y + 4z = 0$$
$$w \ + 3x + y + 2z = 0$$

In Probs. 21 to 30 find the given outer products.

21. $(1,4,-3) \wedge (2,1,6)$.

22. $(4,5,1) \wedge (-1,3,2)$.

23. $(2,-2,1) \wedge (4,-1,3)$.

24. $(0,1,3) \wedge (2,5,-4)$.

25. $\mathbf{i} \wedge \mathbf{j}$.

26. $\mathbf{j} \wedge \mathbf{k}$.

27. $\mathbf{k} \wedge \mathbf{i}$.

28. $(3,1,2) \wedge (6,2,4)$.

29. $(-3,1,4) \wedge (-6,2,8)$.

30. $\mathbf{i} \wedge \mathbf{i}$.

7.13. *Word Problems*

As we pointed out in Chap. 1, the ability to solve a given set of equations is not the only mathematical skill which a scientist requires. He must also be able to translate his physical problems into mathematical terms. In order to develop this ability of translation from nature to mathematics, textbooks usually include sets of "word problems," and we do so here. Since the real problems which a scientist meets are too complicated for you to handle at this stage, these word problems represent situations which have been greatly simplified. They are worth your attention, however, for by solving them you will be preparing yourself to handle less artificial problems.

The following formulas from physics will be helpful in solving some of the problems below:

$s = vt$	$s =$ distance, $v =$ velocity (constant), $t =$ time
$s = s_0 + \frac{1}{2}at^2$	$s =$ distance for general t, $s_0 =$ distance at $t = 0$, $a =$ acceleration (constant), $t =$ time
$v = v_0 + at$	$v =$ velocity for general t, $v_0 =$ velocity at $t = 0$, $a =$ acceleration (constant), $t =$ time
$f = ma$	$f =$ force, $m =$ mass, $a =$ acceleration
$E = IR$	$E =$ voltage, $I =$ current, $R =$ resistance
$PV = KT$	$P =$ pressure of a gas, $V =$ volume, $K =$ universal gas constant, $T =$ absolute temperature

PROBLEMS 7.13

1. The sum of two numbers is equal to one-half the sum of their squares. The difference of the two numbers is equal to one-half the difference of their squares. Find the numbers.

2. The sum of two numbers is 20, and their product is 96. Find the numbers.

3. In an election for the mayor of Oxbridge the Conservative candidate received 5,666 more votes than the Labour candidate. A total of 12,896 votes were cast. How many people voted for the winner?

4. The total cost of 3 milk shakes and 2 coffees is $1.10. The cost of 1 milk shake and 3 coffees is $0.60. Find the price of a milk shake and of a coffee.

5. An eastbound, nonstop flight of 3,500 miles requires 10 hr. A similar westbound flight requires 14 hr. Assuming a constant westerly wind throughout, find the speed of the wind and the airspeed of the airplane.

6. A rocket fired upward from a balloon ascended 2,400 ft in 10 sec. When a similar rocket was fired directly downward, it descended 22,400 ft in 20 sec. Assuming the acceleration of the rocket due to its own thrust to be a constant, find this acceleration. Also compute the acceleration g due to gravity.

7. When two bricklayers, A and B, are working separately, A lays 3 more bricks per minute than B. When they work together, each of their rates of laying drops to $\frac{2}{3}$ of what it was when they worked alone, and together they lay 10 bricks per minute. What are their rates of laying when they work separately?

8. At supermarkets in Suburbia, the price of a pack of cigarettes includes a tax of 20 cents, which is the same for all brands. In Suburbia, 4 packs of Notar cigarettes cost the same as 3 packs of Green Grass cigarettes. In the free port of Utopia, there are no taxes, and hence the price of a pack of cigarettes is 20 cents lower than that in Suburbia. In Utopia, 2 packs of Notar cigarettes cost the same as 1 pack of Green Grass cigarettes. Find the prices of the cigarettes in Suburbia.

9. A force of 5 dynes acts on a body A whose mass is 10 g. A force of 2 dynes acts on a body B whose mass is 15 g. Bodies C and D, the sum of whose masses is 29 g, are now fastened to bodies A and B, respectively, but the forces acting remain unchanged. Find the masses of C and D so that the acceleration produced on $A + C$ is twice that produced on $B + D$.

10. In an electric circuit A, the impressed voltage is 12 volts, and the resistance is 3 ohms. In circuit B, the voltage is 20 volts, and the resistance is 7 ohms. Additional batteries with a total voltage of 28 volts are to be added to these two circuits so that after the addition the currents in the two circuits will be equal. How much voltage should be added to each circuit?

11. In an electric circuit, the voltage is 15 volts. If the current is increased by 2 amp and the resistance decreased by 1 ohm, the voltage is reduced by 1 volt. Find the original current and resistance.

12. The annual cost C of operating a new car is $C = f + cm$, where f is the fixed cost (depreciation, insurance, license, etc.), c is the operating cost per mile, and m is the number of miles driven. The total cost for 10,000 miles is $1,800, and the cost for 15,000 miles is $2,300. Find the fixed cost and the cost per mile.

13. In a certain gas, the product of the pressure (pounds per square inch) and the volume (cubic inches) is 24 in.-lb. If the pressure is decreased by 5 lb/sq in. and the volume is increased by 5 cu in., the temperature is unchanged. Find the original pressure and volume.

14. Two different rockets are fired vertically at the same instant. The acceleration (constant) of one rocket is twice that of the other. After 3 sec one rocket is 90 ft higher than the other. Find their accelerations.

15. The second stage of a rocket is fired vertically with a constant acceleration a at a time $(t = 0)$ when the first stage has a vertical velocity v_0. One second

after $t = 0$ the velocity of the second stage is 1,100 ft/sec, and after 2 sec it is 1,400 ft/sec. Find v_0 and a.

16. A citizen of the nation of Nancago has an annual income of $9,800. The income tax rate in Nancago is 20 per cent. Moreover, the province of Camford also imposes an income tax of 10 per cent. The arrangement is that the national tax is based upon the annual income less the provincial tax paid, and the provincial tax is based upon the annual income less the national tax paid. Find the tax payable to Nancago and also that payable to its province, Camford.

17. On certain days of the week a family of father, mother, and teen-aged children traveling by first-class rail can take advantage of "family-plan" rates. Under one version of this scheme the father pays full fare and his wife and teen-aged children pay half fare. On the other hand the family could travel by coach, in which case each member would pay the full coach fare, which is $\frac{2}{3}$ of the first-class fare. For what number of children is the total cost of first-class family plan equal to the total cost of coach?

18. This problem is the same as Prob. 17, except that the family now consists of father, mother, teen-aged children, and one eight-year-old child. The eight-year-old pays half the full first-class fare under family plan or half the full coach fare if they travel by coach. For what number of teen-aged children are the two costs equal?

19. At a time when the world is balanced between war and peace, an investor finds himself forced to place his funds in a suitable combination of three types of stocks: munitions, utilities, and department stores. He estimates that his expected gains (or losses), per $100 invested, in the next year are as given in the table below:

	Munitions	Utilities	Department stores
War...............	$20	−$3	−$5
Peace..............	−$15	$5	$3

Since he does not know whether war or peace is coming, he decides to distribute his funds in such a way that he may expect to break exactly even in either eventuality. (As you see, he is a peculiar fellow and doesn't trust banks.) In what proportion should his investments be made?

20. A tourist has a collection of 18 coins consisting of Belgian francs (worth 2 cents each), British shillings (14 cents each), and German marks (25 cents each). The total value of his collection is $1.87. He has twice as many francs as marks. How many coins of each kind has he?

REFERENCES

Beaumont, R. A., and R. W. Ball: "Introduction to Modern Algebra and Matrix Theory, "Chaps. I, II, III, IV, Rinehart, New York (1954).

Birkhoff, Garrett, and Saunders MacLane: "A Survey of Modern Algebra," Chaps. 7, 8, Macmillan, New York (1941).

Also consult the following papers in the *American Mathematical Monthly:*

Greenspan, Donald: Methods of Matrix Inversion, vol. 62, p. 303 (1955).

Mendelsohn, N. S.: Some Elementary Properties of Ill Conditioned Matrices and Linear Equations, vol. 63, p. 285 (1956).

CHAPTER EIGHT

Inequalities

8.1. *Introduction*

In Chap. 2 we introduced the concept of inequality between two real numbers. We said there that $a < b$, "a less than b," if and only if $b - a$ is positive. Similarly $a > b$, "a greater than b," if and only if $b - a$ is negative. We also introduced the symbols $a \leq b$ and $a \geq b$, meaning "less than or equal to" and "greater than or equal to," respectively. In this chapter we treat these concepts in more detail.

Let us look first at $b - a$. This is positive, negative, or zero. Hence we may state the following property of real numbers with respect to inequality. We call this property "R12" and add it to properties R1 to R11 of Sec. 2.4.

R12. For each pair of real numbers a and b one and only one of the following relations is true:

$$a < b \qquad a = b \qquad a > b$$

Now consider the pair of inequalities

$$a < b \qquad b < c$$

From these we can conclude that $a < c$. To see this we note that

$$b - a \text{ is positive}$$
$$c - b \text{ is positive}$$

Hence the sum $(b - a) + (c - b) = c - a$ is positive, which shows that $a < c$. We call this the *transitive law* for inequalities and write it as property R13.

R13. If a, b, and c are real numbers, and if $a < b$ and $b < c$, then $a < c$.

Illustration 1. Since $-3 < 2$ and $2 < 8$, it follows that $-3 < 8$.

Next let us suppose that $a < b$ so that $b - a$ is positive. Then it follows that $a + c < b + c$, for $(b + c) - (a + c) = b - a$, which is assumed to be positive. We write this as property R14.

R14. If a, b, and c are real numbers and if $a < b$, then

$$a + c < b + c$$

Illustration 2. Since $3 < 5$, it follows that $3 + 2 < 5 + 2$, or $5 < 7$. Also we have $3 - 8 < 5 - 8$, or $-5 < -3$.

Finally we again suppose that $a < b$ and that c is positive. Then $bc - ac = c(b - a)$ is positive, for each factor is positive. Therefore $ac < bc$. We write this as property R15.

R15. If a, b, and c are real numbers, and if $a < b$ and c is positive, then $ac < bc$.

Illustration 3. Since $2 < 6$, it follows that $3 \times 2 < 3 \times 6$, or $6 < 18$.

Exercise A. The conclusion of R15 is false if c is negative. Find a counter-example which illustrates this fact.

Properties R12 to R15 are thus established for real numbers. In terms of R1 to R15 we can now derive all the rules for operating with inequalities. In more advanced mathematics a system having properties R12 to R15 is said to be "linearly ordered." A system having properties R1 to R15 is called an "ordered field."

Exercise B. Do the rational numbers have properties R12 to R15?
Exercise C. Do the complex numbers have properties R12 to R15?
Exercise D. Show that $a > 0$ if and only if a is positive.
Exercise E. Show that $a < b$ if and only if $b > a$.

8.2. *Theorems about Inequalities*

From R1 to R15 we shall now derive the chief theorems on inequalities. These will enable us to manipulate our inequalities and to solve problems involving them. In this section all letters refer to real numbers.

Theorem 1. If $a < b$ and $c < d$, then $(a + c) < (b + d)$.
  Proof:
  (1) $a + c < b + c$ [R14]
  (2) $b + c < b + d$ [R14]
  (3) $a + c < b + d$ [R13]

Illustration 4. From $-3 < 6$ and $4 < 8$ we conclude from Theorem 1 that $-3 + 4 < 6 + 8$, or $4 < 14$. Note that Theorem 1 says nothing about adding two inequalities, one of which contains a "less than" ($<$) and the other a "greater than" ($>$).

Exercise A. Prove that, if $a > b$ and $c > d$, then $a + c > b + d$.

Theorem 2. If $a < 0$, then $(-a) > 0$. This theorem should be obvious from first principles, but let us give a formal proof.
  Proof:
  (1) $a + (-a) < 0 + (-a)$ [Hypothesis and R14]
  (2) $0 < -a$ [R3 and R4]

Exercise B. Prove that, if $a > 0$, then $(-a) < 0$.

Theorem 3. If $a < b$, then $(-a) > (-b)$.
  Proof: Adding $-a - b$ to both sides of $a < b$, we have: $a - a - b < b - a - b$, or $-b < -a$.

Illustration 5. From $2 < 7$, we conclude that $-2 > -7$.
              From $-3 < 10$, we conclude that $3 > -10$.
              From $-8 < -4$, we conclude that $8 > 4$.

This theorem is sometimes stated in the form: *If we change the signs of both sides of an inequality, we change its "sense."* By changing the sense of an inequality we mean that we have replaced $<$ by $>$ or $>$ by $<$. We combine Theorem 3 with R15 to give Theorem 4:

Theorem 4. If $a < b$ and $c < 0$ (that is, c is negative), then $ac > bc$.
  This means that, if we multiply both sides of an inequality by a negative number, we change its sense.
  As our last theorem we wish to discover what happens to an inequality when we divide both sides by the same number. First we need to observe two minor facts. The first of these is that the square, a^2, of any real number $a \neq 0$ is positive. The second is that, if $a > 0$, then

$1/a > 0$. This is trivial; for $(1/a)^2$ is positive, and hence from R15 $a(1/a)^2 > 0$ or $1/a > 0$. Similarly, if $a < 0$, then $1/a < 0$.

Theorem 5. If $a < b$ and $c > 0$, then $a/c < b/c$. If $a < b$ and $c < 0$, then $a/c > b/c$.

To prove these statements, multiply both sides by $1/c$, and apply R15 and Theorem 4, respectively.

The net result of these theorems is that inequalities behave *almost* like equalities. We can add two inequalities having the same sense. We can add (or subtract) equal quantities to (or from) both sides of an inequality. We can multiply or divide both sides of an inequality by a *positive* number. The only difference between inequalities and equations is that, when we multiply or divide by a *negative* number, we *must change the sense of the inequality.*

8.3. *Linear Inequalities*

In many practical situations we meet inequalities such as:

$$3x + 5 < x - 7 \quad \text{or} \quad 2x^2 - 4x + 9 < 0$$

We wish to "solve" each of these inequalities; i.e., we seek to identify those values of x which satisfy the inequalities. In other words, we are interested in the sets: $\{x \mid 3x + 5 < x - 7\}$ and $\{x \mid 2x^2 - 4x + 9 < 0\}$ and wish to rewrite the definitions of these sets in a simpler form from which we can read off their elements at once. These sets will be subsets of the real numbers and will generally consist of intervals or unions of intervals.

Let us first examine linear inequalities, i.e., those like $ax + b < 0$, $ax + b > 0$, $ax + b \leq 0$, $ax + b \geq 0$. We can solve these at once by using the theorems of Sec. 8.2. We proceed as in the illustration below.

Illustration 1

(a) Solve: $3x + 5 < x - 7$.

By R14 we may subtract $x + 5$ from each side. Doing this, we obtain $2x < -12$. By Theorem 5 we may divide both sides by 2, and we thus conclude that $x < -6$. The solution is then the open interval $]-\infty, -6[$.

(b) Solve $x + 8 \geq 5x - 12$.

$$-4x + 8 \geq -12$$
$$-4x \geq -20$$
$$x \leq 5$$

The solution is the half-open interval $]-\infty, 5]$. Note that we changed the sense in the last inequality, for we were dividing both sides by -4.

Thus we see that the method of solving inequalities is very similar to that for solving equations. By using the operations which we justified in Sec. 8.2 we convert the given inequality into a series of equivalent inequalities, i.e., inequalities which define the same set as the given inequality. From the last of these we can read off the answer.

8.4. *Quadratic Inequalities*

Quadratic inequalities are of the form: $ax^2 + bx + c < 0$, $ax^2 + bx + c \geq 0$, etc., where $a \neq 0$ and a, b, and c are real numbers. There are two cases to consider. Let us first assume that $ax^2 + bx + c = 0$ has real roots, i.e., that $b^2 - 4ac \geq 0$. Then we can factor, so that $ax^2 + bx + c = a(x - r_1)(x - r_2)$, where r_1 and r_2 are real numbers. To proceed to the next step, we need the following theorem:

Theorem 6.   If $ab > 0$, then either:

$$a < 0 \quad \text{and} \quad b < 0$$
$$\text{or} \qquad a > 0 \quad \text{and} \quad b > 0$$

This follows easily from the rules for the multiplication of signed numbers. We can also prove it by the indirect method. Suppose that the conclusion is false. Then one of the following must be true:
    (1) $a < 0$, and $b > 0$.
    (2) $a > 0$, and $b < 0$.
    (3) $a = 0$, b arbitrary.
    (4) $b = 0$, a arbitrary.
Each of these leads to a contradiction. (1) and (2) contradict Theorem 4, and (3) and (4) contradict Theorem 3, Sec. 2.3.

Exercise A.   Prove: If $ab < 0$, then either $a < 0$ and $b > 0$, or $a > 0$ and $b < 0$.
Exercise B.   Prove: If $ab \geq 0$, then either $a \leq 0$ and $b \leq 0$, or $a \geq 0$ and $b \geq 0$.
Exercise C.   Prove: If $ab \leq 0$, then either $a \leq 0$ and $b \geq 0$, or $a \geq 0$ and $b \leq 0$.

We now return to our quadratic inequality, which we suppose to be in the reduced form: $(x - r_1)(x - r_2) > 0$. Other cases have similar treatments. From Theorem 6 we find that either $x - r_1 > 0$ and $x - r_2 > 0$; or $x - r_1 < 0$ and $x - r_2 < 0$. We can express this most clearly in set language as follows:

Theorem 7
$$\{x \mid (x - r_1)(x - r_2) > 0\}$$
$$= \{\{x \mid x > r_1\} \cap \{x \mid x > r_2\}\} \cup \{\{x \mid x < r_1\} \cap \{x \mid x < r_2\}\}$$

Illustration 1

(a) Solve $x^2 - 5x + 6 > 0$.

Factoring, we have: $x^2 - 5x + 6 = (x - 2)(x - 3)$. Hence the solution is:

$$\{\{x \mid x > 2\} \cap \{x \mid x > 3\}\} \cup \{\{x \mid x < 2\} \cap \{x \mid x < 3\}\}$$

This can be simplified, for

$$\{x \mid x > 2\} \cap \{x \mid x > 3\} = \{x \mid x > 3\} =]3, \infty[$$

and

$$\{x \mid x < 2\} \cap \{x \mid x < 3\} = \{x \mid x < 2\} =]-\infty, 2[$$

So write the answer in either of the forms:

$$\{x \mid x > 3\} \cup \{x \mid x < 2\} =]3, \infty[\cup]-\infty, 2[$$

The solution can be visualized in Fig. 8.1

Figure 8.1   **Figure 8.2**

(b) Solve $x^2 - 2x - 3 \leq 0$.

Factoring we have: $(x - 3)(x + 1) \leq 0$.

From Exercise C above we see that the solution is:

$$\{\{x \mid x - 3 \leq 0\} \cap \{x \mid x + 1 \geq 0\}\} \cup \{\{x \mid x - 3 \geq 0\} \cap \{x \mid x + 1 \leq 0\}\}$$

or $\quad \{\{x \mid x \leq 3\} \cap \{x \mid x \geq -1\}\} \cup \{\{x \mid x \geq 3\} \cap \{x \mid x \leq -1\}\}$

This can be written in the form:

$$[-1, 3] \cup \emptyset = [-1, 3]$$

Finally let us consider what happens when $ax^2 + bx + c = 0$ does not have real roots, i.e., when $b^2 - 4ac < 0$. Then the factors involve complex numbers, to which inequalities do not apply. So we must adopt another method. The method of completing the square (Sec. 6.6) tells us that:

$$ax^2 + bx + c = a\left(x + \frac{b}{2a}\right)^2 - a\left(\frac{b^2 - 4ac}{4a^2}\right)$$

This enables us to solve our inequalities. Assume that $a > 0$; then

$$ax^2 + bx + c > 0$$

is equivalent to

$$a\left(x + \frac{b}{2a}\right)^2 - a\left(\frac{b^2 - 4ac}{4a^2}\right) > 0$$

or to

$$\left(x + \frac{b}{2a}\right)^2 > \frac{b^2 - 4ac}{4a^2}$$

But the left side is nonnegative for all real x, and the right side is negative by assumption. Therefore the inequality is verified for *all* x.

Since $ax^2 + bx + c > 0$ for *all* real x, $ax^2 + bx + c < 0$ for *no* x. Thus $\{x \mid ax^2 + bx + c < 0\} = \emptyset$.

Since these arguments work also in the reverse direction we have proved the result:

Theorem 8.   The quadratic expression $ax^2 + bx + c$ with $a > 0$ is positive for all real values of x if and only if $b^2 - 4ac < 0$.

Exercise D.   Prove: When $a > 0$, $ax^2 + bx + c \geq 0$ for all real x if and only if $b^2 - 4ac \leq 0$.

Exercise E.   Restate Theorem 8 and Exercise D for the case $a < 0$.

Illustration 2

(a) Solve $2x^2 - 3x + 10 > 0$.

$$b^2 - 4ac = 9 - 80 = -71 < 0$$

Therefore the inequality is true for all x.

(b) Solve $-3x^2 + 4x - 11 > 0$.

Rewrite this with $a > 0$ in the form

$$3x^2 - 4x + 11 < 0$$
$$b^2 - 4ac = 16 - 132 = -116 < 0$$

Therefore there are no x for which the inequality is true.

PROBLEMS 8.4

In Probs. 1 to 20 solve the stated inequalities:

1. $x + 2 < 0$.
2. $3x + 5 > 0$.
3. $-2x + 3 > 0$.
4. $2x + 5 \leq x - 6$.
5. $3x - 2 \geq 5x + 8$.
6. $-7x + 4 > 3x - 2$.
7. $2(x - 8) > -3(x + 5)$.
8. $6(-2x + 3) < 5(3x + 4)$.
9. $x^2 + 3x - 8 \leq x^2 + 8x - 16$.
10. $2x^2 - x + 4 \geq 2x^2 + 4x - 5$.
11. $x^2 + 3x + 2 > 0$.
12. $x^2 + x - 2 > 0$.
13. $x^2 - 4x + 3 \leq 0$.
14. $x^2 - 6x + 5 \leq 0$.
15. $x^2 - 6x + 9 > 0$.
16. $x^2 + 4x + 4 < 0$.
17. $x^2 + x + 1 > 0$.
18. $2x^2 + x + 4 > 0$.
19. $-2x^2 + 3x - 8 > 0$.
20. $-3x^2 + x - 7 > 0$.

Applications

21. Prove: Let $a > 0$ and $b > 0$. Then, if $a^2 > b^2$, it follows that $a > b$.   HINT: Consider $a^2 - b^2 > 0$ or $(a + b)(a - b) > 0$.
22. From the Pythagorean relation $a^2 + b^2 = c^2$, prove that the hypotenuse of a right triangle is longer than either leg.
23. Apply the result of Prob. 22 to the general triangle given in the figure to show that $a + b > c + d$.   Hence the sum of two sides of a triangle is greater than the third side.

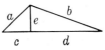

24. In the figure assume that $c > a$. Use the result of Prob. 23 to show that $c - a < b$. Hence any side of a triangle is greater than the absolute value of the difference of the other two sides.

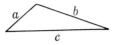

25. Prove that $|a + b| \leq |a| + |b|$.   HINT: Since $|a|^2 = a^2$, etc., let us consider

$$(a + b)^2 = a^2 + 2ab + b^2$$
$$\leq a^2 + 2|a|\,|b| + b^2$$
$$\leq [|a| + |b|]^2$$

When does equality hold in the above relation?

26. Using the result of Prob. 25, prove that

$$|a - b| \geq |a| - |b|$$

27. Prove that $\sqrt{ab} \leq \dfrac{a + b}{2}$ if a and b are positive.   HINT: Show that this is equivalent to

$(a+b)^2 \geq 0$

$$0 \leq a^2 - 2ab + b^2$$

$\sqrt{ab}$ is called the "geometric mean" of a and b; $(a + b)/2$ is called the "arithmetic mean."

    The above result is a special case of the general theorem that, for a set of positive quantities $a_1, \ldots, a_n$, the geometric mean $\sqrt[n]{a_1 a_2 \cdots a_n}$ is less than or equal to the arithmetic mean $\dfrac{1}{n}(a_1 + \cdots + a_n)$.

    When does equality hold in the above relation?

28. Prove that for any real numbers $a_1, a_2, b_1,$ and b_2

$$(a_1 b_1 + a_2 b_2)^2 \leq (a_1{}^2 + a_2{}^2)(b_1{}^2 + b_2{}^2)$$

This is known as "Cauchy's inequality."   HINT: Consider

$$(a_1 x + b_1)^2 = a_1{}^2 x^2 + 2a_1 b_1 x + b_1{}^2 \geq 0$$
$$(a_2 x + b_2)^2 = a_2{}^2 x^2 + 2a_2 b_2 x + b_2{}^2 \geq 0$$

Adding, we find that

$$(a_1{}^2 + a_2{}^2)x^2 + 2(a_1 b_1 + a_2 b_2)x + (b_1{}^2 + b_2{}^2) \geq 0 \qquad \text{for all } x$$

Now apply the result of Exercise D, (p. 158). When does equality hold in the above relation?

29. Generalize the result of Prob. 28 to two sets of numbers: $a_1, \ldots, a_n$ and $b_1, \ldots, b_n$. The formula so obtained is of great importance in statistics and higher geometry.

30. Let $\mathbf{A}$ be the vector $(a_1, \ldots, a_n)$; $\mathbf{B}$ be the vector $(b_1, \ldots, b_n)$; $|\mathbf{A}|$ be the length of $\mathbf{A}$; and $|\mathbf{B}|$ be the length of $\mathbf{B}$. Then from Cauchy's inequality show that:

$$\left(\frac{\mathbf{A} \cdot \mathbf{B}}{|\mathbf{A}|\,|\mathbf{B}|}\right)^2 \leq 1$$

8.5. *The Graph of a Linear Inequality*

Here we are concerned with the graph of the linear inequality $ax + by + c > 0$, or more properly of the set $\{(x,y) \mid ax + by + c > 0\}$.

In order to study this graph, we must first discuss some properties of the plane. We begin with the axiom:

Axiom. A line divides the plane into two half planes.

You are unlikely to have met this axiom in your study of geometry, for Euclid does not mention it. Nevertheless, this axiom and a few others must be added to Euclid's axioms if plane geometry is to be placed on a firm foundation.

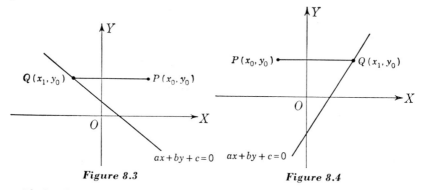

Figure 8.3   Figure 8.4

If the line $ax + by + c = 0$ is not parallel to the X-axis (that is, $a \neq 0$), we can speak of its "right half plane" and its "left half plane." Let us define these analytically in the following way: Let P have coordinates (x_0, y_0), and draw PQ parallel to the X-axis intersecting $ax + by + c = 0$ in the point (x_1, y_0) (Figs. 8.3 and 8.4). Then we have the definition:

Definition: P lies in the *right half plane* if $x_0 > x_1$; it lies in the *left half plane* if $x_0 < x_1$.

Since $a \neq 0$ by assumption, we choose a to be positive and consider the behavior of the expression $ax + by + c$. This is stated in Theorem 9.

Theorem 9. The expression $ax + by + c$ with $a > 0$ is:
   (a) Positive if and only if (x,y) is in the right half plane determined by the line $ax + by + c = 0$.
   (b) Negative if and only if (x,y) is in the left half plane determined by the line $ax + by + c = 0$.
   (c) Zero if and only if (x,y) is on the line $ax + by + c = 0$.

Proof: We shall prove (a) only. Let us suppose that P is a point (x_0, y_0) such that $ax_0 + by_0 + c > 0$. Let Q be the point (x_1, y_0) such that $ax_1 + by_0 + c = 0$ (see Figs. 8.3 and 8.4). Then

$$(ax_0 + by_0 + c) - (ax_1 + by_0 + c) > 0$$

or

$$a(x_0 - x_1) > 0$$

Since $a > 0$, it follows that $x_0 - x_1 > 0$, or that P is in the right half plane. A reversal of this argument shows that, if P is in the right half plane, then $ax_0 + by_0 + c > 0$.

Exercise A. Write out the details of the reversed argument just mentioned.

Exercise B. Prove cases (b) and (c) of Theorem 9.

Exercise C. Restate Theorem 9 when $a < 0$.

Exercise D. When $a = 0$, our expression reduces to $by + c$, where we can assume $b > 0$. Prove that: $by + c$ with $b > 0$ is:

(a) Positive if and only if (x, y) is in the upper half plane determined by the line $by + c = 0$.

(b) Negative if and only if (x, y) is in the lower half plane determined by the line $by + c = 0$.

(c) Zero if and only if (x, y) is on the line $by + c = 0$.

We can now find the graph of the sets like $\{(x, y) \mid ax + by + c > 0\}$. First we draw the line $ax + by + c = 0$. Then we know that the graph is one of the half planes determined by this line. Theorem 9 tells us which half plane. As shown in the illustrations below, we can determine which half plane even more simply by checking one particular point.

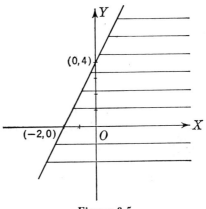

Figure 8.5

Illustration 1

(a) Graph $2x - y + 4 > 0$. The intercepts of $2x - y + 4 = 0$ are $(0,4)$ and $(-2,0)$, which give us the line. To determine which half plane is involved use Theorem 9, or find the sign of $2x - y + 4$ at a convenient point. At the origin O, $2x - y + 4$ equals 4. Hence $2x - y + 4$ is positive on the side of the line which contains O, that is, the right half plane, which is shaded in Fig. 8.5.

(b) Graph $-3x + y - 6 > 0$. The intercepts of $-3x + y - 6 = 0$ are $(0,6)$ and $(-2,0)$. Draw the line. At the origin, $-3x + y - 6$ equals -6; so $-3x + y - 6$ is positive on the side of the line which does *not* contain O, that is, the left-hand side, which is shaded in Fig. 8.6.

If you wish to determine which half plane by Theorem 9, you must first rewrite the inequality with $a > 0$ or in the form: $3x - y + 6 < 0$.

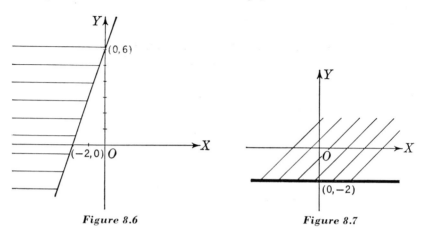

Figure 8.6   Figure 8.7

(c) Graph $4y + 8 \geq 0$. The line $4y + 8 = 0$ is the line $y = -2$. At the origin $4y + 8$ equals 8; so $4y + 8$ is positive on the side of the line containing O, namely, the upper half plane. Since the inequality contains the symbol $\geq$, its graph consists of the upper half plane plus the line $y = -2$.

8.6. *Simultaneous Linear Inequalities*

We now extend our treatment of inequalities (Sec. 8.5) to the case of systems of inequalities. So that we may graph these, we shall limit the discussion to those involving only two unknowns. A typical system of two inequalities is:

(1)
$$a_1x + b_1y + c_1 > 0$$
$$a_2x + b_2y + c_2 > 0$$

Each inequality of (1) determines a subset of the plane (i.e., a half plane), and the system (1) determines another set given by:

$$\{(x,y) \mid a_1x + b_1y + c_1 > 0 \text{ and } a_2x + b_2y + c_2 > 0\} =$$
$$\{(x,y) \mid a_1x + b_1y + c_1 > 0\} \cap \{(x,y) \mid a_2x + b_2y + c_2 > 0\}$$

That is, we are looking for those points which lie in both of the two given half planes. The best method of procedure is graphical.

Illustration 1. Graph the set determined by:

$$2x + y - 3 > 0$$
$$x - 2y + 1 < 0$$

First draw the two lines, which intersect at (1,1). From Sec. 8.5 we find that $2x + y - 3 > 0$ determines its right half plane and that $x - 2y + 1 < 0$ determines its left half plane. The region common to the two is shaded in Fig. 8.8. It is the interior of an angle whose vertex is (1,1).

This illustration is typical for two inequalities. But we can consider three or more simultaneous inequalities. The ideas and procedure are the same.

Illustration 2. Graph the set determined by

$$2x + y - 3 > 0$$
$$x - 2y + 1 < 0$$
$$y - 3 < 0$$

The first two inequalities are the same as in Illustration 1; so we merely add the third line to Fig. 8.8. This gives a triangle with vertices (1,1), (0,3), and (5,3).

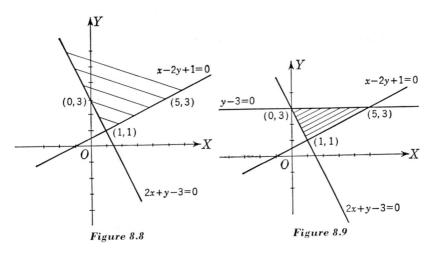

Figure 8.8   **Figure 8.9**

This line divides the shaded region of Fig. 8.8 into two parts. From Sec. 8.5 we see that $y - 3 < 0$ determines its lower half plane. Hence the desired set is the interior of the triangle shaded in Fig. 8.9.

Illustration 3. Let us add one more inequality to our picture, and consider the system:

$$2x + y - 3 > 0$$
$$x - 2y + 1 < 0$$
$$y - 3 < 0$$
$$x + y - 5 < 0$$

Since $x + y + 5 < 0$ determines its left-hand half plane, the desired set is the quadrilateral shaded in Fig. 8.10.

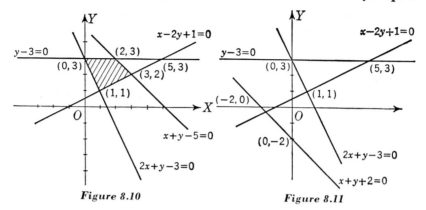

Figure 8.10   Figure 8.11

Illustration 4. Instead of the system of Illustration 3 consider

$$\begin{array}{rrrr} 2x + & y & - 3 > 0 \\ x & - 2y & + 1 < 0 \\ & y & - 3 < 0 \\ x + & y & + 2 < 0 \end{array}$$

The inequality $x + y + 2 < 0$ determines its left half plane, which has no points in common with the triangle of Fig. 8.9. Hence the desired set is empty; and nothing is shaded in Fig. 8.11.

We see in this way that the graph of a system of linear inequalities can take many forms. In the usual cases it is the interior of a convex polygon, which may be closed as in Figs. 8.9 and 8.10 or open as in Fig. 8.8. In other cases it may be the empty set. When the inequalities include $\geq$ or $\leq$, the possibilities are even more numerous.

8.7. *Applications*

Since you have probably not met inequalities and systems of inequalities in your previous mathematical education, you may wonder how they arise in practice and what they are good for. In the first place the acceptable solution of a problem may be limited by practical considerations such as unavoidable restrictions on space, cost, use of materials, man power, or time. Each of these would be expressed analytically as an inequality. On the other hand, the solution may have to satisfy certain minimum requirements such as load-carrying capacity, food intake necessary to maintain health, serviceable life of a product, or volume of sales necessary to justify the production of a certain item.

Our objectives are often stated in terms of inequalities. We do not try to manufacture a bolt whose diameter is exactly $\frac{1}{2}$ in.; we are quite content if it is $\frac{1}{2}$ in. plus or minus certain tolerances, which are expressed as inequalities. Our missiles do not have to hit an exact spot in enemy territory; we are happy if they land within, say, half a mile of their objective. But to handle the analysis of their behavior we need inequalities.

Inequalities are of importance in modern mathematical economics and in recent theories such as game theory and linear programming. Space does not permit us to describe these here, and we refer you to Kemeny, Snell, and Thompson, "Introduction to Finite Mathematics," pages 249 to 306, for an elementary discussion of them.

PROBLEMS 8.7

On squared paper plot the graphs of the following:

1. $x + y + 1 > 0.$
2. $2x - y - 2 > 0.$
3. $-3x + 2y + 12 \geq 0.$
4. $-x + 4y + 8 \geq 0.$
5. $3x + 7y > 0.$
6. $2x - 5y < 0.$
7. $3y + 5 \geq 0.$
8. $-y + 7 > 0.$
9. $4x + 12 < 0.$
10. $-7x + 21 \geq 0.$
11. $x^2 + y^2 \leq 1.$
12. $x^2 + y^2 = 0.$
13. $x^2 + y^2 < 0.$
14. $(x + 1)^2 + (y + 1)^2 \leq 0.$
15. $3x + y - 8 > 0.$
    $x - 2y + 2 < 0.$
16. $4x - 5y + 26 > 0.$
    $5x + 3y + 14 > 0.$
17. $3x + y - 8 > 0.$
    $x - 2y + 2 < 0.$
    $2x + 3y - 24 < 0.$
18. $4x - 5y + 26 > 0.$
    $5x + 3y + 14 > 0.$
    $9x - 2y + 3 > 0.$
19. $3x + y - 8 > 0.$
    $x - 2y + 2 < 0.$
    $2x + 3y - 24 < 0.$
    $3x + y - 15 < 0.$
20. $4x - 5y + 26 > 0.$
    $5x + 3y + 14 > 0.$
    $2x - 7y - 19 < 0.$
21. $3x + y - 8 > 0.$
    $x - 2y + 2 < 0.$
    $2x + 3y - 24 < 0.$
    $3x + y < 0.$
22. $4x - 5y + 26 > 0.$
    $5x + 3y + 14 > 0.$
    $2x - 7y - 19 < 0.$
    $7x + 5y - 37 < 0.$

REFERENCE

Kemeny, J. G., J. L. Snell, and G. L. Thompson: "Finite Mathematics," Chap. 6. Prentice-Hall, Englewood Cliffs, N.J. (1957).

CHAPTER NINE

Functions and Relations

9.1. *Relations*

In this chapter we shall be dealing with subsets of the set $X \times Y$, the set of all ordered pairs of real numbers (x,y). We have already met two important subsets of this type:

$$\{(x,y) \mid ax + by + c = 0\} \quad [\text{Sec. 7.1}]$$
$$\{(x,y) \mid ax + by + c > 0\} \quad [\text{Sec. 8.5}]$$

Here we are interested in other examples, and in the general situation as a whole. In order to have a name for these subsets, we define a *relation* as follows:

Definition: A *relation* is a subset of the set of ordered pairs of real numbers, $X \times Y$.

There are a good many ways of defining specific relations, and so we give the most important of these below:

Methods of Defining Relations

(1) LIST OF ORDERED PAIRS. When the subset consists of a reasonably small (finite) number of ordered pairs, we just write them down. This list of pairs defines the relation.

166

Illustration 1. An example of such a relation is the set:

$$\{(0,3),\ (2,-1),\ (2,4),\ (1,3),\ (0,0)\}$$

A relation consisting of a single ordered pair is the set $\{(1,3)\}$.

Illustration 2. As a physical illustration of such a set consider the pairs (T,D), where T represents the time of revolution in years of a planet and D represents its mean distance from the sun in units such that D for the earth is 1. Then we have the table:

	Mer-cury	Venus	Earth	Mars	Jupiter	Saturn	Uranus	Nep-tune	Pluto
T	0.241	0.615	1.00	1.88	11.9	29.5	84.0	165	265
D	0.387	0.723	1.00	1.52	5.20	9.54	19.2	30.1	41.3

The relation so defined is the set:

$$\{(0.241, 0.387),\ (0.615, 0.723),\ \dots\ ,\ (265,\ 41.3)\}$$

Illustration 3. Relations of this type frequently appear as tables. You have probably met tables of logarithms which are good examples of this. In these the ordered pairs are of the form $(x,\log x)$. The set of all such pairs of entries is the relation so defined.

(2) EQUATIONS. The subset is often defined to consist of those ordered pairs which satisfy a certain equation. Then the relation is

$$\{(x,y)\ |\ (x,y)\ \text{satisfy the given equation}\}$$

Illustration 4. Examples of such relations are:

$$\{(x,y)\ |\ 3x + 2y = 5\} \qquad \{(x,y)\ |\ 4x^2 - 6xy + y^2 = 0\}$$
$$\{(x,y)\ |\ 2x^4 + y^2 - xy^2 + 7 = 0\}$$

(3) INEQUALITIES. Here the subset is defined to consist of those ordered pairs which satisfy a certain inequality. An example is the relation $\{(x,y)\ |\ x + 3y > 2\}$.

(4) SIMULTANEOUS SYSTEMS. Relations may also be defined (as in Secs. 7.3 and 8.6) by a simultaneous system of equalities, or inequalities, or mixtures of these.

Illustration 5. The following simultaneous systems define relations:

$$\begin{matrix} 2x + y = 3 & 3x + 2y = 9 & 2x - y < 0 \\ x > 1 & x + y = 1 & x + y \geq 1 \end{matrix}$$

Exercise A. Write down the relations of Illustration 5.

(5) GRAPHS. In science relations sometimes are defined by a graph. This amounts to a curve in the plane, to a shaded region, or to a discrete set of points. The coordinates (x,y) of all points in the graph give us the desired subset of $X \times Y$ and define the relation.

A relation R defines a subset of X called its *domain* and a subset of Y called its *range*.

Definitions: The *domain* of a relation is the subset of X: $\{x \mid x$ is the first element of at least one of the pairs (x,y) of $R\}$. The *range* of a relation is the subset of Y: $\{y \mid y$ is the second element of at least one of the pairs (x,y) of $R\}$.

Illustration 6. Consider the relation $\{(x,y) \mid 2x + 3y + 1 = 0\}$. For every x there is a pair (x,y) which satisfies this equation (solve for y in terms of x). Hence the domain is X. Similarly the range is Y.

For the relation $\{(x,y) \mid y = 3\}$, the domain is X, and the range is $\{3\} \subset Y$.

For the relation $\{(x,y) \mid x^2 + y^2 = 9\}$, x must lie in the interval $-3 \leq x \leq 3$ if y is to be real. Hence the domain is $[-3,3] \subset X$. Similarly the range is $[-3,3] \subset Y$.

The methods of defining relations are often referred to as *rules*. Thus the relation $\{(x,y) \mid x + 2y - 1 > 0\}$ is defined by the rule which, in this case, is the inequality $x + 2y - 1 > 0$.

PROBLEMS 9.1

In Probs. 1 to 20 discuss the domain and range of each relation whose defining rule is:

1. $y = 3x + 1$.

2. $y = 2x - 1$.

3. $y = x^2$.

4. $y = -2x^2$.

5. $x^2 + y^2 = 1$.

6. $x^2 + y^2 = 4$.

7. $y = x^4$.

8. $y = -x^4$.

9. $x^2 + y^2 \leq 4$.

10. $x^2 + y^2 \geq 4$.

11. $x + y < 1$.

12. $x + y \leq 1$.

13. $\begin{cases} 2x + y < 1. \\ x > 0. \end{cases}$

14. $\begin{cases} x + y = 1. \\ x > 3. \end{cases}$

15. $\begin{cases} 3x - y = 2. \\ y < -3. \end{cases}$

16. $\begin{cases} 2x + y = 1. \\ x + 2y = 1. \end{cases}$

17. $\{(1,7), (3,14)\}$.

18. $\{(0,1), (1,1), (2,1)\}$.

19. $\{(2,2), (2,3)\}$.

20. $\{(-3,4), (-3,-4), (3,-4)\}$.

9.2. Functions

There is a special kind of a relation called a function which is of great importance.

Definition: A *function* f is a relation in which no two ordered pairs have the same first element.

This means that, given an x in the domain of f, there is a unique pair (x,y) belonging to the function. This determines a value y uniquely associated with the given x. We denote this value by the symbol $f(x)$, read "f of x," called the value of the function f at x.

Definition: The *value $f(x)$ of the function f at x* (in the domain of f) is the second element of that unique ordered pair (x,y) belonging to f which has x as its first element.

In a relation there may be many pairs (x,y_1), (x,y_2), . . . with x as first element. Hence we do not speak of the "value of a relation."

Illustration 1. The relation $\{(x,y) \mid 3x - 2y + 4 = 0\}$ is also a function since there is a unique $y = f(x) = (3x + 4)/2$ associated with each x. The domain is X, and the range is Y.

Illustration 2. The relation $\{(x,y) \mid y = x^2\}$ is also a function with $f(x) = x^2$. The domain is X, and the range is $[0, \infty[\subset Y$.

Illustration 3. The relation $\{(x,y) \mid x^2 + y^2 = 4\}$ is *not* a function. For to each x in the open interval $]-2,2[$ there are associated two values of y, namely, $y = \pm \sqrt{4 - x^2}$.

Illustration 4. The relation $\{(x,y) \mid x^2 + y^2 < 4\}$ is *not* a function. For to each x in the open interval $]-2,2[$ there are associated infinitely many values of y, namely, those such that $y^2 < 4 - x^2$.

Illustration 5. We may define a function by giving its values for each x in its domain. For example,

$$f(x) = \begin{cases} 1 & \text{if } x \geq 0 \\ -1 & \text{if } x < 0 \end{cases}$$

defines the function f whose ordered pairs are $(x, f(x))$. The domain is X; the range is $\{-1,1\} \subset Y$.

As in Illustration 5, we regularly define functions by stating what their values $f(x)$, or y, are to be. Thus we speak of "the function f whose values are $f(x) = 4x^2 - 9$" or "whose values are $y = 4x^2 - 9$." It is common practice to abbreviate this and to speak of the "function $f(x) = 4x^2 - 9$" or the "function $y = 4x^2 - 9$" or even the function "$4x^2 - 9$." These abbreviations can be misleading, for they confuse the function itself with its set of values. However, once you have understood the true meaning of a function, there is then no real harm in your using a convenient abbreviation. Consequently, we shall use the full, correct language while you are learning about functions in this chapter, but later we shall not hesitate to use abbreviations and to speak of the functions x, $3x^2 - 4$, sin x, tan x, e^x, log x, etc., when we mean the functions whose values are given by these expressions.

In connection with functions the terms variable and constant are frequently used. They are defined as follows:

Definition: A letter used to represent an arbitrary element of a set of numbers (containing more than one element) is called a *variable*. If the set contains only a single element, the letter used to represent this element is called a *constant*.

When the numbers in the given set are real (as in this chapter), we speak of a *real variable;* when they are complex, we speak of a *complex variable.*

Given a function, we have defined two subsets of the real numbers: the domain which is a subset of X and the range which is a subset of Y. The letter x is an arbitrary element of the domain and is called the *independent variable.* We have seen that, given f and x, a unique y is determined. Hence we call y, which is an element of the range, the *dependent variable.* When x is the independent variable of f, we say that "f is a function of x."

So far we have considered functions f whose ordered pairs are (x,y). It is often necessary or desirable to use other letters to represent the function and the independent and dependent variables. To say what we are doing in such cases, we shall use notations such as $f:(x,y)$; $g:(w,z)$; $\phi(r,T)$; etc. For instance, $f:(x,y)$ means "the function f whose ordered pairs are (x,y)"; $g:(w,z)$ means "the function g whose pairs are (w,z)"; etc.

PROBLEMS 9.2

In Probs. 1 to 4, find the domain and range of the functions whose values are:

1. $f(x) = x$.   2. $f(x) = -3x$.
3. $f(x) = x^2$.   4. $f(x) = -3x^3$.
5. If $f(x) = 3x^3 - 2x^2 + 1$, find $f(-1)$, $f(3)$, $f(0)$.
6. The table defines a function:

x	1	2	4
y	0	1	3

Write down the ordered pairs of this function.

7. The table defines a function:

x	1	2	3
y	1	2	2

Write down the ordered pairs of this function. What is the domain? What is the range?

In Probs. 8 to 11 which of the tables define a relation that is not a function?

8.

x	1	2
y	1	3

9.

x	1	2
y	1	1

10.

x	1	0
y	1	1

11.

x	0	4
y	0	4

In Probs. 12 to 15 which sets of ordered pairs are functions?

12. $\{(1,2), (2,3), (3,4)\}$.

13. $\{(1,2), (2,2), (3,2)\}$.

14. $\{(1,2), (1,3), (1,4)\}$.

15. $\{(2,1), (3,1), (2,3)\}$.

In Probs. 16 to 19 discuss the domain and range of the functions whose values are:

16. $f(x) = \begin{cases} 1, & x \text{ rational.} \\ 0, & x \text{ irrational.} \end{cases}$

17. $f(x) = \begin{cases} 1, & x \geq 0. \\ -1, & -1 \leq x < 0. \\ 0, & \text{otherwise.} \end{cases}$

18. $f(x) = \begin{cases} 1, & x \text{ an integer.} \\ \text{undefined}, & x \text{ not an integer.} \end{cases}$

19. $f(x) = \begin{cases} \sqrt{x}, & x \geq 0. \\ -\sqrt{-x}, & x < 0. \end{cases}$

20. The equation $x^2 + y^2 = 25$ defines a relation. What is the relation? Write down three functions which are special cases (i.e., subsets) of this relation. State the domain, range, and defining rule of each.

21. For f such that $f(x) = (\sqrt{x} - x)/3$, compute the values of the function for $x = 0, 1, 2, 3, -1, -2$.

22. Given that $f(x) = x^2 - 1$, find the following: $f(2)$, $f(1 + \sqrt{2})$, $f(t)$, $f(a + h)$, $f(2) - f(3)$.

In Probs. 23 to 26 find the value of $\dfrac{f(a + h) - f(a)}{h}$ for the functions whose values are:

23. $f(x) = x^2$.

24. $f(x) = 4x^2 + 2x - 3$.

25. $y = x$.

26. $y = k$, k a fixed number.

27. Construct a table showing the average number (assumed) of automobile accidents in the United States per day of the week. Will this table constitute a function? Explain.

28. Why must $x = 2$ be excluded from the domain of the function f whose values are $f(x) = 3/(x - 2)$?

29. A bookstore reduces the price of a certain book for quick sale. In the first five days of the sale, the numbers sold are, respectively, 5,000, 3,000, 1,000, 500, and 500. Write this in functional notation. State domain and range.

30. At a carnival there is the usual strength-testing machine: a vertically supported wire up which a ball is driven by striking a pin with a sledge hammer. The distance the ball is driven upward is a function of how "hard" the pin is struck. (The physical unit is impulse = mass $\times$ velocity, but we shall not need the details.) Let us suppose that for a hypothetical machine the ball can rise a maximum of 20 ft, that height is directly proportional to impulse, and that an impulse of 1 unit sends the ball up 2 ft. Find the following:

(a) The minimum impulse required to drive the ball to the top.

(b) (BT) The height to which the ball rises under an impulse of 5 units; again for 12 units.

(c) If the value of this function f at x is $f(x)$, what is $f(x)$? What is the domain; the range?

31. An automobile wheel 20 in. in diameter settles in quicksand as in the following table:

x = revolutions of wheel per second	0	5	10	15	20
y = rate at which vertical sinking takes place, in./min	1	2	3	4	5

(a) What is the function f; its domain; its range? State explicitly the assumptions you make.

(b) How long will it be before the automobile is mired (i.e., its axle is on the ground) if the wheels revolve at 10 rev/sec; 1 rev/min?

32. Find the domain and range of the functions whose values are

(a) $y = \dfrac{1}{x(x+1)}$.

(b) $y = \dfrac{1}{(x-1)(x+1)}$.

In Probs. 33 to 36 state the domain for the functions whose values are:

33. $y = \dfrac{1}{x(x-1)(x-2)}$.

34. $y = \dfrac{x-1}{x^2+1}$.

35. $y = \dfrac{x-1}{x^2-1}$.

36. $y = x^3 + x - 3$.

37. For $y = (x-1)(x-2)$, state the range if

(a) The domain is considered to be

$$\{x \mid 1 \leq x \leq 2\}$$

(b) The domain is considered to be

$$]-\infty,1] \cup [2,+\infty[$$

38. A rectangle has two (opposite) sides each 2 in. long; the length of another side is to be called x. Show that the area A is then a function of x. State domain and range.

9.3. *Absolute-value Function*

In the course of your studies you will meet some of the especially important functions such as the polynomial, logarithmic, exponential, and trigonometric functions. Now we should like to introduce you to an unusual but very useful function. The domain is the set X of real numbers.

The function is the absolute-value function f whose values are given by $f(x) = |x|$, read "$f(x)$ is the absolute value of x," defined by

$$y = |x| = \begin{cases} x & x > 0 \\ 0 & x = 0 \\ -x & x < 0 \end{cases}$$

Some of the elements of the set f are $(3,3)$, $(-3,3)$, $(-8,8)$; regardless of the sign of x in the ordered pair (x,y) the corresponding value y is positive. Sometimes the "absolute value" is called the "numerical value" for this reason.

Exercise A. Show that the two functions f and g whose values, respectively, are given by $f(x) = |x|$ and $g(x) = \sqrt{x^2}$ are identical.

Exercise B. Compute $|x|$ for $x = 2$, -1, π, 0, $-\sqrt{3}$, $\frac{1}{2}$.

9.4. *Algebra of Functions*

We have studied the four elementary operations of arithmetic $+$, $-$, $\times$, $\div$ in connection with numbers (Chap. 2). These ideas can also be applied to functions according to the following definitions.

Definitions: Consider the functions $f: (x,y)$ and $g: (x,z)$ whose domains are, respectively, indicated by d_f and d_g. The *sum* $f + g$, the *difference* $f - g$, the *product* fg, and the *quotient* f/g are defined as follows:

(1) $f:(x,y) + g:(x,z) = (f + g):(x, y + z)$.

(2) $f:(x,y) - g:(x,z) = (f - g):(x, y - z)$.

(3) $f:(x,y) \times g:(x,z) = (fg):(x,yz)$.

(4) $\dfrac{f:(x,y)}{g:(x,z)} = \left(\dfrac{f}{g}\right):\left(x, \dfrac{y}{z}\right)$.

(1′) In the addition $f + g$ of two functions, the functional values are added.

(2′) In the subtraction $f - g$, the functional values are subtracted (in the proper order).

(3′) In the multiplication fg, the functional values are multiplied.

(4′) In the division f/g, the functional values are divided (in the proper order).

The functional values of f and g are $f(x)$ and $g(x)$, respectively. Thus the values of their algebraic combinations are:

$$(f + g)(x) = f(x) + g(x)$$
$$(f - g)(x) = f(x) - g(x)$$
$$(fg)(x) = f(x) \times g(x)$$
$$\left(\frac{f}{g}\right)(x) = \frac{f(x)}{g(x)}$$

The domain of each of $f + g$, $f - g$, and fg is the set of all elements x common to the domains of f and g; that is, it is the intersection of the sets d_f and d_g. Thus in symbols $d_{f+g} = d_f \cap d_g$, $d_{f-g} = d_f \cap d_g$, and $d_{fg} = d_f \cap d_g$. The domain $d_{f/g} = d_f \cap d_g$ except for those x's for which $g(x) = 0$. (Division by zero is impossible.)

Illustration 1. Given the two functions f and g whose values are $f(x) = x^2$ and $g(x) = x^3$, the domain of each is a set of real numbers. Then

$$(f + g)(x) = x^2 + x^3 \qquad\qquad d_{f+g} = X$$
$$(f - g)(x) = x^2 - x^3 \qquad\qquad d_{f-g} = X$$
$$(fg)(x) = x^2 \times x^3 = x^5 \qquad\qquad d_{fg} = X$$
$$\left(\frac{f}{g}\right)(x) = \frac{x^2}{x^3} = \frac{1}{x} \qquad\qquad d_{f/g} = X \text{ except } \{0\}$$

Note that $x = 0$ is not in the domain of f/g since $g(0) = 0$.

Illustration 2. Let f and g have the values $f(x) = 1 + 1/x$, $g(x) = \sqrt{1 - x^2}$. The domain d_f is the set of all real numbers excluding 0; the domain d_g is the set of all real numbers between -1 and 1 inclusive. Then

$$(f + g)(x) = 1 + \frac{1}{x} + \sqrt{1 - x^2} \qquad d_{f+g} = \{x \mid (-1 \le x < 0) \cup (0 < x \le 1)\}$$

$$(f - g)(x) = 1 + \frac{1}{x} - \sqrt{1 - x^2} \qquad d_{f-g} = d_{f+g}$$

$$f(g)x = 1 + \frac{1}{x}\sqrt{1 - x^2} \qquad d_{fg} = d_{f+g}$$

$$\left(\frac{f}{g}\right)(x) = \frac{1 + (1/x)}{\sqrt{1 - x^2}} \qquad d_{f/g} = \{x \mid (-1 < x < 0) \cup (0 < x < 1)\}$$

In f/g we must exclude $x = \pm 1$, since $g(-1) = g(1) = 0$.

One further operation in the algebra of functions is of great importance; it is the operation of forming the *composite* of two functions.

We illustrate with a special example. Consider first the two functions $f:(x,y)$ and $g:(y,z)$, whose values are given, respectively, by

$$f(x) = 2x \qquad \begin{cases} \text{domain } X \\ \text{range } Y \end{cases}$$

$$g(y) = +\sqrt{y^3 - 1} \qquad \begin{cases} \text{domain } \{y \mid y^3 - 1 \ge 0\}, \text{ that is, } \{y \mid y \ge 1\} \\ \text{range} \quad \{z \mid z \ge 0\} \end{cases}$$

If there is no connection between these two functions f and g, then there is nothing but a notational difference intended in using ordered pairs of the form (x,y) for f and ordered pairs of the form (y,z) for g.

However, mathematics is filled with situations in which there *is* a connection—situations in which range values of one function f must serve as the domain values of another function g. In the above example, only those values $y \ge 1$ of the range of f can be used in the domain of g. This process leads to a *third* function whose ordered pairs are (x,z), where $z = +\sqrt{y^3 - 1} = +\sqrt{(2x)^3 - 1}$. This third and new function is called the *composite of g and f*, and we choose the symbol $g \circ f$ to represent it.

Now let us describe the general situation where we are given two functions $f:(x,y)$ and $g:(y,z)$. Choose an x such that the y which f assigns to it is in the domain of g. Then g assigns a z to this y. This gives us the pair (x,z). The set of all pairs (x,z) which can be constructed in this fashion is the composite function $g \circ f$. The domain of $g \circ f$ is the set of all x's for which this process can be defined; if there are no such x's the function $g \circ f$ is not defined.

Definition. For two given functions $f:(x,y)$ and $g:(y,z)$, the set of ordered pairs (x,z) described above defines a function called the *composite* of g and f and written $g \circ f:(x,z)$.

Illustration 3. Let $z = g(y) = 3y^2 - 2y + 1$ and $y = f(x) = 4x + 7$. The composite $g \circ f$ is given by

$$z = g(y) = 3y^2 - 2y + 1 = 3(4x + 7)^2 - 2(4x + 7) + 1$$

This can be simplified to yield

$$z = 48x^2 + 160x + 134$$

which defines $g \circ f: (x,\, 48x^2 + 160x + 134)$.

Illustration 4. A stone is dropped into a liquid, forming circles which increase in radius with time according to the formula $r = 4t$. How does the area of a given circle depend upon time?

    Solution: The area A of a circle is $A = \pi r^2$, and we are given that $r = 4t$. These define two functions $g:(r,A)$ and $f:(t,r)$; and we seek the composite $g \circ f:(t,A)$.

$$A = \pi r^2 = \pi(4t)^2$$

or, reduced,

$$A = 16\pi t^2$$

Hence $g \circ f:(t, 16\pi t^2)$ is the composite of g and f. Here we are not interested in negative values of t, although, mathematically, the maximal domain is the set of all real numbers. For the physical problem, a subset such as $0 \le t \le t_1$, where t_1 is sufficiently large, would suffice.

Since the letters used to represent the independent and dependent variables of a function can be replaced by other letters without change of meaning, we can speak of the composite $g \circ f$, where the functions f and g are given in the usual form $f:(x,y)$ and $g:(x,y)$. For we can rewrite g in the form $g:(y,z)$ if we wish. If we were interested in the composite $f \circ g$ we would rewrite f in the form $f:(y,z)$.

Illustration 5. Given f and g whose values are $f(x) = x^2 + 2$ and $g(x) = 1 - 1/x$, form the composite functions $g \circ f$ and $f \circ g$.

Solution:

For $g \circ f$	*For $f \circ g$*
Rewrite the defining equations in the form	Rewrite the defining equations in the form

$$y = f(x) = x^2 + 2$$
$$z = g(y) = 1 - 1/y$$

$$z = f(y) = y^2 + 2$$
$$y = g(x) = 1 - 1/x$$

Then $z = 1 - 1/y = 1 - 1/(x^2 + 2)$ and the composite $g \circ f$ is $g \circ f: (x,z)$ or $g \circ f: [x,\ 1 - 1/(x^2 + 2)]$

Then $z = y^2 + 2 = (1 - 1/x)^2 + 2$ and the composite $f \circ g$ is $f \circ g: (x,z)$ or $f \circ g: [x,\ (1 - 1/x)^2 + 2]$

Illustration 6. Find $g \circ f$ when g and f have the values $g(x) = |x|$ and $f(x) = x^2 - 3x + 1$.

Solution: Write $z = g(y) = |y|$ and $y = f(x) = x^2 - 3x + 1$. Then $z = |y| = |x^2 - 3x + 1|$. Thus $g \circ f: (x,\ |x^2 - 3x + 1|)$. To evaluate $|x^2 - 3x + 1|$ for a given x, say $x = 1$, we first find $x^2 - 3x + 1$, which equals -1. Then we take its absolute value, which is $+1$.

PROBLEMS 9.4

In Probs. 1 to 7 find the values $(f + g)(x)$, $(f - g)(x)$, $(fg)(x)$, and $(f/g)(x)$. In each case state domain.

1. $f(x) = \dfrac{1}{x} + \dfrac{1}{x - 1}$, $g(x) = x$.

2. $f(x) = \sqrt{x - 1}$, $g(x) = \sqrt{x + 2}$.

3. $f(x) = \dfrac{1}{x - 1}$, $g(x) = x + 1$.

4. $f(x) = \dfrac{1}{x - 1}$, $g(x) = (x - 1)^2$.

5. $f(x) = x - 1$, $g(x) = \dfrac{1}{(x - 1)^2}$.

6. $f(x) = x - 1$, $g(x) = \dfrac{1}{x - 1}$.

7. $f(x) = \begin{cases} \dfrac{1}{x - 1}, & x \neq 1. \\ 16, & x = 1. \end{cases}$ $g(x) = \begin{cases} \dfrac{2}{(x - 1)(x + 1)}, & x \neq 1,\ -1. \\ \sqrt{15},\ x = 1. \\ \text{undefined},\ x = -1. \end{cases}$

In Probs. 8 to 10 form the composite $g \circ f$. State domain.

8. $z = g(y) = y^4 + y - 1$, $y = f(x) = x + x^{-2}$.

9. $z = g(y) = 1/(1 - y)$, $y = f(x) = 1/(1 - x)$.

10. $z = g(y) = y^2 - 2y$, $y = f(x) = c$.

In Probs. 11 to 16 form $g \circ f$ and also $f \circ g$. State domain.

11. $f(x) = 2 - (1/x) + |x|$, $g(x) = x^2 - 4$.

12. $f(x) = |x|$, $g(x) = |x| + 1$.

13. $f(x) = |x|$, $g(x) = x - 1$.

14. $f(x) = \sqrt{x}$, $g(x) = |x|$.

15. $f(x) = x$, $g(x) = x$.

16. $f(x) = |x|$, $g(x) = |x|$.

17. Evaluate $|3x^2 - x - 5|$ for $x = -1,\ 0,\ 2$.

18. Simplify (a) $\sqrt{x^2 + 4x + 4}$; (b) $\sqrt{3/x^2}$. HINT: Use absolute values.

9.5. *Graphs*

In Chap. 7 and 8 (Secs. 7.1 and 8.5) we plotted the graphs of certain special relations and in Sec. 7.2 we discussed the general concept of the

graph of a relation.   Here we shall study general methods for graphing relations and functions.   By way of review, we define graph as
follows:

Definition: The *graph* of a relation whose ordered pairs are (x,y) is
the set of points in the XY-plane whose coordinates are the given pairs.

When the relation is defined by an equation, the basic method of
plotting its graph is to find a reasonable number of points (x,y) whose
coordinates satisfy the equation.   Then we join these points by a
smooth curve.   There are two disadvantages to this method: (1) We
may need to compute a rather large number of points in order to see
just how the graph should look.   (2) Even then, we may overlook
some abnormal features of the graph which occur in the gaps between
the plotted points.   It is, therefore, desirable for us to develop some
general aids to graphing which will cut down on your work and improve
your accuracy.   These apply only to relations (or functions) which
are defined by equations.

(1) *Intercepts.*   The x-intercepts are the x-coordinates of the points
at which the graph crosses (or meets) the X-axis, and the y-intercepts
are the y-coordinates of the corresponding points on the Y-axis.   To
find the x-intercepts, put $y = 0$ in the equation which defines the
relation, and solve for x.   To find the y-intercepts, put $x = 0$, and
solve for y.

When the relation is a function, the x-intercepts correspond
to those x's for which the value
of the function is zero.   These
x's are called the *zeros of the
function*.   We shall devote considerable attention in Chap. 10
to methods for finding the zeros
of polynomial functions.

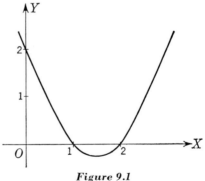

Figure 9.1

Illustration 1.   Find the intercepts
of the graph of $y = x^2 - 3x + 2$.

Solution: Setting $y = 0$, we find that the solutions of $x^2 - 3x + 2 = 0$ are
$x = 1$ and $x = 2$.   The x-intercepts are 1 and 2.   By setting $x = 0$ we find $y = 2$,
which is the y-intercept (Fig. 9.1).

(2) *Domain and Range.*   It is very useful to know the domain and
range of a relation, for this knowledge tells us about regions of the
plane to which the graph is confined or from which it is excluded.
It is useless to try to plot points in excluded regions.   There are two

common situations in which the domain or range is restricted to a subset of the whole axis.

The first of these is based upon the principle that y cannot take on values which require x to be complex and similarly that x cannot take on values which require y to be complex.

Illustration 2.   Discuss the domain and range of $x^2 + y^2 = 4$.
   Solution: First solve for x, and obtain

$$x = \sqrt{4 - y^2}$$

The right-hand side is real if and only if $4 - y^2 \geq 0$, or $4 \geq y^2$.   Hence y must lie in the interval $[-2,2]$.   Solving for y, we obtain $y = \sqrt{4 - x^2}$ and arrive at the similar conclusion that x is in the interval $[-2,2]$.

Illustration 3.   Discuss the domain and range of $y = x^2 - 3x + 2$.
   Solution: Since all values of x give real values of y, there is no restriction on x and the domain is the real line X.   To find any possible restrictions on the range, solve for x.   We have:

$$x^2 - 3x + (2 - y) = 0$$

which yields

$$x = \frac{3 \pm \sqrt{9 - 4(2 - y)}}{2}$$
$$= \tfrac{3}{2} \pm \tfrac{1}{2} \sqrt{1 + 4y}$$

Since x must be real, this requires that y satisfy the inequality $1 + 4y \geq 0$, or $y \geq -\frac{1}{4}$.   No part of the graph can therefore lie below the horizontal line $y = -\frac{1}{4}$ (Fig. 9.1).

The second principle is that expressions equal to a perfect square can never be negative.   The application of this may give us inequalities which x or y must satisfy.

Illustration 4.   Discuss the domain and range of $y^2 = (x - 1)(x + 3)$.
   Solution: Since $y^2 \geq 0$, we must have $(x - 1)(x + 3) \geq 0$.   This is a quadratic inequality of the type discussed in Sec. 8.4.   Using the methods developed there, we find that x cannot lie in the interval $]-3,1[$.
   Solving for x, we find,

$$x = -1 \pm \sqrt{4 + y^2}$$

Since $4 + y^2$ can never be negative, there are no restrictions on y (Fig. 9.2).

(3) *Symmetry.*   The points (x,y) and $(x,-y)$ are symmetric with respect to the X-axis, the one being the mirror image of the other. Either point is called a *reflection* of the other about the X-axis.   The graph will be symmetric about the X-axis if for every point (x,y) on

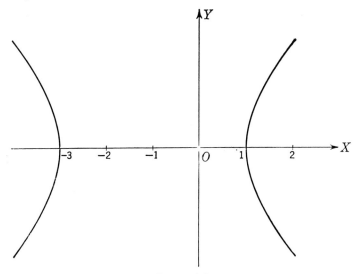

Figure 9.2

the graph the corresponding point $(x, -y)$ also lies on it. To test for symmetry, we therefore replace y in the equation of our relation by $-y$. If the resulting equation is the same as the given one, the graph is symmetric about the X-axis. In particular the graph is symmetric about the X-axis when y appears in the given equation to an *even* power only, for $y^{2k} = (-y)^{2k}$.

In a similar manner, a graph is symmetric about the Y-axis when replacement of x by $-x$ leaves the equation unchanged, e.g., when x occurs to an even power only.

Further, since a line joining (x, y) and $(-x, -y)$ passes through the origin and the distance from (x, y) to the origin is the same as the distance from $(-x, -y)$ to the origin, the graph will be symmetric about the origin if replacement of (x, y) with $(-x, -y)$ leaves the given equation unchanged.

Exercise A. Examine $|y| - x = 0$, $y - |x| = 0$, $|x| + |y| - 1 = 0$ for symmetry.

Exercise B. Show that if there is symmetry with respect to both axes there is, necessarily, symmetry with respect to the origin, but not conversely.

Illustration 5
  (a) The graph of $x^2 - x + y^4 - 2y^2 - 6 = 0$ is symmetric about the X-axis, but not about the Y-axis or the origin.
  (b) The graph of $x^2 - x^4 + y - 5 = 0$ is symmetric about the Y-axis, but not about the X-axis or the origin.

(c) The graph of $x^4 + 2x^2y^2 + y^4 - 10 = 0$ is symmetric about both axes and the origin.

(d) The graph of $xy = 1$ is symmetric about the origin, but not about either axis.

(4) *Asymptotes.* When we solve the given equation for x or y, we may get an expression which contains a variable in the denominator. For example, we may have

$$y = \frac{x}{x - 1}$$

We have seen before that we cannot substitute $x = 1$ on the right, for this would make the denominator zero. We can, however, let x take values nearer and nearer to 1 and see how the graph behaves. Construct the table of values:

x	1.1	1.01	1.001	1.0001
y	11	101	1,001	10,001

It is clear that, as x approaches 1 from the right, y is becoming very large in the positive direction. Similarly, as x approaches 1 from the left, y becomes very large in the negative direction (Fig. 9.3).* The line $x = 1$ is now called a *vertical asymptote.*

If we solve the above equation for x, we obtain

$$x = \frac{y}{y - 1}$$

The same argument can now be applied to show that $y = 1$ is a *horizontal asymptote.*

To find asymptotes, the procedure is as follows: Solve for y and x if possible. Values of x or y which make the corresponding denominator zero correspond to vertical or horizontal asymptotes. The behavior of the graph near an asymptote must be determined by examining points near it, as was done above.

There is a more general definition of asymptote which applies to lines in other directions, but we shall not give it here.

Illustration 6. Find the horizontal and vertical asymptotes, if any, of

$$y = \frac{x(x - 1)}{x + 2}$$

---

* The language here is very imprecise, but is the best that can be presented to you at this stage. Later (Chap. 15) we shall write $\lim_{x \to 1^+} \dfrac{x}{x - 1} = +\infty$ and $\lim_{x \to 1^-} \dfrac{x}{x - 1} = -\infty$ and will define these terms more precisely.

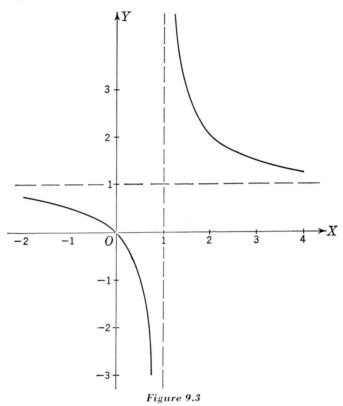

Figure 9.3

Solution: Since the denominator is zero for $x = -2$, there is a vertical asymptote at $x = -2$. Solving for x, we find:

$$x = \frac{1 + y \pm \sqrt{y^2 + 10y + 1}}{2}$$

Since y does not occur in the denominator, there are no horizontal asymptotes.

In the illustrations below we shall use these methods as needed to plot a number of graphs.

Illustration 7. Plot the graph of the function whose values are $y = 4x^2 - 3$.
Solution: To determine the x-intercepts, or the zeros of the function, we set $4x^2 - 3 = 0$ and compute $x = \pm \sqrt{3}/2$. The y-intercept is $y = -3$.
Since any x gives a real value of y, the domain is the entire X-axis. We solve for x to determine the range. We find that $x = \pm 2 \sqrt{y + 3}$. Therefore, the graph does not lie below the line $y = -3$. There is symmetry about the Y-axis.

We construct a short table of values:

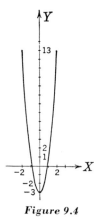

x	0	± 1	± 2
y	-3	1	13

The graph is plotted in Fig. 9.4.

Illustration 8. Plot the graph of the function whose values are

$$y = \frac{x}{(x-1)(x+2)}$$

Solution: The origin is both the x-intercept and the y-intercept. The domain is the entire X-axis with the exception of $x = 1$ and $x = -2$, where the function is not defined. In order to find the range, we solve for x and find:

Figure 9.4

$$x = \frac{1 - y \pm \sqrt{9y^2 - 2y + 1}}{2y}$$

Hence we must choose y so that $9y^2 - 2y + 1 \geq 0$. This is a quadratic inequality of the type discussed in Sec. 8.4. According to the method of this section we compute $b^2 - 4ac$, which equals -32. Hence by Theorem 8 of Sec. 8.4, the inequality is satisfied for all y, and there is no restriction on y. The appearance of y in the denominator suggests, however, that we must exclude $y = 0$. But when we put $x = 0$ in the original equation, we get $y = 0$; so it is not to be excluded from the range.

There is no symmetry, but we find a vertical asymptote at $x = 1$ and at $x = -2$ and a horizontal asymptote at $y = 0$. We construct the following table of values:

x	0	1	2	3	-1	-2	-3	-4	$\frac{1}{2}$	$\frac{3}{2}$	$-\frac{1}{2}$	$-\frac{3}{2}$	$-\frac{5}{2}$
y	0	—	$\frac{1}{2}$	$\frac{3}{10}$	$\frac{1}{2}$	—	$-\frac{3}{4}$	$-\frac{2}{5}$	$-\frac{2}{5}$	$\frac{6}{7}$	$\frac{2}{9}$	$\frac{6}{5}$	$-\frac{10}{7}$

The graph is plotted in Fig. 9.5.

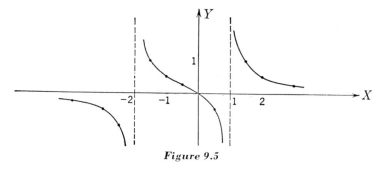

Figure 9.5

Illustration 9. Plot the graph of each of the functions defined by the equations (a) $y = \sqrt{x^3 - x^2}$ and (b) $y = -\sqrt{x^3 - x^2}$.

Solution: The domain of definition is restricted to those values of x for which $x^3 - x^2 \geq 0$. This requires that $x^2(x - 1) \geq 0$. This is satisfied if $x \geq 1$ or $x = 0$. The domain of each is therefore $1 \leq x < \infty$ and also $x = 0$. When $x = 0$, $y = 0$. The range of (a) is $0 \leq y < \infty$; the range of (b) is $-\infty < y \leq 0$. For the zeros, we set $x^3 - x^2 = 0$; that is, $x^2(x - 1) = 0$ or $x = 0,1$. Construct tables.

For $y = \sqrt{x^3 - x^2}$

x	0	1	2	3
y	0	0	2	$3\sqrt{2}$

For $y = -\sqrt{x^3 - x^2}$

x	0	1	2	3
y	0	0	-2	$-3\sqrt{2}$

Each graph has an isolated point $(0,0)$. Each graph is shown in Fig. 9.6.

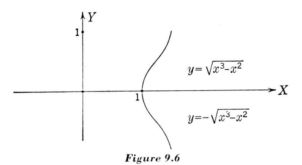

Figure 9.6

PROBLEMS 9.5

In Probs. 1 to 31 plot the graphs of the relations.

1. $y = 3x - 1$.

2. $y = 2 - x$.

3. $y = 6$.

4. $y = x^2 + 2$.

5. $y = x^2 - 1$.

6. $y = 4\sqrt{x}$.

7. $y = 1/x$.

8. $y = \sqrt{4 - x}$.

9. $y = 2 - x - x^2$.

10. $y = (x - 5)(1 - x)$.

11. $y = x^2 + x + 1$.

12. $y = -2x^2 + 3x + 4$.

13. $y = \sqrt{1 + x^2}$.

14. $y = -\sqrt{1 + x^2}$.

15. $y^2 = x(x^2 - 4)$.

16. $y^2 = x(x^2 - 9)$.

17. $x^2 + y^2 = x^3$.

18. $x^2 + y^2 = -x^3$.

19. $y^2 = x^3$.

20. $y^3 = x^2$.

21. $y = x^4$.

22. $x = -y^4$.

23. $x^4 + y^4 = 1$.

24. $y = \frac{3}{2}\sqrt{x}$.

25. $y = 2/\sqrt{x + 1}$.

26. $y = \dfrac{(x + 1)(x - 1)}{x - 1}$.

27. $y = 1/x^3$.

28. $y = x(x - 1)(x + 1)$.

29. $y = \dfrac{x - 1}{x(x + 1)}$.

30. $y = 2\sqrt{4 - x^2}$.

31. $y = -2\sqrt{4 - x^2}$.

32. Can the graph of a function be symmetric with respect to the Y-axis?
33. Can the graph of a function be symmetric with respect to the X-axis?

In Probs. 34 to 47 analyze and sketch the graphs of the relations.

34. $4x + 5y + 1 = 0.$
35. $4x - 5y + 1 = 0.$
36. $4x^2 + 4y^2 = 1.$
37. $x^2 + y^2 = 1.$
38. $x^2 - y^2 = 1.$
39. $x^2 - y^2 = 0.$
40. $x^2 - 4y^2 = 1.$
41. $4x^2 - y^2 = 1.$
42. $y^2 = 9x.$
43. $y^2 = 4x.$
44. $y^2 = (x - 1)(x + 2)(x + 3).$
45. $y = (x - 1)(x + 2)(x + 3).$
46. $y^2 = \dfrac{x(x - 2)}{x + 3}.$
47. $y = \dfrac{x(x - 2)}{x + 3}.$

9.6. Graphs (Continued)

When the given relation is defined by an inequality or in some other way, additional ideas may be needed in order to plot its graph. We have seen (Sec. 8.5) how to plot the graph of a linear inequality. The following illustration extends this idea to a quadratic inequality:

Illustration 1. Plot the graph of the relation defined by the inequality $x^2 - 4y < 0.$

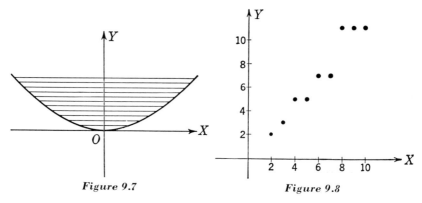

Figure 9.7   Figure 9.8

Solution: As in the case of linear inequalities, we first plot the graph of $x^2 - 4y = 0.$ This divides the plane into two regions, in one of which $x^2 - 4y > 0$ and in the other $x^2 - 4y < 0.$ To see which region we want, test a typical point, say $(0,1).$ At this point

$$x^2 - 4y = 0 - 4 < 0$$

Hence this lies in the desired region, and we shade the graph as shown.

When the relation is defined in a different way, we must use methods suitable to the case in hand.

Illustration 2. Plot the graph of the function f defined to be the set:

$$\{(x,y) \mid x \text{ is a positive integer} > 1, \text{ and } y \text{ is the least prime not less than } x\}$$

The domain is the set of positive integers > 1, and the range is the set of primes. The graph is a discrete set of points which must not be joined by a continuous curve (Fig. 9.8).

PROBLEMS 9.6

In Probs. 1 to 25 plot the graphs of the relations.

1. $x + y^2 = 0$.
2. $x + y^2 < 0$.
3. $x - y^2 = 0$.
4. $x - y^2 > 0$.
5. $x^2 + y^2 = 0$.
6. $x^2 - y^2 = 0$.
7. $x - y^4 \leq 0$.
8. $x + y^4 \geq 0$.
9. $y \geq x$.
10. $y + x > 0$.
11. $3x + 2y - 12 > 0$.
12. $3x + 2y - 12 < 0$.
13. $|y| = x$.
14. $|y| = |x|$.
15. $x^2 + y^2 < 1$.
16. $x^2 + y^2 \geq 1$.
17. $|x| + |y| = 1$.
18. $|x| + |y| \leq 1$.
19. $y = \begin{cases} 1 + x, \ x > 0. \\ x, \ x \leq 0. \end{cases}$
20. $y = \begin{cases} 2, \ x \text{ an integer.} \\ -1, \text{ otherwise.} \end{cases}$
21. $y = \begin{cases} 0, \ x \text{ an even integer.} \\ 1, \ x \text{ an odd integer} \\ \text{otherwise undefined.} \end{cases}$
22. $y = \begin{cases} 1, \ x \text{ rational.} \\ -1, \ x \text{ irrational.} \end{cases}$
23. $y = |x|$.
24. $y = x - |x|$.
25. $y = |x - 1|$.
26. Let $[x]$ stand for the greatest integer not exceeding x. Plot $y = [x]$.
27. The rate of postage on first-class letters is 4 cents per ounce or fraction thereof. This defines a function. Plot it.

9.7. *Inverse Functions*

A function $f:(x,y)$ is a set of ordered pairs such that no two of the ordered pairs have the same first element x. Several ordered pairs could have the same second element y, however. If a function f is of such character that no two pairs have the same second element, then there exists a function f^{-1} called the inverse function of f defined below.

Definition: Given the function f such that no two of its ordered pairs have the same second element, the *inverse function* f^{-1} is the set of ordered pairs obtained from f by interchanging in each ordered pair the first and second elements.

Thus the function f has elements (ordered pairs) of the form (a_1,b_1), (a_2,b_2), . . . , while the inverse function has elements (ordered pairs) of the form (b_1,a_1), (b_2,a_2), ... We may write $f:(a,b)$ and $f^{-1}:(b,a)$. The range of f is the domain of f^{-1}, and the domain of f is the range of f^{-1}.

In the usual notation for real numbers, there can be some confusion here. For it is customary to use the variable x as the independent variable and to use y as the dependent variable. Thus in f we should write $a = x$ and $b = y$, and in f^{-1} we should have $b = x$ and $a = y$. This means that when we pass from f to f^{-1} we must interchange the independent and dependent variables if we wish to follow the usual notation.

If f is given by a simple expression, we can often find f^{-1} by the following procedure: To find f^{-1} when f is defined by the equation $y = f(x)$, we first switch variables, getting $x = f(y)$, and then solve this for $y = f^{-1}(x)$. There are a number of difficulties with this procedure, which will be clarified by the following illustrations.

Illustration 1. Let f be defined by the equation $y = 3x + 1$ over the domain which is the set of real numbers from 0 to 1; otherwise, f is not defined. The range is the set of real numbers from 1 to 4 inclusive. Find the inverse function f^{-1}, its domain and range.

Solution: First we switch variables, getting

$$x = 3y + 1$$

Next we solve this equation for y, getting

$$y = \frac{x - 1}{3}$$

This last equation defines our inverse function f^{-1}: (x,y) [where f^{-1} is given by $y = (x - 1)/3$].

Note that ordered pairs such as $(0,1)$, $(\frac{1}{3},2)$, and $(1,4)$ belong to the set of elements constituting f, whereas f^{-1} contains the ordered pairs $(1,0)$, $(2,\frac{1}{3})$, and $(4,1)$. The domain of f is the set 0 to 1, and the range is the set 1 to 4. For f, we should write: The domain is $0 \le x \le 1$; the range is $1 \le y \le 4$. For f^{-1}, we should write: The domain is $1 \le x \le 4$; the range is $0 \le y \le 1$. We have switched domain and range as we should but have retained the more appropriate notations after the interchange. The graphs of f and f^{-1} are given in Fig. 9.9.

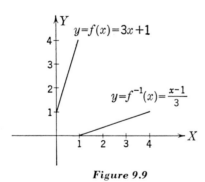

Figure 9.9

If f is defined by $y = 3x + 1$ over the (maximal) domain of the real numbers, then so is f^{-1} and the graphs become straight lines rather than line segments. We gave the illustration as we did in order to place emphasis on computing the domain and range of the inverse function.

Illustration 2. If f is defined by $y = \frac{1}{2}\sqrt{4 - x^2}$, find the inverse function f^{-1}, its domain and range. We suppose that the domain of f is given by $-2 \leq x \leq 0$; the range is, then, given by $0 \leq y \leq 1$.

Solution: First note that a function F is determined by $y = \frac{1}{2}\sqrt{4 - x^2}$ over the larger domain $-2 \leq x \leq 2$ but that then F has ordered pairs such as $(-2,0)$ and $(2,0)$. Hence F has no inverse F^{-1}.

We interchange variables in the equation $y = \frac{1}{2}\sqrt{4 - x^2}$; this yields

(1) $$x = \tfrac{1}{2}\sqrt{4 - y^2}$$

To solve (1) for y, we must square both sides; but here we must be careful, since the square of (1) is also the square of $x = -\frac{1}{2}\sqrt{4 - y^2}$, which is not our function. We have

$$x^2 = \tfrac{1}{4}(4 - y^2)$$

that is,

$$4x^2 = 4 - y^2$$

or

$$y^2 = 4 - 4x^2$$

Now, to obtain y, we must extract the square root of both sides, and this gives

(2) $$y = \pm 2\sqrt{1 - x^2}$$

This is not exactly what we want, since we cannot use both signs. Equation (2) does not define a function; it defines a relation. We look back and note that the domain of f was the set -2 to 0. All of these are negative (with the exception of 0). Since the range of f^{-1} must be given by $-2 \leq y \leq 0$, we must choose the negative sign in (2). Finally, therefore, the inverse function f^{-1} is given by

$$y = -2\sqrt{1 - x^2}$$

the domain of which is the set of reals defined by the inequality $0 \leq x \leq 1$. The graphs are given in Fig. 9.10.

This illustration emphasizes an important point which will come up later on: *If f does not have an inverse, we may be able to restrict its domain so that this restricted function does have an inverse* (see Sec. 13.9).

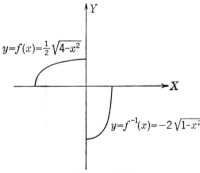

Figure 9.10

Exercise A. The function

$$y = x^2 (-\infty < x < \infty)$$

does not have an inverse. Find a domain for x such that the restricted function does have an inverse. How many such domains can you find?

Illustration 3. If f is defined by $y = 2^x$, find the inverse f^{-1}. The inverse certainly exists since no two choices of x give the same value of y. The graph of f is given in Fig. 9.11.

We switch variables in $y = 2^x$ and obtain $x = 2^y$. Now we wish to solve for y, but we have no method for doing so. In this case the inverse function f^{-1} has no simple formula like those in Illustrations 1 and 2. Still there exists a well-defined inverse, which is in fact a new function unnamed at present. If we have frequent occasion to refer to this function, we shall find it convenient to give it a name and to investigate its properties. This is indeed a common method of obtaining new functions from known functions. You may already know the name of f^{-1} when $f(x) = 2^x$. It is called the "logarithm of x to the base 2," written $\log_2 x$. We shall study this function in detail in Chap. 11.

This illustration emphasizes another point of importance: *If a function f has an inverse which cannot be calculated by elementary means, we shall often give this inverse a name and add it to our list of useful functions.*

Exercise B.   Give a definition of $\sqrt[3]{x}$ ($x > 0$) as the inverse of some function.
Exercise C.   If you have studied trigonometry, you can show that $y = \sin x$ ($-90° \leq x \leq +90°$) has an inverse. What is the name of this inverse?

In order to introduce a final important property of inverse functions, let us define the identity function whose domain and range are the same set X.

Definition: The function $E:(x,x)$, whose elements are the ordered pairs (x,x), is called the *identity function*. (See Fig. 9.12.)

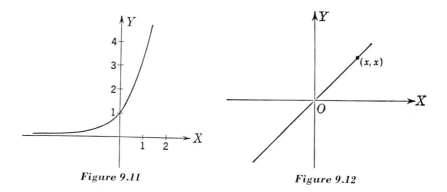

Figure 9.11   Figure 9.12

Now let us consider a function $f:(x,y)$ and its inverse $f^{-1}:(y,x)$. The composite function $f^{-1} \circ f$ sends each x into some y (under f) and then back into itself (under f^{-1}). We see then that

$$f^{-1} \circ f = E$$

and similarly

$$f \circ f^{-1} = E$$

PROBLEMS 9.7

In Probs. 1 to 12 discuss domain and range, and plot the graphs of f and f^{-1}, where f is defined by the following:

1. $y = 2x - 5$.
2. $y = 3x + 1$.
3. $y = ax$.
4. $y = ax + 1$.
5. $y = x$.
6. $y = -x$.
7. $y = x + k$.
8. $y = x - k$.
9. $y = f(x) = \sqrt{x^2 - 4}$; d_f is the set of real numbers $[2, \infty[$.
10. $y = f(x) = \sqrt{4 - x^2}$; d_f is the set of real numbers $[0,2]$.
11. $y = f(x) = -\frac{2}{3} \sqrt{9 - x^2}$; d_f is the set of real numbers $[-3,0]$.
12. $y = f(x) = -\frac{2}{3} \sqrt{x^2 - 9}$; d_f is the set of real numbers $[3, \infty[$.
13. Show that the graphs $y = f(x)$ and $y = f^{-1}(x)$ are symmetric with respect to the line $y = x$; that is, one is the mirror image of the other, the mirror being the line $y = x$.

9.8. *Functions Derived from Equations*

At first sight it may seem that any equation can be used to define a function by solving it for one of the variables. This process, however, often has a number of difficulties which are suggested by the illustrations below

Illustration 1. The equation $2x - 3y + 1 = 0$ is called a "linear equation" because the pairs (x,y) which satisfy it lie on a straight line (see Sec. 14.8). From this equation we can derive two functions:

$$y = f(x) = \frac{2x + 1}{3} \qquad x = g(y) = \frac{-1 + 3y}{2}$$

Exercise A. Show that $f^{-1} = g$.

Illustration 2. The equation $s = 16t^2$ gives the distance s in feet through which a body falls from rest under the influence of gravity in t sec. As such it defines a function. We may ask, however: "How long does it take for the body to fall 64 ft?" To answer this, we solve for t:

$$t^2 = \frac{s}{16} \qquad t = \pm \frac{1}{4} \sqrt{s}$$

This gives two functions defined by: $t = \frac{1}{4} \sqrt{s}$; $t = -\frac{1}{4} \sqrt{s}$. In terms of the physical situation only the first makes *practical* sense, but *both* make *mathematical* sense. Therefore we choose $t = \frac{1}{4} \sqrt{s}$, put $s = 64$, and find $t = 2$.

Exercise B. Are there any physical situations in which $t = -\frac{1}{4} \sqrt{s}$ makes *practical* sense?

This illustration makes the point that, although an equation may lead to several functions, not all of these necessarily have meaning in a practical situation.   You will have to use your head and discard those which are nonsense.

Illustration 3.   Consider the equation $x^2 + y^2 = 4$, which represents a circle of radius 2.   If we solve for y, we obtain $y = \pm \sqrt{4 - x^2}$.   Of the many functions which can be obtained from this, two have outstanding importance:

$$y = f(x) = \sqrt{4 - x^2} \qquad -2 \leq x \leq 2$$
$$y = g(x) = -\sqrt{4 - x^2} \qquad -2 \leq x \leq 2$$

The graph of f is the upper semicircle, and the graph of g is the lower semicircle.

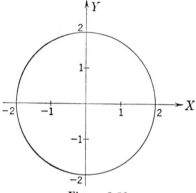

Figure 9.13

Exercise C.   Solve for x, and describe the graphs of the two functions so obtained.   Call these F and G.

Exercise D (BT).   Does F^{-1} equal f or g?

Illustration 4.   The equation

$$x^2 + xy + 4 = 0$$

is quadratic in x and thus has the solution

$$x = \frac{-y \pm \sqrt{y^2 - 16}}{2}$$

This yields two functions defined by:

$$x = f(y) = \frac{-y + \sqrt{y^2 - 16}}{2} \qquad |y| \geq 4$$

$$x = g(y) = \frac{-y - \sqrt{y^2 - 16}}{2} \qquad |y| \geq 4$$

When we solve for y, we obtain

$$y = -\frac{x^2 + 4}{x}$$

which gives the function h, where

$$y = h(x) = -\frac{x^2 + 4}{x} \qquad x \neq 0$$

Exercise E.   What is the domain of $f \circ h$?   Show that in this domain $f \circ h = E$.   Answer the same questions for $g \circ h$.

All these functions derived from equations have a common property: their elements (x,y) satisfy the equation.   This suggests the more general definition.

Definition: If the elements (x,y) of a function f satisfy an equation in x and y, the function f is said to be *derived* from this equation.

In many textbooks and older works a function thus derived from an equation is said to be given "implicitly" by the equation. The functions themselves are called "implicit functions."

In the examples given above the functions derived from an equation were obtained by solving for one of the variables. It is important to note that derived functions may exist even when we are unable to carry through such a solution. We shall sometimes wish to consider such functions, an example of which is given below.

Illustration 5. The equation $x^5y + xy^5 = 2$ has a graph given by Fig. 9.14.

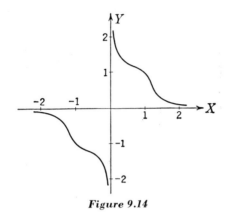

Figure 9.14

There is no simple way of solving this equation for x or y, but the graph indicates that functions $y = f(x)$ and $x = g(y)$ exist which are derived from this equation.

PROBLEMS 9.8

In Probs. 1 to 12 find functions derived from the given equation, and state their domain and range.

1. $3x - 4y = 3$.
2. $6x - 8y = 10$.
3. $2x^2 + y^2 = 1$.
4. $x^2 + 2y^2 = 1$.
5. $x^2y + y = 2$.
6. $x^2y - y = 1$.
7. $|x| + |y| = 1$.
8. $|x| - |y| = 1$.
9. $v^2 - 2gs = 0$, where v is the velocity of a body falling from rest, s is the distance fallen, and g is a given positive constant.
10. $x + y \geq 1$, $x \geq 0$, $y \geq 0$.
11. $2^x = 2^y$.
12. $x < y$.

REFERENCES

Johnson, R. E., and Fred L. Kiokemeister: "Calculus with Analytic Geometry," Allyn and Bacon, Boston (1957).

Menger, Karl: "Calculus—A Modern Approach," Ginn, Boston (1955).

Also consult the following paper in the *American Mathematical Monthly:*

Thielman, H. P.: On the Definition of Functions, vol. 60, p. 259 (1953).

CHAPTER TEN

Algebraic Functions

10.1. *Introduction*

The numerical functions that we have discussed thus far have been for the most part functions given by such expressions as

(I) $y = 2x^2 - 3x + 7$ (II) $y = \dfrac{x^2 - 3x}{x + 2}$ (III) $y = \sqrt{x^2 - 1}$

These are examples of explicit algebraic functions (to be defined later), and we devote this chapter to a study of their properties.

Let us return for the moment, however, to recall some properties of complex numbers. We know how to add, subtract, multiply, and divide (except by zero). These four operations are called the *rational operations* of arithmetic. When to these four we added the process of taking roots, we had what are called the *algebraic operations* of arithmetic.

We wish now to apply these algebraic operations to a *variable x* so as to produce what are commonly called algebraic functions. We shall consider the domain of x to be the set of complex numbers; and, likewise, any arbitrary constant involved shall be considered an element of this set unless otherwise stated.

10.2. *Polynomial Functions*

To generate the simplest type of algebraic function, we first restrict ourselves to the three operations of addition, subtraction, and multiplication. Since there is really no distinction here between addition and subtraction, we do not need to mention subtraction. With these three operations we build up such functions as those given by

(a) 2.   (b) $(3x - 5)(x + 6)$.

(c) $\sqrt{3}\, x^5 - \pi x^2 - 1$.   (d) $(2^{\frac{1}{3}}x - x^2)(x + 2)^3 + (7 - 3i)x - i$.

But we do not obtain such functions as those defined by

(e) $1/x - 3i$.   (f) $\sqrt{x}$.

(g) 2^x.   (h) $|x|$.

The functions illustrated by (a), (b), (c), and (d) are special cases of what are called polynomial functions according to the following definition.

Definition: A function P is called a *polynomial function* if it is given by

$$(1) \qquad y = P(x) = a_0 x^n + a_1 x^{n-1} + \cdots + a_{n-1}x + a_n$$

where n is a positive integer or zero and the coefficients $a_0, a_1, \ldots, a_n$ are complex numbers. Its domain is the set of complex numbers, and its range is some subset of the set of complex numbers.

     Exercise A. Show that (d) above can be written in the form (1).

We say that P is of *degree n*, provided that $a_0 \neq 0$. In the theory of polynomial functions it is customary to call the right-hand side of (1), namely, the expression

$$(2) \qquad a_0 x^n + a_1 x^{n-1} + \cdots + a_{n-1}x + a_n$$

a *polynomial*, which we designate by the symbol $P(x)$, read "polynomial in the variable x." $P(x)$ also stands for the value of P at x, but this should not lead to any confusion. Note that, since n may be zero, a constant is to be considered a polynomial (and a polynomial function).

We have stated that the domain of P is the set of complex numbers, and its range is some subset of the complex numbers. It is possible to discuss polynomial functions with other sets as domain and range and with other types of coefficients as well. For example, we may consider real polynomials in which x, y, and the a's are all real numbers. Or we may require that the a's be rational numbers or even integers and then let x and y be real or complex. All of these are special cases of the general definition given above. In discussing these special cases, we shall have to take great pains in stating the types of coefficients and variables which are under consideration.

Exercise B.   Prove that the sum of two polynomials is a polynomial.
Exercise C.   Prove that the product of the two polynomials $(ax^2 + bx + c)$ and $(Ax^2 + Bx + C)$ is a polynomial.   (As a matter of fact, the product of any two polynomials is a polynomial.)
Exercise D.   Show by an example that the quotient of two polynomials may be a polynomial.   Find another example in which the quotient is not a polynomial.
Exercise E.   Prove that the composite $g \circ f$ of the two polynomial functions given by $f(x) = ax^2 + bx + c$, $g(x) = Ax^2 + Bx + C$ is a polynomial function. (As a matter of fact, the composites of any two polynomial functions are polynomial functions.)

10.3.   *Rational Functions*

The next simplest type of algebraic function is a *rational function* which is so called because we now permit the use of division along with the other rational operations.

Definition: A function R defined by $y = R(x) = P(x)/Q(x)$, where $P(x)$ and $Q(x)$ are polynomials, is called a *rational function.*

The remarks made above about the domain and range of a polynomial function apply equally well to a rational function but here we must be a little careful: the function R is not defined at points where $Q(x) = 0$.   This is made clear by the following illustrations:

Illustration 1
   (a) $y = 1/x$ is not defined at $x = 0$.
   (b) $y = (x - 1)/(x + 2)$ is not defined at $x = -2$.
   (c) $y = 3x^3/(x - 1)(x^2 + 1)$ is not defined at either $x = 1$ or at $x = \pm i$.

Illustration 2
   (a) $y = x/x$ is not defined at $x = 0$.   For other values of x, however, $x/x = 1$. The two functions x/x and 1 are consequently not identical.   This illustration brings up an important point: the cancellation of a common factor in the numerator and denominator may change the function involved.
   (b) As a similar example, consider the two rational functions:

$$y = \frac{x(x - 1)}{x - 1} \qquad \text{and} \qquad y = x$$

These have the same values for $x \neq 1$, but at $x = 1$ the first is undefined, whereas the second has the value 1.   Hence they are different functions.

Illustration 3.   Some functions which are not written in the explicit form $y = P(x)/Q(x)$ are nevertheless equivalent to rational functions.   Consider

$$y = \left(\frac{1}{x} - \frac{4}{x+1}\right)\left(1 + \frac{1}{x-1}\right)$$

$$= \frac{x+1-4x}{x(x+1)} \cdot \frac{x-1+1}{x-1}$$

$$= \frac{(1-3x)(x)}{x(x+1)(x-1)}$$

$$= \frac{-3x^2+x}{x^3-x}$$

In this bit of algebra we did not cancel out the x in numerator and denominator. For the function

$$y = \frac{-3x+1}{x^2-1}$$

is not equivalent to the given function. Why?

In Exercises A to D below assume that the sum, product, and composites of two polynomials are each polynomials.

    Exercise A. Prove that the product of two rational functions is a rational function.
    Exercise B. Prove that the sum of two rational functions is a rational function.
    Exercise C. Prove that the quotient of two rational functions is a rational function.
    Exercise D. Prove that the composites of two rational functions are rational functions.

10.4. *Explicit Algebraic Functions*

Explicit algebraic functions constitute the next important class of functions. These include the polynomial and rational functions as special cases. They are generated by a finite number of the five algebraic operations, namely, addition, subtraction, multiplication, division, and root extraction. Thus the function whose values are given by

$$\frac{\sqrt{1+x} - \sqrt[3]{x^5}}{\sqrt[6]{(2+x-x^2)^3} - 8}$$

is an example of an explicit algebraic function. Because of the possible appearance of (even) roots in the equation defining such a function, it may happen that the value y of the function is real only when x is restricted to a very limited subset of the real numbers. For the example above, it is seen first of all that x (real) must be greater than or equal to -1 if $\sqrt{1+x}$ in the numerator is to be real. Similarly in $\sqrt[6]{(2+x-x^2)^3} - 8$ it must be true that $(2+x-x^2)^3 > 8$, that is, $2 + x - x^2 > 2$ or $x(1 - x) > 0$. This says that x must lie between 0 and 1 exclusive. The domain of definition is therefore $0 < x < 1$.

Of course if x and y are not required to be real, then the only values of x for which the above function is not defined are $x = 0$ and $x = 1$.

PROBLEMS 10.4

In Probs. 1 to 4 state which of the following define polynomial functions:

1. (a) $y = x^2 + 2^x$.   (b) $y = \dfrac{4}{x}$.   (c) $y = \sqrt{x}$.

2. (a) $y = 1 + x + \dfrac{1}{i}$ (b) $y = x - \sqrt{6}\,x^2 + \pi x^0$.   (c) $y = 2 - x + x^2 - 3x^3$.

3. (a) $y = 1 - \dfrac{x^2}{2!} + \dfrac{x^4}{4!}$ (b) $y = \dfrac{x + i}{2 - i}$ (c) $y = (x + 2)^{100}$.

4. (a) $f : \left(x,\ x + \dfrac{1}{x} \right)$.   (b) $g : (z, z^{-1})$.   (c) $h : (t,t)$.

In Probs. 5 to 8 state which of the following define rational functions:

5. (a) $y = \dfrac{1}{x}$ (b) $y = \sqrt{x}$.   (c) $y = |x|$.

6. (a) $y = x^2 + 2^x$.   (b) $y = \dfrac{x}{x - 1}$.   (c) $y = \dfrac{1 - 3x^2 + x}{x^4 - 2x^5 + 1}$.

7. (a) $y = 1$.   (b) $y = (-1)^x$.   (c) $y = x + x^2$.

8. (a) $y = \dfrac{x - 1}{\pi + i}$.   (b) $y = \dfrac{\sqrt{2x} + 1}{x - 1}$.   (c) $f : \left(x,\ \dfrac{x}{x^2} \right)$.

In Probs. 9 to 12 state which of the following define explicit algebraic functions:

9. (a) $y = \dfrac{1}{x}$ (b) $y = \sqrt{x}$.   (c) $y = 1 - \dfrac{x^2}{2!} + \dfrac{x^4}{4!}$.

10. (a) $y = 1 - \dfrac{x^2}{2!} + \dfrac{x^4}{4!} - \cdots + (-1)^{n-1} \dfrac{x^{2n-2}}{(2n - 2)!} + \cdots$

     (b) $y = |x| + x$.   (c) $y = \sqrt{1 + \sqrt{x}}$.

11. (a) $y = x^2 + 2^x$.   (b) $y = |x|^4$.   (c) $y = \begin{cases} 1, & x \text{ rational.} \\ -1, & x \text{ irrational.} \end{cases}$

12. (a) $f : (x,1)$.   (b) $g : (\theta, 3^\theta)$.   (c) $h : (u, |u^2|)$.

In Probs. 13 to 18 state kind of function and domain (we assume x, y, etc., real and n a positive integer).

13. (a) $y = 1 - \sqrt{3}\,x + x^{17}$.   (b) $y = 1 - \sqrt{3x} + x^{17}$.

     (c) $y = \dfrac{1 - \sqrt{3}\,x}{x^{17}}$.

14. (a) $y = \sqrt[3]{x}$.   (b) $y = \sqrt{x - 1} - \sqrt{x - 1}$.   (c) $y = \sqrt{x - x^2}$.

15. (a) $y = \sqrt{x^2 - 1}$.   (b) $y = \dfrac{\sqrt{1 - x^2}}{\sqrt{x^2 - 1}}$.   (c) $y = \dfrac{x}{x(x + 1)}$.

16. (a) $y = \dfrac{\sqrt{x} - \sqrt{x}}{\sqrt{x}}.$ (b) $y = 1 + \dfrac{1}{1 + \dfrac{1}{1 + x}}.$ (c) $y = \left(\dfrac{1}{1/x}\right)^n.$

17. (a) $f:(v, -3).$ (b) $g:\left(y, \left(y - \dfrac{1}{y}\right)^n\right).$ (c) $\phi:(\theta, \sqrt{-\theta}).$

18. (a) $r:(s, \sqrt{1 - s^2}).$ (b) $A:(r, \pi r^2).$ (c) $v:(r, \frac{4}{3}\pi r^3).$

10.5. *Graphs and Continuity*

We have already considered methods of plotting the graphs of functions and relations, or, what amounts to the same thing, of plotting the graph of an equation (Chap. 9). We must still rely upon intuition when we speak about the *continuity* of a function or about a *continuous graph*, but we wish at this time to make some pertinent remarks on the continuity of an algebraic function. For this discussion we restrict ourselves to the field of real numbers, since we plot only the real elements of a function. An element (x,y) is real when and only when x and y are both real. We shall refer indifferently to a continuous function or a continuous graph, the latter being merely descriptive geometric language.

(i) *Polynomial Functions.* A polynomial function, defined by $y = P(x)$, where $P(x)$ is a polynomial, is continuous everywhere. The graph of a polynomial function is a continuous curve. The domain of definition is the set of real numbers; the range is a subset of the real numbers (which could be the whole set). As an example, see Illustration 7, Sec. 9.5.

Definition: The *zeros* of P are the values of x for which $P(x) = 0.$

Illustration 1. Sketch the graph of the polynomial function given by $y = x^4 - 2x^2.$

Solution: For purposes of graphing we now consider the domain as the set of real numbers. Since

$$x^4 - 2x^2 \equiv x^2(x^2 - 2)$$

the zeros are seen to be $x = 0, 0, \pm\sqrt{2}.$ (For the factor x^2, we write $x = 0,0$; see Theorem 4, and following remark, Sec. 10.6.)

The graph is continuous everywhere. It is symmetric with respect to the Y-axis since x appears to even powers only. Some values of the function defined by this equation are given in the following table.

x	-2	$-\sqrt{2}$	-1	0	1	$\sqrt{2}$	2
y	8	0	-1	0	-1	0	8

The graph is shown in Fig. 10.1. The least value of y occurs when $x = \pm 1$, although we cannot prove this. (See Sec. 16.7 where maxima and minima are treated by methods of the calculus.) The range is $-1 \leq y < \infty$.

(ii) *Rational Functions.* A rational function, defined by

$$y = \frac{P(x)}{Q(x)}$$

where $P(x)$ and $Q(x)$ are polynomials, is continuous everywhere with the exception of at most a finite number of isolated values of x, namely, those for which $Q(x) = 0$. These values must be excluded from the domain. The range is a subset of the reals. The graph of a rational function is a continuous curve with the exception of at most a finite number of points. A point of discontinuity is a point x_1 such that $Q(x_1) = 0$. At such a point the function is undefined, as in $(x - 5)/(x - 5)$ at $x = 5$ or as in $1/x$ at $x = 0$.

Illustration 2. Sketch the graph of the rational function defined by $y = f(x) = (x + 2)/(x - 1)^3$.

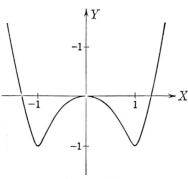

Figure 10.1

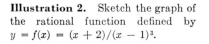

Figure 10.2

Solution: The domain is the set of real numbers excluding $x = 1$. The following intuitive argument will tell us something about the range: If x is just a little larger than 1, y is positive and very large; if x is a very large number, y is positive and very small. For $x > 1$, the range is, therefore, the set of positive real numbers. There is no value of y for $x = 1$. The only discontinuity occurs at $x = 1$. Further, at $x = -2$, $y = 0$ and $x = -2$ is the only zero of the function. If x is negative and a little larger than -2, y is negative and in absolute value very small; if x is positive and a little less than 1, y is negative and very large in absolute value. Therefore, for $-2 \leq x < 1$, y ranges over all nonpositive real numbers. Hence the range is the set of real numbers.

We compute the following table of values.

x	-4	-3.5	-3	-2	-1	0	$\frac{1}{2}$	1	1.5	2	3	11
y	$\dfrac{1}{62.5}$	$\dfrac{1}{60.75}$	$\dfrac{1}{64}$	0	$-\dfrac{1}{8}$	-2	-20	—	28	4	$\dfrac{5}{8}$	$\dfrac{13}{1,000}$

We have included the value of y at $x = -3.5$ because it is the largest value of y for $x < 1$. (Methods of the calculus are needed to prove this.) The graph is plotted in Fig. 10.2.

(iii) *Explicit Algebraic Functions.* Explicit algebraic functions as defined include the rational functions as special cases. An explicit algebraic function may have, therefore, the same type of discontinuities as does a rational function. In addition it may have isolated points as indicated in the examples of Illustration 9, Sec. 9.5. It may also have end-point discontinuities as indicated in Illustration 3 below. The domain and range are subsets of the reals.

Illustration 3. Sketch the graph of the explicit algebraic function defined by

$$y = \sqrt{x^2 - 1}$$

Since y must be real, we must have $x^2 - 1 \geq 0$, or $x^2 \geq 1$. Hence the domain of the function is $-\infty < x \leq -1$; $1 \leq x < +\infty$. The range is $0 \leq y < \infty$. The graph is symmetric with respect to the Y-axis, since substitution of $-x$ for x in $\sqrt{x^2 - 1}$ does not change this expression. Thus we compute a table of values.

x	± 1	± 2	± 3	± 4
y	0	1.73	2.83	3.87

The graph is shown in Fig. 10.3. It is discontinuous at $x = \pm 1$.

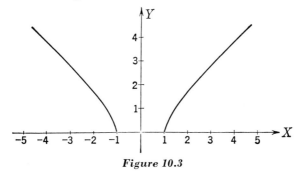

Figure 10.3

It is interesting to compare Fig. 10.3 with the graph of $y = x^2 - 1$ (Fig. 10.4) plotted from the table of values.

x	0	± 1	± 2	± 3
y	-1	0	3	8

The ordinates of Fig. 10.3 are the square roots of those of Fig. 10.4 except in the interval $-1 < x < 1$ in which these square roots become imaginary. In cases like this considerable information about graphs such as Fig. 10.3 can be obtained by first plotting the related graph such as Fig. 10.4.

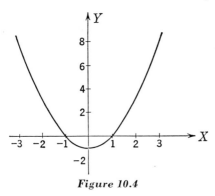

Figure 10.4

Illustration 4. Sketch the graph of

$$y = \frac{x}{\sqrt{x - 1}}$$

Since $\sqrt{x - 1}$ must be real and nonzero, we must have $x > 1$. The domain is therefore $1 < x < +\infty$, and $x = 0$. At $x = 1$ there is a vertical asymptote. The value of y diminishes as x increases; but later, as x gets very large, y increases again. (By the methods of Sec. 16.7 it can be shown that, for $x > 1$, y is least when $x = 2$.)

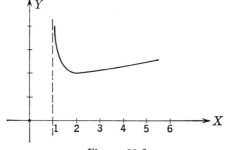

Figure 10.5

We plot the table of values.

x	0	1	1.5	2	3	4	5
y	0	...	2.12	2	2.12	2.31	2.5

The graph is shown in Fig. 10.5. The point $(0,0)$ is an isolated point, and the graph is discontinuous at $x = 1$.

PROBLEMS 10.5

In Probs. 1 to 21 discuss type of algebraic function, domain, range (if possible), zeros, and points of discontinuity. Sketch.

1. $y = x^3 - x$.

2. $y = x^3 - 4x$.

3. $y = \sqrt{x^3 - x}$.

4. $y = \sqrt{x^3 - 4x}$.

5. $y = x^2 - x^4$.

6. $y = x^4 - x^2$.

7. $y = \sqrt{x^2 - x^4}$.

8. $y = \sqrt{x^4 - x^2}$.

9. $y = x^3 + 1$.

10. $y = 8 - x^3$.

11. $y = \sqrt{x^3 + 1}$.   **12.** $y = \sqrt{8 - x^3}$.

13. $y = \sqrt[3]{x^3 + 1}$.   **14.** $y = 1/(x^2 + 1)$.

15. $y = (1 - x^{\frac{1}{2}})^2$ [portion of a parabola].

16. $y = 3x^4 - x^3 + 2$ [minimum value occurs at $x = \frac{1}{4}$ and is $\frac{511}{256}$].

17. $y = 8/(4 + x^2)$ [the Witch of Agnesi].

18. $y = \sqrt{(1 - x^{\frac{2}{3}})^3}$ [portion of a hypocycloid].

19. $y = \sqrt{x^3/(2 - x)}$ [portion of the cissoid of Diocles].

20. $y = \sqrt{x(x - 1)(x + 3)}$.

21. $y = -\sqrt{x(x - 1)(x + 3)}$.

In Probs. 22 to 27 sketch the graph of each equation, and discuss.

22. $x^{\frac{1}{2}} + y^{\frac{1}{2}} = 1$ (see Prob. 15).

23. $x^{\frac{2}{3}} + y^{\frac{2}{3}} = 1$ (see Prob. 18).

24. $(2 - x)y^2 - x^3 = 0$ (see Prob. 19).

25. $y^2 - 4x^2 = 0$.

26. $y^2 - x^3 + x^2 = 0$.

27. $(x + y)(xy + 1) = 0$.

28. Sketch the graph of the function defined jointly by $y = 4/(x^2 - 3x)$ and the condition $y > 1$.

29. Discuss the graph of $y = x^n$, n an even integer; again for n odd.

10.6. *Properties of Polynomials*

We have defined a polynomial as an expression of the form

$$P(x) = a_0x^n + a_1x^{n-1} + \cdots + a_{n-1}x + a_n$$

We now wish to discuss some of the more important properties of polynomials and polynomial functions.

Definitions: A polynomial with complex coefficients we shall call a *complex* polynomial. A polynomial with real coefficients we shall call a *real* polynomial. A polynomial with rational coefficients we shall call a *rational* polynomial. The domain of definition in any case is the set of complex numbers. Associated with every polynomial $P(x)$ is the polynomial function P defined by $y = P(x)$, whose zeros are also called the *roots* of the polynomial equation $P(x) = 0$. A polynomial equation is called complex, real, or rational according as the coefficients are complex, real, or rational, respectively.

We have previously referred to the following theorem:

Theorem 1. The Fundamental Theorem of Algebra. Every complex polynomial equation $P(x) = 0$ of degree ≥ 1 has at least one root.

The proof of this theorem is beyond the scope of this text.

We pause here to tell you of a remarkable theorem first proved by the Norwegian mathematician Abel (1802–1829). The nature of the problem is easily described. You know that the general equations of the first and second degree

$$ax + b = 0 \qquad a \neq 0$$
$$ax^2 + bx + c = 0 \qquad a \neq 0$$

can be solved explicitly for x, giving, respectively,

$$x = -\frac{b}{a}$$

and
$$x = \frac{-b \pm \sqrt{b^2 - 4ac}}{2a}$$

So can the general equations of the third and fourth degree, namely,

$$ax^3 + bx^2 + cx + d = 0 \qquad a \neq 0$$
and
$$ax^4 + bx^3 + cx^2 + dx + e = 0 \qquad a \neq 0$$

be solved explicitly for x, using only a finite number of the algebraic operations. Abel proved that it is impossible to solve the general fifth-degree equation, using only a finite number of these operations. The proof is difficult. It is now known that no general equation of degree greater than four can be solved algebraically, i.e., by a finite number of the algebraic operations.

We seek properties of the roots of polynomial equations. First, we derive Theorem 2.

Theorem 2. Remainder Theorem. If a complex polynomial $P(x)$ is divided by $x - b$ (where b is a complex number) until a remainder R free of x is obtained, then $P(b) = R$.

Proof: Let us divide $P(x)$ by $x - b$ until we obtain a remainder not containing x. In accordance with the Division Algorithm (Sec. 3.5), this division may be written

(3) $$P(x) = (x - b)Q(x) + R$$

where $Q(x)$ is a complex polynomial of degree $n - 1$ called the quotient and R is a complex number.

Since Eq. (3) is true for all complex values of x, we may substitute b for x and obtain

$$P(b) = 0 + R \qquad \text{or} \qquad P(b) = R$$

Illustration 1. Let $P(x) = x^3 + 2x^2 - 3$. Find $P(2)$ by the remainder theorem. By division, we have

$$\frac{x^3 + 2x^2 - 3}{x - 2} = x^2 + 4x + 8 + \frac{13}{x - 2}$$

Hence $R = 13$ and $P(2) = 13$. This can be checked by noting that

$$P(2) = 8 + 8 - 3 = 13$$

Theorem 3. Factor Theorem. If r is a root of a complex polynomial equation $P(x) = 0$, then $x - r$ is a factor of $P(x)$.

Proof: The statement "r is a root of $P(x) = 0$" is equivalent to the statement "$P(r) = 0$." Divide $P(x)$ by $x - r$ as in Eq. (3). By the Remainder Theorem, $R = P(r) = 0$. Hence $x - r$ is a factor of $P(x)$.

Exercise A. Prove the converse of the Factor Theorem: If $(x - r)$ is a factor of $P(x)$, then r is a root of $P(x) = 0$.

Illustration 2. We may use the Factor Theorem to find a polynomial equation with given roots. Suppose we are given $r_1 = 1$, $r_2 = -2$, $r_3 = 0$ and are asked to find an equation with these roots. From the Factor Theorem $x - 1$, $x + 2$, and x are factors. Hence an equation with the desired property is

$$(x - 1)(x + 2)x = x^3 + x^2 - 2x = 0$$

Illustration 3. We use the converse of the Factor Theorem to help us solve polynomial equations which we can factor. Consider the problem: Solve

$$(x + 2)(x - 1)(x^2 + x + 1) = 0$$

Solution: Since $x + 2$ and $x - 1$ are factors, we know that two roots are $r_1 = -2$, $r_2 = 1$. The other roots are solutions of

$$x^2 + x + 1 = 0$$

or
$$x = \frac{-1 \pm i\sqrt{3}}{2}$$

Theorem 4. Number-of-roots Theorem. A complex polynomial equation $P(x) = 0$ of degree n $(n \geq 1)$ has exactly n roots.

It is possible, of course, for two or more of these roots to be equal. If k roots are all equal to r, say, the common language used is "r is said to be a root of multiplicity k." For Theorem 4 to be true, it is necessary to count a root of multiplicity k as k roots.

Proof: We have one root r_1 of $P(x) = 0$ from the Fundamental Theorem of Algebra. Therefore, from the Factor Theorem,

$$P(x) = (x - r_1)Q(x)$$

where $Q(x)$ is a polynomial of degree $n - 1$. Unless $Q(x)$ is a constant, the equation $Q(x) = 0$ also has a root r_2; thus $Q(x) = (x - r_2)S(x)$, where $S(x)$ is a polynomial of degree $n - 2$. Thus

$$P(x) = (x - r_1)(x - r_2)S(x)$$

Continue this process as long as possible. It must stop when n factors have been obtained; for the product of more factors would have a degree higher than n. Hence we have

$$P(x) = (x - r_1)(x - r_2) \cdots (x - r_n)a_0$$

This theorem tells us how many roots to look for. If we have an equation of fifth degree and have found three roots, we still have two more to find.

PROBLEMS 10.6

In Probs. 1 to 10 find a polynomial equation of lowest degree which has the given roots:

1. $1, -1$.

2. $0, 1, 2$.

3. $2 + i$.

4. $2 + i, 2 - i$.

5. $1, 2, 3, 4$.

6. $1, 2, 1 + i, 1 - i$.

7. $0, i, -1$.

8. $1, -\dfrac{1}{2} + \dfrac{i\sqrt{3}}{2}, -\dfrac{1}{2} - \dfrac{i\sqrt{3}}{2}$.

9. $1, 1, 1$.

10. i, i, i.

In Probs. 11 to 18 find a polynomial of third degree which has the following zeros:

11. $1, -1, 0$.

12. $i, -i, 0$.

13. $-2, \sqrt{2}, -\sqrt{2}$.

14. $1, 2 + 3i, 2 - 3i$.

15. $0, a + ib, a - ib$.

16. 2 and two other zeros.

17. $2, 2$, and one other zero.

18. (BT) $2, 2, 2, 2$.

In Probs. 19 to 23 use the Remainder Theorem to find:

19. $P(1)$ when $P(x) = x^2 - x + 3$.

20. $P(-2)$ when $P(x) = 2x^2 + 3x - 4$.

21. $P(0)$ when $P(x) = 3x^3 + x^2 - 5$.

22. $P(i)$ when $P(x) = x^2 + 1$.

23. $P(2)$ when $P(x) = 3x^4 - x^2 + 15$.

In Probs. 24 to 27 by using the converse of the Factor Theorem find all the roots of:

24. $x^3 - 8 = 0$.

25. $x^4 - 1 = 0$.

26. $x^4 + 2x^2 + 1 = 0$.

27. $x^5 + x^3 + x = 0$.

28. How many roots does the equation $x^3 - 1 = 0$ have? Hence, how many numbers are cube roots of 1? Find them.

29. How many roots does $x^2 + 3x^4 - x + 5 = 0$ have?

30. How many roots does $x^5 - x^2 + 1 = 0$ have?

31. How many zeros does the polynomial $(3 + i)x^2 - (2 - i)x^3 + (6 - 4i)$ have?

32. How many zeros does the polynomial $x(x - r_1)(x - r_2)(x - r_3) \cdots (x - r_k)$ have?

33. Show that a polynomial equation of degree n cannot have more than $n/2$ double roots. (A double root is a root of multiplicity 2.)

34.* As a consequence of Theorem 4 show that, if

$$P(x) = a_0 x^n + a_1 x^{n-1} + \cdots + a_{n-1} x + a_n = 0$$

has $n + 1$ roots, then each coefficient a_i is zero.

35.* Prove that $P(x) = 0$ and $Q(x) = 0$ have all their roots equal if and only if there is some constant c such that, for all x, $P(x) - cQ(x) = 0$.

10.7. *Synthetic Division*

The Remainder Theorem gives us a convenient short cut for finding the value $P(b)$, say, for it tells us that $P(b) = R$ and R is easy to compute. To perform the division called for in the Remainder Theorem, we use a short method, called synthetic division. To illustrate the method, we consider the case of the general cubic (complex) polynomial

$$P(x) = a_0 x^3 + a_1 x^2 + a_2 x + a_3$$

which is to be divided by $x - b$. The work is exhibited in all detail below, where R is the remainder.

$$
\begin{array}{l}
x - b \,\big|\, a_0 x^3 + a_1 x^2 + a_2 x + a_3 \,\big|\, a_0 x^2 + (a_0 b + a_1)x + (a_0 b^2 + a_1 b + a_2) \\
\quad\; \underline{a_0 x^3 - a_0 b x^2} \\
\qquad\quad (a_0 b + a_1)x^2 + a_2 x \\
\qquad\quad \underline{(a_0 b + a_1)x^2 - (a_0 b^2 + a_1 b)x} \\
\qquad\qquad\qquad (a_0 b^2 + a_1 b + a_2)x + a_3 \\
\qquad\qquad\qquad \underline{(a_0 b^2 + a_1 b + a_2)x - (a_0 b^3 + a_1 b^2 + a_2 b)} \\
\qquad\qquad\qquad\qquad\qquad a_0 b^3 + a_1 b^2 + a_2 b + a_3 = R
\end{array}
$$

But, surely, we have written down more detail than we actually need; the following, where we have suppressed every x, is quite clear:

$$
\begin{array}{l}
-b \,\big|\, a_0 + a_1 + a_2 + a_3 \,\big|\, a_0 + (a_0 b + a_1) + (a_0 b^2 + a_1 b + a_2) \\
\quad\; \underline{-\, a_0 b} \\
\qquad (a_0 b + a_1) + a_2 \\
\qquad \underline{-\, (a_0 b^2 + a_1 b)} \\
\qquad\qquad (a_0 b^2 + a_1 b + a_2) + a_3 \\
\qquad\qquad \underline{-\, (a_0 b^3 + a_1 b^2 + a_2 b)} \\
\qquad\qquad\qquad a_0 b^3 + a_1 b^2 + a_2 b + a_3 = R
\end{array}
$$

We have also omitted the second writing of a_0, $a_0 b + a_1$, and $a_0 b^2 + a_1 b + a_2$ inasmuch as they are going to cancel by subtraction anyway. We will further simplify the process by changing the sign of $-b$ to $+b$ in the divisor, and hence the subtractive process to an additive one. Also there is no need of writing the quotient Q in the little box to the right since every term there is to be found in the work below, which is finally written on just three lines:

$$b \mid a_0 \quad a_1 \qquad\qquad a_2 \qquad\qquad\qquad a_3$$
$$\underline{ a_0b \qquad a_0b^2 + a_1b \qquad\quad a_0b^3 + a_1b^2 + a_2b}$$
$$a_0 \quad a_0b + a_1 \quad a_0b^2 + a_1b + a_2 \quad a_0b^3 + a_1b^2 + a_2b + a_3 = R$$

Although we have skeletonized the work, the details can still be extracted: We are dividing $a_0x^3 + a_1x^2 + a_2x + a_3$ by $x - b$, and we get a quotient of $a_0x^2 + (a_0b + a_1)x + (a_0b^2 + a_1b + a_2)$ and a remainder of $a_0b^3 + a_1b^2 + a_2b + a_3$. Note that the remainder is $P(b)$ as it should be by the Remainder Theorem.

Illustration 1. Divide $x^4 - 3x^3 + x + 3$ by $x - 2$ synthetically.
   Solution: Form the array, noting that the coefficient of x^2 is zero. (We normally place the "2" associated with the divisor $x - 2$ on the right.)

$$
\begin{array}{rrrrr|r}
1 & -3 & 0 & 1 & 3 & 2 \\
  & 2 & -2 & -4 & -6 & \\
\hline
1 & -1 & -2 & -3 & -3 = R
\end{array}
$$

The quotient $Q(x) = x^3 - x^2 - 2x - 3$, and the remainder $R = -3$. By direct computation we also find that $P(2) = -3$.

Illustration 2. Given $P(x) = 3x^4 - 4x^3 - 2x^2 + 1$, compute $P(-1)$, $P(0)$, $P(1)$, $P(2)$, $P(3)$, $P(-0.3)$, and sketch $y = P(x)$.
   Solution: Directly from $P(x)$ we compute $P(0) = 1, P(1) = -2,$ and $P(-1) = 6$. In the slightly more complicated cases of $P(2), P(3),$ and $P(-0.3)$ we use synthetic division:

$$
\begin{array}{rrrrr|r}
3 & -4 & -2 & 0 & 1 & 2 \\
  & 6 & 4 & 4 & 8 & \\
\hline
3 & 2 & 2 & 4 & 9 = P(2) \\
3 & -4 & -2 & 0 & 1 & 3 \\
  & 9 & 15 & 39 & 117 & \\
\hline
3 & 5 & 13 & 39 & 118 = P(3) \\
3 & -4 & -2 & 0 & 1 & -0.3 \\
  & -0.9 & 1.47 & 0.159 & -0.0477 & \\
\hline
3 & -4.9 & -0.53 & 0.159 & 0.9523 = P(-0.3)
\end{array}
$$

The preceding table is self-explanatory. Note especially the value $P(-0.3) = 0.9523$ and the corresponding dip in the graph (Fig. 10.6). This kind of variation cannot be discovered in general without the methods of the calculus (Chap. 16).

Exercise A. Compute $P(-1)$ by synthetic division, and note the alternating signs in the last line of your work. Explain why this tells us there are no real zeros of P to the left of $x = -1$. Generalize for the case where $P(x)$ is a real polynomial.

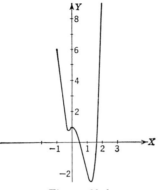

Figure 10.6

Exercise B. Examine the line where $P(2) = 9$, and state what follows about real zeros of P to the right of $x = 2$. Generalize for the case where $P(x)$ is a real polynomial.

PROBLEMS 10.7

In Probs. 1 to 6 use synthetic division to find:

1. $P(2)$ and $P(-2)$, if $P(x) = 2x^3 - x + 5$.

2. $P(-1)$ and $P(3)$, if $P(x) = x^3 + x^2 - 5$.

3. $P(1)$ and $P(2)$, if $P(x) = 3x^4 - x^3 + x^2 + x - 1$.

4. $P(1)$ and $P(2)$, if $P(x) = 2x^4 + x^3 - x^2 + 2x$.

5. $P(\frac{1}{2})$ and $P(\frac{1}{4})$, if $P(x) = 3x^2 - x + 4$.

6. $P(\frac{1}{2})$ and $P(\frac{1}{3})$, if $P(x) = 4x^2 - 3x + 2$.

In Probs. 7 to 16 use synthetic division to find quotient and remainder.

7. $(3x^3 + 2x^2 + x - 1)/(x - 3)$.   **8.** $(3x^3 + 2x^2 + x - 1)/(x + 3)$.

9. $(x^4 - x^3 - 2x + 3)/(x + 2)$.   **10.** $(x^4 - x^3 - 2x + 3)/(x - 2)$.

11. $(x^5 + 3x^3 - 1)/(x - 1)$.   **12.** $(2x^5 + 3x^3 - 4)/(x + 1)$.

13. $(x^3 - 2x^2 + x + 1)/(x - \frac{1}{2})$.   **14.** $(3x^3 + 2x^2 + x + 1)/(x + \frac{1}{2})$.

15. $(x^2 - 3x + 7)/(x - \frac{1}{3})$.   **16.** $(2x^2 - \frac{1}{2}x - 3)/(x + \frac{2}{3})$.

In Probs. 17 to 22 use synthetic division to show that the first polynomial is a factor of the second.

17. $x - 3,\ 2x^3 - 9x^2 + 14x - 15$.   **18.** $x - 2,\ x^3 - 5x^2 - 3x + 18$.

19. $x + 2,\ x^4 + 5x^3 + 5x^2 - 3x - 2$.   **20.** $x - 1,\ x^4 - 2x^2 + 1$.

21. $x - \frac{1}{2},\ 2x^3 + 3x^2 - 8x + 3$.   **22.** $x - \frac{1}{3},\ 3x^3 + 8x^2 - 21x + 6$.

23. Divide $ax^2 + bx + c$ by $x - r$ by long division and also by synthetic division. Compare the results.

24. Divide $ax^2 + bx + c$ by $x + r$ by long division and also by synthetic division. Compare the results.

25. For what value of k does $x^2 + kx + 2$ yield the same remainder when divided by either $x - 1$ or $x + 1$?

26. For what values of k is $x^2 + 2x + k$ exactly divisible by $x - k$?

27. If the polynomial $P(x) = x^5 + Ax^3 + Ax + 4$ is such that $P(2) = 6$, find $P(-2)$.

28. If the polynomial $P(x) = kx^3 - x + 4$ is such that $P(1) = 9$, find $P(2)$.

29. When $x^2 + x - 3$ is divided by $x - r$, the remainder is -1.   Find r.

30. When $2x^2 - x - 3$ is divided by $x + r$, the remainder is 9.   Find r.

31. Use the factor theorem to prove that $x^n - a^n$ is divisible by $x - a$ when n is a positive integer.

32. Use the factor theorem to prove that $x^n + a^n$ is divisible by $x + a$ when n is an odd positive integer.

10.8. *Roots of Polynomial Equations*

Because of its practical importance, much effort has been spent on the question of how to calculate the roots of a polynomial equation. We have mentioned that formulas for the roots exist for $n = 1, 2, 3,$ and 4; but there is no simple method of handling equations of higher degree.   The general procedure consists of two steps:

(I) Find all roots which can be obtained by elementary means; then use the factor theorem or other methods to factor the polynomial into polynomials of lower degree.

(II) Find the zeros of the factors by known formulas or by approximate methods.

When the coefficients of $P(x)$ are general complex numbers, there is little that can be said here which will help you in these steps, for the known methods are too complicated to be treated in this book.   We can make progress, however, if we consider only polynomials whose coefficients are real numbers.   In this case we can prove the theorem:

Theorem 5.   A real polynomial $P(x)$, with real coefficients, can always be represented as a product of factors each of which is either of the form $ax + b$ or $cx^2 + dx + e$, where $a, b, c, d,$ and e are real numbers.

Proof: We know that the roots of $P(x) = 0$ are complex numbers, but some of them may actually be real.   Corresponding to each real root r, the Factor Theorem tells us that there is a factor $(x - r)$. Therefore we can write

$$P(x) = (x - r_1)(x - r_2) \cdots (x - r_s)Q(x) = 0$$

where $r_1, r_2, \ldots, r_s$ are its real roots and $Q(x)$ is a polynomial of degree $n - s$ which has no real zeros.   We must show that $Q(x)$ can be factored into quadratic factors of the form $cx^2 + dx + e$.

Suppose that $\alpha + i\beta$ with $\beta \neq 0$ is a root of $Q(x) = 0$.   Construct the quadratic polynomial:

$$(x - \alpha - i\beta)(x - \alpha + i\beta) = (x - \alpha)^2 + \beta^2 = S(x)$$

Note that $S(\alpha + i\beta) = 0$ and $S(\alpha - i\beta) = 0$.   Now divide $Q(x)$ by

$S(x)$, and obtain

$$Q(x) = S(x) \cdot R(x) + px + q$$

Substitute $x = \alpha + i\beta$ into this equation. Since $Q(\alpha + i\beta) = 0$ and $S(\alpha + i\beta) = 0$, we get

$$p(\alpha + i\beta) + q = 0$$

or
$$p\alpha + q = 0 \qquad p\beta = 0$$

Since $\beta \neq 0$, this shows that $p = 0$ and $q = 0$. Therefore $S(x)$ is a factor of $Q(x)$ and hence of $P(x)$. The same process can now be applied to $R(x)$, and we continue until we get

$$P(x) = (x - r_1) \cdot \cdot \cdot (x - r_s)S_1(x) \cdot \cdot \cdot S_t(x)a_0$$

where $s + 2t = n$. This is of the required form.

Corollary. If $\alpha + i\beta$ is a root of a real polynomial equation, then $\alpha - i\beta$ is also a root of this equation.

Exercise A. Construct an example which shows this corollary false when the coefficients of $P(x)$ are no longer real.

Exercise B. Show that the degree of $Q(x)$ must be even.

This theorem tells us a lot about the nature of the roots of $P(x) = 0$, but it does not help us to find them. Special methods for finding the roots of certain simple types of equations are given in the next two sections.

PROBLEMS 10.8

Solve the following equations by factoring:

1. $2x^2 - 7x + 5 = 0$.
2. $2x^2 + 13x - 7 = 0$.
3. $2x^3 + 13x^2 + 6x = 0$.
4. $3x^3 - 17x^2 - 6x = 0$.
5. $(3x + 1)^2 - 7(3x + 1) + 12 = 0$.
6. $(2x - 1)^2 + 3(2x - 1) - 10 = 0$.
7. $x^4 - 1 = 0$.
8. $(x - 1)^4 - 1 = 0$.
9. $1/x^2 - 1 = 0$.
10. $1/(x + 3)^2 = 4$.
11. $x^3 - 2x^2 - 5x + 6 = 0$.
12. $2x^3 + x^2 - 5x + 2 = 0$.

Solve the following equations:

13. $x^3 + x = 0$.
14. $y^3 + y^2 = 0$.
15. $1/x^2 - x^2 = 0$.
16. $1/x^2 + 1/x = 6$.

17. $t^4 - 3t^3 + 2t^2 = 0$.
18. $\dfrac{1}{t^4} - \dfrac{3}{t^3} + \dfrac{2}{t^2} = 0$.

19. $z^5 - z^3 = 0$.
20. $w^5 + w^3 - 2w = 0$.
21. $(x^2 - 2x - 8)^2 + 13(x^2 - 2x - 8) + 40 = 0$.
22. $(x^2 + x - 3)^2 - (x^2 + x - 3) - 6 = 0$.

10.9. *Rational Roots of Rational Polynomial Equations*

We now restrict ourselves to rational polynomial equations, i.e., to polynomial equations of the form $P(x) = 0$, where the coefficients in $P(x)$ are rational numbers.

Exercise A. Show that a rational polynomial can be written in the form $A \cdot P(x)$, where A is a rational number and where $P(x)$ has integer coefficients. Hence show that a given rational polynomial equation has the same roots as a certain polynomial equation in which the coefficients are integers. [Multiplying both sides of an equation by a constant ($\neq 0$) does not change the roots.]

There is a simple method in this case for obtaining quickly all those roots of $P(x) = 0$ which happen to be rational numbers. Of course, there is no necessity that any of these roots be rational; therefore this method may not produce any of the roots at all since it exhibits only the rational roots.

Theorem 6.   Rational-root Theorem.   If

$$P(x) = a_0 x^n + a_1 x^{n-1} + \cdots + a_{n-1} x + a_n$$

has integers for coefficients, and if $r = p/q$ is a rational root (in lowest terms) of $P(x) = 0$, then p is a factor of a_n and q is a factor of a_0.

Proof: We are given that

$$a_0 \frac{p^n}{q^n} + a_1 \frac{p^{n-1}}{q^{n-1}} + \cdots + a_{n-1} \frac{p}{q} + a_n = 0$$

Multiply through by q^n; the result is

(4) $$a_0 p^n + a_1 p^{n-1} q + \cdots + a_{n-1} p q^{n-1} + a_n q^n = 0$$

This may be written

$$p(a_0 p^{n-1} + a_1 p^{n-2} q + \cdots + a_{n-1} q^{n-1}) = -a_n q^n$$

Now p is a factor of the left-hand side of this equation and therefore p is a factor of the right-hand side, $-a_n q^n$. Since p/q is in lowest terms, p and q^n are relatively prime; and since p is a factor of $a_n q^n$, it follows (from Theorem 5, Chap. 2) that p *is a factor of* a_n.

Equation (4) can also be written

$$a_0 p^n = -q(a_1 p^{n-1} + \cdots + a_{n-1} p q^{n-2} + a_n q^{n-1})$$

By a similar argument q *is a factor of* a_0.

Illustration 1.   Solve the equation $2x^4 + 5x^3 - x^2 + 5x - 3 = 0$.

Solution: The possible rational roots are ± 1, ± 3, $\pm\frac{1}{2}$, $\pm\frac{3}{2}$. Using synthetic division, we find that -3 is a root, for

$$
\begin{array}{rrrrr|r}
2 & 5 & -1 & 5 & -3 & -3 \\
 & -6 & 3 & -6 & 3 & \\
\hline
2 & -1 & 2 & -1 & 0 &
\end{array}
$$

Therefore

$$2x^4 + 5x^3 - x^2 + 5x - 3 = (x + 3)(2x^3 - x^2 + 2x - 1)$$

The remaining roots of the given equation are thus roots of the "reduced" equation

$$2x^3 - x^2 + 2x - 1 = 0.$$

Its possible rational roots are ± 1, $\pm\frac{1}{2}$. Using synthetic division, we find that $\frac{1}{2}$ is a root, for

$$
\begin{array}{rrrr|r}
2 & -1 & 2 & -1 & \frac{1}{2} \\
 & 1 & 0 & 1 & \\
\hline
2 & 0 & 2 & 0 &
\end{array}
$$

The new reduced equation is

$$2x^2 + 2 = 0 \quad\text{or}\quad x^2 + 1 = 0$$

This is solved by the usual methods for quadratic equations and yields $x = \pm i$.

The roots of the original equation are therefore $\frac{1}{2}$, -3, i, $-i$. In this case each real root is a rational number.

PROBLEMS 10.9

In the following equations find the rational roots, and, where possible, solve completely.

1. $x^3 - 2x^2 - 2x + 3 = 0.$ 2. $4x^3 + 3x^2 - 9x + 2 = 0.$
3. $2x^3 + 5x^2 - 4x - 3 = 0.$ 4. $2x^3 - 3x^2 - 3x + 2 = 0.$
5. $x^4 + 2x^3 + 4x^2 + 3x + 2 = 0.$ 6. $x^4 - 5x^3 - 3x^2 + 17x - 10 = 0.$
7. $x^4 - x^3 - 27x^2 + 25x + 50 = 0.$ 8. $x^4 - 9x^3 + 30x^2 - 44x + 24 = 0.$
9. $3x^4 + 2x^3 + 2x^2 - x = 0.$ 10. $4x^3 + 17x^2 - 55x + 30 = 0.$
11. $x^3 + x^2 + x + 1 = 0.$
12. $x^2 - 2 = 0.$ How does this prove that $\sqrt{2}$ is irrational?
13. $x^2 - 3 = 0.$ How does this prove that $\sqrt{3}$ is irrational?
14. $x^2 - 5 = 0.$ How does this prove that $\sqrt{5}$ is irrational?

10.10. *Real Roots of Real Polynomial Equations*

In Sec. 10.9 we discussed the general method of obtaining the roots of rational polynomial equations when those roots are rational numbers. There is no simple general way in which a root can be determined exactly when it is not rational and when the degree of the polynomial exceeds 4. Indeed, about the only method available to us is an approximation method which is best described as a graphical one.

This method will yield those roots of $P(x) = 0$ which are real but gives no information concerning other roots.   The method applies equally to other types of equations as well, provided that the graphs of these equations are continuous.

A real root of $f(x) = 0$ or a zero of $f:(x,y)$ corresponds to a value of x at which the graph of $y = f(x)$ crosses or touches the X-axis.   Hence the procedure is to construct an accurate graph from which the zeros may be read off (approximately).

Most graphs will only be accurate enough to locate the desired zero between successive integers, and a refined technique is needed to obtain more decimal places.   To be definite, suppose that we have located a single root between 2 and 3, so that $f(2)$ and $f(3)$ have opposite signs.   We may calculate $f(2)$, $f(2.1)$, $f(2.2)$, . . . , $f(2.9)$, $f(3)$ in turn and thus locate the root between the adjacent pair of these which have opposite signs.   Since this process is tedious, we try to speed it up graphically by a procedure which suggests which of these tenths to try first.

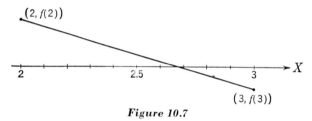

Figure 10.7

Suppose the situation is as in Fig. 10.7.   Draw a straight line between the points $(2,f(2))$ and $(3,f(3))$, and observe where this crosses the axis.   Now try tenths in the neighborhood of this crossing.   When the root is located between successive tenths, the process may be repeated for hundredths, etc., as far as desired.   Usually, however, the graphic method is abandoned after the tenths have been obtained, and refined numerical techniques (beyond the scope of this book) are employed.

We should say a final word about the use of a straight line with which to approximate a (continuous) curve.   Our remarks must necessarily be somewhat vague since we have not presented the mathematical background necessary to a full understanding of the problem. (A thorough knowledge of Chaps. 15 and 16 is a necessary condition for such an understanding.)   Consider a continuous curve in a very small interval from $x = a$ to $x = b$, say.   It can be proved that if $|b - a|$ is sufficiently small, then $|f(b) - f(a)|$ is small.   In effect this says that a small portion of a decently behaving graph is somewhat

like a straight line.   This is the basis on which (linear) interpolation
is made in various tables (such as a table of logarithms).

Illustration 1.   Find the real zeros of the function defined by

$$y = x^3 - 2x^2 + x - 3$$

Solution: We find the table of values

x	-1	1	0	2	3
$f(x)$	-7	-3	-3	-1	9

and plot the graph as in Fig. 10.8.   We see that there is a zero between 2 and 3.
We cannot prove it with our present knowledge, but this is the only real zero of

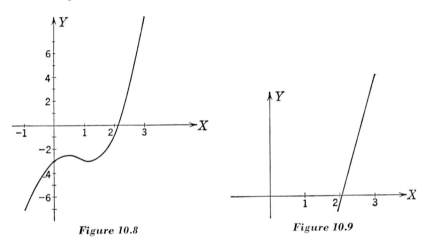

Figure 10.8   *Figure 10.9*

this function.   We plot Fig. 10.9.   The line crosses the axis at exactly **2.1**; therefore we calculate the following table.

x	2.0	2.1	2.2
$f(x)$	-1	-0.459	$+0.168$

Thus the zero is between 2.1 and 2.2.

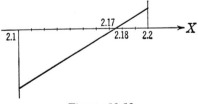

Figure 10.10

To obtain the next decimal place, we plot Fig. 10.10. The line crosses the axis between 2.17 and 2.18; therefore we calculate the following table.

x	2.17	2.18
$f(x)$	-0.03	0.04

Hence the zero is 2.17 $+$.

Repeated, this process will determine the decimal expansion of the root in question. But note that to obtain the best approximation to, say, two decimal places we should compute the expansion to three places and then round off to two places.

PROBLEMS 10.10

Find the first two decimal places (and round to one decimal place) of the numerically smallest real zero of the function defined as follows:

1. $y = x^3 - x^2 + 5x + 5$.
2. $y = x^3 - 4x^2 + 2x + 2$.
3. $y = 4x^3 + 13x + 6$.
4. $y = x^3 - 4x^2 + x + 1$.
5. $y = x^4 + 2x^3 + x^2 - 1$.
6. $y = x^4 + x^3 - 2x^2 + x - 3$.
7. $y = x^2 - 2$; check by solving.
8. $y = x^3 - 2$; check by solving.
9. $y = -x^3 - x + 6$.
10. $y = x^3 + x + 6$.
11. $y = (x - 3.14)(x + 2.57)(x + 2.61)$.
12. $y = (x - 3.13)(x - \pi)(x + 3.12)$.
13. $y = (x^2 + 1)(x^3 - x - 1)$.
14. $y = (x^2 + x + 1)^2(x - 1)^3$.
15. $y = \dfrac{1}{x^3} - \dfrac{5}{x} + 8$.
16. $y = \dfrac{1}{x^3} + \dfrac{1}{x} - 3$.

CHAPTER ELEVEN

Exponential and
Logarithmic Functions

11.1. *Exponential Functions*

In your earlier studies you have become acquainted with powers such as 2^3, $(-3)^4$, π^5, and the like. You have also met

$$7^{-2} = \frac{1}{7^2} \qquad 4^0 = 1 \qquad \pi^{-3} = \frac{1}{\pi^3}$$

The general expression for symbols like these is a^n, where a is any real number and n is an integer. You will also recall the use of fractional exponents to represent roots, such as,

$$3^{\frac{1}{2}} = \sqrt{3} \qquad 5^{\frac{1}{3}} = \sqrt[3]{5} \qquad 2^{-\frac{1}{7}} = \frac{1}{\sqrt[7]{2}}$$

Although we have discussed (Chap. 5) the question of the roots of real numbers, at this stage we wish to consider roots of positive real numbers only, and indeed we consider only the *positive, real* roots of such numbers. The general symbol for such a root will be $a^{1/n}$, where a is positive and n is an integer.

Also we recall that $a^{p/q}$ is defined to be $(a^{1/q})^p = (a^p)^{1/q}$, where p and q are integers and a is positive. Hence we know the meaning of the function defined by

$$y = a^x \qquad a \text{ positive, } x \text{ rational}$$

We should like to extend the domain of definition of this function to the entire set of real numbers and thus give sense to numbers such as 2^π, $\pi^{-\sqrt{3}}$, and $4^{\sin 1}$. A complete discussion of this matter is not feasible here, for it would require a study of the real numbers in more detail than we have treated them in Chap. 2. We shall content ourselves with the remarks that this extension is possible and that the value of a number like those above can be obtained to any desired approximation by choosing an expansion of each irrational to a sufficient number of decimal places. Thus

$$2^\pi \approx 2^{3.1416} = 9.437 \qquad 3^{\sqrt{2}} \approx 3^{1.414} = 4.728$$

where the symbol $\approx$ means "approximately equal to."

In summary we define a new function as follows.

Definition: The function f defined by $y = a^x$ $(a > 0)$ is called the *exponential function* with base a. Its domain of definition is the set of real numbers. We observe that its range of values is $0 < y < \infty$.

We now wish to develop some of its properties.

Theorem 1.   For $a > 0$ and $b > 0$ and x and y real:
(a) $a^x \times a^y = a^{x+y}$.
(b) $(a^x)^y = a^{xy}$.
(c) $(ab)^x = a^x \times b^x$.
These theorems are proved in Chap. 5 for rational values of x. We do not give the proof for irrational values of x.

Theorem 2
(a) $a^x > 1$ for $a > 1$, x real and > 0.
(b) $a^x = 1$ for $a = 1$, x real and > 0.
(c) $a^x < 1$ for $0 < a < 1$, x real and > 0.
Proof: Part (a) is immediate when x is a positive integer; for the product of two numbers each of which is greater than 1 must itself exceed 1. When $x = 1/n$ (n a positive integer), part (a) also is true. For if $a^{1/n}$ were to be less than 1 in this case, its nth power $(a^{1/n})^n = a$ would be less than 1. This follows from the fact that the product of two numbers each between zero and one must itself be less than 1. Finally, part (a) is true for rational x by combining the above cases. We omit the proof for irrational values of x. Part (b) is immediate

since all powers and roots of 1 are themselves 1. Part (c) is proved similarly to part (a).

Exercise A. Write out the details of the proof of part (c) for rational x.

Theorem 3. Let x and y be real numbers such that $x < y$. Then
 (a) $a^x < a^y$ for $a > 1$.
 (b) $a^x = a^y$ for $a = 1$.
 (c) $a^x > a^y$ for $0 < a < 1$.
The proof depends on Theorem 2. In all cases we know from Theorem 1 that $a^y = a^{y-x} \cdot a^x$. By hypothesis $y - x$ is positive. Thus, if $a > 1$, $a^{y-x} > 1$ and $a^y > a^x$, and similarly for the other cases.

Exercise B. Complete the proof of Theorem 3.

When $a > 1$, Theorem 3 shows that the graph of the function rises as x increases. Such a function is called monotone increasing. A typical graph for $a > 1$ is given in Fig. 11.1.

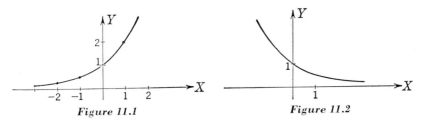

Figure 11.1   Figure 11.2

When $0 < a < 1$, Theorem 3 shows that the graph of the function falls as x increases. Such a function is called monotone decreasing. A typical graph for $0 < a < 1$ is given in Fig. 11.2.

There is an interesting symmetry between the graphs of $y = a^x$ and $y = (1/a)^x$. For $(1/a)^x = a^{-x}$, and the graph of $y = a^{-x}$ is just like the graph of $y = a^x$ with the X-axis reversed in direction.

Exercise C. Draw the graph of $y = 1^x$.

We state without proof that the exponential functions are continuous for all values of x.

For reference later, we also state the general definitions of monotone functions.

Definitions: A function such that $f(a) < f(b)$ for $a < b$ is called *strictly monotone increasing*. A function such that $f(a) > f(b)$ for $a < b$ is called *strictly monotone decreasing*.

PROBLEMS 11.1

1. Show that $a^x \times a^y$ defines an exponential function.
2. Show that $a^x \div a^y$ defines an exponential function.

In Probs. 3 to 13, simplify.

3. $10^{-1}5^2$.
4. $10^{-2}5^2$.
5. $1/10^3 3^{-6}$.
6. $4^{-3}/2^{-7}$.
7. $2^8 4^{-6} (\sqrt{2})^5$.
8. $3^3 9 (27)^{-\frac{1}{3}}$.
9. $9^{-3} 9^{-\frac{3}{2}}$.
10. $\sqrt{2\sqrt{64}}$.
11. $5(16)^{\frac{3}{4}}$.
12. $\sqrt[3]{8/\sqrt{50}}$.
13. $\sqrt{(1.23)10^6}$.

In Probs. 14 to 20 simplify, but leave the answer in exponential form.

14. $a^{4x} \cdot a^{-3x}/a^x$.
15. $a^x \cdot a^{2x} \cdot a^{-3x}$.
16. $c^y \cdot c^{-3y} \cdot d^y$.
17. $b^{-\frac{1}{2}x} \cdot b^{4x} \cdot a^{\frac{2}{3}x}$.
18. $\sqrt{10}\sqrt[3]{10}\sqrt[4]{10}/10$.
19. $10^2 \cdot 10^{\frac{1}{2}} \cdot 10^{-\frac{1}{3}} \cdot 10^{-6} \cdot 10^x \cdot 10^{\frac{1}{2}x}$.
20. $(BT)3^x + 3^{2x}$.

In Probs. 21 to 24 plot on the same axes and to the same scales:

21. $y = 3x$.
22. $y = (\frac{3}{2})^x$.
23. $y = (\frac{1}{3})^x$.
24. $y = (\frac{2}{3})^x$.
25. Plot the graph of $y = 3^x$. Now change the scale on the Y-axis so that the graph you have drawn is that of $y = 2 \cdot 3^x$.
26. Plot the graph of $y = 4 \cdot 1^x$.
27. Prove: If f strictly is monotone, then f has an inverse f^{-1}.

State the converse; show by a counterexample that the converse is false.   HINT: Let f be discontinuous.

11.2. *The Number e*

We have defined the function $f:(x,y)$ whose values are given by $y = a^x$. Now there is a particular number $a > 1$ of great importance in mathematics; it is an irrational number and approximately equal to 2.71828. It bears the name e; thus

$$e \approx 2.71828$$

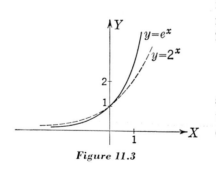

Figure 11.3

It is impossible for us to explain at this time why the number e and the associated exponential function defined by

$$y = e^x$$

are of such importance.

This exponential function is in fact so important that we speak of it as *the* exponential function and neglect to mention its base. Sometimes this function is written

$$y = \exp x$$

where no base appears at all; the base is assumed to be e unless otherwise specified. Its values are tabulated in many convenient tables ("Standard Mathematical Tables," pages 179 to 185). Its graph is plotted in Fig. 11.3. *153 to 159*

PROBLEMS 11.2

In Probs. 1 to 10 obtain from a table

1. $e^{1.2}$.

2. $e^{4.15}$.

3. $e^{6.01}$.

4. $e^{9.00}$.

5. e^{-3}.

6. $e^{-3.25}$.

7. $2e^{-2}$.

8. $-3e^{-5.35}$.

9. $e^{\sqrt{2}}$ (approximate).

10. $e^{\sqrt{3}}$ (approximate).

In Probs. 11 to 18 plot the graph.

11. $y = \frac{1}{3}e^{3x}$.

12. $y = 2e^{-\frac{1}{2}x}$.

13. $y = 5e^{-3x}$.

14. $y = \frac{1}{2}e^{-2x}$.

15. $y = -10e^{\frac{1}{2}x}$.

16. $y = -3e^{\frac{1}{5}x}$.

17. $y = 50e^{-1.2x}$.

18. $y = \frac{1}{10}e^{3x}$.

19. Plot the graph of $y = (e^x + e^{-x})/2$.

20. Plot the graph of $y = (e^x - e^{-x})/2$.

11.3. *Logarithmic Functions*

Since $y = a^x$ defines a strictly monotone function, for $a \neq 1$, each value of y is obtained from a single x. Therefore the inverse function exists, and this is called the logarithmic function.

Definition: The function inverse to that given by $y = a^x$, $a > 0$, $a \neq 1$ is written $y = \log_a x$ and is called the *logarithm* of x to the base a.

For computational purposes, the base is usually taken to be 10 so that properties of our decimal system may be used to simplify the needed tables. For theoretical purposes, the base is always taken to be e. In advanced books, this base is omitted, and $\log x$ is to be understood to mean $\log_e x$. Frequently the notation $\ln x$ is used for $\log_e x$. Logarithms to the base 10 are called "common" logarithms; those to the base e are called "natural" logarithms. Tables of both kinds are available in most collections of elementary tables. ("Standard Mathematical Tables," pages 24 to 45 and 171 to 178.)

Exercise A. Prove that $\log_a a^x = x$ and that $a^{\log_a x} = x$.

The graph of $y = \log_a x$ is obtained from that of $y = a^x$ by reflecting it in the line $y = x$. It is given in Figs. 11.4 and 11.5.

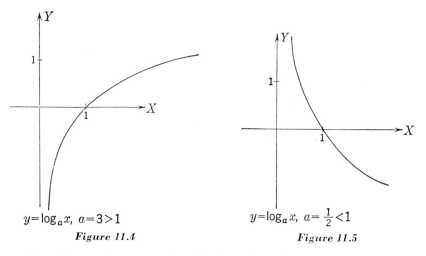

$y = \log_a x,\ a = 3 > 1$

Figure 11.4

$y = \log_a x,\ a = \frac{1}{2} < 1$

Figure 11.5

From the graphs we see that the domain and range are as follows.

Domain and *Range*.   The domain of definition of $\log_a x$ is the set of positive real numbers. Its range of values is the set of all real numbers.

Note that the logarithms of negative numbers are not defined here. In advanced books you will learn how to extend the definition of $\log_a x$ so that x can be negative. Its value turns out to be complex in this case. We do not consider this case.

Properties.   The logarithmic function defined by $y = \log_a x$ is strictly monotone increasing for $a > 1$, strictly monotone decreasing for $0 < a < 1$, and not defined for $a = 1$. It is continuous for all values of x for which it is defined. The following theorems have useful applications.

Theorem 4. $\log_a xy = \log_a x + \log_a y$.

  Proof:

  Let $z = \log_a xy$, then $a^z = xy$.

  Let $u = \log_a x$, then $a^u = x$.

  Let $v = \log_a y$, then $a^v = y$.

Therefore, $a^z = xy = a^u \cdot a^v = a^{u+v}$

or

$$z = u + v$$

from which the theorem follows.

Theorem 5. $\log_a \dfrac{1}{x} = -\log_a x.$

Proof.   Let $z = \log_a \dfrac{1}{x}$; then $a^z = \dfrac{1}{x}$, and $a^{-z} = x$.   Therefore, $-z = \log_a x.$ Hence the theorem follows.

Theorem 6. $\log_a \dfrac{y}{x} = \log_a y - \log_a x.$

Proof: Combine Theorems 4 and 5.

Theorem 7. $\log_a (x^y) = y \log_a x.$
  Proof:
  Let $z = \log_a (x^y)$; then $a^z = x^y$.
  Let $u = \log_a x$; then $a^u = x$.

Therefore $(a^u)^y = a^z$ or $uy = z$

from which the theorem follows.

Exercise B.   Prove $\log_b a = \dfrac{1}{\log_a b}.$

Exercise C.   Prove $\log_a x = \dfrac{\log_b x}{\log_b a}.$ A special case of this is $\log_a x = \dfrac{\log_e x}{\log_e a}.$

Theorems 4, 5, and 6 are useful for numerical computations involving only products and quotients.   Logarithms to the base 10 are generally employed.

Illustration 1.   Find $\dfrac{(33.0)(27.2)}{15.8}.$

Solution: We compute

$$\log_{10} \frac{(33.0)(27.2)}{15.8} = \log_{10} 33.0 + \log_{10} 27.2 - \log_{10} 15.8$$

To find these logarithms, we consult a table of common logarithms.   Since instructions for the use of these tables are usually printed with the tables, we refer to these instructions and do not repeat this material here.
  We find

$$
\begin{aligned}
\log_{10} 33.0 &= & 1.51851 \\
\log_{10} 27.2 &= & 1.43457 \\
\hline
 & & 2.95308 \\
-\log_{10} 15.8 &= & -1.19866 \\
\hline
\log_{10} \frac{(33.0)(27.2)}{15.8} &= & 1.75442
\end{aligned}
$$

Working backward from the table, we obtain

$$\frac{(33.0)(27.2)}{15.8} = 56.81$$

The importance of logarithms in problems of this sort is not as great as it was in former years. Calculations such as that above can be performed more rapidly on a slide rule, provided that the numbers involved do not contain more than three essential digits. When the numbers are more complicated, or when greater accuracy is desired, rapid results can be obtained from a desk computing machine. For this reason most students do not need to develop great skill in this use of logarithms.

On the other hand, logarithms must be used to compute exponentials such as $2^{1.42}$ by the use of Theorem 7.

Illustration 2. Compute $2^{1.42}$.
Solution: From Theorem 7,

$$\log_{10} 2^{1.42} = 1.42 \log_{10} 2$$
$$= (1.42)(0.30103)$$
$$= 0.42746$$
Therefore
$$2^{1.42} = 2.6758$$

PROBLEMS 11.3

In Probs. 1 to 6 compute, using common logarithms:

1. $5^{3.2}$.   2. $7^{1.5}$.
3. $e^{0.4}$.   4. $e^{1.25}$.
5. $10^{6.1}$.   6. $10(10)^{1.4}$.

In Probs. 7 to 12 compute, using natural logarithms:

7. $5^{3.2}$.   8. $7^{1.5}$.
9. $e^{0.4}$.   10. $e^{1.25}$.
11. $10^{6.1}$.   12. $10(10)^{1.4}$.

HINT: Tables of natural logarithms are complete. No "characteristic" needs to be supplied.

In Probs. 13 to 18 evaluate or simplify:

13. $2^{\log_2 2}$.   14. $3^{\log_3 9}$.
15. $9^{\log_9 3}$.   16. $5^{\log_{125} 5}$.
17. $16^{\log_{64} 8}$.   18. $e^{\log_e x}$.
19. Show that $x^x = a^{x \log_a x}$, $x > 0$.
20. Show that $[f(x)]^{g(x)} = a^{g(x) \log_a f(x)}$, $f(x) > 0$.
21. Write the function f defined by $y = a^x b^x$ as an exponential function with base a.
22. Pick out the pairs of inverse functions, and state domain and range: 5^{6x}, 6^{5x}, 2^{-x}, $5 \log_6 x$, $6 + \log_5 x$, $\log_6 (5x)$, $\frac{1}{6} \log_5 x$, $\log_2 (-x)$, $-\log_2 x$.
23. Compute $(1 + \tfrac{1}{10})^{10}$, $(1 + \tfrac{1}{100})^{100}$, and $\left(1 + \dfrac{1}{1,000}\right)^{1,000}$ by common logarithms. Compare with the value of e.

11.4. *Graphs*

With a set of the standard mathematical tables at our disposal, we can now make light work of graphing various exponential, logarithmic, and related functions.

Illustration 1. Plot the graph of the function given by $y = xe^{-x}$.

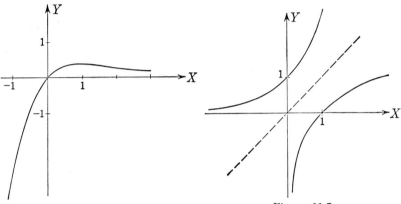

Figure 11.6   *Figure 11.7*

Solution: Again we prepare a table of x's and corresponding values of y and sketch the graph in Fig. 11.6.

x	-3	-2	-1	0	1	2	3
e^{-x}	20.09	7.39	2.72	1	0.37	0.14	0.05
$y = xe^{-x}$	-60.27	-14.78	-2.72	0	0.37	0.28	0.15

[By methods of the calculus (Chap. 15) we find that a maximum value of the function occurs at $x = 1$.]

Illustration 2. On the same axes and to the same scale plot the graphs of $y = e^x$, $y = \log_e x$.
Solution: The functions defined by these equations are inverses of each other. We use a table of natural logarithms to prepare the following entries.

x	-3	-2	-1	0	0.2	0.5	1	2	3
$y = \log_e x$	......	......	......	$-\infty$	-1.61	-0.69	0	0.69	1.10
$y = e^x$	0.05	0.14	0.37	1	1.22	1.65	2.72	7.39	20.09

The graphs are plotted in Fig. 11.7.

Exercise A. In Prob. 13, Sec. 9.7, we were to prove that $y = f(x)$ and $y = f^{-1}(x)$ are symmetric with respect to the line $y = x$. Prove this for the special functions given by $y = e^x$ and $y = \log_e x$.

PROBLEMS 11.4

In Probs. 1 to 13, sketch the graphs.

1. $y = \log_e |x|$.   2. $y = \log_e |2x|$.
3. $y = |\log_e x|$.   4. $y = |\log_e 2x|$.
5. $y = \log_e \sqrt{x}$.   6. $y = \log_e \sqrt{4x}$.
7. $y = 10^{\sqrt{x}}$.   8. $y = \log_e x$.
9. $y = \log_{10} x$.   10. $y = x \log_e x$.
11. $y = e^{-x^2}$. (This graph is called the "probability curve.")
12. (BT) $y = \log_e e^x$.
13. $y = e^{-2}2^x/x!$, for $x = 0, 1, 2, 3, 4$, etc. (This defines an important function in statistics; note that the domain is the positive integers and zero. It is called the "Poisson distribution function.")

In Probs. 14 to 19 solve the equation for x.

14. $3^x = 10$.   15. $(3.5)^x = 10$.
16. $2^{-x} = 4$.   17. $3^{-x} = 9$.
18. $e^x - e^{-x} + 1 = 0$.   19. $e^x + e^{-x} = 2$.

In Probs. 20 and 21 solve simultaneously for x and y.

20. $4^x = 5^y$, $2(4^x) = 7^y$.   21. $2^x = 3^y$, $3(2^x) = 6^y$.
22. If $\log_b a = x$ and $\log_a b = y$, what is the value of x/y?

11.5. *Applications*

There are many problems in biology, chemistry, economics, etc., involving growth and decay for which the natural mathematical model is the exponential function. Our basic illustration is from the field of economics.

Illustration 1. (a) An amount P dollars (principal) is invested at 100 per cent interest (rate), compounded annually. (The accrued interest is to be added to the principal.) Find the total amount A after 1 year. (b) Same problem compounded monthly. (c) Same problem compounded daily (360 days/year). (d) Same problem compounded continuously.
Solution
(a) $A = P(1 + 1)$.
(b) $A = P(1 + \frac{1}{12})^{12}$.
(c) $A = P(1 + \frac{1}{360})^{360}$.
(d) In order to arrive at something meaningful in this case we should begin with a description of what is meant by compounding "continuously." At this time we can give only an intuitive explanation since a precise explanation involves the theory of limits. We would have an approximate answer if we compounded each second. A year (360 days) has 31,104,000 seconds. The amount, at the end of 1 year, would be

$$A_{31,104,000} = P\left(1 + \frac{1}{31,104,000}\right)^{31,104,000}$$

We should like to know what, if anything, $A = P(1 + 1/n)^n$ would approach with ever-increasing n. The answer (beyond the scope of this text to develop) is Pe. That is, in technical language: "The limit of $(1 + 1/n)^n$, as n grows without bound, is e." Or, in symbols,

$$\lim_{n \to \infty} \left(1 + \frac{1}{n}\right)^n = e$$

If continuous compounding took place over a period of kt years the amount would be given by

$$A = P \lim_{n \to \infty} \left(1 + \frac{1}{n}\right)^{nkt} = P \lim_{n \to \infty} \left[\left(1 + \frac{1}{n}\right)^n\right]^{kt} = Pe^{kt}$$

The same kind of problem arises in biology where each of P cells in a given culture splits into two cells in a certain time t.

Illustration 2.   The number of bacteria in a culture at time t was given by

$$y = N_0 e^{5t}$$

What was the number present at time $t = 0$? When was the colony double this initial size?

Solution: When $t = 0$, $y = N_0 e^0 = N_0$. The colony will be $2N_0$ in size when t satisfies the equation $2N_0 = N_0 e^{5t}$, that is, when $5t = \log_e 2$ or when $t = \frac{1}{5} \log_e 2 = 0.69315/5 \approx 0.1386$ unit of time.

In chemistry certain disintegration problems are similarly explained.

Illustration 3.   Radium decomposes according to the formula $y = k_0 e^{-0.038t}$, where k_0 is the initial amount (corresponding to $t = 0$) and where y is the amount undecomposed at time t (in centuries). Find the time when only one-half of the original amount will remain. This is known as the "half-life" of radium.

Solution: We must solve $\frac{1}{2}k_0 = k_0 e^{-0.038t}$ for t.

$$\log_e \tfrac{1}{2} = -0.038t$$
$$-0.69315 = -0.038t$$
$$t = \frac{693.15}{38} = 18.24 \text{ centuries}$$

Illustration 4.   Given that the half-life of a radioactive substance is 10 min, how much out of a given sample of 5 g will remain undecomposed after 20 min?

Solution: The substance decays according to the formula:

$$y = 5e^{-kt}$$

First we must find k. From the given data

$$\tfrac{5}{2} = 5e^{-10k}$$

or

$$\tfrac{1}{2} = e^{-10k}$$

Taking natural logarithms of both sides, we have:

$$-\log_e 2 = -10k$$
$$k = \frac{\log_e 2}{10}$$

Substituting back, we find:

$$y = 5e^{-(\log_e 2)(t/10)}$$
$$= 5e^{-0.069315t}$$

When $t = 20$ min,

$$y = 5e^{-1.3863}$$
$$= 1.25 \text{ g}$$

We could have seen this at once, for half remains after 10 min and so half of a half, or a quarter, remains after 20 min. The above method, however, will give us the answer for any time t.

PROBLEMS 11.5

In Probs. 1 to 6 solve for the unknown.

1. $2 = 5e^{0.1t}$.
2. $3 = 2e^{0.5t}$.
3. $1.2 = 3.1e^{-0.12x}$.
4. $2.5 = 6.4e^{-0.48x}$.
5. $6 = 7ke^{0.5}$.
6. $4 = 3ke^{0.6}$.
7. An approximation for the pressure p in millimeters of mercury at a height h km above sea level is given by the equation $p = 760e^{-0.144h}$. Find the height for which the pressure is one-half that of sea level.
8. One "healing law" for a skin wound is $A = Be^{-n/10}$, where A (square centimeters) is the unhealed area after n days and B (square centimeters) is the original wound area. Find the number of days required to cut the wound down to one-half the area.
9. A special case of Newton's Law for the rate r at which a hot body cools is $50 = 75e^{-20r}$. Find r.
10. Find how long it will take a sum to double at 100 per cent interest, compounded continuously.
11. Given that the half-life of a radioactive substance is 5 sec, how much out of a given sample of 1 g will remain after 7 sec?
12. A radioactive substance decays from 3 g to 2 g in 1 hr. Find the half-life.

11.6. *The Logarithmic Scale*

Ordinary addition can be performed mechanically quite simply by sliding one ruler along another as in Fig. 11.8. We assume that the

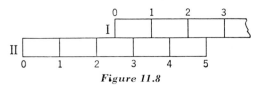

Figure 11.8

rulers are graduated in the usual way with linear scales. A linear scale is one in which the marks 1, 2, 3, . . . are placed 1, 2, 3, . . . units from one end (say the left). Thus with ruler I in its present position we could add $2.5 + 1.5 = 4$, $2.5 + 3 = 5.5$, $2.5 + n = 2.5 + n$.

If logarithmic instead of linear scales were used, we could perform multiplication. Examine the scale in Fig. 11.9. The distance from

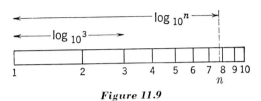

Figure 11.9

the left end to the mark 3 is not 3 units but is the logarithm (to base 10) of 3 units; that is, the distance is $\log_{10} 3 = 0.47712$ of the whole length. Similarly the mark n is placed at a distance of $\log_{10} n$ units from the left end. Note that the left end itself is marked 1 as it should be since $\log_{10} 1 = 0$. If we placed two such scales side by side as in Fig. 11.10, we could add the logarithms of numbers and hence multiply

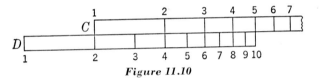

Figure 11.10

the numbers themselves. Thus $\log_{10} 2 + \log_{10} 3 = \log_{10} 6$. But since the scales are *marked* with units 2, 3, 6, etc., we *read* 2 (on the D scale) $\times$ 3 (on the C scale) $= 6$ (back on the D scale). In the same way we compute $2 \times 3\frac{1}{2} = 7$, $2 \times n = 2n$, etc.

Reading "backward" we perform division; thus $\dfrac{6(\text{on } D)}{3(\text{on } C)} = 2$ (on D, opposite 1 on C), etc. The usual slide rule also has scales that permit raising to powers and extraction of square and cube root. A slide rule is a useful aid in calculating where only two- or three-place accuracy is required. Instructions come with a rule.

In all of our graph work up to this point we have described and used but one type of graph paper, called rectangular coordinate paper, in which the rulings are laid out on linear scales. Many other types are available for special purposes. We shall devote Sec. 14.15 to a type called polar coordinate paper.

It is appropriate at this time to mention briefly two other types that are in common use and are available at a bookstore. These are:

(a) Semilogarithmic (semilog) paper in which one axis has a linear scale, the other a logarithmic scale (see Fig. 11.11).

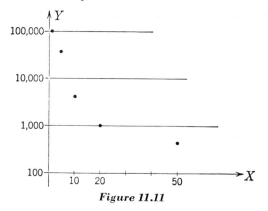

Figure 11.11

(b) Double-logarithmic (log-log) paper in which each axis is marked with a logarithmic scale (see Fig. 11.12).

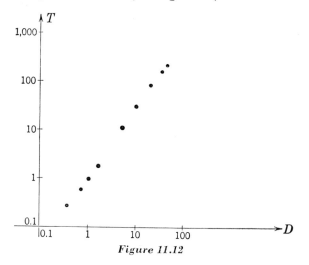

Figure 11.12

Exercise A. Why is there no zero on a logarithmic scale?

One use for semilog paper is for graphing functions that have both small and relatively large values in their range, such data as, for example, in the following illustration:

Illustration 1. Graph the function whose total set of elements is given by the following table.

x	50	20	8	3	1
y	500	1,000	5,000	25,000	100,000

Solution: First note that the domain is the set X of the five integers 50, 20, 8, 3, and 1. The range is the set Y of the five corresponding integers 500, 1,000, 5,000, 25,000, and 100,000. You can see that ordinary rectangular paper is inadequate because of the tremendous differences in magnitude of the values of y. These data might refer to the number of bank depositors x each writing checks (for an average month) with a total value y.

In order to get some geometric picture of this function, we resort to semilog paper with the linear scale on the X-axis and the logarithmic scale on the Y-axis. The graph is shown in Fig. 11.11. We do not connect the points, since there are no other elements of this function.

Note that a logarithmic scale goes by repetitive blocks, the set of marks representing 100, 200, 300, . . . , 900 being repeated in the same pattern for 1,000, 2,000, 3,000, . . . , 9,000. This is because of the decimal characteristics of the base 10 and is made clear by the following partial table. By blocks the mantissas repeat; the characteristics increase by 1. Semilog (and log-log) paper comes in several block styles. The one of Fig. 11.11 is three-block paper. In the printed forms the scales in each block run from 1 to 10; you will have to relabel them to fit the given problem.

y	$\log_{10} y$
.	.
.	.
.	.
100	2.00000
200	2.30103
300	2.47712
.	.
.	.
.	.
900	2.95424
1,000	3.00000
2,000	3.30103
3,000	3.47712
.	.
.	.
.	.
9,000	3.95424
.	.
.	.
.	.

Another use for logarithmic paper is in the search for an equation which might be satisfied by a set of data obtained, perhaps, as the result of some kind of an experiment. In running a given experiment, a research worker may feel that there is possibly a simple "law" that the data should or might follow.   If he were able to discover this law in the form of an equation, he could then use the equation for purposes of prediction.

Before we illustrate with an example we must make a few remarks about equations of the form

(1) $y = ae^{bx}$ [This defines an *exponential function*]
(2) $y = ax^b$ [This defines a *power function*]
(3) $y = ax + b$ [This defines a *linear function*]

We shall prove in Chap. 14 that the graph of (3) is a straight line when plotted on rectangular coordinate paper.   We have considered special cases of (1) and (2) before.

Let us take the logarithms of each side of (1) and (2); we do this in the following double column:

(4) $y = ae^{bx}$
$\log_{10} y = \log_{10} a + bx \log_{10} e$
$\qquad = \log_{10} a + 0.43429\, bx$

$\qquad\qquad y = ax^b$
$\qquad\qquad \log_{10} y = \log_{10} a + b \log_{10} x$

Rewrite these in the form

(5) $Y = A + Bx$ $Y = A + bX$

where $Y = \log_{10} y$, $A = \log_{10} a$, $B = 0.43429b$, $X = \log_{10} x$.

With the introduction of the new variables X and Y, we see that each equation (4) can be written as a linear equation (5).   Therefore each equation (5) will plot a straight line.   Thus, if we had data such as

x	x_1	x_2	$\cdots$	x_n
y	y_1	y_2	$\cdots$	y_n

and suspected that they followed (approximately) an exponential law (power law), we could look up the logarithms and write them down in a table as follows:

x	x_1	x_2	$\cdots$	x_n	I
y	y_1	y_2	$\cdots$	y_n	
$X = \log_{10} x$	X_1	X_2	$\cdots$	X_n	II
$Y = \log_{10} y$	Y_1	Y_2	$\cdots$	Y_n	III

Plotting I against III on rectangular paper would yield a straight line if the original data followed an exponential law.   Plotting II against

III on rectangular paper would yield a straight line if the original data followed a power law.

But we can do better. If we plot x against y (original data) on semilog paper, we will get a straight line if the law is exponential since, in effect, the paper looks up the logarithms for us. Similarly x plotted against y on log-log paper will yield a straight line if the data follow a power law.

By plotting data on semilog or log-log paper it is therefore a simple matter to tell whether the law is exponential or power (or approximately so) by determining whether the points lie along a line (or nearly so). If the points lie along some other curve, we must resort to other methods to find a suitable equation. The general process is called *curve fitting*.

Illustration 2. The mean distance D of the planets from the sun and their periods of revolution (T years) are given by the table. (The distance of the earth from the sun is taken as one unit.) Discover the (approximate) law.

	Mercury	Venus	Earth	Mars	Jupiter	Saturn	Uranus	Neptune	Pluto
T	0.241	0.615	1.00	1.88	11.9	29.5	84.0	165	265
D	0.337	0.723	1.00	1.52	5.20	9.54	19.2	30.1	41.3

Solution: We plot the data on rectangular, semilog, and log-log paper. The results are shown in Fig. 11.12 (p. 228) for log-log paper (four-block by three-block). We take D as independent variable.

The points lie (almost) on a straight line, and thus the law is (approximately) given by $T = aD^b$. It turns out (we will not compute it here) that $a = 1$ and $b = \frac{3}{2}$ (approximately) so that the final answer is $T = D^{\frac{3}{2}}$ or $T^2 = D^3$. Thus the square of the time is the cube of the distance. This is known as *Kepler's Law*.

Exercise B. For illustration 2, show the graphs of the data on rectangular and semilog paper.

Exercise C. Plot the graph of the equation $T = D^{\frac{3}{2}}$ on rectangular paper.

PROBLEMS 11.6

1. The number N of bacteria in a culture at time t (hours) is given by the following table:

t	0	1	2	3
N	100	700	5,500	40,300

Discover the (approximate) law, and compute a and b.

2. Discover an approximate law for the following data:

x	1	2	4	7
y	1	4	10	19

3. The speed s with which a certain chemical reaction takes place trebles every time the temperature $T°$ is raised 5°. Make out a table of some of the elements of the function $f:(T,s)$ thus defined, and discover the type of law. Let one element be $(0°,1)$.

4. The total absorption (x cubic units) of a certain gas by another chemical varied with time (t units) as follows:

x	2	4	6	7
t	12	48	108	147

Discover an approximate law.

In Probs. 5 to 16 name the kind of paper on which the graph is a straight line.

5. $y = 2e^{-3x}$.

6. $y = 5e^{2x}$.

7. $y = 2x^{-e}$.

8. $y = ex^e$.

9. $xy = 1$.

10. $3xy = 4$.

11. $x^2y = 10,000$.

12. $y = 7/x^3$.

13. $y = 4/x^2$.

14. $x^2y^2 = 100$.

15. $y = 2^x$.

16. $y = 3^x$.

REFERENCES

In addition to the many standard textbooks on algebra, the reader should consult the following articles in the *American Mathematical Monthly*.

Cairns, W. D.: Napier's Logarithms as He Developed Them, vol. 35, p. 64 (1928).

Cajori, Florian: History of the Exponential and Logarithmic Concepts, vol. 20, pp. 5, 20, 35, 75, 107, 148, 173, 205 (1913).

Huntington, E. V.: An Elementary Theory of the Exponential and Logarithmic Functions, vol. 23, p. 241 (1916).

Lenser, W. T.: Note on Semi-logarithmic Graphs, vol. 49, p. 611 (1942).

Sandham, H. F.: An Approximate Construction for e, vol. 54, p. 215 (1947).

Thomas, J. M.: Pointing Off in Slide Rule Work, vol. 55, p. 567 (1948).

CHAPTER TWELVE

Trigonometric Functions
of Angles

12.1. *Introduction*

Trigonometry was originally developed in connection with the study of the relationships between the sides and angles of a triangle. You have probably already met some of the trigonometric functions, such as the sine and cosine, and have applied them to simple problems about triangles. This aspect of trigonometry was investigated extensively by the early Greeks, especially by Hipparchus (circa 180–125 B.C.), who, because of his work in astronomy, actually developed spherical rather than plane trigonometry. The trigonometry of the triangle continues to be of importance in modern technology in such areas as surveying, navigation, and the applications of vectors to mechanics. The present chapter is concerned with those portions of this material which deal with the geometry of the plane. You will need to consult other books for material on spherical trigonometry.

It would be a serious error, however, to limit the study of trigonometry to its applications to triangles. Its modern uses are widespread in many theoretical and applied fields of knowledge. The trigonometric functions force themselves on you in a very surprising fashion when you study the calculus of certain algebraic functions. You will also meet them when you study wave motion, vibrations, alternating current, and sound. In none of these subjects, however, do angles appear in any natural fashion. It is therefore essential that we extend the concept of a trigonometric function so that it is a function of a general real variable, and no longer merely a function of an angle. These more general trigonometric functions become, then, members of our arsenal of functions which have been developed in the previous chapters. Their definitions and properties are given in the following chapter.

The complete set, consisting of the algebraic functions, the exponential function, the logarithmic functions, and the trigonometric functions, is called the set of "elementary functions." Virtually all undergraduate courses in mathematics restrict themselves to these elementary functions. In more advanced work, however, it is necessary to introduce additional functions which carry curious names such as the "gamma function," "Bessel function," "theta function," etc. We shall not need to refer to these hereafter in this book.

12.2. *Distance in the Plane*

We begin our study of trigonometry by developing certain properties of plane geometry which we shall need. Naturally we assume that you are already familiar with much of this subject from your study of it in high school. We shall be using all the logical structure of this geometry, including the undefined words, axioms, definitions, and theorems. Of course, we must assume these here, for a review of this material would take us too far afield. As a minimum, you should be familiar with the properties of similar triangles and with the theorem of Pythagoras.

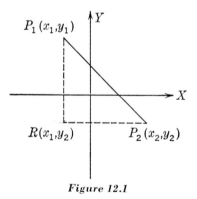

Figure 12.1

We shall employ the usual system of rectangular axes which was discussed in Secs. 2.11 to 2.13. In our work so far in this book we have permitted you to use quite different units on the two axes according to your immediate needs. Here, however, we must be more particular. In this chapter, coordinates on the X-axis and the Y-axis will represent *distance* in the *same* units of measurement.

Let us now consider two points P_1 and P_2 which do not lie on a line parallel to one of the axes (Fig. 12.1). The length of the segment, or the "distance P_1P_2," can be computed from the Theorem of Pythagoras. Construct the right triangle P_1RP_2 with P_1R parallel to the Y-axis and RP_2 parallel to the X-axis. R has coordinates (x_1,y_2). From the Theorem of Pythagoras,

$$(P_1P_2)^2 = (RP)^2 + (P_1R)^2$$

We know (Chap. 2) that

$$RP_2 = |x_2 - x_1| \quad \text{and} \quad P_1R = |y_1 - y_2|$$

Hence

$$(P_1P_2)^2 = (x_2 - x_1)^2 + (y_2 - y_1)^2$$

We observe that this is also true even if the line P_1P_2 is parallel to one of the axes. We have thus proved the general theorem.

Theorem 1. The distance d between any two points in the plane $P_1(x_1,y_1)$ and $P_2(x_2,y_2)$ is given by

$$d = \sqrt{(x_2 - x_1)^2 + (y_2 - y_1)^2}$$

Illustration 1. Find the distance between $A(4,-3)$ and $B(-2,5)$.
 Solution: The distance $d = AB$ is given by

$$
\begin{aligned}
d &= \sqrt{[4 - (-2)]^2 + [-3 - 5]^2} \\
&= \sqrt{36 + 64} \\
&= 10
\end{aligned}
$$

Illustration 2. Find the lengths of the diagonals of the quadrilateral $A(1,2)$, $B(-2,1)$, $C(-3,-4)$, $D(5,-7)$.
 Solution: The diagonals are AC and BD, and their lengths are given by

$$
\begin{aligned}
AC &= \sqrt{4^2 + 6^2} = \sqrt{52} \\
BD &= \sqrt{(-7)^2 + 8^2} = \sqrt{113}
\end{aligned}
$$

PROBLEMS 12.2

In Probs. 1 to 6 find the distance d between the pairs of points.

1. $(4,0)$, $(0,-3)$.
2. $(0,5)$, $(-2,-2)$.
3. $(2,1)$, $(2,-1)$.
4. $(3,7)$, $(4,16)$.
5. $(8,-2)$, $(-3,9)$.
6. $(20,0)$, $(-5,100)$.
7. Show that the triangle $A(-1,2)$, $B(3,10)$, $C(3,0)$ is a right triangle.
8. Show that the triangle $A(1,-1)$, $B(-\frac{1}{5},\frac{7}{5})$, $C(3,3)$ is a right triangle.
9. Show that the triangle $A(0,0)$, $B(\frac{5}{2},\frac{5}{2}\sqrt{3})$, $C(5,0)$ is an equilateral triangle.
10. Show that the triangle $A(-1,0)$, $B(0,\sqrt{3})$, $C(1,0)$ is an equilateral triangle.
11. Show that the points $A(1,0)$, $B(0,1)$, $C(-4,-1)$, $D(-3,-2)$ are the vertices of a parallelogram.
12. Show that the points $A(0,1)$, $B(-3,-2)$, $C(1,0)$, $D(4,3)$ are the vertices of a parallelogram.

In Probs. 13 to 14 show that the point P is on the perpendicular bisector of the line segment AB.

13. $P(1,\frac{1}{2})$, $A(4,1)$, $B(-2,0)$.   **14.** $P(4,3)$, $A(3,-2)$, $B(-1,4)$.

15. Show that $A(-1,0)$, $B(1,4)$, $C(2,3)$, $D(-2,1)$ are the vertices of a rectangle.

16. Show that $A(-1,2)$, $B(0,3)$, $C(0,1)$, $D(1,2)$ are the vertices of a square.

12.3. *Directed Angles*

In plane geometry *angle* was introduced as a rather intuitive concept. For our purposes we need a precise definition of *angle* and also of *directed angles*. To define these, we must first introduce the notion of a *ray*. (The intuitive idea is that of a ray of light issuing from a point-source.)

Definition: Let A be an arbitrary point and l an arbitrary directed line through A. Then the points of l which are "beyond A" (Sec. 2.11) together with the given direction constitute a *ray* with initial point A.

Let us draw two rays p and q, with initial point O, and let points P and Q (different from O), respectively, lie on p and q such that $OP = OQ$. Now rotate p about O into q so that P traverses the arc

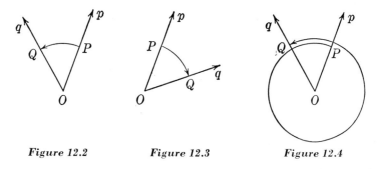

Figure 12.2   Figure 12.3   Figure 12.4

PQ. This rotation may be counterclockwise, as in Fig. 12.2, or clockwise, as in Fig. 12.3. Moreover, it may include one or more complete revolutions, as in Fig. 12.4. In order to describe this rotation, we must know not only the positions of p and q but also the arc PQ, which tells us how p is rotated into q.

In order to be specific about the arc PQ, we wish to define a measure for it. First we note that PQ lies on a circle. It is customary to divide a circle into 360 equal arcs, the measure of each of which is defined to be "one degree," written "1°." Each degree is further divided into 60 minutes (60′) and each minute into 60 seconds (60″). Our rotation imposes a direction on the arc PQ which is counterclockwise or clockwise. By general agreement, the measure of a counter-clockwise rotation is given a positive sign and that of a clockwise rotation a negative sign. This is purely a convention adopted in mathematics, and we could easily have chosen it the other way round. In fact clocks and compasses do assign a positive value to a clockwise rotation. We shall, however, stick to the usual mathematical convention and call counterclock-wise rotations positive.

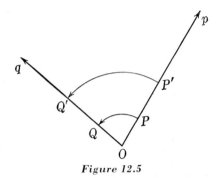

We have seen that, in a rotation of a ray p into a ray q, a point P on p traverses an arc PQ. Similarly another point P' on p traverses another arc $P'Q'$ (Fig. 12.5). Although arcs PQ and $P'Q'$ have different radii, it follows from ele-mentary geometry that *they have the same measure.* This permits us to define a directed angle and its measure as follows:

Figure 12.5

Definitions:

(1) A *directed angle* is the rotation of a ray p into a ray q.
(2) The *initial side* of the directed angle is the ray p.
(3) The *terminal side* of the directed angle is the ray q.
(4) The *measure* (in degrees) of the directed angle is the measure (in degrees), together with *its algebraic sign, of any of the arcs PQ with which the angle is associated.*

Exercise A. Show that:
(a) The measure of a quarter revolution counterclockwise is 90°.
(b) The measure of a half revolution clockwise is −180°.
(c) The measure of a $1\frac{1}{2}$ revolutions counterclockwise is 540°.
(d) The measure of a full revolution clockwise is −360°.

PROBLEMS 12.3

In Probs. 1 to 16 sketch roughly the directed angle θ.

1. $\theta = 30°$.	**2.** $\theta = 45°$.
3. $\theta = 60°$.	**4.** $\theta = 120°$.
5. $\theta = 135°$.	**6.** $\theta = 150°$.
7. $\theta = 210°$.	**8.** $\theta = 225°$.
9. $\theta = 240°$.	**10.** $\theta = 300°$.
11. $\theta = 315°$.	**12.** $\theta = 330°$.
13. $\theta = -120°$.	**14.** $\theta = -240°$.
15. $\theta = -300°$.	**16.** $\theta = -390°$.

In Probs. 17 to 30 draw, with the aid of a protractor, the directed angle θ.

17. $\theta = 70°$.
18. $\theta = 170°$.
19. $\theta = 200°$.
20. $\theta = 345°$.
21. $\theta = -17°$.
22. $\theta = -27°$.
23. $\theta = -99°$.
24. $\theta = -165°$.
25. $\theta = 560°$.
26. $\theta = 620°$.
27. $\theta = -410°$.
28. $\theta = -545°$.
29. $\theta = 1,000°$.
30. $\theta = -2,000°$.

12.4. *Polar Coordinates*

We have seen earlier how to locate a point in the plane by means of its rectangular coordinates (x,y). For many purposes, however, it is more convenient to locate points by using a different system of coordinates (r,θ), called polar coordinates. The intuitive idea is quite familiar. Suppose we are on a mountain top and wish to locate another peak. We can do so if we are told that it is 50 miles away in a direction 35° east of north. The essentials are that we know the distance r from a fixed point and the angle θ relative to a fixed reference line. The formal definition is as follows (Fig. 12.6):

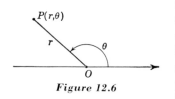

Figure 12.6

Definitions:

(1) The origin O is called the *pole*.

(2) The horizontal ray, directed to the right from O, is called the *polar axis*.

(3) Given a point P in the plane, the directed segment OP is called the *radius vector*. Its length—which we assume to be positive in this chapter—is denoted by r.

(4) A directed angle (positive or negative) with the polar axis as initial side and the radius vector on its terminal side is denoted by θ.

(5) In the ordered pair (r,θ), r and θ are called *polar coordinates* of P.

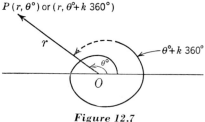

Figure 12.7

We observe, first of all, that any pair (r,θ) determines a unique point P. On the other hand, a fixed point P has many sets of polar coordinates. Indeed, if P has coordinates (r,θ), then it also has coordinates $(r, \theta° + k360°)$ for every integer k, positive or negative (Fig.12.7).

We now have two sets of coordinates for locating a point in the plane: (1) rectangular (x,y) and (2) polar (r,θ). So that we can use these interchangeably, we need to be able to go from one to the other at will. We observe at once that $r = \sqrt{x^2 + y^2}$, but, to make further progress, we need to introduce the trigonometric functions sine and cosine. These are treated in the following section.

12.5. *Sine and Cosine of a Directed Angle*

A directed angle will be said to be in *standard position* when the initial ray p coincides with the polar axis. Clearly any directed angle can be rotated into standard position. To find the trigonometric functions of a directed angle, we first put it in standard position and then proceed as follows:

Let θ be a directed angle in standard position with terminal ray q. Choose any point Q on q, and let the segment OQ have length r. Then Q has the polar coordinates (r,θ); let its rectangular coordinates be (x,y). Then we define the sine of θ (written $\sin \theta$) and the cosine of θ (written $\cos \theta$) as follows:

Definition: $\sin \theta = y/r$; $\cos \theta = x/r$.

This definition appears to depend upon our choice of Q, but this is not really the case. Let us choose Q' with coordinates (r',θ) and (x',y'). Then, from the elementary properties of similar triangles, we see that $y/r = y'/r'$ and $x/r = x'/r'$. Thus the definitions of $\sin \theta$ and $\cos \theta$ do not depend upon the choice of the point Q on the terminal side of θ. We see in this way that, given a directed angle θ, the real numbers $\sin \theta$ and $\cos \theta$ are uniquely determined. The sets of ordered pairs $\{\theta, \sin \theta\}$ and $\{\theta, \cos \theta\}$ thus *define*

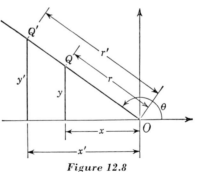

Figure 12.8

two functions which we call "sine" and "cosine," respectively. The domain of definition of each is the set of all directed angles, and their respective ranges of values are subsets of the real numbers, which will be discussed in Sec. 13.3.

Let us now return to the problem of determining the rectangular coordinates of a point from its polar coordinates, and vice versa. If we are given the polar coordinates (r,θ), the rectangular coordinates are obtained from the formulas:

$$x = r \cos \theta \qquad y = r \sin \theta$$

which are immediate consequences of the definitions of $\sin \theta$ and $\cos \theta$. For a point P we call the number x the *abscissa*, the number y the *ordinate*, and the positive number r the *radius vector*, or, simply, the *distance* (from the origin).

In order to go from (x,y) to (r,θ), we use the formulas:

$$r = \sqrt{x^2 + y^2} \qquad \frac{\sin \theta}{\cos \theta} = \frac{y}{x}$$

We shall presently be able to simplify the second of these two formulas.

We can use these formulas to derive an important relation between $\sin \theta$ and $\cos \theta$. Let us substitute $x = r \cos \theta$ and $y = r \sin \theta$ in $x^2 + y^2 = r^2$. Then we obtain

$$r^2 \cos^2 \theta + r^2 \sin^2 \theta = r^2$$

or, dividing by r^2 and rearranging,

$$\sin^2 \theta + \cos^2 \theta = 1$$

This equation is called an *identity* because it is true for *all* values of θ. It is the most useful identity in the whole subject of trigonometry.

We can also find the distance between two points in terms of their polar coordinates. Suppose that we have two points whose polar coordinates are $P_1(r_1,\theta_1)$ and $P_2(r_2,\theta_2)$ and whose rectangular coordinates are (x_1,y_1) and (x_2,y_2), respectively. We have seen that the distance d between P_1 and P_2 is given by the formula

$$d^2 = (x_2 - x_1)^2 + (y_2 - y_1)^2$$

Substituting in this formula, we find:

$$\begin{aligned}
d^2 &= (r_2 \cos \theta_2 - r_1 \cos \theta_1)^2 + (r_2 \sin \theta_2 - r_1 \sin \theta_1)^2 \\
&= r_2^2 \cos^2 \theta_2 - 2r_1r_2 \cos \theta_2 \cos \theta_1 + r_1^2 \cos^2 \theta_1 \\
&\quad + r_2^2 \sin^2 \theta_2 - 2r_1r_2 \sin \theta_2 \sin \theta_1 + r_1^2 \sin^2 \theta_1 \\
&= r_1^2(\sin^2 \theta_1 + \cos^2 \theta_1) + r_2^2(\sin^2 \theta_2 + \cos^2 \theta_2) \\
&\quad - 2r_1r_2(\cos \theta_1 \cos \theta_2 + \sin \theta_1 \sin \theta_2)
\end{aligned}$$

Hence

$$d^2 = r_1^2 + r_2^2 - 2r_1r_2(\cos \theta_1 \cos \theta_2 + \sin \theta_1 \sin \theta_2)$$

12.6. *Sine and Cosine of Special Angles*

If we are to make any use of the sine and cosine functions, we must know their values for any directed angle. We begin the discussion of this matter by treating some special angles of great importance.

(*a*) sin 0° *and* cos 0°. When $\theta = 0$, it is clear that the terminal side q lies along the initial side p, which we take to be horizontal (the polar axis or the X-axis). Choose Q to be the point $(1,0)$. Then $x = 1$, $y = 0$, $r = 1$. Hence

$$\sin 0° = \frac{y}{r} = \frac{0}{1} = 0$$

$$\cos 0° = \frac{x}{r} = \frac{1}{1} = 1$$

(*b*) sin 90° *and* cos 90°. Here we can choose Q to be the point $(0,1)$; so $x = 0$, $y = 1$, $r = 1$, and

$$\sin 90° = \frac{1}{1} = 1$$

$$\cos 90° = \frac{0}{1} = 0$$

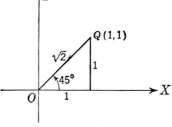

Figure 12.9

(*c*) sin 45° *and* cos 45°. From Fig. 12.9 we see that we can choose Q to be the point $(1,1)$; so $x = 1$, $y = 1$, $r = \sqrt{2}$. Hence

$$\sin 45° = \frac{1}{\sqrt{2}} = \frac{\sqrt{2}}{2} \approx \frac{1.414}{2} \approx 0.707$$

$$\cos 45° = \frac{1}{\sqrt{2}} = \frac{\sqrt{2}}{2} \approx \frac{1.414}{2} \approx 0.707$$

(*d*) sin 30° *and* cos 30°. From Fig. 12.10 we see that we can choose Q to be the point $(\sqrt{3},1)$; so $x = \sqrt{3}$, $y = 1$, $r = 2$. Hence

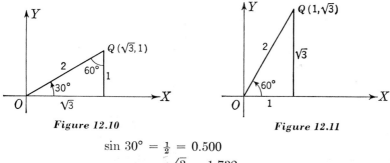

Figure 12.10   Figure 12.11

$$\sin 30° = \tfrac{1}{2} = 0.500$$

$$\cos 30° = \frac{\sqrt{3}}{2} \approx \frac{1.732}{2} \approx 0.866$$

(*e*) sin 60° *and* cos 60°. From Fig. 12.11 we see that we can choose Q to be the point $(1,\sqrt{3})$; so $x = 1$, $y = \sqrt{3}$, $r = 2$. Hence

$$\sin 60° = \frac{\sqrt{3}}{2} \approx 0.866$$
$$\cos 60° = \tfrac{1}{2} = 0.500$$

In the cases just treated every angle lay in the first quadrant. Similar constructions permit us to compute the values of these functions for related angles in other quadrants. The details are contained in the problems below.

PROBLEMS 12.6

In Probs. 1 to 30 find $\sin \theta$ and $\cos \theta$.

1. $\theta = 120°$.
2. $\theta = 150°$.
3. $\theta = 135°$.
4. $\theta = 180°$.
5. $\theta = 210°$.
6. $\theta = 240°$.
7. $\theta = 225°$.
8. $\theta = 270°$.
9. $\theta = 300°$.
10. $\theta = 330°$.
11. $\theta = 315°$.
12. $\theta = 360°$.
13. $\theta = 450°$.
14. $\theta = 750°$.
15. $\theta = 600°$.
16. $\theta = -30°$.
17. $\theta = -45°$.
18. $\theta = -60°$.
19. $\theta = -90°$.
20. $\theta = -120°$.
21. $\theta = -135°$.
22. $\theta = -150°$.
23. $\theta = -210°$.
24. $\theta = -225°$.
25. $\theta = -300°$.
26. $\theta = -330°$.
27. $\theta = -600°$.
28. $\theta = -750°$.
29. $\theta = -855°$.
30. $\theta = -1575°$.

In Probs. 31 to 46 find x and y for the given values of r and θ.

31. $r = 2$, $\theta = 30°$.
32. $r = 2$, $\theta = 135°$.
33. $r = 5$, $\theta = 180°$.
34. $r = 5$, $\theta = 210°$.
35. $r = 10$, $\theta = 240°$.
36. $r = 10$, $\theta = 270°$.
37. $r = 3$, $\theta = 300°$.
38. $r = 3$, $\theta = 315°$.
39. $r = \sqrt{2}$, $\theta = 45°$.
40. $r = \sqrt{2}$, $\theta = 225°$.
41. $r = 4$, $\theta = -150°$.
42. $r = 4$, $\theta = -270°$.
43. $r = \sqrt{3}$, $\theta = 45°$.
44. $r = \sqrt{3}$, $\theta = -45°$.
45. $r = 100$, $\theta = 855°$.
46. $r = 100$, $\theta = -750°$.

In Probs. 47 to 62 find r and the least positive value of θ for the given values of x and y.

47. $x = 2$, $y = 0$.
48. $x = 0$, $y = 1$.
49. $x = 1$, $y = 1$.
50. $x = \sqrt{3}$, $y = 1$.
51. $x = 1$, $y = \sqrt{3}$.
52. $x = -1$, $y = \sqrt{3}$.
53. $x = -4$, $y = 4$.
54. $x = -4$, $y = -4$.
55. $x = -1$, $y = 0$.
56. $x = 0$, $y = -1$.
57. $x = -1$, $y = -\sqrt{3}$.
58. $x = 1$, $y = -\sqrt{3}$.
59. $x = 2\sqrt{3}$, $y = -2$.
60. $x = -2$, $y = -2\sqrt{3}$.
61. $x = 5$, $y = -5$.
62. $x = -5$, $y = -5$.

In Probs. 63 to 70 find r and also find the θ whose absolute value is least.

63. $x = 1, y = -1$.

64. $x = 0, y = -2$.

65. $x = -\sqrt{3}, y = 1$.

66. $x = -1, y = -1$.

67. $x = 1, y = -\sqrt{3}$.

68. $x = -1, y = -\sqrt{3}$.

69. $x = 1, y = \sqrt{3}$.

70. $x = -\sqrt{3}, y = -1$.

In Probs. 71 to 76 find the distance between the given pairs of points.

71. $(2,30°)$ and $(5, 180°)$.

72. $(10, 240°)$ and $(3, 300°)$.

73. $(\sqrt{2},45°)$ and $(4, -150°)$.

74. $(2,60°)$ and $(2, 135°)$.

75. $(5, 210°)$ and $(10, 270°)$.

76. $(\sqrt{2},225°)$ and $(4, -270°)$.

12.7. *Other Trigonometric Functions*

Although the sine and cosine are adequate for the study of trigonometry, certain combinations occur so often that they are given special names. We therefore introduce the following four additional trigonometric functions:

Definitions:

(a) The set of ordered pairs $\{\theta, \sin \theta/\cos \theta\}$ defines a function called *tangent*, or, simply, *tan*. That is, for a given θ, $\tan \theta = \sin \theta/\cos \theta$, $\cos \theta \neq 0$.

(b) The set of ordered pairs $\{\theta, \cos \theta/\sin \theta\}$ defines a function called *cotangent*, or, simply, *cot*. That is, for a given θ, $\cot \theta = \cos \theta/\sin \theta$, $\sin \theta \neq 0$.

(c) The set of ordered pairs $\{\theta, 1/\cos \theta\}$ defines a function called *secant*, or *sec*. That is, for a given θ, $\sec \theta = 1/\cos \theta$, $\cos \theta \neq 0$.

(d) The set of ordered pairs $\{\theta, 1/\sin \theta\}$ defines a function called *cosecant*, or *csc*. That is, for a given θ, $\csc \theta = 1/\sin \theta$, $\sin \theta \neq 0$.

(e) The functions cosine, cotangent, cosecant are called the cofunctions of sine, tangent, secant, respectively.

Exercise A. What is the domain of definition of each of the functions tangent, cotangent, secant, cosecant?

Exercise B. Show that

(a) $\tan \theta = y/x, x \neq 0$.

(b) $\cot \theta = x/y, y \neq 0$.

(c) $\sec \theta = r/x$.

(d) $\csc \theta = r/y$.

The signs of the six trigonometric functions of θ depend upon the quadrant in which the terminal side of θ lies. We shall say that "θ is a *second quadrantal angle* if its terminal side lies in the second quadrant" and shall use similar expressions for the other quadrants. We see that $\sin \theta = y/r$ is positive when θ is a first or second quadrantal angle, since y is positive in the first and second quadrants and r is

always positive. However, sin θ is negative when θ is a third or fourth quadrantal angle, for y is negative in these quadrants. The situation is summarized in the following table, which you should verify for yourself.

Quadrant	Sine	Cosine	Tangent	Cosecant	Secant	Cotangent
I	+	+	+	+	+	+
II	+	−	−	+	−	−
III	−	−	+	−	−	+
IV	−	+	−	−	+	−

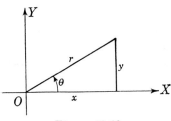

Figure 12.12

The following mnemonic scheme will help you to remember the signs of the sine, cosine, and tangent: "All Scholars Take Chemistry," or "ASTC." This says that *A*ll functions are positive in the first quadrant, only the *S*ine in the second quadrant, only the *T*angent in the third quadrant, and only the *C*osine in the fourth quadrant.

The identity

(1) $$\sin^2 \theta + \cos^2 \theta = 1$$

can be written in the form

$$\frac{\sin^2 \theta}{\cos^2 \theta} + 1 = \frac{1}{\cos^2 \theta} \qquad \cos \theta \neq 0$$

From this it follows that

(2) $$1 + \tan^2 \theta = \sec^2 \theta$$

for every value of θ for which tan θ and sec θ have meaning.

Exercise C. Name one value of θ for which (2) has no meaning.

Similarly we arrive at the identity

(3) $$1 + \cot^2 \theta = \csc^2 \theta$$

You should memorize these three basic identities (1), (2), and (3).

The values of tan θ, cot θ, sec θ, and csc θ for the special angles treated in the previous section can be readily determined. These are of considerable importance both in pure mathematics and in applica-

tions in science and engineering. For example, to determine tan 30°, we write

$$\tan 30° = \frac{\sin 30°}{\cos 30°} = \frac{1/2}{\sqrt{3}/2} = 1/\sqrt{3} = \frac{1}{3}\sqrt{3} = 0.57735$$

Again

$$\sec 60° = \frac{1}{\cos 60°} = \frac{1}{\frac{1}{2}} = 2$$

$$\cot 135° = \frac{\cos 135°}{\sin 135°} = \frac{-1/\sqrt{2}}{1/\sqrt{2}} = -1$$

$$\csc 270° = \frac{1}{\sin 270°} = \frac{1}{-1} = -1$$

Note that tan 90° = sin 90°/cos 90° is not defined since cos 90° = 0 and in defining tan θ we excluded the case where cos θ = 0.

The problems below are designed for a systematic study of these special angles.

PROBLEMS 12.7

In Probs. 1 to 33 compute the values of the six trigonometric functions for the indicated angle. Draw a figure.

1. 0°.	2. 30°.
3. 45°.	4. 60°.
5. 90°.	6. 120°.
7. 135°.	8. 150°.
9. 180°.	10. 210°.
11. 225°.	12. 240°.
13. 270°.	14. 300°.
15. 315°.	16. 330°.
17. 360°.	18. −30°.
19. −45°.	20. −60°.
21. −90°.	22. −120°.
23. −135°.	24. −150°.
25. −180°.	26. −210°.
27. −225°.	28. −240°.
29. −270°.	30. −300°.
31. −315°.	32. −330°.
33. −360°.	

12.8. *Some Important Identities*

There are many useful identities in trigonometry, and, as a scientist or mathematician, you will find it necessary at times to make use of some of them. This is particularly true when the angle involved is,

in absolute value, greater than 90°. For example, the tables of values of the natural trigonometric functions—and these we discuss in the next section—are made up for angles ranging between 0 and 90° only. We need, therefore, methods of reducing expressions like sin $(90° + \theta°)$, cos $(180° + \theta°)$, tan $(270° - \theta°)$, etc., to some simpler form involving only the angle $\theta°$, where $0° \leq \theta° \leq 90°$.

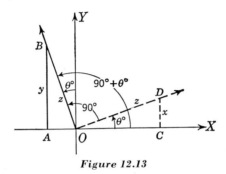

Figure 12.13

By way of illustration let us reduce sin $(90° + \theta°)$. Examine Fig. 12.13. You should be able to show, by methods of plane geometry, that $\triangle OAB$ is congruent to $\triangle OCD$ if, say, $|OA| = CD$.

Exercise A. Prove that $\triangle OAB$ is congruent to $\triangle OCD$ if $|OA| = CD$. Now sin $(90° + \theta°) = y/z = \cos \theta°$, which is the reduction sought. Similarly, keeping in mind that, as pictured, OA is negative, cos $(90° + \theta°) = -x/z = -\sin \theta°$.

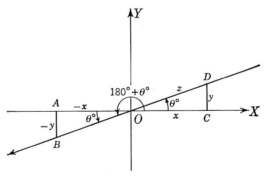

Figure 12.14

Again, from Fig. 12.14 if $AB = -CD$, it follows that

$$\cos (180° + \theta°) = -x/z = -\cos \theta°$$

Similarly, sin $(180° + \theta°) = -y/z = -\sin \theta°$.

From Fig. 12.15, with $OA = CD$ (each is negative), you should see that tan $(270° - \theta°) = -y/-x = y/x = \cot \theta°$.

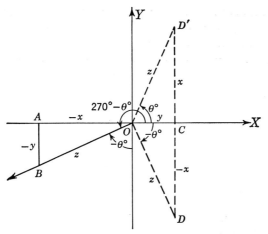

Figure 12.15

These are typical reduction formulas; the general situation is described in the following theorem, which is readily proved:

Theorem 2. Any trigonometric function of the angle $(k90° \pm \theta°)$ is equal to $(\pm)$ the same function of $\theta°$, if k is an even integer, and is equal to $(\pm)$ the cofunction of $\theta°$, if k is an odd integer. The $(+)$ sign is used if the original function of the original angle $(k90° \pm \theta°)$ is positive; the $(-)$ sign is used if the original function is negative.

The special cases, where $k = 0$ and where $-\theta$ is used, are worthy of further mention. For example, from Fig. 12.16,

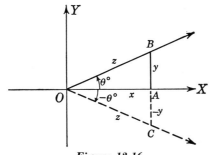

Figure 12.16

$$\sin (-\theta°) = -y/z = -\sin \theta°$$
$$\cos (-\theta°) = x/z = \cos \theta°, \tan (-\theta°) = -y/x = -\tan \theta°, \text{ etc.}$$

The following problems are designed for a systematic and detailed study of reduction formulas.

PROBLEMS 12.8

In Probs. 1 to 45 use Theorem 2 to simplify the expression. Assume that $0° \leq \theta° \leq 90°$, and draw an appropriate figure.

1. $\sin (90° + \theta°)$.
2. $\cos (90° + \theta°)$.
3. $\tan (90° + \theta°)$.
4. $\sin (90° - \theta°)$.
5. $\cos (90° - \theta°)$.
6. $\tan (90° - \theta°)$.
7. $\sin (180° + \theta°)$.
8. $\cos (180° + \theta°)$.
9. $\tan (180° + \theta°)$.
10. $\sin (180° - \theta°)$.
11. $\cos (180° - \theta°)$.
12. $\tan (180° - \theta°)$.
13. $\sin (270° + \theta°)$.
14. $\cos (270° + \theta°)$.
15. $\tan (270° + \theta°)$.
16. $\sin (270° - \theta°)$.
17. $\cos (270° - \theta°)$.
18. $\tan (270° - \theta°)$.
19. $\sin (5 \times 90° + \theta°)$.
20. $\cos (5 \times 90° + \theta°)$.
21. $\tan (5 \times 90° + \theta°)$.
22. $\sin (5 \times 90° - \theta°)$.
23. $\cos (5 \times 90° - \theta°)$.
24. $\tan (5 \times 90° - \theta°)$.
25. $\sin (6 \times 90° + \theta°)$.
26. $\cos (6 \times 90° + \theta°)$.
27. $\tan (6 \times 90° + \theta°)$.
28. $\sin (6 \times 90° - \theta°)$.
29. $\cos (6 \times 90° - \theta°)$.
30. $\tan (6 \times 90° - \theta°)$.
31. $\sin (2k90° + \theta°)$.
32. $\cos (2k90° + \theta°)$.
33. $\tan (2k90° + \theta°)$.
34. $\sin [(2k + 1)90° + \theta°]$.
35. $\cos [(2k + 1)90° + \theta°]$.
36. $\tan [(2k + 1)90° + \theta°]$.
37. $\sin [(2k + 1)90° - \theta°]$.
38. $\cos [(2k + 1)90° - \theta°]$.
39. $\tan [(2k + 1)90° - \theta°]$.
40. $\cot (2k90° + \theta°)$.
41. $\sec (2k90° + \theta°)$.
42. $\csc (2k90° + \theta°)$.
43. $\cot [(2k + 1)90° + \theta°]$.
44. $\sec [(2k + 1)90° + \theta°]$.
45. $\csc [(2k + 1)90° + \theta°]$.

12.9. *Trigonometric Tables*

The values of the six trigonometric functions have been computed for each minute of angle from 0 to 90°, and in the next chapter we indicate how some of these values were computed. Tables are available, along with much other mathematical material in several handbooks. Typical portions of these tables are produced on the opposite page. From it we read $\sin 32° = 0.52992$, $\cos 32°10' = 0.84650$, $\tan 32°16' = 0.63136$. For these we read the *left-hand* column of minutes and the *upper* column headings sin, cos, and tan. To get $\cot 57°5' = 0.64734$, $\sec 57°39' = 1.8688$, we read the *right-hand* minute column and the *bottom* column headings cot and sec.

Interpolation within any such table is carried out as follows: Suppose we want to compute $\cos 32°51.4'$. We first write

$$1.0' \left[0.4' \left[\begin{array}{l} \cos 32°51' = 0.84009 \\ \cos 32°51.4' = ? \\ \cos 32°52' = 0.83994 \end{array} \right] \Delta \right] 0.00015$$

32°

′	Sin	Cos	Tan	Cot	Sec	Csc	′
0	.52992	.84805	.62487	1.6003	1.1792	1.8871	**60**
1	.53017	.84789	.62527	1.5993	1.1794	1.8862	59
2	.53041	.84774	.62568	1.5983	1.1796	1.8853	58
3	.53066	.84759	.62608	1.5972	1.1798	1.8844	57
4	.53091	.84743	.62649	1.5962	1.1800	1.8836	56
5	.53115	.84728	.62689	1.5952	1.1803	1.8827	**55**
6	.53140	.84712	.62730	1.5941	1.1805	1.8818	54
7	.53164	.84697	.62770	1.5931	1.1807	1.8810	53
8	.53189	.84681	.62811	1.5921	1.1809	1.8801	52
9	.53214	.84666	.62852	1.5911	1.1811	1.8792	51
10	.53238	.84650	.62892	1.5900	1.1813	1.8783	**50**
11	.53263	.84635	.62933	1.5890	1.1815	1.8775	49
12	.53288	.84619	.62973	1.5880	1.1818	1.8766	48
13	.53312	.84604	.63014	1.5869	1.1820	1.8757	47
14	.53337	.84588	.63055	1.5859	1.1822	1.8749	46
15	.53361	.84573	.63095	1.5849	1.1824	1.8740	**45**
16	.53386	.84557	.63136	1.5839	1.1826	1.8731	44
17	.53411	.84542	.63177	1.5829	1.1828	1.8723	43
18	.53435	.84526	.63217	1.5818	1.1831	1.8714	42
19	.53460	.84511	.63258	1.5808	1.1833	1.8706	41
20	.53484	.84495	.63299	1.5798	1.1835	1.8697	**40**
21	.53509	.84480	.63340	1.5788	1.1837	1.8688	39
22	.53534	.84464	.63380	1.5778	1.1839	1.8680	38
23	.53558	.84448	.63421	1.5768	1.1842	1.8671	37
24	.53583	.84433	.63462	1.5757	1.1844	1.8663	36
25	.53607	.84417	.63503	1.5747	1.1846	1.8654	**35**
26	.53632	.84402	.63544	1.5737	1.1848	1.8646	34
27	.53656	.84386	.63584	1.5727	1.1850	1.8637	33
28	.53631	.84370	.63625	1.5717	1.1852	1.8629	32
29	.53705	.84355	.63666	1.5707	1.1855	1.8620	31
30	.53730	.84339	.63707	1.5697	1.1857	1.8612	**30**
31	.53754	.84324	.63748	1.5687	1.1859	1.8603	29
32	.53779	.84308	.63789	1.5677	1.1861	1.8595	28
33	.53804	.84292	.63830	1.5667	1.1863	1.8586	27
34	.53828	.84277	.63871	1.5657	1.1866	1.8578	26
35	.53853	.84261	.63912	1.5647	1.1868	1.8569	**25**
36	.53877	.84245	.63953	1.5637	1.1870	1.8561	24
37	.53902	.84230	.63994	1.5627	1.1872	1.8552	23
38	.53926	.84214	.64035	1.5617	1.1875	1.8544	22
39	.53951	.84198	.64076	1.5607	1.1877	1.8535	21
40	.53975	.84182	.64117	1.5597	1.1879	1.8527	**20**
41	.54000	.84167	.64158	1.5587	1.1881	1.8519	19
42	.54024	.84151	.64199	1.5577	1.1883	1.8510	18
43	.54049	.84135	.64240	1.5567	1.1886	1.8502	17
44	.54073	.84120	.64281	1.5557	1.1888	1.8494	16
45	.54097	.84104	.64322	1.5547	1.1890	1.8485	**15**
46	.54122	.84088	.64363	1.5537	1.1892	1.8477	14
47	.54146	.84072	.64404	1.5527	1.1895	1.8468	13
48	.54171	.84057	.64446	1.5517	1.1897	1.8460	12
49	.54195	.84041	.64487	1.5507	1.1899	1.8452	11
50	.54220	.84025	.64528	1.5497	1.1901	1.8443	**10**
51	.54244	.84009	.64569	1.5487	1.1903	1.8435	9
52	.54269	.83994	.64610	1.5477	1.1906	1.8427	8
53	.54293	.83978	.64652	1.5468	1.1908	1.8419	7
54	.54317	.83962	.64693	1.5458	1.1910	1.8410	6
55	.54342	.83946	.64734	1.5448	1.1912	1.8402	**5**
56	.54366	.83930	.64775	1.5438	1.1915	1.8394	4
57	.54391	.83915	.64817	1.5428	1.1917	1.8385	3
58	.54415	.83899	.64858	1.5418	1.1919	1.8377	2
59	.54440	.83883	.64899	1.5408	1.1921	1.8369	1
60	.54464	.83867	.64941	1.5399	1.1924	1.8361	**0**
′	Cos	Sin	Cot	Tan	Csc	Sec	′

As the angle increases by 1', the value of the cosine decreases by 0.00015. In linear interpolation we assume that, if the angle increases by 0.4', then the value of the cosine decreases by a proportional amount; i.e., the decrease is $(0.4)(0.00015) = 0.00006$. Formally we write

$$\frac{0.4}{1.0} = \frac{\Delta}{0.00015}$$

from which it follows that $\Delta = 0.00006$. Therefore

$$\cos 32°51.4' = 0.84003$$

Inverse interpolation, where the value of the function is given and the angle is to be determined, is performed in essentially the same manner. For example, if we wish to find θ having given that $\tan \theta = 0.63530$, we proceed as follows: From the table we find

$$1.0' \left[\Delta \begin{bmatrix} \tan 32°25' = 0.63503 \\ \tan \theta° = 0.63530 \\ \tan 32°26' = 0.63544 \end{bmatrix} \begin{matrix} 0.00027 \end{matrix} \right] 0.00041$$

Hence

$$\frac{\Delta}{1.0} = \frac{0.00027}{0.00041}$$

$$\Delta = \tfrac{27}{41} \approx 0.658 \approx 0.7$$

Therefore $\theta° = 32°25.7'$.

PROBLEMS 12.9

In Probs. 1 to 60 angles are given. Use tables of the natural trigonometric functions to find:

	sin		cos		tan
1.	16°16'	11.	9°29'	21.	11°11'
2.	73°25'	12.	45°45'	22.	62°55'
3.	40°19.7'	13.	30°18.2'	23.	20°46.6'
4.	67°51.4'	14.	54°40.1'	24.	50°22.2'
5.	109°16'	15.	97°7.7'	25.	122°35.5'
6.	153°44.6'	16.	165°28.7'	26.	170°56.3'
7.	200°10.8'	17.	250°50.1'	27.	307°4.4'
8.	−22°16.8'	18.	−17°39.9'	28.	−25°34.2'
9.	−47°40.1'	19.	−50°23.3'	29.	−82°12.3'
10.	1,000°	20.	2,000°	30.	3,000°

	cot		sec		csc
31.	15°25'	41.	21°14'	51.	38°9'
32.	46°50'	42.	63°36'	52.	53°40'
33.	72°27.4'	43.	20°20.1'	53.	36°11.2'
34.	12°49.9'	44.	49°38.7'	54.	45°3.3'
35.	130°30'	45.	116°16'	55.	129°44'

cot	sec	csc
36. 184°48.5′	**46.** 192°16.2′	**56.** 226°56.4′
37. 327°41.1′	**47.** 303°0.4′	**57.** 271°1.4′
38. −35°55.3′	**48.** −6°41.7′	**58.** −39°22.3′
39. −97°18.8′	**49.** −52°26.1′	**59.** −100°31.9′
40. 700°	**50.** 877°	**60.** 4,000°

In Probs. 61 to 84 values of the functions are given. Find the indicated angles to the nearest $\frac{1}{10}$ minute. Assume $0° \leq \theta° < 360°$.

61. $\sin \theta° = 0.58712$ [1st quadrantal angle].
62. $\sin \theta° = 0.12758$ [2d quadrantal angle].
63. $\sin \theta° = -0.34567$ [3d quadrantal angle].
64. $\sin \theta° = -0.72743$ [4th quadrantal angle].
65. $\cos \theta° = 0.81432$ [1st quadrantal angle].
66. $\cos \theta° = -0.27435$ [2d quadrantal angle].
67. $\cos \theta° = -0.60260$ [3d quadrantal angle].
68. $\cos \theta° = 0.54256$ [4th quadrantal angle].
69. $\tan \theta° = 0.42316$ [1st quadrantal angle].
70. $\tan \theta° = -1.1258$ [2d quadrantal angle].
71. $\tan \theta° = 2.2465$ [3d quadrantal angle].
72. $\tan \theta° = -0.92603$ [4th quadrantal angle].
73. $\cot \theta° = 3.4258$ [1st quadrantal angle].
74. $\cot \theta° = -1.7213$ [2d quadrantal angle].
75. $\cot \theta° = 0.26941$ [3d quadrantal angle].
76. $\cot \theta° = -0.61354$ [4th quadrantal angle].
77. $\sec \theta° = 1.4143$ [1st quadrantal angle].
78. $\sec \theta° = -4.2758$ [2d quadrantal angle].
79. $\sec \theta° = -2.0011$ [3d quadrantal angle].
80. $\sec \theta° = 1.2004$ [4th quadrantal angle].
81. $\csc \theta° = 5.1273$ [1st quadrantal angle].
82. $\csc \theta° = 1.1111$ [2d quadrantal angle].
83. $\csc \theta° = -3.1769$ [3d quadrantal angle].
84. $\csc \theta° = -4.6755$ [4th quadrantal angle].

12.10. *Right Triangles*

The simplest applications of trigonometry involve the solution of right triangles. We are given any two of the following "parts" (including at least one side): the angles A and B, and the sides a, b, and c. Then we are asked to find the remaining three parts.

For a right triangle the definitions of sine, cosine, tangent given in Sec. 12.5 reduce to the following.

$$\text{The sine of an acute angle} = \frac{\text{opposite side}}{\text{hypotenuse}}$$

$$\text{The cosine of an acute angle} = \frac{\text{adjacent side}}{\text{hypotenuse}}$$

$$\text{The tangent of an acute angle} = \frac{\text{opposite side}}{\text{adjacent side}}$$

As an illustration of the application of these formulas, consider the following problem:

Illustration 1.   A gable roof has rafters that are 10 ft long.   If the eaves are 17 ft apart, how much headroom is there in the center of the attic and how steep is the roof?
   Solution: Directly from Fig. 12.17 we see that

$$\text{Headroom} = x = \sqrt{100 - 72.25}$$
$$= \sqrt{27.75}$$
$$= 5.26 \text{ ft} \qquad \text{from a table of square roots}$$

The steepness of the roof is measured by θ, where

$$\cos \theta = \frac{8.5}{10} = 0.85$$

and, from a table of natural cosines (degree measure),

$$\theta = 31°47.3' \qquad \text{to the nearest } \tfrac{1}{10} \text{ minute}$$

A second example is given in Illustration 2.

Illustration 2.   A radio tower stands on top of a building 200 ft high.   At a point on the ground 500 ft from the base of the building the tower subtends an angle of 10°.   How high is the tower?

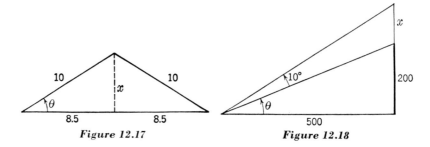

Figure 12.17   Figure 12.18

   Solution: From Fig. 12.18 we have

$$\tan \theta = \tfrac{200}{500} = 0.40000$$
$$\theta = 21°48.1' \qquad \text{to the nearest } \tfrac{1}{10} \text{ minute}$$

Now
$$\tan 31°48.1' = \frac{200 + x}{500}$$
$$0.62007 = \frac{200 + x}{500}$$
$$200 + x = 310.04$$
$$x = 110.04 \text{ ft}$$

PROBLEMS 12.10

In Probs. 1 to 10 solve for the unknown parts in the right triangle with angles
A, B, $C = 90°$ and opposite sides a, b, c, respectively.

1. $a = 1$, $c = 4$. 　　　　　　　**2.** $a = 1$, $b = 4$.
3. $a = 2$, $c = 4$. 　　　　　　　**4.** $a = 2$, $b = 1$.
5. $a = 10$, $A = 27°34.6'$. 　　　　**6.** $b = 10$, $A = 27°34.6'$.
7. $c = 100$, $B = 40°$. 　　　　　　**8.** $c = 25$, $A = 65°32.4'$.
9. $a = 22.1$, $c = 31.2$. 　　　　　　**10.** $a = 25.0$, $b = 16.5$.

In Probs. 11 to 16 find the perimeter of the following regular polygons:

11. A hexagon inscribed in a circle of radius 10 in.
12. A hexagon circumscribed about a circle of radius 10 in.
13. An octagon inscribed in a circle of radius 10 in.
14. An octagon circumscribed about a circle of radius 10 in.
15. A decagon inscribed in a circle of radius 10 in.
16. A decagon circumscribed about a circle of radius 10 in.
17. From the top of a lighthouse 70 ft high the angle of depression of a boat is
found to be 35°; how far away from the base of the lighthouse is the boat?
18. What angle does the diagonal of the face of a cube make with a diagonal of the
cube (drawn from the same vertex)?
19. (*a*) What is the area of a regular pentagon inscribed in a circle of radius 5 in.;
(*b*) circumscribed?
20. A wheel 3 ft in diameter is driven, by means of a (noncrossed) belt, by a wheel
1 ft in diameter. If the wheel centers are 8 ft apart, how long is the belt?
21. A 10-ft ladder, with its foot anchored in an alleyway, will reach 9 ft up a building on one side of the alley and 6 ft up a building on the other. How wide is
the alley?
22. Discover a way of measuring the width of a stream by making all of the meas-
urements on one bank.
23. Find the area of the traffic island shown in the figure; distances are in feet.

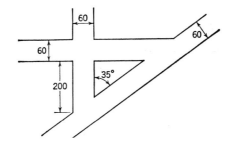

24. If the angle of elevation of the sun is 37°20′, how long a shadow will a 6-ft man
cast on level ground?
25. Prove that the area S of a right triangle with hypotenuse c is given by $S = \frac{1}{2}c^2$
$\sin A \cos A$.
26. In a triangle ABC, $BC = 100$ ft, angle $ABC = 40°$, angle $ACB = 120°$. Find
AB.

12.11. *Vectors*

We have already defined vectors and discussed their algebra (Sec. 7.6). In this section we shall show how trigonometry helps us to use them in practical problems. By way of review, we remind you that a vector whose initial point is at the origin is graphed as a directed

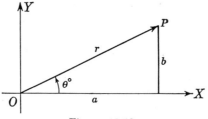

Figure 12.19

line segment $\overrightarrow{OP}$. The vector is determined by the coordinates (a,b) of the end point P, and we call a the x-component of $\overrightarrow{OP}$ and b its y-component. Indeed we previously indentified $\overrightarrow{OP}$ with the pair (a,b).

We can, however, describe $\overrightarrow{OP}$ in another important way. We can give its *length* (or *magnitude*) $r = |\overrightarrow{OP}|$ and the angle θ which it makes with the positive X-axis. This pair of numbers (r,θ) are nothing but the polar coordinates of the end point P.

Our discussion in Sec. 12.5 now permits us to use these two aspects of a vector interchangeably. If we are given the magnitude r and the direction θ, we find:

The x-component a of the vector (r,θ) is $a = r \cos \theta$.

The y-component b of the vector (r,θ) is $b = r \sin \theta$.

Suppose, on the other hand, that we know the components (a,b) of a vector. Then:

The magnitude r of (a,b) is $r = \sqrt{a^2 + b^2}$

The direction θ of (a,b) is given by $\tan \theta = b/a$.

We can generalize the notion of the x- and y-components of a vector by considering its projections on any pair of perpendicular lines.

Definition: Given a directed line l and a vector $\overrightarrow{AB}$, the *component* of $\overrightarrow{AB}$ on l is $CD = |\overrightarrow{AB}| \cos \theta$ where θ is any of the angles between the positive directions of $\overrightarrow{AB}$ and l (Fig. 12.20).

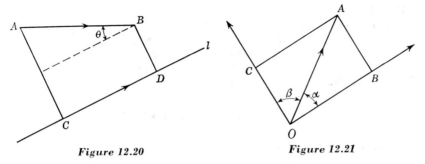

Figure 12.20   Figure 12.21

Thus the vector $\overrightarrow{OA}$ (Fig. 12.21) is readily resolved into its components

$$OB = |\overrightarrow{OA}| \cos \alpha \text{ and } OC = |\overrightarrow{OA}| \cos \beta = |\overrightarrow{OA}| \sin \alpha$$

Let us use these ideas to find the *sum* or *resultant* of two vectors. We recall that the sum of $\overrightarrow{OA_1}$ and $\overrightarrow{OA_2}$ is the vector $\overrightarrow{OB}$, where B completes the parallelogram determined by $\overrightarrow{OA_1}$ and $\overrightarrow{OA_2}$. We recall that in component language the sum is given by:

$$(a,b) + (c,d) = (a + c, b + d)$$

Suppose, however, that our two vectors are given in the form (r_1,θ_1) and (r_2,θ_2) and that we wish to find their sum. This is usually the situation in problems in physics and mechanics. First we must compute their components along two perpendicular directions.

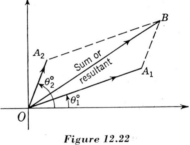

Figure 12.22

For convenience we choose the X- and Y-axes. These are:

$$a_1 = r_1 \cos \theta_1 \qquad b_1 = r_1 \sin \theta_1$$
$$a_2 = r_2 \cos \theta_2 \qquad b_2 = r_2 \sin \theta_2$$

Then the sum is the vector:

$$(r_1 \cos \theta_1 + r_2 \cos \theta_2, \; r_1 \sin \theta_1 + r_2 \sin \theta_2)$$

From this we can find the magnitude and direction of the vector sum by the formulas above.

Illustration 1. Two forces F_1 and F_2 of 20 and 10 lb, respectively, act on a body. If F_1 acts at $\theta_1 = 30°$ and F_2 at $\theta_2 = 60°$, find the resultant force F and its direction.

Solution:

(F_1, θ_1) has components: $a_1 = 20 \cos 30° = 10\sqrt{3} = 17.32$
$\qquad\qquad\qquad\qquad\quad b_1 = 20 \sin 30° = \frac{20}{2} = 10$
(F_2, θ_2) has components: $a_2 = 10 \cos 60° = \frac{10}{2} = 5$
$\qquad\qquad\qquad\qquad\quad b_2 = 10 \sin 60° = 5\sqrt{3} = 8.66$

Hence the resultant has components:

$$a_1 + a_2 = 22.32 \qquad b_1 + b_2 = 18.66$$

The magnitude of the resultant is

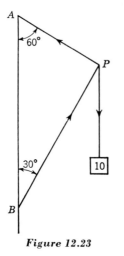

$$\sqrt{22.32^2 + 18.66^2} = \sqrt{846.4} = 29.1 \text{ lb}$$

The direction of the resultant is given by:

$$\tan \theta = \frac{18.66}{22.32} = 0.8360$$

So $\qquad\qquad\qquad \theta = 39°54'$

The resultant is the vector $(29.1, 39°54')$

This method applies equally to the sum of three or more vectors. It is particularly useful in analyzing statics problems where the body is at equilibrium. This implies that the vector sum of the forces involved is zero, and hence that the sum of the components in any direction is zero.

Figure 12.23

Good applications of this are given in the next illustrations.

Illustration 2. A weight of 10 lb is supported by a rod BP and a rope AP (Fig. 12.23). Find the tension in the rope.
   Solution: The sum of the horizontal components is:

$$-|\overrightarrow{AP}| \sin 60° + |\overrightarrow{BP}| \sin 30° = 0$$

The sum of the vertical components is:

$$|\overrightarrow{AP}| \cos 60° + |\overrightarrow{BP}| \cos 30° - 10 = 0$$

We are asked to find $|\overrightarrow{AP}|$ and can do this by solving the above pair of simultaneous equations. This gives:

$$|\overrightarrow{AP}| = \frac{10 \sin 30°}{\cos 60° \sin 30° + \sin 60° \cos 30°}$$
$$= 5 \text{ lb}$$

Illustration 3.   A block of wood weighing 5.0 lb rests on an inclined plane making 20° with the horizontal.   Disregarding all forces except that of gravity, determine the force (a vector quantity) required to keep the block from moving (Fig. 12.24).

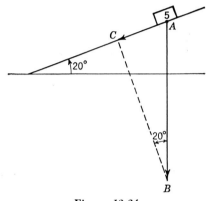

Figure 12.24

Solution: We draw the vector $\overrightarrow{AB}$ of length 5.0 and downward to represent the force (in pounds).   The component of this force in the direction down the inclined plane is $AC = |\overrightarrow{AB}| \sin 20°$.   Now

$$AC = 5.0 \sin 20°$$
$$= (5.0)(0.34202)$$
$$= 1.71010 \approx 1.7$$

The answer to the question is given by the vector $\overrightarrow{CA}$.   That is, a force of 1.7 lb acting *up* the plane is required to keep the body from moving.

Exercise A.   Find the component of the force in the upward direction perpendicular to the inclined plane.

PROBLEMS 12.11

1. Two forces of magnitudes 8 and 10 act at right angles to each other.   Find the resultant, describing the direction of the resultant with respect to the force with magnitude 8.
2. Find the resultant $R(L,\theta)$ of the two forces $F_1(20,45°)$, $F_2(30,60°)$ with initial points at the origin.

3. Find the resultant $R(L,\theta)$ of the two forces $F_1(5,0°)$, $F_2(6,45°)$ with initial points at the origin.
4. An airplane points itself due north, and its northerly speed is 400 mi/hr. A west wind blows the airplane east at 50 mi/hr. Find the velocity vector, i.e., the speed = |velocity| and direction, of the airplane.
5. A woman swims at 2 mi/hr at 45° up a current which flows at 6 mi/hr. Describe her motion.
6. In an east-to-west flight across the United States (a distance of 3,000 miles) an airplane traveling west at 600 mi/hr is blown off course by a 20 mi/hr northeast wind. How far off course is it at the end of the trip?
7. A 3,000-lb automobile rests on a 15° hill. What force is required of the brakes to hold the automobile at rest?
8. A 10-lb block of wood W (tied to A with a piece of string) rests on a scale S.

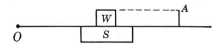

If the whole assembly is rotated 12°36.2′ counterclockwise about O, what will be the reading on the scale?
9. A 21.301-lb box is to be lifted vertically by $F_1(10,28°)$ and $F_2(x,118°)$. Find x.
10. A 100-lb box is to be lifted vertically by $F_1(x,40°)$ and $F_2(y,130°)$. Find x and y.
11. A force $F(100,45°)$ is the sum of the forces $F_1(a,0°)$, $F_2(b,70°)$. Find a and b.
12. If a force of 500 lb is resolved into components of 300 lb and 400 lb, respectively, find the angle these components make with each other.
13. Two forces F_1 and F_2 of 5 and 15 lb, respectively, make 40° with each other. Describe the resultant.
14. A weight W of 20 lb is supported by a rod BP and a rope AP as in the figure. Find the tension in the rope and the compression in the rod.

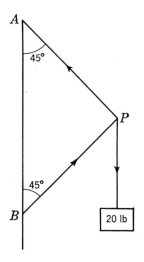

15. A weight of W lb is supported by a rod BP and a rope AP as in the figure. Find general expressions for the tension in the rope and the compression in the rod.

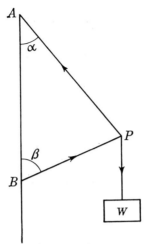

16. Three forces of 100, 200, and 300 lb, respectively, are in equilibrium. What angles do they make with each other?

17. A force $F(a,\theta)$ is the sum of the forces $F_1(50,30°)$, $F_2(100,80°)$, and $F_3(150,130°)$. Find a and θ.

18. (BT) Ropes extend from tractors up over a pulley at the top of a haymow and down to a load of hay. If one tractor pulls with a force of 75 lb at 34° with the vertical and another pulls with a force of 100 lb at 26° with the vertical, what is the weight of hay they lift?

12.12. *Law of Sines*

So far we have been working with right triangles. In this section and in the next we wish to develop methods for dealing with any triangle. To "solve" a triangle means to find the angles and sides which are not given in the problem.

The solutions of general triangles may be obtained by using the Laws of Sines and Cosines. To derive the Law of Sines, examine Fig. 12.25,

Figure 12.25

in which it is assumed that angle A is acute. We have $h/a = \sin B$ and $h/b = \sin A$ or $h = a \sin B = b \sin A$. Therefore

$$\frac{a}{\sin A} = \frac{b}{\sin B}$$

Similarly $a:b:c = \sin A : \sin B : \sin C$

This is known as the Law of Sines. The proof of this law when A is obtuse is posed in Prob. 7 of this section. It enables us to solve a triangle when given (*a*) two sides, one opposite angle, and (*b*) two angles, one side.

When two sides and the angle opposite one of these are given, we have a situation called the *ambiguous case*. Let a, b, and A be given. Then by the Law of Sines

$$\sin B = \frac{b \sin A}{a}$$

Three cases can occur, as follows:

(*a*) $\sin B > 1$. This is impossible, and there is no solution. (See Illustration 1.)

(*b*) $\sin B = 1$. Then $B = 90°$, the triangle is a right triangle, and there is one solution.

(*c*) $\sin B < 1$. Then two values of B must be examined, namely: B_1 in the first quadrant and B_2 in the second quadrant. B_1 always gives a solution. If $B_2 + A < 180°$, there is a second solution; but if $B_2 + A \geq 180°$, B_2 is impossible and there is only one solution. (See Illustration 2.)

Illustration 1. Given $a = 2$, $b = 10$, $A = 30°$, find B.

Solution: $\sin B = \dfrac{10 \sin 30°}{2}$

$$= \frac{10 \ (0.5000)}{2}$$

$$= 2.5$$

Since $2.5 > 1$, there is no angle B for which $\sin B = 2.5$. Hence there is no solution.

Illustration 2. Given $a = 10.537$, $b = 5.0261$, $A = 40°37.6'$, find B.

Solution: The Law of Sines is to be used, but the computation is now more difficult. However, with a desk computer at hand, B can be determined very quickly. First we find $\sin 40°37.6' = 0.65113$ and write

$$\frac{10.537}{0.65113} = \frac{5.0261}{\sin B}$$

$$\sin B = \frac{(0.65113)(5.0261)}{10.537} = 0.31058$$

Since B can possibly lie in either the first or second quadrants, two values of B must be examined, namely:

$$B_1 = 18°5.6' \quad \text{and} \quad B_2 = 180° - B_1 = 161°54.4'$$

Since $A + B_2 > 180°$, the value B_2 is impossible. Hence $B = 18°5.6'$.

If a desk calculator is not available, you can save time by using logarithms for computing sin B. (Review Chap. 11.)

$$\log \sin B = \log 0.65113 + \log 5.0261 - \log 10.537$$
$$= 9.81367 - 10 + 0.70123 - 1.02272$$
$$= 9.49218 - 10$$

At this point we use a table of the *logarithms* of the trigonometric values and find $B = 18°5.4'$. The discrepancy in the answers is due to rounding errors.

SPECIAL NOTE: In this book we do not stress the use of logarithms for solving such problems as the above. Desk computers are almost as common as typewriters, and we assume that you will have the use of one.

When two angles and a side are given (or computed as in the case just discussed), we can find the third angle immediately by using the fact that the sum of the angles of a triangle is 180°. Then the remaining sides can be found by use of the Law of Sines.

Illustration 3. Given $a = 10$, $A = 40°$, $B = 50°$, find b.
  Solution: From the Law of Sines,

$$b = \frac{a \sin B}{\sin A}$$
$$= \frac{10(0.76604)}{0.64279}$$
$$= 11.917$$

PROBLEMS 12.12

Solve the triangle, given the following:

1. $a = 10$, $B = 30°$, $C = 40°$.   2. $a = 7$, $A = 25°$, $B = 35°$.
3. $A = 45°$, $b = 4.04$, $C = 60°$.   4. $b = 100$, $c = 150$, $C = 38°8'$.
5. $A = 120°$, $B = 15°7'$, $c = 6.2583$.
6. $a = 5.6$, $b = 20$, $B = 20°35'$.
7. $b = 10$, $c = 9.3$, $C = 56°$ (two solutions).
8. $B = 18°25'$, $b = 20.62$, $c = 30.45$.
9. $a = 2$, $A = 25°$, $c = 5$.
10. $C = 52°28'$, $c = 4.75$, $a = 6.00$.
11. Develop completely the Law of Sines, $a:b:c = \sin A : \sin B : \sin C$, in the case of a triangle where angle A is obtuse. HINT: $\sin A = \sin (180° - A)$.
12. If s represents half the perimeter of a triangle and R the radius of the circumscribed circle, show that
    (a) $R(\sin A + \sin B + \sin C) = s$.
    (b) $2R = \dfrac{a}{\sin A} = \dfrac{b}{\sin B} = \dfrac{c}{\sin C}.$
13. Prove that the area K of triangle ABC is given by the formula

$$K = \tfrac{1}{2}bc \sin A$$

14. An observation balloon B and two points A and C on the ground are in the same vertical plane. From A the angle of elevation of the balloon is 65° and from C 35°. If the balloon is between the two points A and C, what is its elevation if A and C are 1,000 ft apart?

15. The magnitudes of two forces are 5 and 6, and their resultant makes an angle of 22° with the first. Describe the system.

16. Two vectors make 70° with each other; their resultant is $R(10,50°)$. The vectors issue from the origin, and one makes 5° with the horizontal. Describe the system.

12.13. *Law of Cosines.*

The Law of Sines is not directly applicable in case three sides of a triangle are given or in case two sides and the included angle are given. To develop a usable formula for these two cases, we proceed as follows

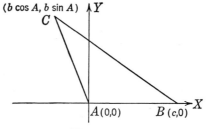

Figure 12.26

(Fig. 12.26): Place the triangle on the axes so that A is at the origin and side c lies along the positive X-axis. Then B has the coordinates $(c,0)$ and C the coordinates $(b \cos A, b \sin A)$. For this construction, A may be acute or obtuse.

The distance BC is equal to a and is given by the distance formula:

$$a^2 = (b \cos A - c)^2 + (b \sin A - 0)^2$$
$$= b^2 \cos^2 A - 2bc \cos A + c^2 + b^2 \sin^2 A$$
$$= b^2 + c^2 - 2bc \cos A$$

Using other letters, this formula may be written

$$b^2 = a^2 + c^2 - 2ac \cos B$$
$$c^2 = a^2 + b^2 - 2ab \cos C$$

Any of these formulas is called the Law of Cosines, and by means of them a triangle can be solved, given (*a*) three sides and (*b*) two sides, included angle.

Illustration 1.   Given $C = 100°$, $a = 15$, $b = 20$, find c.
  Solution: Substituting in the third form of the Law of Cosines, we get

$$c^2 = (15)^2 + (20)^2 - 2(15)(20)(-0.17365)$$

recalling that $\cos 100° = -\cos 80° = -0.17365$.   Hence

$$c^2 = 729.19$$
$$c = \sqrt{729.19}$$
$$= 27.0037$$
$$\approx 27$$

Exercise A.   Find A and B in the above illustration.

Illustration 2.   Given $C = 100°$, $a = 15.277$, $b = 20.593$, find c.
  Solution: As in Illustration 2 in the preceding section, the problem is now one of more difficult computations.   However, with a desk calculator, we compute

$$c^2 = (15.277)^2 + (20.593)^2 - 2(15.277)(20.593)(-0.17365)$$
$$= 767.37$$
$$c = 27.701 \approx 27.7$$

Note that the Law of Cosines is not well adapted to logarithmic treatment.

We are now in a position to explain the geometric interpretation of the inner product of two vectors (Sec. 7.7).   We recall that if $\mathbf{A} = (a_1, a_2)$ and $\mathbf{B} = (b_1, b_2)$, then $\mathbf{A} \cdot \mathbf{B} = a_1 b_1 + a_2 b_2$.

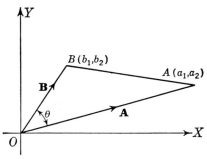

Figure 12.27

Construct the triangle OAB as in Fig. 12.27.   Then, by the law of cosines:

$$\overline{AB}^2 = \overline{OA}^2 + \overline{OB}^2 - 2\overline{OA} \times \overline{OB} \times \cos \theta$$

Using the formula of Sec. 12.2 for the length of a segment, we can write this as:

$$(a_1 - b_1)^2 + (a_2 - b_2)^2 = (a_1^2 + a_2^2) + (b_1^2 + b_2^2)$$
$$- \sqrt{a_1^2 + a_2^2} \sqrt{b_1^2 + b_2^2} \cos \theta$$

or $$-2(a_1 b_1 + a_2 b_2) = -2 \sqrt{a_1^2 + a_2^2} \sqrt{b_1^2 + b_2^2} \cos \theta$$

Since $|\mathbf{A}| = \sqrt{a_1^2 + a_2^2}$ and $|\mathbf{B}| = \sqrt{b_1^2 + b_2^2}$, this becomes:

$$\mathbf{A} \cdot \mathbf{B} = |\mathbf{A}|\,|\mathbf{B}|\cos\theta$$

In words, *the inner product of two vectors is the product of their lengths times the cosine of their included angle.*

Exercise B.   Show that $\mathbf{A} \cdot \mathbf{B} = 0$ if $\mathbf{A}$ and $\mathbf{B}$ are at right angles.

PROBLEMS 12.13

In Probs. 1 to 12 solve for:

1. Angle B, given $a = 6$, $b = 7$, $c = 10$.
2. Angle B, given $a = 5$, $b = 10$, $c = 12$.
3. Angle A, given $a = 5$, $b = 4$, $c = 8$.
4. Angle A, given $a = 2$, $b = 3$, $c = 4$.
5. Angle C, given $a = 15.357$, $b = 20.219$, $c = 25.483$.
6. Angle C, given $a = 10.197$, $b = 15.488$, $c = 15.488$.
7. Side a, given $A = 13°$, $b = 4.1937$, $c = 5.0275$.
8. Side a, given $A = 11°$, $b = 5.4327$, $c = 6.2189$.
9. Side c, given $a = 10$, $b = 15$, $C = 95°$.
10. Side c, given $a = 5$, $b = 9$, $C = 100°46'$.
11. Side b, given $a = 25$, $B = 36°15'$, $c = 15$.
12. Side b, given $a = 20$, $B = 31°15'$, $c = 15$.
13. The diagonals of a parallelogram are 15 ft and 10 ft, respectively, and they form an angle of 33°.   Find the lengths of the sides.
14. Find a formula for the area of a triangle, given a, b, and C.
15. Show that the area of a regular polygon of n sides is $\frac{1}{4}na^2 \cot (180°/n)$, where a is the length of one side.
16. The magnitudes of two forces and their resultant are 4, 5, and 6, respectively. Describe the system.
17. The magnitudes of two forces and their resultant are 3, 8, and 10, respectively. Describe the system.
18. From an airport at noon one airplane flies northeast at 300 mi/hr, another due south at 400 mi/hr.   How far apart are they at 2 P.M.?
19. The angle between two forces, 5 and 10, is 52°.   Describe the resultant.
20.* Derive the Law of Sines from the Law of Cosines.

12.14. *Law of Tangents*

The Law of Cosines and a desk computer offer the best methods for solving triangles where three sides or two sides and the included angle are given.   To solve these two cases with logarithms, it is best to use the Law of Tangents.   Even though we do not recommend the latter procedure, it is still a good exercise in trigonometry to develop the Law of Tangents.   This is done in the next chapter (Prob. 30, Sec. 13.6).

CHAPTER THIRTEEN

Trigonometric Functions
of Real Numbers

13.1. *Arc Length and Radian Measure*

We are now ready to generalize the concepts of the trigonometric functions. In Chap. 12 they were functions of an angle measured in degrees. Here we shall define them as functions of a real number so that sin x, say, has the same domain of definition as e^x, $2x^2 - 4$, etc.

Consider a unit circle with center placed at the origin of a rectangular coordinate system (Fig. 13.1). We have already seen that the equation of such a circle is $x^2 + y^2 = 1$, where, of course, the coordinates (x,y) of a point on the circle satisfy the above equation.

Next we lay off on the circle an arc of (positive) length θ beginning at the point $(1,0)$ and running counterclockwise. An arc running clockwise will be called an arc of negative length. The set of all arcs is in 1 to 1 correspondence with the set of all real numbers. Figures 13.1e and 13.1f show arcs that lap over more than one circumference. Before proceeding, let us say that the concept of *arc length*, as yet undefined, is a very profound one and is not to be lightly passed over. Length measured along a straight line is one thing; but what could be the meaning of length measured along a circle or some other curve? If all of the known history of mathematics is any indication of the truth, Archimedes was the only one of the ancients who had any clear notion of how to treat arc length, and after his death the subject languished for almost two thousand years!   We do not treat this matter, and therefore must ask you to rely simply upon your intuition.

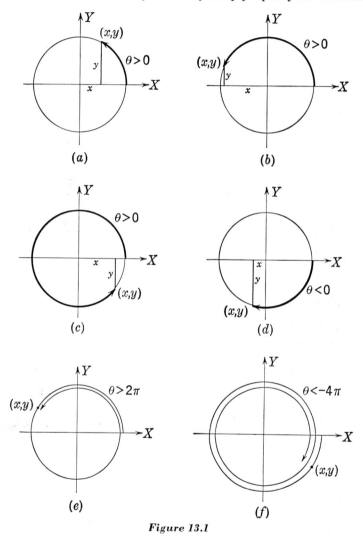

Figure 13.1

The total length of the circumference of the unit circle is 2π units. (For a circle of radius r, the circumference C is given by $C = 2\pi r$.) The number π is irrational, and, approximately, $\pi = 3.14159$.

Returning now to Fig. 13.1, we note that associated with each real number θ there is a unique, ordered pair (x,y) which are the coordinates of the end point of the arc θ whose initial point is $(1,0)$.

Exercise A. Is there a unique arc beginning at $(1,0)$ the coordinates of whose end point are a given pair (x,y)?

Definitions. We define x and y, respectively, to be $\cos \theta$ and $\sin \theta$ and write

$$x = \cos \theta$$
$$y = \sin \theta$$

These are to be read "x is the cosine of the real number θ" and "y is the sine of the real number θ." The sine and cosine are, therefore, functions of the real number θ. The other four trigonometric functions (tan, cot, sec, and csc) of a real number θ are defined in terms of $\sin \theta$ and $\cos \theta$ by the formulas given in Sec. 12.7. Consequently all the identities and formulas developed in Chap. 12 are valid also in the present context.

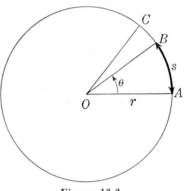

In order to explain the relationship of these new definitions to those in Chap. 12, where θ was

Figure 13.2

interpreted as an angle measured in degrees, we must introduce a new idea, namely the radian measure of an angle, which we write $\theta^{(r)}$.

Definition. An angle which, on a circle of radius r, subtends an arc of length r is said to have a measure of one radian.

We may find the radian measure of any angle by considering Fig. 13.2. From plane geometry

(1) $$\frac{\text{Arc } AB}{\text{Arc } AC} = \frac{\text{measure of angle } AOB}{\text{measure of angle } AOC}$$

Now let arc $AC = r$ so that the measure of angle AOC is one radian, and let Arc $AB = s$ and $\theta^{(r)}$ be the measure (in radians) of angle AOB. Then (1) becomes

$$\frac{s}{r} = \frac{\theta^{(r)}}{1^{(r)}}$$

Hence $\theta^{(r)} = s/r$ and $s = r\theta^{(r)}$

Since a complete circumference has length $2\pi r$, it subtends an angle of $2\pi r/r = 2\pi^{(r)}$. This angle also has a measure of 360°. Therefore

$$(2) \qquad\qquad 2\pi^{(r)} = 360° \qquad \text{or} \qquad \pi^{(r)} = 180°$$

From (2) we can effect a transfer from degrees to radians or from radians to degrees. Thus, for example,

$$30° = \frac{180°}{6} = (\pi/6)^{(r)}$$

Let us now return to our real number θ. We have drawn an arc of length θ on the unit circle, and hence this arc subtends an angle whose measure is $\theta^{(r)}$. Moreover the endpoint of the arc θ is on the terminal side of the angle $\theta^{(r)}$. According to our definitions we now see that:

$$\sin \theta = \sin \theta^{(r)} \qquad \text{and} \qquad \cos \theta = \cos \theta^{(r)}$$

the first of which can be read: the sine of the real number θ equals the sine of the angle whose radian measure is θ radians. There is consequently no further point in distinguishing between $\sin \theta$ and $\sin \theta^{(r)}$, etc., and we shall write $\sin \theta$ to mean either the sine of the real number θ or the sine of an angle whose measure is θ radians. Hereafter the variables in all trigonometric functions will have this interpretation unless we explicitly mention degrees.

Exercise B.   Distinguish between $\sin 2$ and $\sin 2°$.

13.2. *Computations*

In order to calculate the values of the trigonometric functions of a real number, we can refer to either of two types of standard tables. To illustrate the first method consider Illustrations 1 and 2.

Illustration 1.   Find $\cos \pi/4$.
   Solution: Since $(\pi/4)^{(r)} = 45°$, $\cos \pi/4 = \cos (\pi/4)^{(r)} = \cos 45° = \sqrt{2}/2$.

Illustration 2.   Find $\tan 1.5$.
   Solution: Since $1.5^{(r)} = (180°)(1.5)/\pi = 85°56.6'$

$$\tan 1.5 = \tan 1.5^{(r)} = \tan 85°56.6' = 14.100$$

We may also refer to a table of the values of trigonometric functions of angles expressed in radian measure.[1]

[1] For example see "Standard Mathematical Tables," 11th ed., pp. 140–144, Chemical Rubber Publishing Company, New York, 1957.

Illustration 3.   Find tan 1.5.

    Solution: From such a table we find

$$\tan 1.5 = \tan 1.5^{(r)} = 14.101$$

The discrepancy in the last place between this answer and that of Illustration 2 is due to rounding errors in Illustration 2. Hence the method of Illustration 3 is a more reliable one which should be used if the needed tables are available.

You may be interested in knowing how such a table is prepared. How do we compute $\sin \frac{1}{2}$, $\cos (\pi/7)$, etc., anyway? We cannot give you at this time the details, but at least we can say a few words. By methods of the calculus it can be shown that $\sin x$, where x is any real number, is given by the following "infinite series":

$$\sin x = x - \frac{x^3}{3!} + \frac{x^5}{5!} - \frac{x^7}{7!} + \cdots + (-1)^{n+1} \frac{x^{2n-1}}{(2n-1)!} + \cdots$$

and similarly

$$\cos x = 1 - \frac{x^2}{2!} + \frac{x^4}{4!} - \frac{x^6}{6!} + \cdots + (-1)^{n+1} \frac{x^{2n-2}}{(2n-2)!} + \cdots$$

These hold for every real number x. A table of values of sine and cosine *correct to five decimal places* can be prepared from them by considering the approximations

$$(3) \qquad\qquad \sin x \approx x - \frac{x^3}{3!} + \frac{x^5}{5!} - \frac{x^7}{7!}$$

$$(4) \qquad\qquad \cos x \approx 1 - \frac{x^2}{2!} + \frac{x^4}{4!} - \frac{x^6}{6!}$$

There is a general theorem which says, for such series, that the numerical value of the error made in taking a finite number of terms as an approximation does not exceed the numerical value of the *first* term omitted. In the case of $\sin x$ this term is $x^9/9!$ and $9! = 362{,}880$. The largest value of x we need consider is $\pi/4 = 0.78540$. Since $(0.78540)^9/362{,}880 = 0.0000003$, we see that this will not affect the fifth decimal.

    Exercise A. Explain why we need only consider $0 \leq x \leq \pi/4$ in order to prepare a complete table for $\sin x$ and $\cos x$.

PROBLEMS 13.2

In Probs. 1 to 8 write the equivalent number of degrees.

1. 0, $\pi/6$, $\pi/4$, $\pi/3$.

2. $\pi/2$, $2\pi/3$, $3\pi/4$, $5\pi/6$.

3. π, $7\pi/6$, $5\pi/4$, $4\pi/3$.

4. $3\pi/2$, $5\pi/3$, $7\pi/4$, $11\pi/6$, 2π.

5. $\pi/5$, $2\pi/5$, $\pi/7$, 1.

6. $\pi/10$, $\pi/12$, $\pi/16$, 0.2.

7. $5\pi/2$, $11\pi/2$, 7π, 3.

8. -4π, $-7\pi/16$, $-\frac{1}{10}$, -4, $-\frac{1}{2}$.

In Probs. 9 to 12 write the equivalent number of radians.

9. $0°, 30°, 45°, 60°, 90°$.

10. $1°, 10°, 22\frac{1}{2}°, 67\frac{1}{2}°, 1'$.

11.. $200°, 220°, 307°, 355°, 1''$.

12. $-10°, -100°, -206°, -328°, -0.1°$.

For each real number θ, in Probs. 13 to 20, find the value (if it exists) of each of the six trigonometric functions.

13. $\theta = 0$.

14. $\theta = \pi/2$.

15. $\theta = \pi$.

16. $\theta = \frac{3}{2}\pi$.

17. $\theta = 2\pi$.

18. $\theta = 3\pi$.

19. $\theta = -8\pi$.

20. $\theta = -71\pi$.

In Probs. 21 and 22 draw a figure indicating approximately every arc θ (where $0 \leq \theta \leq 2\pi$) for which

21. $\tan \theta = 3$.

22. $|\tan \theta| = \frac{1}{3}$ and $\cos \theta$ is negative.

23. Prove that $\sin \theta = -\sin(-\theta)$, for all θ.

24. Prove that $\cos \theta = \cos(-\theta)$, for all θ.

25. Find a counterexample for the following false statement:
For all θ and φ

$$\sin(\theta + \phi) = \sin \theta + \sin \phi$$

26. Find a counterexample for the following false statement:
For all θ

$$\cos 2\theta = 2 \cos \theta$$

27. Draw an appropriate figure and prove that, for all θ,

$$\sin(\theta + 2\pi) = \sin \theta$$

and
$$\sin(\theta + \pi) = -\sin \theta$$

28. By making use of the equation of the unit circle, find all θ for which

$$\tan \theta = \cot \theta$$

29. Show that

$$\sec^2 \theta - \tan^2 \theta = \csc^2 \theta - \cot^2 \theta$$

30. (BT) Is $\dfrac{1 + \tan^2 \theta - \sec^2 \theta}{1 + \cot^2 \theta - \csc^2 \theta} = 1$ an identity?

31. Use Eq. (3) to compute $\sin 0.1$.   Check with a table.

32. Use Eq. (4) to compute $\cos 0.1$.   Check with a table.

In Probs. 33 to 36 find $\sin \theta$.

33. $\theta = 1.76$.

34. $\theta = 1.00$.

35. $\theta = 0.86$.

36. $\theta = 0.75 + 2\pi$.

In Probs. 37 to 40 find $\cos \theta$.

37. $\theta = 0.61$.

38. $\theta = 0.29$.

39. $\theta = 1.85$.

40. $\theta = 2 + 2\pi$.

In Probs. 41 to 44 find $\tan \theta$ when θ is

41. $\theta = 1.50$.

42. $\theta = 1.50 - 2\pi$.

43. $\theta = 1.50 + \pi$.

44. $\theta = 1.50 + 5\pi$.

13.3. *Range and Graphs of the Functions*

As the arc θ increases from 0 to 2π, the trigonometric functions vary. It is relatively simple to see how each varies; we discuss only the cases of sin, cos, and tan. Draw the unit circle, and consider several arcs such that $0 < \theta_1 < \cdots < \theta_3 < \pi/2$ (Fig. 13.3). Remember that for a given θ, which is a real number, the abscissa x is $\cos\theta$ and the ordinate y is $\sin\theta$. Now erect a line tangent to the circle at $P(1,0)$; also draw the several lines from the origin to the end points of θ_1, $\theta_2, \ldots, \theta_3$ extending these to intersect the tangent line at A_1, $A_2, \ldots, A_3$, respectively. It is seen that the length of the segment of the tangent PA_1 is actually equal to $\tan\theta_1$, by proportional parts of the triangles OPA_1 and OCB. Indeed this is the source of the name

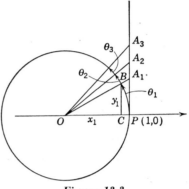

Figure 13.3

"tangent" of θ. By observing the variation of the length of PA as θ varies we can obtain the behavior of $\tan\theta$ as θ varies. From Fig. 13.1 we can read off the variations of $\sin\theta$ and $\cos\theta$. The results are tabulated below.

Quadrant	As θ varies from	$\sin\theta$ varies from	$\cos\theta$ varies from	$\tan\theta$ varies from
I	0 to $\pi/2$	0 to 1	1 to 0	0 to ∞
II	$\pi/2$ to π	1 to 0	0 to -1	$-\infty$ to 0
III	π to $\frac{3}{2}\pi$	0 to -1	-1 to 0	0 to ∞
IV	$\frac{3}{2}\pi$ to 2π	-1 to 0	0 to 1	$-\infty$ to 0

The entries $\pm\infty$ under $\tan\theta$ need further explanation. It is quite evident that, as θ $(0 < \theta < \pi/2)$ gets nearer and nearer to $\pi/2$, $\tan\theta$ gets larger and larger. When the arc is exactly $\pi/2$, the value of the tan ceases to exist. We indicate this here by writing $\tan(\pi/2) = \infty$. However, in the second quadrant, the tan is negative; hence the entry of $-\infty$ on the second line. Similarly for III and IV quadrant entries.

Exercise A. Draw a figure similar to Fig. 13.3 but for arcs θ where

$$\pi/2 < \theta < \pi$$

Moreover, the variations are "essentially" the same for a given function, quadrant by quadrant: a function may increase or decrease, be positive or turn negative, but the range is the same if sign be disregarded. This will become clearer as we begin to graph the functions. We are already in a position to make up the following detailed table for the first quadrant. The entries below were found in the problems at the end of Sec. 13.2.

θ	$\sin \theta$	$\cos \theta$	$\tan \theta$
0	0	1	0
$\pi/6$	$\frac{1}{2} = 0.500$	0.866	$\frac{1}{3}\sqrt{3} = 0.577$
$\pi/4$	$\frac{1}{2}\sqrt{2} = 0.707$	0.707	1
$\pi/3$	$\frac{1}{2}\sqrt{3} = 0.866$	0.5	$\sqrt{3} = 1.732$
$\pi/2$	1	0	∞

For your own understanding you should extend this table through the other three quadrants. Figure 13.4 is helpful. With the aid of

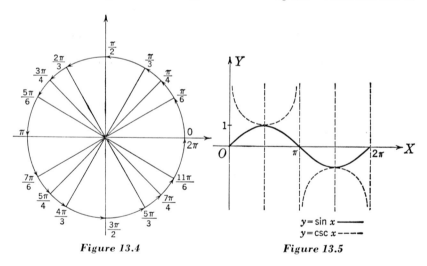

Figure 13.4   Figure 13.5

$y = \sin x$ ———
$y = \csc x$ ----

this information we sketch the graphs as in Figs. 13.5, 13.6, and 13.7, which also include the graphs of the sec, csc, and cot. To plot a more accurate graph, we could obtain other elements from a table of these functions. Note that sin, cos, sec, csc repeat after 2π but that tan and cot repeat after π, that is, sin, cos, sec, csc are periodic functions of period 2π and tan and cot are periodic functions of period π according to the following definitions.

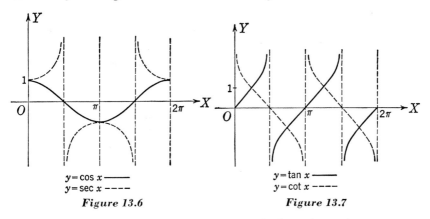

$y = \cos x$ ———
$y = \sec x$ - - - -

Figure 13.6

$y = \tan x$ ———
$y = \cot x$ - - - -

Figure 13.7

Definitions: A nonconstant function f such that $f(x + a) = f(x)$ for some positive a and all x is said to be a *periodic function*. The least positive a for which this is true is called the *period of the function*.

Exercise B. Prove that no periodic function can be a rational function. HINT: Use the theorem that if a polynomial of degree n has more than n zeros then the polynomial is identically zero (see Prob. 34*, Sec. 10.6).

Exercise C. Prove that $f(x + 2a) = f(x)$ if f is a periodic function of period a.

Illustration 1. Sketch on the same axes and to the same scale the graphs of $y = \sin x$ and $Y = 3 \sin \frac{1}{2}x$, $0 \le x \le 4\pi$.

Solution: We compute the following entries, treating $\sin x$ and $3 \sin \frac{1}{2}x$ separately and making use only of the special values we know about. (For a more accurate graph, we should make use of a table.)

x	$\frac{1}{2}x$	$y = \sin x$	$\sin \frac{1}{2}x$	$Y = 3 \sin \frac{1}{2}x$
0	0	0.000	0.000	0.000
$\pi/6$	...	0.500		
$\pi/4$	...	0.707		
$\pi/3$	$\pi/6$	0.866	0.500	1.500
$\pi/2$	$\pi/4$	1.000	0.707	2.121
$2\pi/3$	$\pi/3$	0.866	0.866	2.598
$3\pi/4$	...	0.707		
$5\pi/6$	...	0.500		
π	$\pi/2$	0.000	1.000	3.000

Now the graph of $y = \sin x$ is "essentially" the same in the second, third, and fourth quadrant as it is in the first quadrant. By this we mean that it is the same shape but placed differently. Also $\sin x$ is periodic of period 2π, while $\sin \frac{1}{2}x$ is periodic of period 4π. With this information we sketch the graphs below. (The whole of a given curve is sketched by means of a template with which the heavy portion was drawn; Fig. 13.8.)

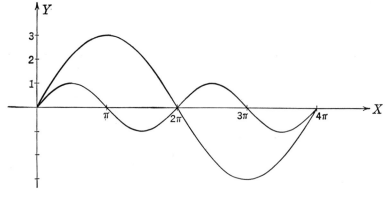

Figure 13.8

Illustration 2. Sketch the graph of $y = \sin x + \frac{1}{3}\sin 3x$.
  Solution: We should now know enough to sketch

$$Y_1 = \sin x \quad \text{and} \quad Y_2 = \tfrac{1}{3}\sin 3x$$

They are dashed and labeled in Fig. 13.9. Then we sketch $y = Y_1 + Y_2$ by adding the ordinates of the two curves.

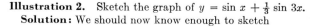

Figure 13.9

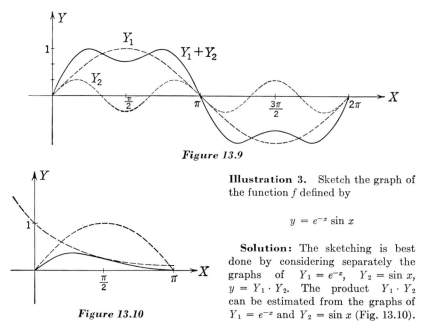

Figure 13.10

Illustration 3. Sketch the graph of the function f defined by

$$y = e^{-x}\sin x$$

  Solution: The sketching is best done by considering separately the graphs of $Y_1 = e^{-x}$, $Y_2 = \sin x$, $y = Y_1 \cdot Y_2$. The product $Y_1 \cdot Y_2$ can be estimated from the graphs of $Y_1 = e^{-x}$ and $Y_2 = \sin x$ (Fig. 13.10).

The graph of $y = e^{-x}\sin x$ is called an *exponentially damped sine wave* and is important in the theory of electricity.

PROBLEMS 13.3

1. Figure 13.3 gives the so-called *line values* of the three functions sin, cos, tan. Prepare a similar figure for sec, csc, and cot.

In Probs. 2 to 8 sketch on the same axes and to the same scale the following pairs of graphs (complete period of each). Note the change in variables to the usual x and y.

2. $y = \sin x$, $y = \sin 2x$.   3. $y = \sin x$, $y = \frac{1}{2} \sin 2x$.

4. $y = \sin x$, $y = 2 \sin x$.   5. $y = \cos x$, $y = 3 \cos 3x$.

6. $y = \cos x$, $y = \cos (x/2)$.   7. $y = \sin x$, $y = \sin (x + \pi/2)$.

8. $y = \cos x$, $y = \frac{1}{2} \cos (x - \pi/4)$.

In Probs. 9 to 12 sketch (a complete period):

9. $y = \sin x + \cos x$. (Consider this as a sum $f + g$, plot the graphs of f and g separately, and then add ordinates.)

10. $y = 2 \sin x - \cos x$.   11. (BT) $y = \sin^2 x + \cos^2 x$.

12. $y = \sin x + \frac{1}{2} \sin 2x$.

13. What is the range of sec, csc, and cot, quadrant by quadrant?

14. What is the domain of definition of sine; cosine; tangent; cotangent; secant; cosecant?

13.4. *Amplitude, Period, Phase*

One of the most important trigonometric concepts is that of a "sinusoidal wave." It occurs in innumerable ways and places in astronomy, mathematics, and all of the sciences including the social sciences. It is, simply, the graph of $y = A \sin (Bx + C)$, where A, B, C are constants.

We begin with a comparison of the graphs of

$$y = \sin x$$
$$y = A \sin x$$

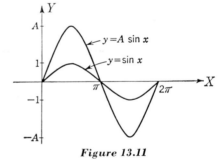

These are exhibited superimposed on the same axes and drawn to the same scales, in Fig. 13.11.

Figure 13.11

Since the maximum value of $|\sin x|$ is 1 and occurs when

$$x = \frac{\pi}{2} + k\pi$$

it is evident that $|A|$ is the maximum value of $A \sin x$. The constant A is called the *amplitude* of the sine wave (sinusoidal wave). The *period* p of $y = \sin x$ (and of $y = A \sin x$) is $p = 2\pi$.

Next we compare

$$y = \sin x$$
$$y = \sin Bx$$

Now when $Bx = 0$, $x = 0$; and when $Bx = 2\pi$, $x = 2\pi/B$.   Therefore the period p of $y = \sin Bx$ is $p = 2\pi/B$ (Fig. 13.12).   Combining these two ideas, we have $y = A \sin Bx$ (Fig. 13.13).

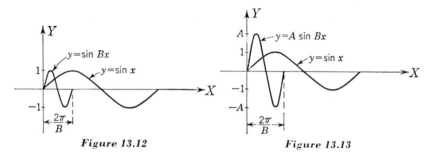

Figure 13.12   Figure 13.13

The frequency of an oscillation is the number of periods which take place in some standard interval of time, usually one second.   Frequency is measured in periods per second, or in more usual language, in cycles per second.   A cycle is the same thing as a period.   In radio broadcasting the convenient unit is kilocycles (one thousand cycles) per second.   These are the numbers on your radio dial.   The usual house current is "60-cycle" current, and this means a frequency of 60 cycles per second.

If an oscillation has a period of p seconds, it has a frequency of $\omega = 1/p$ cycles per second.   The frequency of $A \sin Bx$ is $\omega = B/2\pi$ and the frequency of $A \sin (2\pi\omega t)$ is ω cycles per second.

Consider, now, the graph of $y = \sin (x + C)$.   When $x + C = 0$, $x = -C$, and when $x + C = 2\pi$, $x = 2\pi - C$.   The graph, indicated in Fig. 13.14, is therefore a sine wave shifted to the *left* by an amount C.

The constant C is called the *phase shift*, or *phase angle*.

For the wave $y = \sin (Bx + C)$, we note that when $Bx + C = 0$,

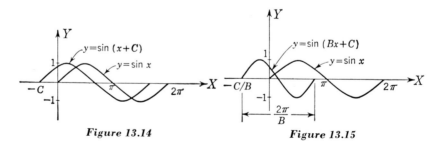

Figure 13.14   Figure 13.15

$x = -C/B$ and when $Bx + C = 2\pi$, $x = (2\pi - C)/B$ (Fig. 13.15).
Here the *phase shift* is represented by the number $-C/B$.

Finally we combine all of these ideas in the representation of the most general sine wave:

$$y = A \sin (Bx + C)$$

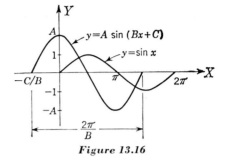

The *amplitude* is A, the *period* is $2\pi/B$, and the *phase shift* is $-C/B$ (Fig. 13.16).

Similar remarks apply to the graphs of the other functions.

Figure 13.16

PROBLEMS 13.4

In Probs. 1 to 22 sketch the graph. Label amplitude (where meaningful), period, and phase shift.

1. $y = 2 \sin (x + \pi/4)$.
2. $y = \frac{1}{2} \sin (x - \pi/4)$.
3. $y = 3 \cos ((x - \pi/4)$.
4. $y = 4 \cos (x + \pi/4)$.
5. $y = \frac{1}{2} \sin (2x + \pi/3)$.
6. $y = 2 \cos (2x - \pi/6)$.
7. $y = 2 \sin (x/2 - \pi/2)$.
8. $y = \frac{1}{2} \cos (x - \pi/2)$.
9. $y = \frac{1}{3} \sin 3x$.
10. $y = \frac{1}{3} \cos 3x$.
11. $y = 2 \tan (x + \pi/4)$.
12. $y = 3 \tan (x - \pi/4)$.
13. $y = \tan (x + \pi/2)$.
14. $y = 2 \tan (2x + \pi/3)$.
15. $y = 2 \cot (x/2 + \pi/6)$.
16. $y = \cot (x - \pi/2)$.
17. $y = \frac{1}{2} \cot (2x + \pi/3)$.
18. $y = 3 \cot (x/3 - \pi/3)$.
19. $y = \frac{1}{2} \sec 2x$.
20. $y = 2 \sec (x/2)$.
21. $y = \frac{1}{2} \csc 2x$.
22. $y = 2 \csc (x/2)$.
23. Prove that, for any A_1, A_2, B, $y = A_1 \sin Bx + A_2 \cos Bx$ represents a sine wave, and determine its amplitude, period, and phase shift.

13.5. *Addition Theorems*

Let us consider a function f and its values $f(x_1)$ and $f(x_2)$, where x_1 and x_2 are to be thought of as any two x's in the domain of definition such that $x_1 + x_2$ is also in the domain. The following general question arises: "What can we say about $f(x_1 + x_2)$ in terms of $f(x_1)$ and $f(x_2)$ separately?" Such a theorem is referred to as an *addition theorem for the function f.* Both classical and modern mathematics place emphasis on the discovery and use of such theorems. They are of special importance in trigonometry where we should like to know the answers to the following questions:

(*a*) Can we express $\sin (\theta \pm \phi)$ and $\cos (\theta \pm \phi)$ in terms of $\sin \theta$, $\sin \phi$, $\cos \theta$, and $\cos \phi$?

(*b*) If so, what are the formulas?

We can easily find one for $\phi - \theta$ by using the Law of Cosines. Suppose that we are given θ and ϕ as in either Fig. 13.17a or Fig. 13.17b. On the terminal side of θ choose $P(\cos \theta, \sin \theta)$ such that $OP = 1$. Similarly choose $Q(\cos \phi, \sin \phi)$ on the terminal side of ϕ with $OQ = 1$. Draw the triangle OPQ. The angle POQ may be equal to $\theta - \phi$ (Fig. 13.17a) or to $\phi - \theta$ (Fig. 13.17b) or to either of these plus or minus $2n\pi$ according to the respective values of θ and ϕ.

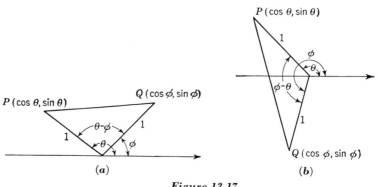

Figure 13.17

The length of PQ can be computed in two ways. First the formula for distance in polar coordinates (Sec. 12.5) gives:

(1) $$\overline{PQ}^2 = 2 - 2(\cos \theta \cos \phi + \sin \theta \sin \phi)$$

From the Law of Cosines

$$\overline{PQ}^2 = 2 - 2 \cos \angle POQ$$

Although $\angle POQ$ may, according to the circumstances, have different expressions in terms of θ and ϕ, all of these have the same cosine; and we can write for all cases:

$$\cos \angle POQ = \cos (\phi - \theta)$$

Hence

(2) $$PQ^2 = 2 - 2 \cos (\phi - \theta)$$

Combining (1) and (2), we have at once:

(3) $$\cos (\phi - \theta) = \cos \theta \cos \phi + \sin \theta \sin \phi$$

This is exactly the kind of formula we are seeking. It is an identity which expresses the cosine of the difference of two real numbers ϕ and θ in terms of the sines and cosines of ϕ and θ separately. You must memorize formula (3); it is one of the "addition theorems" for the

trigonometric functions.   We now derive three others, namely, (6)
(10), and (11) below.
    Directly from the definitions of $\sin \theta$ and $\cos \theta$ it follows that

(4) $$\sin (-\theta) = -\sin \theta$$

and

(5) $$\cos (-\theta) = \cos \theta$$

In (3) put $\theta = -\alpha$.   [We may do this since (6) is an identity.]   We
get $\cos (\phi + \alpha) = \cos \phi \cos (-\alpha) + \sin \phi \sin (-\alpha)$.   Using (4) and
(5), this simplifies to the second important "addition theorem":

(6) $$\cos (\phi + \alpha) = \cos \phi \cos \alpha - \sin \phi \sin \alpha$$

    Next in (3) let us put $\theta = \pi/2$.   We get

$$\cos \left(\phi - \frac{\pi}{2} \right) = \cos \phi \cos \frac{\pi}{2} + \sin \phi \sin \frac{\pi}{2}$$

or

(7) $$\cos \left(\phi - \frac{\pi}{2} \right) = \sin \phi$$

If we put $\alpha = \phi - \pi/2$, or $\phi = \alpha + \pi/2$ in (7), we can write (7) in
the form:

(8) $$\cos \alpha = \sin \left(\alpha + \frac{\pi}{2} \right)$$

Similarly by putting $\theta = -\pi/2$ in (3), we obtain

(9) $$\cos \left(\phi + \frac{\pi}{2} \right) = -\sin \phi$$

    We are now ready to derive the addition theorem for $\sin (\phi - \theta)$.
We use (7) to write

$$\sin (\phi - \theta) = \cos \left[(\phi - \theta) - \frac{\pi}{2} \right] = \cos \left[\phi - \left(\theta + \frac{\pi}{2} \right) \right]$$

Now apply (3) to the right-hand expression, and obtain

$$\sin (\phi - \theta) = \cos \phi \cos \left(\theta + \frac{\pi}{2} \right) + \sin \phi \sin \left(\theta + \frac{\pi}{2} \right)$$

Using (8) and (9), we can simplify this to

$$\sin (\phi - \theta) = -\cos \phi \sin \theta + \sin \phi \cos \theta$$

or

(10) $$\sin (\phi - \theta) = \sin \phi \cos \theta - \cos \phi \sin \theta$$

This is the desired result.

Finally, putting $\theta = -\alpha$ in (10), we obtain

(11) $\sin (\phi + \alpha) = \sin \phi \cos \alpha + \cos \phi \sin \alpha$

We now collect (3), (6), (10), and (11) and write them in the form:

(I) $\sin (\phi \pm \theta) = \sin \phi \cos \theta \pm \cos \phi \sin \theta$
(II) $\cos (\phi \pm \theta) = \cos \phi \cos \theta \mp \sin \phi \sin \theta$

To develop a formula for $\tan (\phi \pm \theta)$, write

$$\tan (\phi \pm \theta) = \frac{\sin \phi \cos \theta \pm \cos \phi \sin \theta}{\cos \phi \cos \theta \mp \sin \phi \sin \theta}$$

$$= \frac{\dfrac{\sin \phi \cos \theta}{\cos \phi \cos \theta} \pm \dfrac{\cos \phi \sin \theta}{\cos \phi \cos \theta}}{\dfrac{\cos \phi \cos \theta}{\cos \phi \cos \theta} \mp \dfrac{\sin \phi \sin \theta}{\cos \phi \cos \theta}}$$

(III) $$= \frac{\tan \phi \pm \tan \theta}{1 \mp \tan \phi \tan \theta}$$

You should study this material until you understand it thoroughly. Be sure to note that I, II, and III are identities which hold for all values of θ amd ϕ. They should be memorized.

PROBLEMS 13.5

In Probs. 1 to 16 make use of (I), (II), (III) to compute without tables. (Leave answer in radical form.)

1. $\sin \left(\dfrac{\pi}{4} + \dfrac{\pi}{6} \right) = \sin 75°.$ **2.** $\sin \left(\dfrac{\pi}{4} - \dfrac{\pi}{6} \right) = \sin 15°.$

3. $\sin \left(\dfrac{\pi}{3} + \dfrac{\pi}{4} \right).$ **4.** $\sin \left(\dfrac{\pi}{3} - \dfrac{\pi}{4} \right).$

5. $\cos \left(\dfrac{\pi}{4} + \dfrac{\pi}{6} \right) = \cos 75°.$ **6.** $\cos \left(\dfrac{\pi}{4} - \dfrac{\pi}{6} \right) = \cos 15°.$

7. $\cos \left(\dfrac{\pi}{3} + \dfrac{\pi}{4} \right).$ **8.** $\cos \left(\dfrac{\pi}{3} - \dfrac{\pi}{4} \right).$

9. $\tan (5\pi/12).$ **10.** $\tan (\pi/12).$
11. $\tan (7\pi/12).$ **12.** $\cot (7\pi/12).$
13. $\sec (5\pi/12).$ **14.** $\sec (7\pi/12).$
15. $\csc (5\pi/12).$ **16.** $\csc (7\pi/12).$

In Probs. 17 to 24 reduce to a function of θ.

17. $\sin \left(\dfrac{\pi}{2} \pm \theta \right).$ **18.** $\cos \left(\dfrac{\pi}{2} \pm \theta \right).$

19. $\sin (\pi \pm \theta).$ **20.** $\cos (\pi \pm \theta).$

21. $\tan \left(\dfrac{\pi}{2} \pm \theta \right).$ **22.** $\tan (\pi \pm \theta).$

23. $\sin\left(\dfrac{3\pi}{2} \pm \theta\right).$ **24.** $\cos\left(\dfrac{3\pi}{2} \pm \theta\right).$

25. Show that $\cos (13\pi/12) = -\frac{1}{4}(\sqrt{2} + \sqrt{6}).$

26. Show that $\sin (13\pi/12) = \frac{1}{4}(\sqrt{2} - \sqrt{6}).$

27. Show that for some numbers α and β $\sin (\alpha + \beta) \neq \sin \alpha + \sin \beta.$

28. Given $\sin \alpha = -\frac{4}{5}(\alpha$ in fourth quadrant) and $\tan \beta = -\frac{5}{12}(\beta$ in second quadrant), find $\sin (\alpha - \beta)$ and $\cos (\alpha - \beta).$

In Probs. 29 to 33 simplify to a single function of some number.

29. $\sin 2 \cos 1 + \cos 2 \sin 1.$ **30.** $\sin 7 \cos 4 - \cos 7 \sin 4.$

31. $\cos 2 \cos 3 + \sin 2 \sin 3.$ **32.** $\cos 2 \cos \frac{1}{2} - \sin 2 \sin \frac{1}{2}.$

33. $\dfrac{\tan 0.1 + \tan 0.2}{1 - \tan 0.1 \tan 0.2}.$

34. Verify the steps in the following proof of the formula for $\sin (\phi - \theta)$, where we assume $0 < \phi - \theta < \pi.$

In Fig. 13.17*b* the area K of the triangle POQ is given in the two following ways:

$$K = \tfrac{1}{2} \sin (\phi - \theta) \qquad \text{[Prob. 13, Sec. 12.12]}$$

$$K = \frac{1}{2} \begin{vmatrix} \cos \theta & \sin \theta & 1 \\ \cos \phi & \sin \phi & 1 \\ 0 & 0 & 1 \end{vmatrix} \qquad \text{[Prob. 27, Sec. 7.11]}$$

$$= \tfrac{1}{2}(\sin \phi \cos \theta - \cos \phi \sin \theta)$$

Therefore $\sin (\phi - \theta) = \sin \phi \cos \theta - \cos \phi \sin \theta.$

35. Derive formula (3) for $\cos (\phi - \theta)$ from the result of Prob. 34.

13.6. *Multiple- and Half-angle Formulas*

The general formulas, or identities, (I), (II), (III) of Sec. 13.5 have some extremely important special cases. These we now derive and we shall mark with Roman numerals the ones you should memorize. They play important roles in all branches of mathematics and in all of the sciences.

From (I), with $\phi = \theta$, it immediately follows that

(IV) $$\sin 2\theta = 2 \sin \theta \cos \theta$$

Similarly from (II)

(V) $$\cos 2\theta = \cos^2 \theta - \sin^2 \theta$$

This can be written in two other ways by making use of the identity $\sin^2 \theta + \cos^2 \theta = 1.$ These are

(VI) $$\cos 2\theta = 1 - 2 \sin^2 \theta$$
(VII) $$\cos 2\theta = 2 \cos^2 \theta - 1$$

Formula (IV) expresses the sine of *twice* a number in terms of the sine and cosine of the number itself. Each of the three formulas (V) to (VII) expresses the cosine of *twice* a number in terms of sine and cosine of the number itself.

Exercise A. Discover a formula for tan 2θ in terms of tan θ.

Now (VI) can be written in the form $\cos x = 1 - 2 \sin^2 (x/2)$ where $2\theta = x$. If we now solve for $\sin^2 (x/2)$ (but now write $\theta/2$ instead of $x/2$), we get

$$\sin^2 \frac{\theta}{2} = \frac{1 - \cos \theta}{2}$$

from which

(VIII) $$\sin \frac{\theta}{2} = \pm \sqrt{\frac{1 - \cos \theta}{2}}$$

The sign before the radical is to be chosen $+$ if $\theta/2$ is a first- or second-quadrantal arc. It is to be chosen $-$ if $\theta/2$ is a third- or fourth-quadrantal arc.

Similarly from (VII) we obtain

(IX) $$\cos \frac{\theta}{2} = \pm \sqrt{\frac{1 + \cos \theta}{2}}$$

Exercise B. State, for (IX), when the $+$ sign is to be used and when the $-$ sign is to be used.

Formulas (VIII) and (IX) express sine and cosine of *half* a number in terms of the cosine of the number itself. From them we develop three formulas for tangent of *half* a number.

(X) $$\tan \frac{\theta}{2} = \frac{\sin (\theta/2)}{\cos (\theta/2)} = \pm \sqrt{\frac{1 - \cos \theta}{1 + \cos \theta}}$$

(XI) $$= \frac{1 - \cos \theta}{\sin \theta}$$

(XII) $$= \frac{\sin \theta}{1 + \cos \theta}$$

Exercise C. State, for (X), when the $+$ sign is to be used and when the $-$ sign is to be used.

Exercise D. Derive (XI) and (XII). HINT for (XI):

$$\cos \frac{\theta}{2} = \cos \left(\theta - \frac{\theta}{2} \right) = \cos \theta \cos \frac{\theta}{2} + \sin \theta \sin \frac{\theta}{2}$$

Now solve for $\dfrac{\sin (\theta/2)}{\cos (\theta/2)}$.

We now return to (I) of Sec. 13.5, write

$$\sin (\phi + \theta) = \sin \phi \cos \theta + \cos \phi \sin \theta$$
$$\sin (\phi - \theta) = \sin \phi \cos \theta - \cos \phi \sin \theta$$

and add, getting, after dividing by 2,

(XIII) $\sin \phi \cos \theta = \frac{1}{2} \sin (\phi + \theta) + \frac{1}{2} \sin (\phi - \theta)$

This identity and the two following, which are derived similarly from (II), are most important in a study of the calculus.

(XIV) $\cos \phi \cos \theta = \frac{1}{2} \cos (\phi + \theta) + \frac{1}{2} \cos (\phi - \theta)$
(XV) $\sin \phi \sin \theta = -\frac{1}{2} \cos (\phi + \theta) + \frac{1}{2} \cos (\phi - \theta)$

Exercise E.   Write out the derivation of (XIV) and (XV).

The fifteen formulas (I) to (XV) constitute the basic identities. You should not only memorize them, but you should know how to derive them. They are written in terms of numbers (arcs) ϕ and θ, but, obviously, other symbols could be used, and, of course, degree measure could be used. The following problems, wherein many other letters are used, are based directly on (I) to (XV).

PROBLEMS 13.6

In Probs. 1 to 6 find a counterexample for the false statements which are asserted for all x:

1. $\frac{1}{2} \sin 2x = \sin x$.   **2.** $\frac{1}{2} \cos 2x = \cos x$.
3. $2 \sin \frac{1}{2}x = \sin x$.   **4.** $2 \cos \frac{1}{2}x = \cos x$.
5. $\frac{1}{2} \tan 2x = \tan x$.   **6.** $2 \tan \frac{1}{2}x = \tan x$.
7. Derive the formula

$$\cot (\alpha + \beta) = \frac{\cot \alpha \cot \beta - 1}{\cot \alpha + \cot \beta}$$

8. Derive the formula

$$\cot (\alpha - \beta) = \frac{\cot \alpha \cot \beta + 1}{- \cot \alpha + \cot \beta}$$

9. Prove: $\sin 3x = 3 \sin x - 4 \sin^3 x$.
10. Prove: $\cos 3x = 4 \cos^3 x - 3 \cos x$.

In Probs. 11 to 16 let $\sin x = \frac{15}{17}$, $\cos x < 0$, $\tan y = -\frac{12}{5}$, and $\sin y < 0$. Then find

11. $\sin (x + y)$.   **12.** $\cos (x + y)$.
13. $\sin (x - y)$.   **14.** $\cos (x - y)$.
15. $\tan (y - x)$.   **16.** $\cot (\pi + x)$.
17. Derive a formula for $\sin 4z$ in terms of $\sin z$ and $\cos z$.
18. Derive a formula for $\cos 4z$ in terms of $\sin z$ and $\cos z$.
19. Derive a formula for $\tan 4z$ in terms of $\tan z$.

In Probs. 20 to 23, let $\sin 4\theta = \frac{1}{2}$ and $\tan 4\theta > 0$.   Then find

20. $\sin 2\theta$. **21.** $\cos 2\theta$.

22. $\sin 8\theta$. **23.** $\cos 8\theta$.

24. Prove: $\sin \left(\dfrac{\pi}{4} - x \right) = \dfrac{\cos x - \sin x}{\sqrt{2}}$.

25. Prove: $\cos \left(\dfrac{\pi}{4} - x \right) = \dfrac{\cos x + \sin x}{\sqrt{2}}$.

Set $x + y = A$ and $x - y = B$, and use the identities (XIII) to (XV) to derive the identities:

26. $\sin A + \sin B = 2 \sin \frac{1}{2}(A + B) \cos \frac{1}{2}(A - B)$.
27. $\sin A - \sin B = 2 \cos \frac{1}{2}(A + B) \sin \frac{1}{2}(A - B)$.
28. $\cos A + \cos B = 2 \cos \frac{1}{2}(A + B) \cos \frac{1}{2}(A - B)$.
29. $\cos A - \cos B = -2 \sin \frac{1}{2}(A + B) \sin \frac{1}{2}(A - B)$.
30. Law of Tangents.   Verify the steps in the following derivation:

$$\frac{a}{b} = \frac{\sin A}{\sin B}$$

$$\frac{a + b}{b} = \frac{\sin A + \sin B}{\sin B}$$

$$\frac{a - b}{b} = \frac{\sin A - \sin B}{\sin B}$$

$$\frac{a + b}{a - b} = \frac{\sin A + \sin B}{\sin A - \sin B}$$

$$= \frac{2 \sin \frac{1}{2}(A + B) \cos \frac{1}{2}(A - B)}{2 \cos \frac{1}{2}(A + B) \sin \frac{1}{2}(A - B)}$$

$$= \frac{\tan \frac{1}{2}(A + B)}{\tan \frac{1}{2}(A - B)}$$

Show how this formula can be used to solve a triangle, given two sides and the included angle.   Compare the advantages and disadvantages of this solution with those of the solution in terms of the Law of Cosines.

13.7. *Identities*

From the basic identities given above it is possible to establish the truth of a whole host of other identities.   These are often useful in applications of mathematics, for they permit us to reduce a formidable looking trigonometric expression to something simpler and more manageable.   Before entering into the details, we must say a few words about the general idea.

Definition: An equation involving trigonometric functions of the real number x is called an *identity* if the two sides are equal for all values of x for which both sides are defined.

For example,

$$\tan x = \frac{1}{\cot x}$$

is an identity, for the two sides are equal for all x except $x = \pi/2 \pm n\pi$ (at which $\tan x$ is not defined and $\cot x = 0$) and $x = \pm n\pi$ (at which $\cot x$ is not defined).

On the other hand,

$$\sin x = \sqrt{1 - \cos^2 x}$$

is not an identity, since it is true only when $\sin x \geq 0$, that is, when x is a first- or second-quadrantal arc.

In order to prove that a given equation is an identity, we use standard algebraic processes to show that it is equivalent to a known identity. In Sec. 6.4 we discussed equivalent equations in terms of the permissible algebraic processes, but here we can be a little more relaxed. We wish to put emphasis on the *all x* part of the definition of an identity, and not on the exceptional values of x which occur when our expressions are not defined. If you will analyze our discussion in Sec. 6.4, you will see that we can now admit any algebraic process *except raising both sides of an equation to an even power (e.g., squaring).* Multiplying or dividing both sides by a nonvanishing expression is now permissible, for this affects only the exceptional values of x and does not alter the *all x* aspect of the problem. Proceed as in the following illustrations, where we have ignored the exceptional values of x.

Illustration 1. Prove the identity:

$$\frac{\sin^2 x}{1 - \cos x} = 1 + \cos x$$

Solution: Multiplying both sides by $1 - \cos x$, we get:

$$\sin^2 x = (1 - \cos x)(1 + \cos x)$$
$$= 1 - \cos^2 x$$
$$= \sin^2 x$$

which is an obvious identity.

Exercise A. What values of x are exceptional for this identity?

Illustration 2. Prove the identity:

$$\frac{\tan^3 x - \cot^3 x}{\tan x - \cot x} = \tan^2 x + \csc^2 x$$

Solution 1. We recall that $\csc^2 x = 1 + \cot^2 x$; so we have:

$$\frac{\tan^3 x - \cot^3 x}{\tan x - \cot x} = \tan^2 x + 1 + \cot^2 x$$

Multiplying both sides by $\tan x - \cot x$, we obtain:

$$\tan^3 x - \cot^3 x = (\tan^2 x + 1 + \cot^2 x)(\tan x - \cot x)$$
$$= \tan^3 x + \tan x + \tan x \cot^2 x - \cot x \tan^2 x - \cot x - \cot^3 x$$

But

$$\tan x = \frac{1}{\cot x}$$

and so this becomes

$$\tan^3 x - \cot^3 x = \tan^3 x + \tan x + \cot x - \tan x - \cot x - \cot^3 x$$
$$= \tan^3 x - \cot^3 x$$

Solution 2. The numerator on the left factors; so we can write:

$$\frac{(\tan x - \cot x)(\tan^2 x + \tan x \cot x + \cot^2 x)}{\tan x - \cot x} = \tan^2 x + 1 + \cot^2 x$$

Dividing out $\tan x - \cot x$ on the left, we have:

$$\tan^2 x + \tan x \cot x + \cot^2 x = \tan^2 x + 1 + \cot^2 x$$

or
$$\tan^2 x + 1 + \cot^2 x = \tan^2 x + 1 + \cot^2 x$$

Exercise B. What values of x are exceptional for this identity?

Illustration 3. Prove the identity:

$$\sec 2x = \frac{\csc^2 x}{\csc^2 x - 2}$$

Solution: Since we have not derived a formula for $\sec 2x$, we convert $\sec 2x$ into $1/\cos 2x$ and obtain:

$$\frac{1}{\cos 2x} = \frac{\csc^2 x}{\csc^2 x - 2}$$

Expressing everything in terms of $\sin x$, we write:

$$\frac{1}{1 - 2\sin^2 x} = \frac{1/\sin^2 x}{(1/\sin^2 x) - 2}$$
$$= \frac{1/\sin^2 x}{(1 - 2\sin^2 x)/\sin^2 x}$$
$$= \frac{1}{1 - 2\sin^2 x}$$

Exercise C. What values of x are exceptional for this identity?

PROBLEMS 13.7

Prove the following identities:

1. $\sin x(\cot x + \csc x) = \cos x + 1$.   **2.** $\dfrac{\sin x \sec x}{\tan x + \cot x} = 1 - \cos^2 x$.

3. $\tan x + \cot x = \sec x \csc x.$

4. $\dfrac{1 + \tan x}{1 - \tan x} + \dfrac{1 + \cot x}{1 - \cot x} = 0.$

5. $\dfrac{\sec x}{\csc x} = \dfrac{1 + \tan x}{1 + \cot x}.$

6. $\dfrac{\sin x + \cos x}{\sec x + \csc x} = \dfrac{\sin x}{\sec x}.$

7. $\dfrac{1 - \sin x}{\cos x} = \dfrac{\cos x}{1 + \sin x}.$

8. $\dfrac{1 + \cos x}{\sin x} + \dfrac{\sin x}{1 + \cos x} = 2 \csc x.$

9. $4 \sin^2 x \cos^2 x = 1 - \cos^2 2x.$

10. $\dfrac{1 - \cos 2x}{\sin 2x} = \tan x.$

11. $\csc x - \cot x = \tan \frac{1}{2} x.$

12. $\sin^2 7x + \cos 14x = \cos^2 7x.$

13. $\cos (x + y) \cos y + \sin (x + y) \sin y = \cos x.$

14. $\sin x = \cos x \tan x = \dfrac{\tan x}{\sec x}.$

15. $\sec x + \tan x = \tan \left(\dfrac{x}{2} + \dfrac{\pi}{4} \right).$

16. $\csc x = \cot x + \tan \dfrac{x}{2}.$

17. $\sin 4x \cos 3x + \cos 4x \sin 3x = \sin 7x.$
18. $\cos \frac{3}{5}x \cos \frac{2}{5}x - \sin \frac{2}{5}x \sin \frac{3}{5}x = \cos x.$

13.8. *Equations*

In Exercises A, B, and C of Sec. 13.7 we encountered such equations as (A), $1 - \cos x = 0$; (B), $\tan x - \cot x = 0$; (C), $\csc^2 x - 2 = 0$. These are quite evidently not identities but are conditional equalities or simply equations. The equation of Exercise A is true if and only if $x = 2n\pi$, where n is an integer; the equations of Exercises B and C are satisfied if and only if $x = \pi/4 + n(\pi/2)$, where n is an integer. A given equation might have no solution; $\sin x = 3$ is an example. In case an equation is complicated, we may not be able to tell offhand whether it is a conditional equation or an identity.

There are practically no general rules which, if followed, will lead to the roots of a trigonometric equation. You might try to factor or to solve by quadratic formula where appropriate. Or, again, you might reduce each and every trigonometric function present to one and the same function of one and the same independent variable. In this section we exhibit some of the obvious ways of solving such an equation.

Illustration 1. Solve the equation

$$2 \sin^2 x + \sin x - 1 = 0$$

for all roots.

Solution: The left-hand member is quadratic in the quantity $\sin x$; that is, it is a polynomial of the second degree in $\sin x$. It is factorable:

$$(2 \sin x - 1)(\sin x + 1) = 0$$

Thus from the first factor we get

$$2 \sin x - 1 = 0$$
$$\sin x = \tfrac{1}{2}$$
$$x = \tfrac{1}{6}\pi + 2n\pi \quad \text{[1st-quadrantal arc]}$$
$$x = \tfrac{5}{6}\pi + 2n\pi \quad \text{[2d-quadrantal arc]}$$

Exercise A.   Draw figures for these arcs.

The second factor yields

$$\sin x + 1 = 0$$
$$\sin x = -1$$
$$x = \tfrac{3}{2}\pi + 2n\pi$$

There are no other roots.

Illustration 2.   Find all values of x in the interval 0 to 2π satisfying the equation

$$\cos^2 2x + 3 \sin 2x - 3 = 0$$

Solution: This appears to offer some difficulty at first thought because of the presence of both sine and cosine.   We use the identity $\sin^2 2x + \cos^2 2x = 1$ and rewrite the equation in the form

$$1 - \sin^2 2x + 3 \sin 2x - 3 = 0$$

which factors into

$$(1 - \sin 2x)(2 - \sin 2x) = 0$$

The first factor yields

$$1 - \sin 2x = 0$$
$$\sin 2x = 1$$

$$2x = \frac{\pi}{2} + 2n\pi$$

whence

$$x = \frac{\pi}{4} + n\pi$$

The second factor leads to the equation

$$\sin 2x = 2$$

which has no solution.

Illustration 3.   Solve the equation $\tan x + 2 \sec x = 1$.

Solution: You should be able to follow each of the steps:

$$\frac{\sin x}{\cos x} + \frac{2}{\cos x} = 1$$

$$\frac{\sin x + 2}{\cos x} = 1$$

$$\sin x + 2 = \cos x \qquad \text{provided } \cos x \neq 0$$

$$= \pm \sqrt{1 - \sin^2 x}$$

$$(\sin x + 2)^2 = 1 - \sin^2 x$$

$$\sin^2 x + 4 \sin x + 4 = 1 - \sin^2 x$$

$$2 \sin^2 x + 4 \sin x + 3 = 0$$

$$\sin x = \frac{-4 \pm \sqrt{16 - 24}}{4}$$

Since we are dealing with the real numbers, we conclude that the original equation is satisfied by no real number.

Illustration 4.   Solve the equation sin $2x$ + sin x = 0.
Solution: We first write sin $2x$ = 2 sin x cos x.

$$2 \sin x \cos x + \sin x = 0$$
$$\sin x(2 \cos x + 1) = 0$$

$$\sin x = 0 \qquad\qquad \cos x = -\tfrac{1}{2}$$
$$x = 2n\pi \qquad\qquad x = \tfrac{2}{3}\pi + 2n\pi \quad \text{[2d-quadrantal arc]}$$
$$\qquad\qquad\qquad\qquad x = \tfrac{4}{3}\pi + 2n\pi \quad \text{[3d-quadrantal arc]}$$

Exercise B.   Draw figures for these arcs.

Illustration 5.   Solve the equation tan² x − 5 tan x − 4 = 0.
Solution: This is a quadratic equation in the quantity tan x.   Solving this by formula, we get

$$\tan x = \frac{5 \pm \sqrt{25 + 16}}{2}$$
$$= \tfrac{5}{2} \pm \tfrac{1}{2} \sqrt{41}$$
$$= 2.50000 \pm 3.20656$$
$$= 5.70656 \text{ and } -0.70656$$

Since these values do not correspond to any of the special arcs, we must resort to a table.   We use a table of "Natural Functions for Angles in Radians."
From tan x = 5.70656 we find that

$$x = 1.3972 + 2n\pi \qquad \text{[1st-quadrantal arc]}$$
$$x = (1.3972 + \pi) + 2n\pi \qquad \text{[3d-quadrantal arc]}$$
$$= 4.5388 + 2n\pi$$

To solve tan x = −0.70656, we first solve

$$\tan x' = +0.70656$$

This gives

$$x' = 0.6151$$

But now we must use the minus sign since at present what we have is

$$\tan 0.6151 = 0.70656$$

whereas we seek x such that tan x = −0.70656.   This means that either

$$x = \pi - x'$$
or
$$x = 2\pi - x'$$

Finally, therefore, we have

$$x = 2.5265 + 2n\pi \qquad \text{[2d-quadrantal arc]}$$
$$x = 5.6681 + 2n\pi \qquad \text{[4th-quadrantal arc]}$$

PROBLEMS 13.8

Solve the following equations for all roots:

1. $2 \cos^2 x - \cos x = 0.$
2. $2 \sin^2 x - \cos x - 1 = 0.$
3. $2 \sin^2 x - \sin x - 1 = 0.$
4. $2 \sin^2 x - \sin x = 0.$
5. $\sin 2x = \frac{1}{2}.$
6. $\cos 2x = \frac{1}{2}.$
7. $\sin 3x = \frac{1}{2}.$
8. $\cos 3x = \frac{1}{2}.$
9. $\sin 2x = \sqrt{2}/2.$
10. $\sin 2x = \sqrt{3}/2.$
11. $\cos 2x = \sqrt{2}/2.$
12. $\cos 2x = \sqrt{3}/2.$
13. $\tan^2 x = 1.$
14. $\cos^2 x = \frac{1}{2}.$
15. $\csc^2 x = \frac{4}{3}.$
16. $\sec x + 1 = 2 \cos x.$
17. $(2 \cos x + \sqrt{3})(\sec x - 2) = 0.$
18. $\csc x/\cot x = \tan x.$
19. $\cos 3x = 1.$
20. $\sin^2 x - \sin x = \frac{1}{4}.$
21. $\cos^2 x + \cos x = \frac{1}{2}.$
22. $3 \tan^2 x + \tan x = 2.$
23. $4 \cot^2 x - 4 \cot x = 5.$

13.9. *Inverse Trigonometric Functions*

When we write $y = \sin x$, we mean that given x we can find y, or "y is the sine of x." But of course, saying that "y is the sine of x" is the same as saying that "x is a real number whose sine is y." In this case we regard y as given and hence determine x.

This process should be recognized as that of forming the inverse of the function $y = \sin x$ (Sec. 9.7). You will recall that the inverse of $y = f(x)$ was obtained by first switching variables, getting $x = f(y)$, and then solving this for $y = f^{-1}(x)$. In the present case we have to invent a new name for the inverse function f^{-1} and also to restrict the domain so that an inverse function is defined. Let the domain of sine

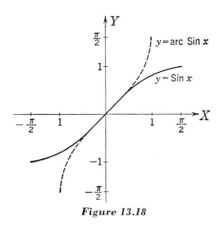

Figure 13.18

be restricted to $-\frac{\pi}{2} \le x \le \frac{\pi}{2}.$ We shall indicate this function by writing $y = \mathrm{Sin}\ x$, using a capital S, read "y equals Cap-Sin x." We shall write its inverse as $y = \mathrm{arc\ Sin}\ x$ and read "y equals arc Cap-Sin x," or "y equals inverse Cap-Sin x." If y is thought of as an angle, we may read this: "y is the angle whose Cap-Sin is x." Sometimes the notation $y = \mathrm{Sin}^{-1} x$ is used.

The two functions whose values are given by Sin x and arc Sin x are different functions; either is said to be the inverse of the other. We sketch in Fig. 13.18 the graph of $y = \mathrm{Sin}\ x$ and that of $y = \mathrm{arc\ Sin}\ x$.

The domain and range of $y = \text{Sin } x$ are $-\dfrac{\pi}{2} \le x \le \dfrac{\pi}{2}$, $-1 \le y \le 1$.

The domain and range of $y = \text{arc Sin } x$ are $-1 \le x \le 1$, $-\dfrac{\pi}{2} \le y \le \dfrac{\pi}{2}$.

Similarly we define other restricted trigonometric functions.

> $y = \text{Cos } x$, $0 \le x \le \pi$, $-1 \le y \le 1$, as cos x restricted to this domain.
>
> $y = \text{arc Cos } x$, $-1 \le x \le 1$, $0 \le y \le \pi$, as the inverse of $y = \text{Cos } x$.
>
> $y = \text{Tan } x$, $-\pi/2 < x < \pi/2$, $-\infty < y < \infty$, as tan x restricted to this domain.
>
> $y = \text{arc Tan } x$, $-\infty < x < \infty$, $-\pi/2 < y < \pi/2$, as the inverse of $y = \text{Tan } x$.

Exercise A.   Define arc Cot x.

Illustration 1.   Find $y = \text{arc Sin } \sqrt{3}/2$.

Solution: We seek the number y, where $-\pi/2 \le y \le \pi/2$, such that the sine of it is $\sqrt{3}/2$. That is, Sin $y = \sqrt{3}/2$, and, from previous knowledge, we know that $y = \pi/3$.

Illustration 2.   Find $y = \text{arc Cos } (-0.87531)$.

Solution: This is the same thing as saying Cos $y = -0.87531$ and, of course, $0 \le y \le \pi$. We use a table of natural cosines (in radian measure or, for that matter, in degree measure).

Radian Measure
("Standard Mathematical Tables," page 140)

$$0.01 \left[\Delta \begin{bmatrix} \cos 0.50 = 0.87758 \\ \cos z \quad = 0.87531 \end{bmatrix} 227 \atop \cos 0.51 = 0.87274 \right] 484$$

(We write 227 instead of 0.00227, etc.)

$$\frac{\Delta}{0.01} = \frac{227}{484}$$

$$\Delta = 0.0047$$
$$z = 0.5047$$

Therefore

Since Cos y is negative, $y > \pi/2$, we get

$$y = \pi - 0.5047$$
$$y = 2.6369$$

or

Degree Measures
("Standard Mathematical Tables," page 108)

$$1' \left[\Delta \begin{bmatrix} \cos 28°55' = 0.87532 \\ \cos z \quad = 0.87531 \end{bmatrix} 1 \atop \cos 28°56' = 0.87518 \right] 14$$

(We write 14 instead of 0.00014, etc.)

$$\frac{\Delta}{1} = \frac{1}{14} \qquad \Delta = 0.07 \approx 0.1$$

Therefore $$z = 28°55.1'$$

But Cos y is negative, and y is therefore a second-quadrantal angle

$$y = 180° - 28°55.1' = 151°4.9'$$

We can reduce 151°4.9′ to radian measure by using the "Standard Mathematical Tables," pages 194 to 197. We have (interpolating for 4.9′ ≈ 5.0′)

$$
\begin{aligned}
5' &= 0.00145 \\
1° &= 0.01745 \\
50° &= 0.87266 \\
100° &= 1.74533 \\
\hline
y = 151°5' &= 2.63689
\end{aligned}
$$

Illustration 3. Evaluate sin arc Sin 0.25837.
Solution: Keep in mind that arc Sin 0.25837 means "the number z whose sine is 0.25837, $0 \le z \le \pi/2$." The problem then can be stated as: "What is the sine of the number whose sine is 0.25837?" This is obviously 0.25837.

Illustration 4. Evaluate arc Tan $\left(\text{Tan } \dfrac{\pi}{7} \right)$.

Solution: Now tangent of $\pi/7$ is a number z. The problem is to find arc Tan z. The whole problem can be stated as: "What is the number whose tangent is tangent of $\pi/7$?" The answer is $\pi/7$.

Illustrations 3 and 4 are special cases of $f(f^{-1}) = f^{-1}(f) = E$ (see Sec. 9.7).

Illustration 5. Find $y = \cos (\text{arc Tan } x + \pi/3)$.
Solution: We use $\cos (\phi + \theta) = \cos \phi \cos \theta - \sin \phi \sin \theta.$

$$
\begin{aligned}
\cos \left(\text{arc Tan } x + \frac{\pi}{3} \right) &= \cos (\text{arc Tan } x) \cdot \cos \frac{\pi}{3} - \sin (\text{arc Tan } x) \cdot \sin \frac{\pi}{3} \\
&= \frac{1}{\sqrt{1 + x^2}} \cdot \frac{1}{2} - \frac{x}{\sqrt{1 + x^2}} \cdot \frac{\sqrt{3}}{2} \\
&= \frac{1 - \sqrt{3}\, x}{2 \sqrt{1 + x^2}}
\end{aligned}
$$

PROBLEMS 13.9

In Probs. 1 to 24 compute

1. arc Sin $\frac{1}{2} \sqrt{2}$.
2. arc Cos $\frac{1}{2} \sqrt{3}$.
3. $\text{Sin}^{-1} \frac{1}{2}$.
4. $\text{Cos}^{-1} \frac{1}{2}$.
5. arc Tan $\sqrt{3}$.
6. arc Cot $\sqrt{3}$.
7. $\text{Tan}^{-1} (-1)$.
8. $\text{Cot}^{-1} \frac{1}{3} \sqrt{3}$.
9. arc Sin $(-\frac{1}{2})$.
10. arc Cos $(-\frac{1}{2})$.
11. arc Tan (sin 270°).
12. arc Tan (cos 180°).
13. Cos (arc Sin $\frac{3}{5}$).
14. cos (arc Sin $\frac{3}{5}$).
15. tan $(\text{Tan}^{-1} 2)$.
16. Tan $(\text{Tan}^{-1} 2)$.
17. $\text{Sin}^{-1} \text{Sin } 0.3$.
18. Sin $\text{Sin}^{-1} 1$.
19. arc Sin 0.59731.
20. arc Cos 0.32987.
21. arc Tan 1.1257.
22. arc Cot -2.1475.
23. arc Sin (arc Cos $\frac{1}{2} \sqrt{2}$).
24. arc Sin (arc Sin $\frac{1}{2} \sqrt{2}$).

In Probs. 25 to 28 verify

25. $\text{Sin}^{-1} \frac{1}{2} + \text{Sin}^{-1} \frac{1}{2} \sqrt{3} = -\text{Sin}^{-1} (-1)$.
26. arc Cos $\frac{1}{2} +$ arc Cos $\frac{1}{2} \sqrt{3} =$ arc Cot 0.
27. $\text{Cos}^{-1} x = \text{Tan}^{-1} (\sqrt{1 - x^2}/x)$, $0 < x \le 1$.
28. $2 \text{Tan}^{-1} \frac{1}{3} + \text{Tan}^{-1} \frac{1}{7} = \pi/4$.

In Probs. 29 to 34 sketch the graph.

29. $y = \text{Cos } x$.
30. $y = \text{Tan } x$.
31. $y = \text{arc Cos } x$.
32. $y = \text{arc Tan } x$.
33. $y = \text{Cot } x$.
34. $y = \text{arc Cot } x$.

13.10. *Complex Numbers*

We have already met (Sec. 2.14) a complex number represented in rectangular form: $a + ib$ (or $a + bi$). There is a 1 to 1 correspond-

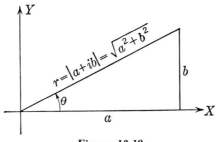

Figure 13.19

ence between such numbers and points in the plane. Now since $a = r \cos \theta$ and $b = r \sin \theta$ (Fig. 13.19),

(1) $$a + ib = r(\cos \theta + i \sin \theta)$$

where $$r = |a + ib| = \sqrt{a^2 + b^2}$$

and $$\tan \theta = \frac{b}{a}$$

The real, nonnegative number r ($= \sqrt{a^2 + b^2}$) is called the *absolute value* (or *modulus*) of the complex number and is written $|a + ib|$.

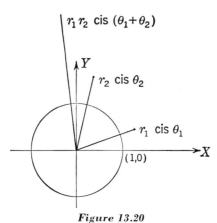

The angle θ associated with the number $a + ib$ is called the *argument* (or *amplitude*) of $a + ib$. The left-hand side of (1) is the *rectangular form* and the right-hand side is the *polar form* of a complex number. A complex number is therefore a vector having both magnitude (absolute value) and direction (argument).

Addition (and subtraction) of complex numbers is best accomplished in rectangular ($a + ib$) form. Thus

Figure 13.20

$$(a + ib) \pm (c + id) = (a \pm c) + i(b \pm d)$$

But multiplication and division are conveniently treated in polar $[r(\cos \theta + i \sin \theta)]$ form. Often, to simplify the notation, we write $r(\cos \theta + i \sin \theta)$ in the form r cis θ.

Multiplication. Consider r_1 cis θ_1 and r_2 cis θ_2, two complex numbers. Their product (Fig. 13.20) is given by

r_1 cis $\theta_1 \cdot r_2$ cis θ_2
$= r_1 r_2$ cis θ_1 cis θ_2
$= r_1 r_2 (\cos \theta_1 + i \sin \theta_1)(\cos \theta_2 + i \sin \theta_2)$
$= r_1 r_2 [(\cos \theta_1 \cos \theta_2 - \sin \theta_1 \sin \theta_2) + i(\sin \theta_1 \cos \theta_2 + \cos \theta_1 \sin \theta_2)]$
$= r_1 r_2 [\cos (\theta_1 + \theta_2) + i \sin (\theta_1 + \theta_2)]$
$= r_1 r_2$ cis $(\theta_1 + \theta_2)$

Therefore the absolute value of the product is the product of the absolute values and the argument of the product is the sum of the arguments (plus or minus a multiple of 2π).

By similar reasoning

$$r_1 \text{ cis } \theta_1 r_2 \text{ cis } \theta_2 r_3 \text{ cis } \theta_3 = r_1 r_2 r_3 \text{ cis } (\theta_1 + \theta_2 + \theta_3)$$

If the three numbers θ_1, θ_2, θ_3 are all equal to θ, and if r_1, r_2, r_3 are all equal to r, we have

$$[r \text{ cis } \theta]^3 = r^3 \text{ cis } 3\theta$$

And similarly

(2) $\qquad [r \text{ cis } \theta]^n = r^n \text{ cis } n\theta \qquad n$ a positive integer

With proper interpretations, (2) is true for any real number n, but we shall not give the proof. This is known as de Moivre's Theorem.

Theorem 1.   de Moivre's Theorem. $[r \text{ cis } \theta]^n = r^n \text{ cis } n\theta$, n real.

Exercise A.   Prove de Moivre's Theorem for the case where n is a positive integer.   HINT: Use induction.

Division.   To find the quotient of two complex numbers, write

$$\frac{r_1 \text{ cis } \theta_1}{r_2 \text{ cis } \theta_2} = \frac{r_1 \text{ cis } \theta_1}{r_2 \text{ cis } \theta_2} \times \frac{r_2 \text{ cis } (-\theta_2)}{r_2 \text{ cis } (-\theta_2)}$$

$$= \frac{r_1 r_2 \text{ cis } (\theta_1 - \theta_2)}{r_2^2 \text{ cis } 0}$$

$$= \frac{r_1}{r_2} \text{ cis } (\theta_1 - \theta_2)$$

Thus we see that the absolute value of the quotient of two complex numbers is the quotient of their absolute values and the argument of the quotient is the argument of the numerator minus the argument of the denominator (Fig. 13.21).

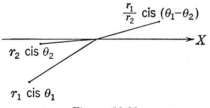

$$\frac{r_1}{r_2} \text{ cis } (\theta_1 - \theta_2)$$

$r_2 \text{ cis } \theta_2$

$r_1 \text{ cis } \theta_1$

Figure 13.21

Roots of Complex Numbers.   First, we note that the argument of a complex number is not uniquely defined.   If

$$a + ib = r \text{ cis } \theta$$

it is also equal to $r[\text{cis } (\theta + 2\pi n)]$ for any integer n.   Up to now this was not important, but we must use it here.

Given the complex number $r \text{ cis } \theta$, we seek to find all complex numbers whose pth powers are equal to $r \text{ cis } \theta$.   These are called its pth roots.   From de Moivre's Theorem we see at once that for every n

$$\left[r^{1/p} \text{ cis } \left(\frac{\theta + 2\pi n}{p} \right) \right]^p = r \text{ cis } (\theta + 2\pi n) = r \text{ cis } \theta$$

Therefore the numbers (Fig. 13.22)

(3)
$$r^{1/p} \operatorname{cis} \left(\frac{\theta + 2\pi n}{p} \right)$$

are pth roots of $r \operatorname{cis} \theta$. It can be shown that these comprise all the pth roots.

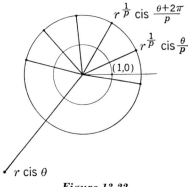

Figure 13.22

Exercise B. If $[R \operatorname{cis} \phi]^p = r \operatorname{cis} \theta$, show that $R \operatorname{cis} \phi$ must have the form (3) for some value of n.

Let us examine (3) for various values of n. Letting $n = 0$, we have

$$r^{1/p} \operatorname{cis} \frac{\theta}{p}$$

In more advanced books this is called the *principal* pth root of $r \operatorname{cis} \theta$ and is denoted by the symbol $(r \operatorname{cis} \theta)^{1/p}$. Letting $n = 1$, we have

$$r^{1/p} \operatorname{cis} \frac{\theta + 2\pi}{p}$$

Each of these two (distinct) numbers is a pth root of $r \operatorname{cis} \theta$. By letting $n = 2, 3, \ldots, p - 1$, we obtain $p - 2$ other distinct pth roots. Letting $n = p$, we have

$$r^{1/p} \operatorname{cis} \frac{\theta + 2\pi p}{p} = r^{1/p} \operatorname{cis} \frac{\theta}{p}$$

which yields the same result as did $n = 0$. And $n = p + 1$ yields the same result as $n = 1$, etc. Therefore there are p (distinct), and only p, pth roots of a complex number, $a + ib = r \operatorname{cis} \theta$.   These are given by

(4) $\qquad r^{1/p} \operatorname{cis} \left(\dfrac{\theta + 2\pi n}{p} \right) \qquad n = 0, 1, 2, \ldots, p - 1$

You should memorize (4).

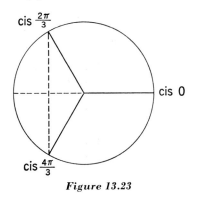

Figure 13.23

Illustration 1.   Find the three cube roots of 1 (Fig. 13.23).   Since

$$1 = 1 + i0$$

$r = 1$, and $\theta = 0$.   Thus $1 = \operatorname{cis}(0 + 2\pi n)$.   The cube roots are

$$1^{\frac{1}{3}} \operatorname{cis} \frac{0 + 2\pi n}{3} \qquad n = 0, 1, 2$$

or $\qquad 1 \operatorname{cis} 0 = 1$

$$1 \operatorname{cis} \frac{2\pi}{3} = \cos \frac{2\pi}{3} + i \sin \frac{2\pi}{3} = -\frac{1}{2} + i \frac{\sqrt{3}}{2}$$

$$1 \operatorname{cis} \frac{4\pi}{3} = \cos \frac{4\pi}{3} + i \sin \frac{4\pi}{3} = -\frac{1}{2} - i \frac{\sqrt{3}}{2}$$

To check the result, multiply out $\left(-\dfrac{1}{2} + i \dfrac{\sqrt{3}}{2} \right)^3$ and $\left(-\dfrac{1}{2} - i \dfrac{\sqrt{3}}{2} \right)^3$.   The results should be 1.

This example is equivalent to solving the equation

$$x^3 - 1 = 0$$

or $\qquad (x - 1)(x^2 + x + 1) = 0$

The roots are

$$x = 1$$

$$x = \frac{-1 \pm \sqrt{1 - 4}}{2} = -\frac{1}{2} \pm i \frac{\sqrt{3}}{2}$$

PROBLEMS 13.10

In Probs. 1 to 10 change the following to polar form:

1. $1 + i \sqrt{3}.$

2. $1 - i \sqrt{3}.$

3. $-1 - i.$

4. $-1 + i.$

5. $-i.$

6. $i.$

7. $-1.$

8. $1.$

9. $\dfrac{1}{2} + i \dfrac{\sqrt{2}}{2}.$

10. $\dfrac{1}{2} - i \dfrac{\sqrt{2}}{2}.$

In Probs. 11 to 20 change the following to rectangular form:

11. cis $0°.$

12. cis $30°.$

13. 2 cis $45°.$

14. 5 cis $60°.$

15. 2 cis $150°.$

16. 10 cis $210°.$

17. 4 cis $270°.$

18. 3 cis $315°.$

19. 4 cis $(-\pi/3).$

20. 3 cis $(-\pi/4).$

In Probs. 21 to 24 find the product of:

21. 2 cis $45°$ and 3 cis $120°.$

22. 3 cis $30°$ and 5 cis $180°.$

23. 4 cis π and 3 cis $(-\pi/2).$

24. cis $(\pi/3)$ and 7 cis $(\pi/6).$

In Probs. 25 to 28 find the quotient of:

25. 2 cis $45°$ by 3 cis $120°.$

26. 3 cis $30°$ by 5 cis $180°.$

27. 100 cis $(5\pi/4)$ by 20 cis $(\pi/4).$

28. 5 cis 3π by 2 cis $(3\pi/2).$

In Probs. 29 to 32 find the fourth power of:

29. 2 cis $220°.$

30. 3 cis $15°.$

31. 2 cis $(7\pi/4).$

32. 5 cis $(\pi/6).$

33. Find the three cube roots of 8 cis $(3\pi/2).$ Plot them and the original number.

34. Find the four fourth roots of -1, and plot all five numbers.

35. Find the four fourth roots of 1, and plot all five numbers.

36. Find the four fourth roots of i, and plot all five numbers.

37. Find the three cube roots of 27 cis π, and plot all four numbers.

38. Find all roots of the equation $x^5 - 1 = 0.$

39. Find all roots of the equation $x^5 - 32 = 0.$

40. Find all roots of the equation $4x^4 - 25 = 0.$

41. Find all roots of the equation $3x^3 - 4 = 0.$

CHAPTER FOURTEEN

Analytic Geometry

14.1. *Introduction*

René Descartes (1596–1650) introduced the subject of analytic geometry with the publishing of his "La Géométrie" in 1637. Accordingly it is often referred to as *cartesian* geometry; it is, essentially, merely a method of studying geometry by means of a coordinate system and an associated algebra. The application of this basic idea enabled the mathematicians of the seventeenth century to make the first noteworthy advances in the field of geometry since the days of Euclid. The next great advance came with the invention of the calculus (see Chaps. 15 and 16).

There are two central problems in plane analytic geometry:

(*a*) Given an equation in x and y, to plot its graph, or to represent it geometrically as a set of points in the plane.

(*b*) Given a set of points in the plane, defined by certain geometric conditions, to find an equation whose graph will consist wholly of this set of points.

The second problem is frequently called a *locus problem*. A locus is the geometric counterpart of a relation, and we define it as follows:

Definition: A *locus* is a subset of the set of points in the plane.

A locus is defined by some geometric conditions, usually expressed in words. Let P represent an arbitrary point in the plane; then the following are examples of loci:

(1) $\{P \mid P$ is at a fixed distance r from a point $C\}$; this locus is then a circle with radius r and center C.

(2) $\{P \mid PA = PB,$ where A and B are fixed points$\}$; this locus is the perpendicular bisector of the segment AB.

(3) $\{P \mid P$ is a fixed point on the rim of a wheel which rolls along a line$\}$; this locus is called a cycloid.

Many loci are defined in terms of a physical notion like example (3). For this reason you may run across statements like: "The locus of a point which moves so that . . . ." Since there is no motion in geometry, we prefer to avoid this language except in applications to mechanics.

When we are given such a locus, the problem before us is to find the corresponding relation. That is, we seek an equation whose graph is the given locus. We call this an *equation of the locus*. Having found such an equation, we study its properties by algebraic means and thus derive properties of the locus.

We have studied the notion of distance between two points (length of a line segment) when the points have given coordinates with respect to rectangular axes. We now wish to consider some related problems.

14.2. *Mid-point of a Line Segment*

Consider a line segment $P_1(x_1,y_1)$, $P_2(x_2,y_2)$. We seek the coordinates $(\bar{x},\bar{y})$ of the mid-point P in terms of x_1, y_1, x_2, and y_2. From Fig. 14.1 it is evident that

$$(1) \qquad \frac{x_2 - x_1}{P_1P_2} = \frac{\bar{x} - x_1}{P_1P}$$

But $P_1P_2 = 2P_1P$. Therefore (1) becomes

$$\frac{x_2 - x_1}{2} = \frac{\bar{x} - x_1}{1}$$

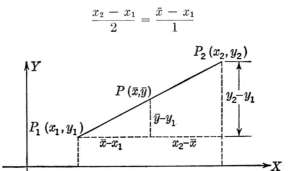

Figure 14.1

from which we get

$$2\bar{x} - 2x_1 = x_2 - x_1$$
$$2\bar{x} = x_1 + x_2$$

or

$$\bar{x} = \frac{x_1 + x_2}{2}$$

Similarly,

$$\bar{y} = \frac{y_1 + y_2}{2}$$

Exercise A. From Fig. 14.1 derive the expression for $\bar{y}$.

Thus the X-coordinate of the mid-point is the average of the X-coordinates of the end points; the Y-coordinate is the average of the Y-coordinates of the end points. For example, the mid-point of the segment whose end points are $(-1,5)$, $(4,-7)$ has coordinates $(\frac{3}{2},-1)$.

Exercise B. Find the coordinates of the mid-points of the sides of the triangle whose vertices are $A(4,7)$, $B(-3,-3)$, $C(2,-5)$.

14.3. *Directed Line Segment*

Often it is desirable to associate with a line segment (or line) the notion of *direction* or *sense*. When sense becomes important, it will

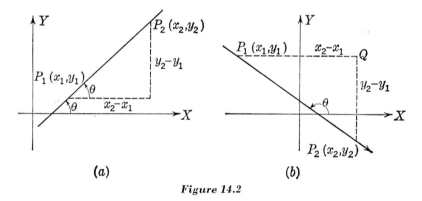

(a)   (b)

Figure 14.2

be specified by the order in which the end points are given, by an arrow appropriately placed in the figure, or in some other unambiguous way. Thus in Fig. 14.2a the line segment P_1P_2 is to be considered without sense, whereas the segment P_1P_2, with the arrow attached as in Fig. 14.2b, has the positive direction $\overrightarrow{P_1P_2}$ and the negative direction $\overrightarrow{P_2P_1}$. We write $\overrightarrow{P_1P_2} = -\overrightarrow{P_2P_1}$. If sense is unimportant, no mention will be made of it.

Definition: The *senses* of the X-axis and the Y-axis are in the positive directions.

14.4. *Rise, Run, Slope, Inclination*

A line which is not parallel to a coordinate axis may *rise from lower left to upper right*, as in Fig. 14.2a, or it may *fall from upper left to lower right*, as in Fig. 14.2b. This language implies that the observer is oriented from left to right even though the line or line segment P_1P_2 may not be! Intuitively we are looking uphill in the first instance and downhill in the second. In order to clarify these ideas, we lay down the following definitions with respect to the line determined by $P_1(x_1,y_1)$ and $P_2(x_2,y_2)$, where $x_2 > x_1$ and $y_2 > y_1$, which is the situation in Fig. 14.2a.

Definitions: The positive number $y_2 - y_1$ is called the *rise*, and the positive number $x_2 - x_1$ is called the *run*.

Remark. When P_1 and P_2 are in other positions, the words *rise* and *run* are, strictly speaking, no longer appropriate although the quantities $x_2 - x_1$ and $y_2 - y_1$ are well defined in all cases. That which is important here is given in the following definition:

Definition: When $x_2 - x_1 \neq 0$, the number

$$m = \frac{y_2 - y_1}{x_2 - x_1}$$

is called the *slope* of the line.

Remarks. The slope of a line parallel to the Y-axis ($x_2 - x_1 = 0$) is not defined. The slope of a line parallel to the X-axis ($y_2 - y_1 = 0$) is zero. Where rise and run apply, slope = rise/run. Since

$$\frac{y_2 - y_1}{x_2 - x_1} = \frac{y_1 - y_2}{x_1 - x_2}$$

it makes no difference how we label the points when computing slope.

If the same units and scales are used on the X- and Y-axes, still another notion is of use according to the following definition:

Definition: If x and y are measured in the same units, we call θ, where $m = \tan \theta$, the *inclination*. That is, $\theta = \text{arc Tan } m$, $0° \leq \theta < 180°$, θ being measured counterclockwise from the positive X-axis.

The inclination of a line parallel to the X-axis is zero, and the inclination of a line parallel to the Y-axis is 90° from other considerations. The notion of inclination is of no value if x and y are in different units such as, for example, if x represents "calendar year" and y represents "dollars per ton-mile." On the other hand, slope defined by

$$\text{Slope} = m = \frac{y_2 - y_1}{x_2 - x_1} = \frac{\text{rise}}{\text{run}} \qquad x_2 \neq x_1$$

is useful regardless of the units employed. If units and scales are the same on the two axes, it is meaningful to say that

$$\tan \theta = \frac{y_2 - y_1}{x_2 - x_1} \qquad x_2 \neq x_1$$

In analytic geometry we always assume equal scales on the two axes.

Directly from Fig. 14.1 or Fig. 14.2 and the Pythagorean theorem, it follows that the positive distance

$$d = P_1 P_2 = \sqrt{(x_2 - x_1)^2 + (y_2 - y_1)^2}$$

This was also developed in Sec. 12.1.

PROBLEMS 14.4

In Probs. 1 to 9 find the coordinates of the mid-point of the line segment joining the given points.

1. (2,5), (4,1).   **2.** (4,6), (8,2).
3. (5,11), (7,7).   **4.** $(-3,6)$, (0,1).
5. $(9,-3)$, $(-5,7)$.   **6.** $(-8,0)$, $(0,-8)$.
7. $(1,k)$, $(2,3k)$.   **8.** $(a,0)$, $(-a,0)$.
9. (a,b), (c,d).

In Probs. 10 to 18 find (a) rise, (b) run, where meaningful, and (c) slope of the line joining the given points.

10. (1,2), (2,4).   **11.** $(-1,2)$, (1,5).
12. $(-3,-1)$, $(2,-1)$.   **13.** $(4,-5)$, $(6,-5)$.
14. $(3,-9)$, (2,7).   **15.** (20,10), $(-5,25)$.
16. (30,6), $(25,-20)$.   **17.** (90,50), (3,17).
18. (BT) (8,0), (8,4).

In Probs. 19 to 30 find (a) slope and (b) inclination of the line joining the given points.

19. (4,0), (11,0).   **20.** (6,20), (20,20).
21. $(-8,-6)$, $(-5,-3)$.   **22.** $(-4,3)$, $(-1,0)$.
23. (0,2), $(1, 2 + \sqrt{3})$.   **24.** $(1,-\sqrt{3})$, (2,0).
25. $(1,-\sqrt{3})$, $(2,-2\sqrt{3})$.   **26.** (4,1), $(3, 1 + \sqrt{3})$.
27. $(\sqrt{3},-1)$, $(0,-2)$.   **28.** $(-5,0)$, $(\sqrt{3} - 5, 1)$.
29. (0,0), (2,4).   **30.** (0,0), $(-3,1)$.

In Probs. 31 to 36 find the rise and run (where meaningful) and distance for the line segment P_1P_2.

31. $P_1(2,-3)$, $P_2(-3,-9)$.   **32.** $P_1(4,0)$, $P_2(-4,-4)$.
33. $P_1(6,16)$, $P_2(7,12)$.   **34.** $P_1(20,30)$, $P_2(20,40)$.
35. $P_1(10,20)$, $P_2(20,20)$.   **36.** $P_1(5,12)$, $P_2(-8,16)$.

In Probs. 37 to 40 the point P is the mid-point of P_1P_2. Find the coordinates of

37. P_2, given $P_1(4,6)$, $P(2,3)$.   **38.** P_2, given $P_1(-3,2)$, $P(2,-5)$.
39. P_1, given $P_2(0,2)$, $P(-3,-2)$.   **40.** P_1, given $P_2(2,-7)$, $P(-1,3)$.
41. Prove that the triangle $A(0,1)$, $B(\frac{9}{2},1)$, $C(5,4)$ is not isosceles and not equilateral.
42. Prove that the triangle $A(0,0)$, $B(10,-4)$, $C(2,5)$ is a right triangle.
43. Show that $A(-1,1)$, $B(-3,-2)$, $C(1,4)$ are on the same straight line.
44. Find the slope of each side of the triangle $A(1,-2)$, $B(-3,0)$, $C(-1,-6)$.
45. Find the slopes of the medians of the triangle $A(0,0)$, $B(2,-3)$, $C(1,-5)$.
46. Prove that $A(2,3)$, $B(8,\frac{5}{2})$, $C(9,-1)$, and $D(3,-\frac{1}{2})$ are the vertices of a parallelogram.
47. Write an equation which states that the point $P(x,y)$ is four units from the point $(-2,1)$.
48. Write an equation which states that $P(x,y)$ is twice as far from $(3,0)$ as it is from $(-3,0)$.
49. The points $A(1,1)$, $B(3,2)$, $C(4,0)$ are vertices of a square. Find the coordinates of the fourth vertex.
50. Plot the four points $A(1,5)$, $B(2,0)$, $C(0,-1)$, and $D(-6,1)$. Find the coordinates of the mid-points of the sides of the quadrilateral whose vertices are $ABCD$. Prove that the mid-points are vertices of a parallelogram.
51. For the directed line segment $\overrightarrow{P_1P_2}$, $P_1(x_1,y_1)$, $P_2(x_2,y_2)$, find the coordinates of $P(x,y)$ such that $P_1P/PP_2 = r_1/r_2$.

14.5. *Direction Cosines*

Since distance, slope, and inclination are related to a right triangle (P_1P_2Q in Fig. 14.3), it is desirable to make further use of trigonometry as in the following definitions.

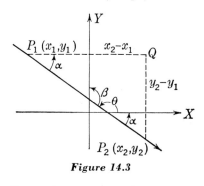

Figure 14.3

Definitions: The angles α and β, between the positive direction $\overrightarrow{P_1P_2}$ and the positive directions of the axes, are called the *direction angles* of the directed line. The two numbers given by $\lambda = \cos \alpha$ and $\mu = \cos \beta$ are called the *direction cosines* of the line. Any two numbers proportional, respectively, to the direction cosines are called *direction numbers* of the line. Thus $a = k\lambda = k \cos \alpha$ and $b = k\mu = k \cos \beta$, where $k \neq 0$, are direction numbers. A line without direction has two sets of direction angles: α, β and $180° - \alpha$, $180° - \beta$, corresponding to the two possible directions.

For a sensed line, since α and β are unique, so are λ and μ. Hence a sensed line has unique direction cosines. But a line without sense has two sets of direction cosines, namely, $\lambda = \cos \alpha$, $\mu = \cos \beta$ and $-\lambda = \cos (180° - \alpha)$, $-\mu = \cos (180° - \beta)$. Note that in any case $m = \tan \theta = \mu/\lambda$, provided that the line is not perpendicular to the X-axis, which would make $\lambda = 0$. The slope of a line perpendicular to the Y-axis is zero; the direction cosines of such a line are $\mu = 0$, $\lambda = \pm 1$. The slope of a line perpendicular to the X-axis does not exist; the direction cosines are $\mu = \pm 1$, $\lambda = 0$. These concepts are of very great importance in higher mathematics.

Now
$$d = \sqrt{(x_2 - x_1)^2 + (y_2 - y_1)^2}$$

Directly from Fig. 14.3, which is typical, we see that

(2)
$$m = \tan \theta = \frac{y_2 - y_1}{x_2 - x_1}$$

(3)
$$\cos \alpha = \frac{x_2 - x_1}{d} \qquad \cos \beta = \frac{y_2 - y_1}{d}$$

Hence

(4)
$$x_2 - x_1 = d \cos \alpha \qquad y_2 - y_1 = d \cos \beta$$

Therefore, for any two points on a line the differences in the respective coordinates, namely, $x_2 - x_1$ and $y_2 - y_1$, are direction numbers of the line. The constant of proportionality is, in this case, the distance d between the two points.

If we square and add in (3), we get

$$\cos^2 \alpha + \cos^2 \beta = \frac{(x_2 - x_1)^2}{d^2} + \frac{(y_2 - y_1)^2}{d^2}$$
$$= \frac{(x_2 - x_1)^2 + (y_2 - y_1)^2}{d^2}$$

which becomes, since $d^2 = (x_2 - x_1)^2 + (y_2 - y_1)^2$,

(5)
$$\cos^2 \alpha + \cos^2 \beta = 1$$

We can also write this as

(6)
$$\lambda^2 + \mu^2 = 1$$

and this relation holds for every pair of direction angles α, β.

Exercise A. Show that if a and b are direction numbers of a line L then

$$\lambda^2 = \frac{a^2}{a^2 + b^2} \quad \text{and} \quad \mu^2 = \frac{b^2}{a^2 + b^2}$$

In Exercise A care must be taken in order to obtain the direction cosines λ and μ themselves. The trouble is apparent when you write

$$\lambda = \pm \frac{a}{\sqrt{a^2 + b^2}} \quad \text{and} \quad \mu = \pm \frac{b}{\sqrt{a^2 + b^2}},$$

There are essentially just two cases:

(I) The line goes from lower left to upper right. If the sense is in the upward direction, the direction cosines are both positive; for the opposite sense, λ and μ are both negative. If the line is not directed, then either $\lambda = +$, $\mu = +$ or $\lambda = -$, $\mu = -$ may be used.

(II) The line goes from lower right to upper left. If the sense is in the upward direction, then λ is negative, μ positive; for the opposite sense, λ is positive, μ negative. If the line is not directed, then either $\lambda = -$, $\mu = +$ or $\lambda = +$, $\mu = -$ may be used.

Illustration 1. Find the slope and direction cosines of the sensed line cutting the X-axis at $32°$.

Solution: Here $\alpha = 32°$, $\beta = 90° - 32° = 58°$. Also $\theta = 32°$. It follows from a table of the natural trigonometric functions that

$$\text{Slope} = m = \tan 32° = 0.62487$$

and $\lambda = \cos 32° = 0.84805$, $\mu = \cos 58° = 0.52992$.

Illustration 2. Find the inclination, slope, and direction cosines of the line joining the two points $(2, -3)$, $(-5, 1)$.

Solution: This line is not sensed. We may take α and β as shown in Fig. 14.4; they correspond to the upward sense of the line.

$$\text{Slope} = m = \tan \theta = \frac{1 - (-3)}{-5 - 2} = -\frac{4}{7}$$

and θ is a second quadrantal angle. Looking up θ in a table of natural tangents, we find first of all that the angle θ', in the first quadrant, whose tangent is $+\frac{4}{7} = 0.57143$ is

$$\theta' = \text{arc Tan} (0.57143) = 29°44.7'$$

Therefore $\text{Inclination} = \theta = 180° - \theta'$
$$= 150°15.3'$$

The direction cosines may be taken as

$$\lambda = \cos \alpha = - \cos \theta' = - \cos 29°44.7' = -0.86823$$

and $\mu = \cos \beta = \cos (90° - \theta') = \cos 60°15.3' = 0.49614$

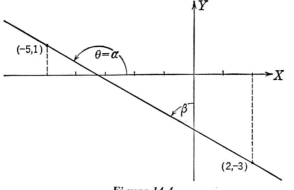

Figure 14.4

Illustration 3. Show that the line AB joining $(2,0)$ and $(0,6)$ and the line PQ joining $(1,-3)$ and $(-2, 6)$ have the same slope.
Solution:

$$m_{AB} = \frac{6 - 0}{0 - 2} = -3$$

$$m_{PQ} = \frac{-3 - 6}{1 - (-2)} = -3$$

Theorem 1. If two lines have the same slope, then they are parallel.

The proof is immediate, since if two lines have the same slope they have the same inclination and hence they are parallel.

    Exercise B. State and prove the converse theorem.

Sometimes directed lines which have the same inclination but opposite sense are called *antiparallel*.

14.6. *Angle between Two Directed Lines*

In Sec. 12.2 we defined the angle between two directed lines. We now prove the following theorem:

Theorem 2. The angle θ between the positive directions of two directed lines L_1 and L_2 with direction cosines λ_1, μ_1 and λ_2, μ_2, respectively, is given by

(7) $$\cos \theta = \lambda_1\lambda_2 + \mu_1\mu_2$$

    Proof: There is no loss in generality if we suppose that L_1 and L_2 meet at the origin (Fig. 14.5). Choose P_1 on L_1 at a distance 1 from 0.

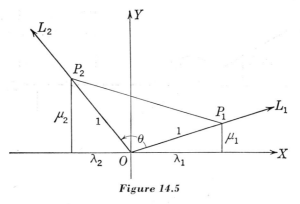

Figure 14.5

Then P_1 has coordinates (λ_1, μ_1). Choose P_2 on L_2 so that $OP_2 = 1$. Similarly P_2 has coordinates (λ_2, μ_2).

We apply the Law of Cosines (Sec. 12.11) to the triangle P_1OP_2; this gives

$$(8) \qquad (P_1P_2)^2 = 1 + 1 - 2 \cos \theta$$

By the distance formula we compute $(P_1P_2)^2$. We get

$$(\lambda_1 - \lambda_2)^2 + (\mu_1 - \mu_2)^2 = 2 - 2 \cos \theta$$
$$(9) \qquad \lambda_1^2 - 2\lambda_1\lambda_2 + \lambda_2^2 + \mu_1^2 - 2\mu_1\mu_2 + \mu_2^2 = 2 - 2 \cos \theta$$

Since $\lambda_1^2 + \mu_1^2 = \lambda_2^2 + \mu_2^2 = 1$, (9) reduces to

$$-2\lambda_1\lambda_2 - 2\mu_1\mu_2 = -2 \cos \theta$$

or finally
$$\cos \theta = \lambda_1\lambda_2 + \mu_1\mu_2$$

which was to be proved.

Corollary 1. Two lines are perpendicular if and only if their direction cosines satisfy

$$(10) \qquad \lambda_1\lambda_2 + \mu_1\mu_2 = 0$$

This follows since $\cos 90° = 0$.

Corollary 2. Two lines are perpendicular if and only if their direction numbers satisfy

$$a_1a_2 + b_1b_2 = 0$$

for $a_1 = k_1\lambda_1$, $b_1 = k_1\mu_1$, $a_2 = k_2\lambda_2$, and $b_2 = k_2\mu_2$. Hence the result follows at once from Corollary 1.

Corollary 3. If neither L_1 nor L_2 is parallel to an axis and if L_1 is perpendicular to L_2, then the slope of one is the negative reciprocal of the slope of the other.

Proof: Since none of λ_1, μ_1, λ_2, μ_2 is zero, we are allowed to write (10) in either of the forms:

$$\frac{\mu_1}{\lambda_1} = -\frac{1}{\mu_2/\lambda_2} \quad \text{or} \quad \frac{\mu_2}{\lambda_2} = -\frac{1}{\mu_1/\lambda_1}$$

We have seen above that $m_1 = \mu_1/\lambda_1$ and $m_2 = \mu_2/\lambda_2$. Hence

$$m_1 = -\frac{1}{m_2} \quad \text{or} \quad m_2 = -\frac{1}{m_1}$$

Sometimes we write this in the form: $m_1 m_2 = -1$.

Illustration 1. Find the slope of a line which is (a) parallel to and (b) perpendicular to the line joining $A(4,-3)$, $B(6,1)$.
Solution:

(a) The slope of a parallel line is the same as the slope of the line AB.

$$m_{AB} = \frac{1 - (-3)}{6 - 4} = \frac{4}{2} = 2$$

(b) The slope of a perpendicular line by Corollary 3 is $-\frac{1}{2}$.

Illustration 2. Find the cosine of the angle B of the triangle $A(0,0)$, $B(2,-1)$, $C(9,2)$.
Solution: In order to obtain an angle (interior) of a triangle, we *think* of the sides as being directed *away* from that particular vertex. To obtain angle B, therefore, we impose the directions $\overrightarrow{BA}$ and $\overrightarrow{BC}$. We compute

$$d_{BA} = \sqrt{5} \qquad d_{BC} = \sqrt{58}$$

$$\lambda_{\overrightarrow{BA}} = -\frac{2}{\sqrt{5}} \qquad \lambda_{\overrightarrow{BC}} = \frac{7}{\sqrt{58}}$$

$$\mu_{\overrightarrow{BA}} = \frac{1}{\sqrt{5}} \qquad \mu_{\overrightarrow{BC}} = \frac{3}{\sqrt{58}}$$

Therefore

$$\cos \theta = \cos B = \lambda_{\overrightarrow{BA}} \lambda_{\overrightarrow{BC}} + \mu_{\overrightarrow{BA}} \mu_{\overrightarrow{BC}}$$

$$= \frac{-14}{\sqrt{5}\sqrt{58}} + \frac{3}{\sqrt{5}\sqrt{58}}$$

$$= \frac{-11}{\sqrt{5}\sqrt{58}}$$

The angle B is obtuse.

Exercise A. Prove that the acute angle between two undirected lines is given by

$$\cos \theta = |\lambda_1\lambda_2 + \mu_1\mu_2|$$

PROBLEMS 14.6

In Probs. 1 to 9 find direction cosines of the line joining the given points.

1. $(1,2)$, $(2,4)$.   2. $(-1,2)$, $(1,5)$.
3. $(-3,-1)$, $(2,-1)$.   4. $(4,-5)$, $(6,-5)$.
5. $(3,-9)$, $(2,7)$.   6. $(20,10)$, $(-5,25)$.
7. $(30,6)$, $(25,-20)$.   8. $(90,50)$, $(3,17)$.
9. $(8,0)$, $(8,4)$.

In Probs. 10 to 15, (a) by using direction cosines, (b) by using slopes, show that triangle ABC is a right triangle.

10. $A(0,0)$, $B(10,-4)$, $C(2,5)$.   11. $A(0,0)$, $B(5,10)$, $C(4,-2)$.
12. $A(-5,2)$, $B(2,16)$, $C(1,-1)$.   13. $A(4,8)$, $B(1,-1)$, $C(-2,0)$.
14. $A(-7,3)$, $B(2,-8)$, $C(3,2)$.   15. $A(2,-11)$, $B(0,-3)$, $C(4,-2)$.

In Probs. 16 to 21 show that $ABCD$ is a parallelogram.

16. $A(0,0)$, $B(-3,4)$, $C(9,9)$, $D(12,5)$.
17. $A(4,0)$, $B(3,2)$, $C(5,4)$, $D(6,2)$.
18. $A(0,2)$, $B(4,1)$, $C(-2,-2)$, $D(-6,-1)$.
19. $A(3,0)$, $B(3,2)$, $C(7,1)$, $D(7,3)$.
20. $A(0,1)$, $B(8,5)$, $C(9,0)$, $D(1,-4)$.
21. $A(-2,-1)$, $B(2,3)$, $C(3,1)$, $D(-1,-3)$.

In Probs. 22 to 25 find the cosine of the smaller angle made by the two lines AB and CD.

22. $A(0,0)$, $B(4,-1)$; $C(1,2)$, $D(-2,2)$.
23. $A(1,2)$, $B(-3,5)$; $C(5,3)$, $D(-4,-1)$.
24. $A(3,3)$, $B(-2,1)$; $C(-3,0)$, $D(3,1)$.
25. $A(1,6)$, $B(-2,8)$; $C(1,-2)$, $D(-1,-3)$.

In Probs. 26 to 33 find the cosine of the angle at B of the triangle.

26. $A(0,0)$, $B(5,10)$, $C(4,-2)$.   27. $A(0,0)$, $B(10,-4)$, $C(2,5)$.
28. $A(4,8)$, $B(1,-1)$, $C(-2,0)$.   29. $A(-5,2)$, $B(2,16)$, $C(1,-1)$.
30. $A(4,0)$, $B(3,2)$, $C(5,4)$.   31. $A(0,2)$, $B(4,1)$, $C(-2,-2)$.
32. $A(3,2)$, $B(7,1)$, $C(7,3)$.   33. $A(8,5)$, $B(9,0)$, $C(1,-4)$.

In Probs. 34 to 39 find the slope of a line which is (a) parallel to and (b) perpendicular to the line joining the mid-points of the segments AB and CD.

34. $A(4,1)$, $B(2,3)$; $C(5,-1)$, $D(3,1)$.
35. $A(0,7)$, $B(3,3)$; $C(2,0)$, $D(-4,3)$.
36. $A(1,1)$, $B(5,5)$; $C(-2,2)$, $D(2,-2)$.
37. $A(6,4)$, $B(-6,-4)$; $C(3,-6)$, $D(-1,2)$.
38. $A(1,2)$, $B(2,-1)$; $C(2,5)$, $D(1,4)$.
39. $A(2,1)$, $B(1,0)$; $C(1,-2)$, $D(4,7)$.

In Probs. 40 to 43 find the cosine of the acute angle θ made by the two lines with given direction cosines.

40. $\lambda_1 = \frac{2}{3}$, $\mu_1 = -\sqrt{5}/3$ and $\lambda_2 = -\frac{3}{5}$, $\mu_2 = \frac{4}{5}$.
41. $\lambda_1 = \frac{3}{7}$, $\mu_1 = 2\sqrt{10}/7$ and $\lambda_2 = \sqrt{5}/5$, $\mu_2 = 2\sqrt{5}/5$.
42. $\lambda_1 = 0.6$, $\mu_1 = -0.8$ and $\lambda_2 = \frac{1}{2}$, $\mu_2 = \sqrt{3}/2$.
43. $\lambda_1 = \sqrt{2}/2$, $\mu_1 = \sqrt{2}/2$ and $\lambda_2 = -\sqrt{2}/2$, $\mu_2 = \sqrt{2}/2$.

In Probs. 44 to 47 find the cosine of the acute angle θ made by the two lines with given direction numbers.

44. $a_1 = 1$, $b_1 = 2$ and $a_2 = -2$, $b_2 = 1$.
45. $a_1 = 0$, $b_1 = 1$ and $a_2 = 4$, $b_2 = -3$.
46. $a_1 = 2$, $b_1 = 3$ and $a_2 = 2$, $b_2 = 1$.
47. $a_1 = 40$, $b_1 = -20$ and $a_2 = 30$, $b_2 = 50$.
48. Show that the diagonals of a square intersect at right angles.
49. Apply Eq. (7) to find the angle between two antiparallel lines.
50. Given $P_1(2, -1)$, $P_2(1,a)$, $Q_1(-3, -2)$, $Q_2(a,3)$, determine a if P_1P_2 is perpendicular to Q_1Q_2.
51. Given $\overrightarrow{P_1P_2}$ and $\overrightarrow{Q_1Q_2}$, where $P_1(2,1)$, $P_2(5,7)$, $Q_1(4,0)$, $Q_2(a,b)$, find values for a and b that the angle made by the positive directions $\overrightarrow{P_1P_2}$ and $\overrightarrow{Q_1Q_2}$ is $45°$.
52. Show that the angle θ_{12} (read, "theta sub 1,2") measured counterclockwise *from* line L_1 *to* line L_2 is given by

$$\tan \theta_{12} = \frac{m_2 - m_1}{1 + m_2m_1}$$

HINT: Use formula for $\tan (\theta_2 - \theta_1)$.
53. In Fig. 14.5 show that $\theta = \alpha_2 - \alpha_1$. Hence prove Theorem 2 by using the addition formula for $\cos (\alpha_2 - \alpha_1)$.
54. A pair of direction cosines (λ, μ) may be interpreted as the components of a unit vector directed along the given line. Show that in Theorem 2 $\cos \theta$ is the inner product of the vectors (λ_1, μ_1) and (λ_2, μ_2). Hence derive Theorem 2 from the formula for $\mathbf{A} \cdot \mathbf{B}$ given at the end of Sec. 12.13.

14.7. *Applications to Plane Geometry*

The properties of a given geometric configuration usually found in Euclidean plane geometry do not in any way depend upon a related coordinate system. It often happens, however, that the introduction of a coordinate system will help to simplify the work of proving a theorem and especially if axes are chosen properly. But the axes must be chosen so that there will be no loss in generality. For example, if the problem is to prove some proposition relating to a triangle, then a coordinate axis can be chosen coincident with a side and one vertex can then be taken as the origin. Consider the following illustration.

Illustration 1. Prove: The line segment joining the mid-points of two sides of a triangle is parallel to the third side and equal to one-half its length.
    Solution: We choose axes as in Fig. 14.6. The mid-points D and E have the coordinates $D\left(\dfrac{b}{2}, \dfrac{c}{2}\right)$ and $E\left(\dfrac{a+b}{2}, \dfrac{c}{2}\right)$. The slope of DE is

$$m_{DE} = \frac{(c/2) - (c/2)}{(a+b)/2 - (b/2)} = \frac{0}{a/2} = 0$$

Since AB also has slope zero, it follows that DE is parallel to AB. The length AB is a. The length of DE is

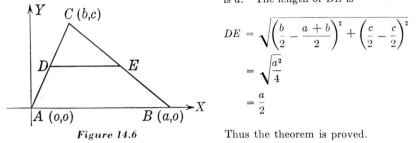

$$DE = \sqrt{\left(\frac{b}{2} - \frac{a+b}{2}\right)^2 + \left(\frac{c}{2} - \frac{c}{2}\right)^2}$$

$$= \sqrt{\frac{a^2}{4}}$$

$$= \frac{a}{2}$$

Figure 14.6   Thus the theorem is proved.

Illustration 2. Prove: The diagonals of a parallelogram bisect each other.

Solution: Choose axes as in Fig. 14.7, letting the coordinates of three vertices be $A(0,0)$, $B(a,0)$, and $C(b,c)$. Then, since the figure $ABCD$ is a parallelogram, the

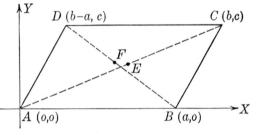

Figure 14.7

coordinates of D are determined. It is easy to see that they must be $D(b - a, c)$. The mid-point of AC has coordinates $E\left(\frac{b}{2}, \frac{c}{2}\right)$. Let F be the mid-point of BD. The coordinates of F are $F\left(\frac{b - a + a}{2}, \frac{c}{2}\right)$, that is, $F\left(\frac{b}{2}, \frac{c}{2}\right)$. Since E and F have the same coordinates, they must coincide. Hence the proposition is proved.

PROBLEMS 14.7

Draw a figure, and prove by analytic geometry.

1. The mid-point of the hypotenuse of a right triangle is equidistant from the vertices.
2. The lines joining the mid-points of the sides of a triangle divide it into four equal triangles.
3. The diagonals of a rectangle are equal.
4. The diagonals of a rhombus are perpendicular. (A rhombus is an equilateral parallelogram.)
5. The distance between the mid-points of the nonparallel sides of a trapezoid is one-half the sum of the parallel sides.

6. The diagonals of a trapezoid are equal if the trapezoid is isosceles. (The non-parallel sides of an isosceles trapezoid are equal.)
7. The diagonals of a trapezoid are equal only if the trapezoid is isosceles.
8. The line segments joining the mid-points of adjacent sides of a quadrilateral form a parallelogram.
9. The sum of the squares of the sides of a parallelogram equals the sum of the squares of the diagonals.
10. The medians of a triangle intersect in a point. HINT: Show that the point $[\frac{1}{3}(x_1 + x_2 + x_3), \frac{1}{3}(y_1 + y_2 + y_3)]$ lies on each median.
11. With respect to skewed axes where the X-axis and Y-axis make an angle $\theta°$ ($<0°$), the distance formula is $d^2 = (x_2 - x_1)^2 + 2(x_2 - x_1)(y_2 - y_1) \cos \theta + (y_2 - y_1)^2$.

14.8. *The Straight Line*

We now wish to study certain curves defined by special equations. About the simplest algebraic relation is that given by the equation

$$Ax + By + C = 0$$

where A, B, and C are real numbers. We exclude the case where $A = B = 0$, $C \neq 0$, and also the case where $A = B = C = 0$ as they are not sensible ones from our present point of view. The equation $Ax + By + C = 0$ is called a linear equation because its graph is a straight line as is proved in Theorem 3.

Theorem 3.　　The graph of a linear equation is a straight line.
　　Proof: Choose a point $P_0(x_0, y_0)$ whose coordinates satisfy the given equation, i.e., such that

$$Ax_0 + By_0 + C = 0$$

Hence
$$C = -Ax_0 - By_0$$

and we can write the given equation in the form:

(11) 　　　　　　　$A(x - x_0) + B(y - y_0) = 0$

Construct the line L through P_0 with direction numbers A, B. Let P be the point $P(x,y)$ where (x,y) satisfies (11). Then Eq. (11) tells us that the segment PP_0 is perpendicular to the line L (Corollary 2, Sec. 14.6). We know from geometry that there is a unique line M passing through P_0 and perpendicular to L. Hence P must lie on M. Our argument also shows that the coordinates of any point on M satisfy (11). Therefore M is the graph of the given equation.

Theorem 4.　　There exists a linear equation whose graph is a given straight line.

Proof: Let the given line be M (Fig. 14.8), and choose a fixed point $P_0(x_0,y_0)$ on it. Let $P(x,y)$ be any other point on M. Construct L perpendicular to M at P_0. Let L have direction numbers (A,B). Since the segment P_0P is perpendicular to L, we can write:

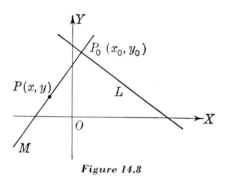

$$A(x - x_0) + B(y - y_0) = 0$$

Figure 14.8

But this is a linear equation which is satisfied by the coordinates of all points on M. Since, moreover, all solutions (x,y) of this equation correspond to points on M, it is the desired equation.

Corollary. A and B are direction numbers of any line perpendicular to the line whose equation is $Ax + By + C = 0$.

When the given line is defined by a pair of points on it $P_1(x_1,y_1)$ and $P_2(x_2,y_2)$, we can find its equation by the following theorem:

Theorem 5. Let $P_1(x_1,y_1)$ and $P_2(x_2,y_2)$ be two points on a given line. Then one equation of this line is:

$$(12) \qquad (y_1 - y_2)x + (x_2 - x_1)y + (x_1y_2 - x_2y_1) = 0$$

Proof: First, if the line is perpendicular to the X-axis, $x_1 = x_2$ and the above equation reduces to

$$(y_1 - y_2)x + x_1(y_2 - y_1) = 0$$

or to

$$x = x_1$$

which is a suitable equation for this line.

Second, on any other line we can find two distinct points $P_1(x_1,y_1)$ and $P_2(x_2y_2)$, where $x_1 \neq x_2$. Directly from Fig. 14.9 we have

$$(13) \qquad \frac{y - y_1}{x - x_1} = \frac{y_2 - y_1}{x_2 - x_1}$$

where $P(x,y)$ is a point different from P_1 on the line joining P_1 and P_2. From (13) we derive (12) at once. Equation (12) is called the *two-point* form of the equation of a straight line.

Exercise A. Derive (12) from (13).

Exercise B. Show that (x_1,y_1) and (x_2,y_2) satisfy (12).

Exercise C. Can you combine Theorems 3 and 4, using "necessary and sufficient" language?

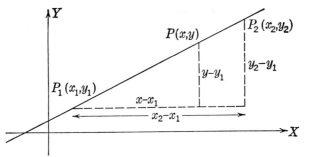

Figure 14.9

It is desirable to find the direction cosines of a line when we are given its equation. Let the equation be

$$Ax + By + C = 0$$

Let us suppose $B \neq 0$. Otherwise we must have $A \neq 0$ and a similar discussion follows. Two points on this line are

$$\left(x_1, -\frac{C + Ax_1}{B}\right) \qquad \left(x_2, -\frac{C + Ax_2}{B}\right)$$

Therefore $a = x_2 - x_1 \qquad b = -\frac{A}{B}(x_2 - x_1)$

are direction numbers of this line. We can get another set of direction numbers by multiplying these by $B/(x_2 - x_1)$. These are

$$a = B \qquad b = -A$$

We have therefore proved the following theorem.

Theorem 6. The direction cosines of the line whose equation is $Ax + By + C = 0$ are

(14) $\lambda = \dfrac{B}{\sqrt{A^2 + B^2}} \qquad \mu = \dfrac{-A}{\sqrt{A^2 + B^2}}$

or $\lambda = \dfrac{-B}{\sqrt{A^2 + B^2}} \qquad \mu = \dfrac{A}{\sqrt{A^2 + B^2}}$

The slope $m = \mu/\lambda$ is therefore equal to $-A/B$, $B \neq 0$.

Illustration 1. Find the direction cosines and slope of the line

$$2x - 3y + 5 = 0$$

Solution:

$$\lambda = \frac{-3}{\sqrt{4 + 9}} = \frac{-3}{\sqrt{13}} \qquad \mu = \frac{-2}{\sqrt{13}} \qquad m = \frac{2}{3}$$

or $\lambda = \dfrac{3}{\sqrt{13}} \qquad \mu = \dfrac{2}{\sqrt{13}}$

Theorem 7.   Let λ and μ be the direction cosines of a line segment OP of positive length p issuing from the origin.   Then $\lambda x + \mu y - p = 0$ is an equation of the line L perpendicular to OP and passing through P.

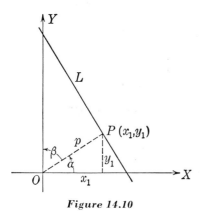

Figure 14.10

Proof: The line perpendicular to OP passing through P will have an equation of the form

(15) $\lambda x + \mu y + k = 0$

by the Corollary to Theorem 4. Keep in mind that λ and μ here are the direction cosines of any line perpendicular to the line whose equation is (15). They are *not* the direction cosines of the line (15) itself.   The coordinates of P, namely, $x_1 = \lambda p$, $y_1 = \mu p$, must satisfy (15).   Hence

$$\lambda^2 p + \mu^2 p + k = 0$$
$$p(\lambda^2 + \mu^2) + k = 0$$

or, since $\lambda^2 + \mu^2 = 1$,

$$p = -k$$

Therefore the equation of L is

(16) $\lambda x + \mu y - p = 0$

and the theorem is proved.

You can easily deduce the following rule for reducing

$$Ax + By + C = 0$$

to (16) which is called the *normal form* of the equation of the straight line.

Rule: Divide $Ax + By + C = 0$ by $\pm \sqrt{A^2 + B^2}$, using the sign opposite to that of $C(\neq 0)$.   If $C = 0$, the sign does not matter. Thus

(17) $\dfrac{Ax}{\pm \sqrt{A^2 + B^2}} + \dfrac{By}{\pm \sqrt{A^2 + B^2}} + \dfrac{C}{\pm \sqrt{A^2 + B^2}} = 0$

is in normal form if the sign of $\sqrt{A^2 + B^2}$ is chosen so that

$$\frac{C}{\pm \sqrt{A^2 + B^2}}$$

is negative.

Illustration 2. Reduce $3x - 2y + 7 = 0$ to normal form.
   Solution:

$$\frac{3}{-\sqrt{13}} x + \frac{-2}{-\sqrt{13}} y + \frac{7}{-\sqrt{13}} = 0$$

$$\frac{-3}{\sqrt{13}} x + \frac{2}{\sqrt{13}} y - \frac{7}{\sqrt{13}} = 0$$

Here $\lambda = -3/\sqrt{13}$, $\mu = 2/\sqrt{13}$, and $p = 7/\sqrt{13}$. Again note that λ and μ are direction cosines of any line perpendicular to $3x - 2y + 7 = 0$.

Exercise D. Find the direction cosines of the line $3x - 2y + 7 = 0$.

Illustration 3. Find the perpendicular distance from the origin to the line $x + y - 6 = 0$.
   Solution: The normal form is

$$\frac{x}{\sqrt{2}} + \frac{y}{\sqrt{2}} - \frac{6}{\sqrt{2}} = 0$$

The distance is $p = 6/\sqrt{2}$ units.

PROBLEMS 14.8

In Probs. 1 to 14 sketch the straight line.

1. $2x - 3y + 6 = 0$.
2. $3x + 2y - 6 = 0$.
3. $x + 2y - 5 = 0$.
4. $2x - y - 5 = 0$.
5. $x - 3 = 0$.
6. $2x - 7 = 0$.
7. $y - 2 = 0$.
8. $3y + 2 = 0$.
9. $y = 3x$.
10. $2y = 3x$.
11. $y = \frac{1}{3}x$.
12. $y = 0.6x$.
13. $\frac{x}{2} + \frac{y}{3} = 1$.
14. $\frac{x}{4} - \frac{y}{5} = 1$.

In Probs. 15 to 23 write down an equation for each straight line.

15. Through $(2, -1)$ and $(-1, 2)$.
16. Through $(4, 3)$ and $(2, -5)$.
17. Through $(0,0)$ and $(3,2)$.
18. Through $(0,0)$ and $(0,2)$.
19. Through $(0,0)$ and rising 2 units for every forward unit x.
20. Through $(0,0)$ and falling 2 units for every forward unit x.
21. Through $(-2,1)$ and rising 2 units for every forward unit x.
22. Through $(4, -3)$ and falling 3 units for every forward unit x.
23. Parallel to $2x + y = 0$ and such that each ordinate exceeds the corresponding ordinate of $2x + y = 0$ by 3 units.
24. Discuss the problem of graphing $(Ax + By + C)^n = 0$, n a positive integer.
25. Graph $(x^2 + y^2 + 1)(x - y + 3) = 0$.
26. Show that Eq. (13) can be written in the form $y - y_1 = m(x - x_1)$, where m is the slope of the line. This is called the *point-slope* form and is useful where the line is determined by its slope and one point.
27. Find the equation of the line passing through $(3, -2)$ and making $30°$ with the X-axis.

28. Show that the line $y = mx + b$ has slope m. What lines cannot be written in this form?

29. Show that Eq. (12) reduces to $(x/a) + (y/b) = 1$ in case the two points given are $(a,0)$ and $(0,b)$.

30. Plot the lines $2x - 3y + 1 = 0$ and $x + y - 2 = 0$, and find, by solving the equations simultaneously, the coordinates of the point of intersection.

31. Given the two straight lines $A_1x + B_1y + C_1 = 0$ and $A_2x + B_2y + C_2 = 0$ with $A_1, A_2, B_1, B_2, C_1, C_2$ in the field of real numbers. Assuming that the two lines intersect in one and only one point, are the coordinates of this point in the field of real numbers? Explain.

32. Find the equation of the line perpendicular to $x - 3y + 6 = 0$ and passing through $(0,0)$.

33. Show that for each value of k the graph of the equation

$$(A_1x + B_1y + C_1) + k(A_2x + B_2y + C_2) = 0$$

is a straight line through the point of intersection of $A_1x + B_1y + C_1 = 0$ and $A_2x + B_2y + C_2 = 0$. What is the situation in case there is no point of intersection?

34. Show that $2x + y - 5 = 0$, $x + y - 2 = 0$, $3x + 2y - 7 = 0$ meet in a common point.

35. Show that the three points $(-2,3)$, $(1,9)$, $(-5,-3)$ lie on one and the same line.

In Probs. 36 to 43 reduce to normal form.

36. $x + y - 5 = 0$.   **37.** $x - y + 5 = 0$.
38. $3x + y - 6 = 0$.   **39.** $x + 3y + 6 = 0$.
40. $2x - y + 4 = 0$.   **41.** $2x - y - 3 = 0$.
42. $4x - 3y + 10 = 0$.   **43.** $6x + 8y + 10 = 0$.

44. Show that the distance from the line $\lambda x + \mu y - p = 0$ to the point (x_1,y_1) is $|\lambda x_1 + \mu y_1 - p|$.

45. Find the distance from the line $x + 2y - 3 = 0$ to the point $(7,9)$ (see Prob. 44).

46. Find the equations of the bisectors of the angles between the lines $\lambda_1x + \mu_1y - p_1 = 0$ and $\lambda_2x + \mu_2y - p_2 = 0$ (see Prob. 44).

47. Find the equations of the bisectors of the angles between the lines $x - y + 6 = 0$ and $2x + y - 2 = 0$ (see Prob. 46).

48. Find the equation of the locus of points P which are at a distance of 3 units from the line $3x + 4y - 15 = 0$.

49. Given $A(0,2)$ and $B(3,7)$, find the equation of the locus of P such that the slope of AB equals that of BP.

14.9. Conic Sections

One way of generalizing $Ax + By + C = 0$, which represents a straight line, is to add all possible quadratic terms (terms of the second degree in x and y). Where an obvious shift has been made in renaming the coefficients, such an equation can be written in the form

(18) $$Ax^2 + Bxy + Cy^2 + Dx + Ey + F = 0$$

It is the general equation of the second degree in each variable (provided it is not true that $A = B = C = 0$).

We shall consider some special cases of (18). The treatment of the general case is complicated; but the total set of points corresponding to the ordered pairs (x,y) satisfying the relation defined by (18) is called a *conic section*. This is because, geometrically, the curve can be obtained by cutting a cone with a plane. This fact was known to the Greek mathematicians of 300 B.C.; we shall give the appropriate geometric illustration as we treat each case.

14.10. Case I. The Circle

Definition: A *circle* is the locus of points P which are at a fixed distance from a fixed point.

Thus consider a fixed point $C(h,k)$. Now the point $P(x,y)$ will be r units from C if and only if the distance PC equals r, that is, if and only if (Fig. 14.11)

$$\sqrt{(x - h)^2 + (y - k)^2} = r$$

This becomes, upon squaring,

$$(19) \quad (x - h)^2 + (y - k)^2 = r^2$$

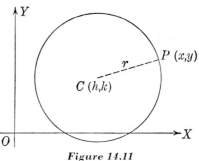

Figure 14.11

which is the equation whose graph is the circle with center at $C(h,k)$ and with radius r since (19) expresses the condition that the point P, with coordinates x and y, shall always be exactly r units from C.

Equation (19) reduces, after a little rearranging, to

$$(20) \quad x^2 + y^2 - 2hx - 2ky + h^2 + k^2 - r^2 = 0$$

This is a special case of (18) where $A = C$ and $B = 0$ [which indeed constitutes a necessary condition that (18) represent a circle].

> **Exercise A.** In (20) what coefficients correspond to $A, B, C, D, E,$ and F in (18)?
> **Exercise B.** Is the necessary condition that (18) represent a circle, namely, $A = C$ and $B = 0$, also sufficient?

The circle is a conic section. Geometrically it is obtained by cutting a right circular cone with a plane parallel to the base (Fig. 14.12).

Illustration 1. Write down the equation of the circle with center at $(-2,1)$ and with radius 3.

Solution: It is

$$(x + 2)^2 + (y - 1)^2 = 9$$

Illustration 2. Plot the curve given by

$$x^2 + y^2 - 3x + 6y - 5 = 0$$

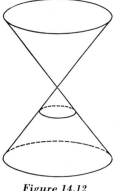

Solution: We complete the square separately on the x terms and on the y terms as follows:

$$x^2 - 3x + [\tfrac{9}{4}] + y^2 + 6y + [9] = 5 + [\tfrac{9}{4}] + [9]$$

The "5" was transposed, and the brackets merely indicate the terms added to complete the square. (To complete the square on the x terms, we must add the square of one-half the coefficient of x; and similarly for the y terms.) This can be rewritten as

$$(x^2 - 3x + \tfrac{9}{4}) + (y^2 + 6y + 9) = \tfrac{65}{4}$$

or, again, as

$$(x - \tfrac{3}{2})^2 + (y + 3)^2 = \tfrac{65}{4}$$

Figure 14.12

This is precisely in the form (19) so that the graph is a circle with center at $(\tfrac{3}{2}, -3)$ and $r = \sqrt{\tfrac{65}{4}} = \tfrac{1}{2}\sqrt{65}$.

The equation

(21) $$x^2 + y^2 = r^2$$

is that of a circle of radius r with center at the origin.

Exercise C. In (21) what coefficients correspond to $A, B, C, D, E,$ and F in (18)?

PROBLEMS 14.10

In Probs. 1 to 12 sketch and find the equation of each circle.

1. Center at $(2,7)$, radius 8.   **2.** Center at $(4,3)$, radius 5.
3. Center at $(-5,3)$, radius 3.   **4.** Center at $(-2,-1)$, radius 7.
5. Ends of diameter at $(4,-3)$, $(6,2)$.   **6.** Ends of diameter at $(6,2)$, $(-2,5)$.
7. Touching (tangent to) the X-axis, center at $(3,7)$.
8. Touching (tangent to) the axes, center in first quadrant, radius 4.
9. Has for diameter the portion of $x + 4y - 8 = 0$ lying in first quadrant.
10. Has radius 5 and is concentric with $x^2 + y^2 + 2x - 4y = 0$.
11. Has radius 4 and is concentric with $(x - 5)^2 + y^2 = 1$.
12. Has for diameter the common chord of $x^2 + y^2 + 2x - 4y = 0$ and $x^2 + y^2 + 4x - 2y = 0$.

In Probs. 13 to 20 find center and radius, and sketch.

13. $x^2 + y^2 + x + y = 0$.   **14.** $x^2 + y^2 - 2x + 4y - 1 = 0$.
15. $x^2 + y^2 - 8x + 7 = 0$.   **16.** $x^2 + y^2 + 9y - 2 = 0$.
17. $2x^2 + 2y^2 - 5x + 3y - 1 = 0$.   **18.** $3x^2 + 3y^2 + x + y - 6 = 0$.
19. $x^2 + y^2 + ax = 0$.   **20.** $x^2 + y^2 + by = 0$.

21. Find the equation of the locus of points P such that the sum of the squares of the distances from P to $(2,-3)$ and to $(-1,1)$ is 17.
22. Find the equation of the locus of points P such that the sum of the squares of the distances from P to $(-3,1)$, to $(4,5)$, and to $(0,0)$ is 104.
23. Write the equation for every circle passing through the origin.
24. Write the equation for every circle of radius 1 with center on the X-axis.
25. Write the equation of every circle of radius 1 with center on the line $y = x$.
26. Consider the set of line segments AB of length a such that A lies on the X-axis and B on the Y-axis. Find the equation of the locus of the mid-points of AB.

14.11. *Case* **II.** *The Parabola*

We are already somewhat familiar with the parabola (Illustrations 1, 3, 7, Sec. 9.5, and Illustration 1, Sec. 9.6).

Definitions: A *parabola* is the locus of points P such that the distance of P from a fixed point is always equal to its distance from a fixed line. The fixed point is called the *focus;* the fixed line is called the *directrix.* The line perpendicular to the directrix and passing through the focus is called the *axis of the parabola.*

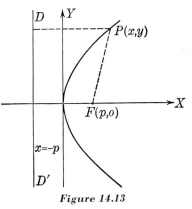

Figure 14.13

In order to arrive at an equation for this locus, we choose the coordinate axes so that the focus F has the coordinates $F(p,0)$ and the directrix line DD' has the equation $x = -p$ (Fig. 14.13). (This choice of axes leads to the simplest equation, although this is not immediately apparent.) By definition, the distance PF must equal the (perpendicular) distance from P to DD'. The distance from P to DD' is $|x + p|$. We have

$$|x + p| = \sqrt{(x - p)^2 + (y - 0)^2}$$

which yields, upon squaring,

$$x^2 + 2px + p^2 = x^2 - 2px + p^2 + y^2$$

This reduces to

(22) $$y^2 = 4px$$

This is the equation sought; it defines a relation. It is a special case of (18).

Exercise A. In (22) what coefficients correspond to $A, B, C, D, E,$ and F in (18)?

The parabola is a conic section (Fig. 14.14). Geometrically, the parabola can be obtained by cutting a right circular cone with a plane parallel to a generator.

Illustration 1. Write down the equation of the parabola with $F(3,0)$ and directrix $x = -3$.
    Solution: In this case $p = 3$, and the equation is consequently $y^2 = 12x$.

Illustration 2. Sketch the parabola whose equation is $y^2 = -7x$. Find the coordinates of the focus and the equation of the directrix.
    Solution: Here $4p = -7$. Hence the focus has coordinates $F(-\frac{7}{4},0)$, and the equation of the directrix DD' is $x = \frac{7}{4}$ (Fig. 14.15).

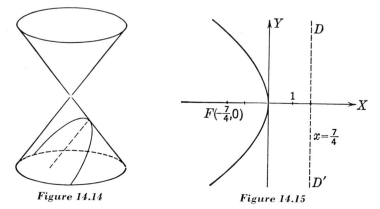

| Figure 14.14 | Figure 14.15 |

PROBLEMS 14.11

In Probs. 1 to 10 sketch and find the coordinates of the focus and the equation of the directrix.

1. $y^2 = x$.   **2.** $y^2 = 6x$.
3. $y^2 = 17x$.   **4.** $y^2 = -2x$.
5. $y^2 = -4x$.   **6.** $x^2 = -3y$.
7. $x^2 = 2y$.   **8.** $2x^2 = 5y$.
9. $(y - 1)^2 = 8(x + 3)$.   HINT: Plot the lines $y - 1 = 0$ and $x + 3 = 0$, and think of these as new axes.
10. $(x + 1)^2 = 4(y + 5)$.   (See hint, Prob. 9.)

In Probs. 11 to 20 sketch and find the equation of the parabola.

11. Focus at $(10,0)$, directrix $x = -10$.
12. Focus at $(4,0)$, directrix $x = -4$.
13. Focus at $(5,0)$, directrix $x = -5$.
14. Focus at $(12,0)$, directrix $x = -12$.
15. Focus at $(-4,0)$, directrix $x = 4$.
16. Focus at $(-10,0)$, directrix $x = 10$.
17. Focus at $(0,5)$, directrix $y = -5$.
18. Focus at $(0,6)$, directrix $y = -6$.
19. Focus at $(0,-3)$, directrix $y = 3$.

20. Focus at $(0, -10)$, directrix $y = 10$.
21. Find the points of intersection of $y^2 = 4x$ and $x^2 = y$.
22. A point has the property that the sum of its distances from $F(3,1)$, $F'(-3,1)$ is 10. Find the equation of the locus of such points.
23. Each circle of a set of circles passes through $(1,0)$ and is tangent to the vertical line $x = -2$. Find the equation of the locus of the centers of the circles.

14.12. *Case* **III.** *The Ellipse*

Definitions: An *ellipse* is the locus of points P such that the sum of the distances from P to two fixed points is a constant. The two fixed points are called *foci*.

A very simple equation results from choosing the axes and scales so that the foci F and F' have the coordinates $F(c,0)$, $F'(-c,0)$. We let the sum of the distances be the constant $2a$. Note that $2a > 2c$; hence $a > c$ (Fig. 14.16). The definition requires that

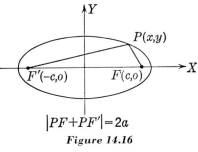

$$|PF+PF'|=2a$$

Figure 14.16

(23) $$\sqrt{(x + c)^2 + y^2} + \sqrt{(x - c)^2 + y^2} = 2a$$

We transpose the second radical and square, getting

$$x^2 + 2cx + c^2 + y^2 = 4a^2 - 4a\sqrt{(x - c)^2 + y^2} + x^2 - 2cx + c^2 + y^2$$

which simplifies to

$$4cx - 4a^2 = -4a\sqrt{(x - c)^2 + y^2}$$

We can now cast out the 4, and the reason for choosing $2a$ as the sum of the distances instead of a is now apparent. Square again. Thus

$$c^2x^2 - 2a^2cx + a^4 = a^2(x^2 - 2cx + c^2 + y^2)$$

which reduces to

(24) $$(a^2 - c^2)x^2 + a^2y^2 = a^4 - a^2c^2$$
$$= a^2(a^2 - c^2)$$

Since $a > c$, it follows that $a^2 > c^2$ and $a^2 - c^2 > 0$. Let us call $a^2 - c^2 = b^2$ (a positive number). We can then write (24) in the form

$$b^2x^2 + a^2y^2 = a^2b^2$$

or, finally,

(25) $$\frac{x^2}{a^2} + \frac{y^2}{b^2} = 1$$

This is the equation of the ellipse.

Exercise A.   In (25) what coefficients correspond to A, B, C, D, E, and F in (18)?
Exercise B.   Show that the points $V(a,0)$ and $V'(-a,0)$ are on the ellipse.
Exercise C.   Show that the points $(0,b)$ and $(0,-b)$ are on the ellipse.

Definitions: The points V and V' are called the *vertices* of the ellipse. The segment joining V and V' is called the *major axis;* its length is $2a$. The segment joining $(0,b)$ and $(0,-b)$ is called the *minor axis;* its length is $2b$.   The *center* of the ellipse is the mid-point of the major axis.

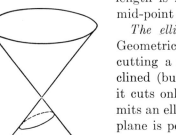

The ellipse is a conic section (Fig. 14.17). Geometrically, the ellipse can be obtained by cutting a right circular cone with a plane inclined (but not parallel to a generator) so that it cuts only one nappe of the cone.   This permits an ellipse to reduce to a circle if the cutting plane is perpendicular to the axis of the cone. Algebraically, this is the case where $a = b$ and where, therefore, Eq. (25) reduces to

$$\frac{x^2}{a^2} + \frac{y^2}{a^2} = 1$$

Figure 14.17

which represents a circle of radius a.

Illustration 1.   Plot the graph of

(26) $$\frac{x^2}{9} + \frac{y^2}{4} = 1$$

Solution: The total graph (Fig. 14.18) will be made up of the graphs of the two algebraic functions f and g derived from (26) and defined by the equations

$$y = \tfrac{2}{3} \sqrt{9 - x^2} \begin{cases} \text{domain, } -3 \le x \le 3 \\ \text{range, } 0 \le y \le 2 \end{cases}$$

$$y = -\tfrac{2}{3} \sqrt{9 - x^2} \begin{cases} \text{domain, } -3 \le x \le 3 \\ \text{range, } -2 \le y \le 0 \end{cases}$$

The zeros of both f and g are $x = \pm 3$; that is, the vertices of the ellipse are $V(3,0)$ and $V'(-3,0)$.   The point $(0,2)$ is on the graph of f, $(0,-2)$ is on the graph of g; each graph is a semiellipse.   The coordinates of the foci are $F(\sqrt{5},0)$ and $F'(-\sqrt{5},0)$ since $c^2 = a^2 - b^2 = 5$.   You should compute a few elements of f and g.

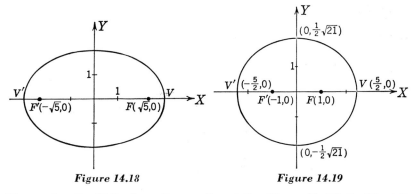

Figure 14.18   *Figure 14.19*

Illustration 2. Write down the equation of the ellipse with $F(1,0)$, $F'(-1,0)$, and major axis 5.

    Solution: Now $c = 1$ and $2a = 5$. Therefore $a = \frac{5}{2}$; and since $b^2 = a^2 - c^2$, we have $b^2 = \frac{25}{4} - 1 = \frac{21}{4}$. Therefore the equation is

$$\frac{x^2}{\frac{25}{4}} + \frac{y^2}{\frac{21}{4}} = 1$$

The graph is drawn in Fig. 14.19.

PROBLEMS 14.12

    In Probs. 1 to 12 sketch and find the coordinates of the foci and of the vertices.

1. $\dfrac{x^2}{16} + \dfrac{y^2}{4} = 1.$ **2.** $\dfrac{x^2}{25} + \dfrac{y^2}{16} = 1.$

3. $\dfrac{x^2}{100} + \dfrac{y^2}{81} = 1.$ **4.** $\dfrac{x^2}{100} + \dfrac{y^2}{64} = 1.$

5. $\dfrac{x^2}{3} + \dfrac{y^2}{2} = 1.$ **6.** $x^2 + 2y^2 = 2.$

7. (BT) $\dfrac{x^2}{25} + \dfrac{y^2}{49} = 1.$ **8.** $\dfrac{x^2}{1} + \dfrac{y^2}{4} = 1.$

9. $\dfrac{(x + 2)^2}{4} + \dfrac{(y - 1)^2}{1} = 1.$ HINT: Plot the lines $x + 2 = 0$ and $y - 1 = 0$,

    and think of these as new axes.

10. $\dfrac{(x - 1)^2}{16} + \dfrac{(y + 5)^2}{9} = 1.$ (See hint in Prob. 9.)

11. $3x^2 + 4y^2 = 6.$ **12.** $9x^2 + 16y^2 = 1.$

    In Probs. 13 to 22 sketch and find the equation of the ellipse.

13. $F(2,0)$, $F'(-2,0)$, and major axis 6.
14. $F(4,0)$, $F'(-4,0)$, and major axis 10.
15. $F(2,0)$, $F'(-2,0)$, and minor axis 6.
16. $F(4,0)$, $F'(-4,0)$, and minor axis 10.
17. Major axis (along X-axis) 10, minor axis 8, and center at $(0,0)$.
18. Major axis (parallel to X-axis) 10, minor axis 8, and center at $(0,2)$.

19. $V(4,0)$, $V'(-4,0)$, $F(3,0)$, $F'(-3,0)$.
20. $V(5,0)$, $V'(-5,0)$, $F(3,0)$, $F'(-3,0)$.
21. $V(0,4)$, $V'(0,-4)$, $F(0,3)$, $F'(0,-3)$.
22. $V(0,6)$, $V'(0,-6)$, $F(0,2)$, $F'(0,-2)$.
23. A point has the property that the numerical difference of its distances from $F(5,2)$, $F'(-5,2)$ is 4. Find the equation of the locus of such points.
24. The hypotenuse of each of a set of right triangles is the segment joining $(0,0)$ and $(2,0)$. Find the equation of the locus of the third vertices.

14.13. Case IV.   The Hyperbola

Definitions: A *hyperbola* is the locus of points P such that the numerical difference of the distances from P to two fixed points is a constant. The two fixed points are called *foci*.

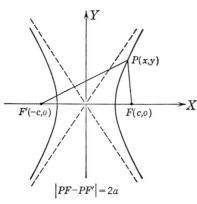

$|PF-PF'| = 2a$

Figure 14.20

We choose axes as we did for the ellipse, writing $F(c,0)$ and $F'(-c,0)$ (Fig. 14.20). We let the numerical difference of the distances be the constant $2a$. The definition requires

$$\left| \sqrt{(x + c)^2 + y^2} - \sqrt{(x - c)^2 + y^2} \right| = 2a$$

This is equivalent to

(27) $$\sqrt{(x + c)^2 + y^2} - \sqrt{(x - c)^2 + y^2} = +2a$$

if $$\sqrt{(x + c)^2 + y^2} > \sqrt{(x - c)^2 + y^2}$$

and to

(28) $$\sqrt{(x + c)^2 + y^2} - \sqrt{(x - c)^2 + y^2} = -2a$$

if $$\sqrt{(x + c)^2 + y^2} < \sqrt{(x - c)^2 + y^2}$$

In either case, (27) or (28), if we square (twice) and simplify as we did in the case of the ellipse, we shall arrive again at Eq. (24). For the hyperbola, however, $2a < 2c$, as can be seen directly from the figure. This means that $a^2 - c^2 < 0$; we set $a^2 - c^2 = -b^2$ (a negative number). Continuing the simplification of (24), we get, on this basis,

$$b^2x^2 - a^2y^2 = a^2b^2$$

or, finally,

(29) $$\frac{x^2}{a^2} - \frac{y^2}{b^2} = 1$$

This is the equation of the hyperbola.

Exercise A.   In (29) what coefficients correspond to $A, B, C, D, E,$ and F in (18)?

Exercise B.   Show that the points $V(a,0)$, $V'(-a, 0)$ are on the hyperbola.

Definitions: The points V and V' are called the *vertices* of the hyperbola. The segment VV' is called the *transverse axis;* its length is $2a$. The segment joining $(0,b)$ and $(0,-b)$ is called the *conjugate axis;* its length is $2b$. The *center* of the hyperbola is the mid-point of the transverse axis.

If we divide (29) by x^2, we get, after a little simplification,

$$\frac{y^2}{x^2 b^2} = \frac{1}{a^2} - \frac{1}{x^2}$$

$$\frac{y^2}{x^2} = \frac{b^2}{a^2} - \frac{b^2}{x^2}$$

$$\frac{y}{x} = \pm \sqrt{\frac{b^2}{a^2} - \frac{b^2}{x^2}}$$

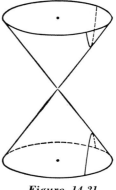

Figure 14.21

This says that, for large x (since b^2/x^2 is then small), the numerical ratio $|y/x|$ is just a very little less than b/a. (See Chap. 15, where the notion of *limit* is treated.) With this information at hand we sketch in the two lines (called the *asymptotes* of the *hyperbola*) whose equations are $y = \pm(b/a)x$ to act as guides in sketching the graph of the hyperbola itself. The asymptotes are *not* part of the locus; they merely serve as aids in plotting.

The hyperbola is a conic section (Fig. 14.21). Geometrically, the hyperbola can be obtained by cutting a right circular cone with a plane that is inclined so as to cut both nappes of the cone but not placed so as to pass through the vertex of the cone.

Illustration 1.   Sketch the graph of the equation

(30) $$\frac{x^2}{9} - \frac{y^2}{4} = 1$$

Solution: The total graph will be made up of the graphs of the two algebraic functions f and g derived from (30) and defined by the equations

$$y = \tfrac{2}{3}\sqrt{x^2 - 9} \begin{cases} \text{domain, } -\infty < x \leq -3, \, 3 \leq x < \infty \\ \text{range, } 0 \leq y < \infty \end{cases}$$

$$y = -\tfrac{2}{3}\sqrt{x^2 - 9} \begin{cases} \text{domain, } -\infty < x \leq -3, \, 3 \leq x < \infty \\ \text{range, } -\infty < y \leq 0 \end{cases}$$

The zeros are $x = \pm 3$ for each function; that is, the vertices of the hyperbola are $V(3,0)$ and $V'(-3,0)$. The coordinates of the foci are $F(\sqrt{13},0)$ and $F'(-\sqrt{13},0)$, since $c^2 = b^2 + a^2 = 13$. You should compute a few elements of f and g.

The length of the transverse axis is 6; the length of the conjugate axis is 4. The equations of the asymptotes are $y = \pm \frac{2}{3}x$ (Fig. 14.22).

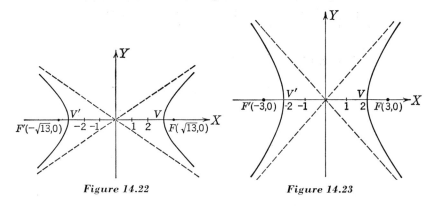

Figure 14.22   Figure 14.23

Illustration 2. Write down the equation of the hyperbola with vertices $V(2,0)$, $V'(-2,0)$ and with foci $F(3,0)$, $F'(-3,0)$.

Solution: We are given $a = 2$ and $c = 3$. Therefore, since $c^2 = b^2 + a^2$, we find $b^2 = c^2 - a^2 = 9 - 4 = 5$. The equation is

$$\frac{x^2}{4} - \frac{y^2}{5} = 1$$

The equations of the asymptotes are

$$y = \pm \frac{\sqrt{5}}{2} x \quad [\text{Fig. 14.23}]$$

PROBLEMS 14.13

Equations 1 to 14 define relations. Sketch the graph of each, following the procedures just outlined. Where appropriate, establish the algebraic functions f and g. In case the figure is a hyperbola, find the equations of the two asymptotes. Find the center and radius in case the figure is a circle.

1. $x^2 + y^2 - x + 2y - 3 = 0$.   2. $2x^2 + 2y^2 + 3x - 4 = 0$.
3. $x^2 + 2x + 1 + y = 0$.   4. $y^2 + y + x = 0$.
5. $x + 4y^2 = 0$.   6. $3x + 4y^2 = 0$.
7. $9x^2 - 4y^2 - 36 = 0$.   8. $9x^2 + 4y^2 = 36$.
9. $x^2 + y^2 - 9 = 0$.   10. $x^2 - y^2 - 9 = 0$.
11. $x^2 - y^2 + 9 = 0$.   12. $(x - 1)^2 + (y + 2)^2 - 16 = 0$.
13. $(x + y - 1)(x + 2y + 1) = 0$.   14. $(x - 1)(x + 4) - y = 0$.
15. Find the equation of the locus of points P such that the distance from P to $(-2,3)$ is always 5 units.
16. Find the equation of the locus of points P such that the distance from P to the line $x = -1$ is always equal to its distance from the point $(1,0)$. Rationalize and simplify your answer.

17. Find the equation of the locus of points P such that the sum of the distances from P to the two points $(-4,0)$ and $(4,0)$ is always 10 units. Rationalize and simplify.
18. What geometric configurations, other than ellipse, parabola, and hyperbola, can be obtained by cutting a cone with a plane? Illustrate with a figure.
19. For the ellipse $x^2/a^2 + y^2/b^2 = 1$ show that the line segment drawn from $(0,b)$ to a focus is of length a.
20. What are the coordinates of the foci of the ellipse $x^2/4 + y^2/4 = 1$?
21. Sketch and discuss: $(y - k)^2 = 4p(x - h)$.
22. Sketch and discuss: $\dfrac{(x - h)^2}{a^2} + \dfrac{(y - k)^2}{b^2} = 1.$
23. Sketch and discuss: $\dfrac{(x - h)^2}{a^2} - \dfrac{(y - k)^2}{b^2} = 1.$
24. Sketch and discuss: $x^2 = 4py$.
25. Sketch on same axes: $y = x^2$, $y = 2mx - 1$. Find the x-coordinates of the points of intersection of this parabola and straight line. Find the condition that there is only one point of intersection. Discuss the geometry for the lines $y = 2x - 1$ and $y = -2x - 1$.
26. Sketch $x^2 - 2y^2 - 2x - 4y - 1 = 0$. HINT: Complete squares.
27. Sketch $x^2 + xy - 2y^2 + 6x - 6y = 0$. HINT: Factor.
28. Show that an ellipse is the locus of points P such that the ratio of the distances of P from a fixed point and from a fixed line is a constant e less than unity. HINT: Take the fixed point $F(ae,0)$ and the fixed line $x = a/e$. Show that the equation of the locus is then

$$\frac{x^2}{a^2} + \frac{y^2}{a^2(1 - e^2)} = 1$$

The constant e is called the *eccentricity* of the ellipse. What is the eccentricity of a circle?

29. Show that a hyperbola is the locus of points P such that the ratio of the distances of P from a fixed point and from a fixed line is a constant e greater than unity. HINT: Take the fixed point $F(ae,0)$ and the fixed line $x = a/e$. Show that the equation of the locus is then

$$\frac{x^2}{a^2} - \frac{y^2}{a^2(e^2 - 1)} = 1$$

The constant e is called the eccentricity of the hyperbola. (See the definition of the parabola where e, defined similarly, would be equal to unity.)

14.14. *Applications*

In order to treat in detail many of the scientific applications of the theory of conic sections, we need especially the methods of the calculus (Chaps. 15 and 16). Therefore at this time we shall just mention some of them briefly.

Parabola

(a) Path of a projectile (neglecting air resistance).
(b) Cable of a suspension bridge (uniformly loaded along the bridge).
(c) Parabolic reflector [surface generated by revolving a parabola about its axis has the property that each light ray coming in parallel to the axis will be reflected to (through) the focus].
(d) Graphs of many equations in physics are parabolas.
(e) The antenna of a radio telescope.

Ellipse

(a) Orbit of a planet (sun at one focus).
(b) Orbits of planetary moons, satellites, some comets.
(c) Elliptic gears for certain machine tools.
(d) Focal property: a ray emanating at one focus is reflected to the other.
(e) Many scientific formulas are equations which plot into ellipses.

Hyperbola

(a) Used in the construction of certain telescopic lenses.
(b) Some comets trace hyperbolas.
(c) Formulas taken from the field of the physical sciences are often of hyperbolic type.

14.15. *Polar Coordinates*

In discussing the trigonometric functions of angles we introduced in Sec. 12.4 the ideas of polar coordinates. Our interest at that time was trigonometry, and certain discussions were simplified by assuming that the radius vector r was positive. For purposes of analytic geometry it is highly desirable to remove this restriction. This we now do according to the following definitions [which are just slightly modified versions of definitions (1)–(5) in Sec. 12.4].

Definitions: Consider a (horizontal) line called the *polar axis* and a point O on it called the *pole*, or *origin*. From the pole to an arbitrary point P, draw the line segment r, called the *radius vector;* the radius vector makes a directed angle θ with the positive direction of the polar axis, which is taken to the right. We assign to P the ordered pair (r,θ); call them the *polar coordinates of P*, and write $P(r,\theta)$.

We permit θ to be positive (counterclockwise) or negative (clockwise). If no restrictions are imposed upon us, we may use any convenient angular unit, radian measure and degree measure being the most common.   Likewise we permit r to be positive or negative, as we shall explain.

First, note that a fixed point P has several sets of polar coordinates.   Indeed, if P has coordinates (r,θ), then it also has coordinates $(r,\ \theta + 2k\pi)$ for every integer k.   Regardless of what integer k is used in the second element of the number pair $(r,\ \theta + 2k\pi)$, r itself is positive.   It is desirable to permit r to be negative.   We agree to call the number pair $(-r,\ \theta + \pi)$ coordinates of P; likewise for the pair

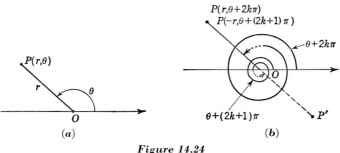

Figure 14.24

$(-r,\ \theta + (2k + 1)\pi)$, k an integer.   The geometric interpretation is evident from Fig. 14.24b: we extend PO in the direction OP' and measure θ to the extension.   For this case r is negative.

In summary, the polar coordinates of the point P are

$$(31) \qquad\qquad (r,\ \theta + 2k\pi) \qquad k \text{ an integer}$$

or

$$(32) \qquad\qquad (-r,\ \theta + (2k + 1)\pi) \qquad k \text{ an integer}$$

The pole itself is a very special point since, when $r = 0$, there is no unique angle θ.

Comment.   There is no 1 to 1 correspondence between points in the plane and polar number pairs. To a given pair (r,θ) there corresponds a unique point, but to a given point there corresponds no unique pair (r,θ).   This is in contrast to the situation in rectangular coordinates.

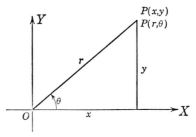

Figure 14.25

There is evidently a connection between the rectangular coordinates and the polar coordinates of a point P. By superposition of the two systems (Fig. 14.25) we find that

(I) $$x = r \cos \theta \qquad y = r \sin \theta$$

Exercise A. Figure 14.25 assumes that r is positive. Draw a figure with r negative, and use it to establish formulas (I).

From these equations we can readily find the rectangular coordinates when we know the polar coordinates. To arrive at polar coordinates when we are first given rectangular coordinates is harder because of the ambiguity in the former. We generally settle upon the least angle θ, where $0 \leq \theta < 360°$, to be associated with P. In this case r is positive. But there are times when we need to consider expressions (31) and (32) from both of which we will then pick out appropriate coordinates (perhaps more than one set) to suit our purpose. Thus, usually,

(II) $$r = \sqrt{x^2 + y^2} \qquad \tan \theta = \frac{y}{x}$$

where θ is determined as the least angle $\theta \geq 0$, which satisfies the above equation and the equations:

(III) $$\sin \theta = \frac{y}{\sqrt{x^2 + y^2}} \qquad \cos \theta = \frac{x}{\sqrt{x^2 + y^2}}$$

By means of (I), (II), and (III) we can transform equations from one system to another. Sometimes one system is more suitable to a given problem than another.

Illustration 1. Transform the polar equation

$$Ar \cos \theta + Br \sin \theta + C = 0$$

to rectangular coordinates.

Solution: We make use of (III) and write the transformed equation

$$A \sqrt{x^2 + y^2} \cdot \frac{x}{\sqrt{x^2 + y^2}} + B \sqrt{x^2 + y^2} \cdot \frac{y}{\sqrt{x^2 + y^2}} + C = 0$$

or $$Ax + By + C = 0$$

In either system the graph is a straight line.

Exercise A. Show that $r \cos (\theta - a) = b$ is the equation of a straight line and compare with $r(A \cos \theta + B \sin \theta) + C = 0$.

Exercise B. Sketch the graph of $r = \sec \theta$.

Exercise C. Write the polar equation of an arbitrary line passing through the pole.

Illustration 2. Transform the rectangular equation $x^2 + y^2 = a^2$ (of a circle of radius a with center at the origin) to polar coordinates.

Solution: Using (I), we write $x^2 + y^2 = a^2$ in the form

$$(r \cos \theta)^2 + (r \sin \theta)^2 = a^2$$
$$r^2 (\cos^2 \theta + \sin^2 \theta) = a^2$$
$$r^2 = a^2$$

The graph of $r = a$ is a circle of radius a with center at the pole; $r = -a$ plots the same circle. Hence there are two different equations in polar coordinates for this circle. This is not an isolated example; certain curves may have several distinct polar equations. This is due to the fact that the polar coordinates of a point are not unique. It is important to note that the *coordinates* (a,θ), satisfying $r = a$, do *not* satisfy $r = -a$.

Exercise D. Write down the polar equation of the circle with unit radius and center at the point $(r = \frac{1}{2}, \theta = \pi/2)$.

PROBLEMS 14.15

In Probs. 1 to 12 transform to polar coordinates.

1. $x^2 + y^2 - 3y = 0$.
2. $x^2 + y^2 + 2x = 0$.
3. $x - y = 0$.
4. $x + y = 0$.
5. $y^2 = 4x$.
6. $x^2 = 7y$.
7. $\dfrac{x^2}{9} + \dfrac{y^2}{4} = 1$.
8. $\dfrac{x^2}{16} + \dfrac{y^2}{25} = 1$.
9. $\dfrac{x^2}{9} - \dfrac{y^2}{4} = 1$.
10. $\dfrac{x^2}{4} - \dfrac{y^2}{9} = 1$.
11. $(x^2 + y^2 + y)^2 = x^2 + y^2$.
12. $(x - x^2 - y^2)^2 = x^2 + y^2$.

In Probs. 13 to 28 transform to rectangular coordinates.

13. $r = 2 \cos \theta$.
14. $r = -2 \cos \theta$.
15. $r = 5 \sin \theta$.
16. $r = -5 \sin \theta$.
17. $r = 1 + \cos \theta$.
18. $r = 1 - \cos \theta$.
19. $r = 1 - 2 \sin \theta$.
20. $r = 2 + \sin \theta$.
21. $r = 1/(1 - \cos \theta)$.
22. $r = 5$.
23. $r = -5$.
24. $\theta = 60°$.
25. $\theta = -60°$.
26. $r\theta = 1$.
27. $r\theta = -1$.
28. $r = 1/(1 + \cos \theta)$.

14.16. *Polar Coordinates* (*Continued*)

In Probs. 28 and 29, Sec. 14.13, we gave new definitions for the ellipse and hyperbolas. For a simple treatment of the conic sections in polar coordinates, we need the following definitions of a conic:

Definitions: The locus of points P such that the ratio of the distances from P to a fixed point F and to a fixed line DD' is a constant e is called a *conic section.* The point F is called the *focus, DD'* is called the *directrix,* and e is called the *eccentricity.*

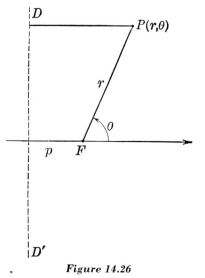

Figure 14.26

If $e = 1$, the locus is a *parabola*
  $e < 1$, the locus is an *ellipse*
  $e > 1$, the locus is a *hyperbola*

Of course these definitions must be consistent with our previous definitions. They are, but we shall not prove it. As you know, it turns out that the ellipse and hyperbola have two foci. They also have two directrices.

To derive the equation of a conic in polar coordinates is quite simple if we choose the focus F for the pole and the line through F and perpendicular to DD' for the polar axis. Consult Fig. 14.26; we let p be the distance from F to DD'. By definition, for every point $P(r,\theta)$ it must be true that

$$\frac{\text{Dist. } PF}{\text{Dist. } P \text{ to } DD'} = e$$

that is,

$$\frac{r}{p + r \cos \theta} = e$$

This reduces to

(33)
$$r = \frac{ep}{1 - e \cos \theta}$$

which is the equation of the conic.

Illustration 1.   Sketch the graph of the parabola $r = 1/(1 - \cos \theta)$.
  Solution: We make out a table of values.

θ	0	$\pi/6$	$\pi/4$	$\pi/3$	$\pi/2$	π
$1 - \cos \theta$	0	0.134	0.293	0.500	1	2
r	$\ldots$	7.47	3.41	2	1	$\frac{1}{2}$

You can easily make out another table for third and fourth quadrants (for the lower half of the curve). It is important to be careful in plotting points for values of θ near 0 since r is not defined for $\theta = 0$ (Fig. 14.27).

Exercise A

(a) Plot the graph of $r = -1/(1 + \cos \theta)$.

(b) Find all pairs (r,θ) which satisfy $r = -1/(1 + \cos \theta)$ and $r = 1/(1 - \cos \theta)$ simultaneously.

Illustration 2. Sketch the graph of $r = \sin 2\theta$.

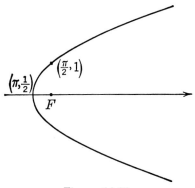

Figure 14.27

Solution: Again we prepare a table of values. This time, for practice, we shall use degree measure.

θ	0°	15°	22.5°	30°	45°	60°	67.5°	75°	90°
2θ	0°	30°	45°	60°	90°	120°	135°	150°	180°
r	0	0.500	0.707	0.866	1	0.866	0.707	0.500	0

The graph of this much is given in Fig. 14.28a.

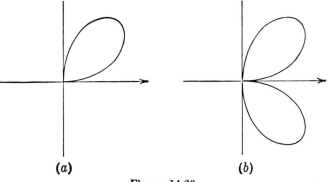

(a)   (b)

Figure 14.28

We continue the table.

θ	105°	112.5°	120°	135°	150°	157.5°	165°	180°
2θ	210°	225°	240°	270°	300°	315°	330°	360°
r	−0.500	−0.707	−0.866	−1	−0.866	−0.707	−0.500	0

The graph of the preceding two tables is given in Figure 14.28b.   So far, no portion of the graph has repeated.   Indeed θ must run the full course of 360° before repetition.   The total graph is the "four-leaved rose" exhibited in Fig. 14.29.

Exercise B.   Make out the remaining portion of the above table for the complete graph (drawn in Fig. 14.29).

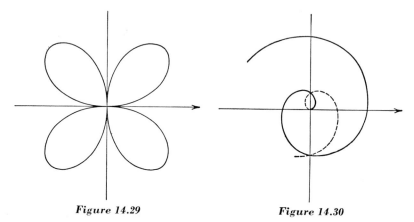

Figure 14.29   *Figure 14.30*

You should study this illustration to see that really all we need is the set of the first five entries in the first portion of the table.   With a knowledge of the behavior of the trigonometric function sine, we can draw the total graph.   The essential variations of sin 2θ take place in the first half of the first quadrant.   This is typical of much of the graph work in polar coordinates involving the trigonometric functions where periodicity plays an important role.

Illustration 3.   Plot the graph of $r = \theta$.
  Solution: Here we must use radian measure; but there is no need of making out a table.   Take note of the portion corresponding to negative values of θ in Fig. 14.30.   The curve is known as the Spiral of Archimedes.

Illustration 4.   Sketch the graph of $r = \cos \theta$.
  Solution: We prepare the following table:

θ	0	$\pi/6$	$\pi/4$	$\pi/3$	$\pi/2$	$2\pi/3$	$3\pi/4$	$5\pi/6$	π	$7\pi/6$
r	1	0.866	0.707	0.500	0	−0.500	−0.707	−0.866	−1	−0.866

The geometric point whose coordinates are $(\pi/6, 0.866)$ is the same as that with coordinates $(7\pi/6, -0.866)$. These are the second and last entries in the preceding table. Extension of the table through third and fourth quadrantal angles shows that the curve is being traced a second time. Therefore the description of the curve is complete after θ runs through the first two quadrants (Fig. 14.31). The curve is actually a circle, as you can immediately verify by transforming $r = \cos\theta$ to the rectangular form

$$(x - \tfrac{1}{2})^2 + y^2 = \tfrac{1}{4}$$

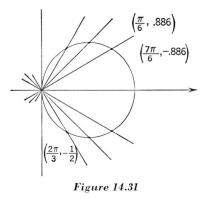

Figure 14.31

Notice that $(x - \tfrac{1}{2})^2 + y^2 = \tfrac{1}{4}$ defines a *relation*, whereas the corresponding polar equation $r = \cos\theta$ defines a *function*. This anomaly is due to the fact that the polar coordinates of a point are not unique.

PROBLEMS 14.16

In Probs. 1 to 28 sketch. Also transform to rectangular coordinates.

1. $r = \dfrac{8}{3 - \cos\theta}$.

2. $r = \dfrac{5}{2 - \cos\theta}$.

3. $r = \dfrac{4}{1 + 2\cos\theta}$.

4. $r = \dfrac{3}{1 - 2\sin\theta}$.

5. $r = \dfrac{10}{5 - \sin\theta}$.

6. $r = \dfrac{2}{3 + \sin\theta}$.

7. $r^2 - 4r\cos(\theta - 30°) = 0$.

8. $r^2 - 4r\sin(\theta - 30°) = 0$.

9. $r = \sin\theta$.

10. $r = -\sin 2\theta$.

11. $r = \sin 3\theta$ (three-leaved rose).

12. $r = \sin 4\theta$.

13. $r = \cos\theta$.

14. $r = \cos 2\theta$ [four-leaved rose].

15. $r = \cos 3\theta$ [three-leaved rose].

16. $r = \cos 4\theta$.

17. $r = 1 - 2\cos\theta$ [limaçon of Pascal].

18. $r = 1 - 2\sin\theta$.

19. $r = 1 - \cos\theta$ [cardioid].

20. $r = 1 - \sin\theta$.

21. $r = 2 - \cos\theta$.

22. $r = 2 - \sin\theta$.

23. $r = \pi/\theta$ [hyperbolic spiral].

24. $r = -\pi/\theta$.

25. $r^2 = \pi/\theta$ [the lituus].

26. $r^2 = -\pi/\theta$.

27. $r^2 = \cos 2\theta$ [the lemniscate].

28. $r^2 = \sin 2\theta$.

29. Sketch and find the points of intersection: $r = \sin\theta$ and $r = \cos\theta$.

30. Sketch and find the points of intersection: $r = \sin\theta$ and $r = 1 - \sin\theta$.

31. Find the equation of the locus of points P such that P is a fixed distance a from $P(r_1, \theta_1)$.

32. Find the equation of the locus of the mid-points of chords of a circle of radius a drawn from a fixed point Q on the circle.

33. Find the equation of the locus of points P such that the radius vector of P is proportional to the square of its vectorial angle.

14.17. *Parametric Equations*

It is often desirable to express each element of a pair, such as (x,y), in terms of a third variable, say t. When this is done, we find that we need a pair of equations of the form

(34) $$x = f(t) \qquad y = g(t)$$

to represent a given curve algebraically. We refer to (34) as *parametric equations;* by eliminating the *parameter* t we obtain the *cartesian equation* of the curve. Many loci problems are best treated in terms of parametric equations. Since the parameter can be chosen in many ways, we expect to find a great variety of parametric equations representing a given locus. In some cases a set of parametric equations will represent only a portion of the locus, and several such sets will be needed to represent it completely.

Illustration 1. Write the equation of a straight line in parametric form.
  Solution: In Eqs. (4) we saw that

$$x_2 - x_1 = d \cos \alpha \qquad y_2 - y_1 = d \cos \beta$$

where (x_1,y_1) and (x_2,y_2) are points on the line and d is the distance between them. If we write (x,y) for (x_2,y_2) and t for the distance between (x,y) and (x_1,y_1), these can be written

$$x = x_1 + t \cos \alpha \qquad y = y_1 + t \cos \beta$$

These are parametric equations of the line. They may also be written in the form

$$x = x_1 + u(x_2 - x_1) \qquad y = y_1 + u(y_2 - y_1)$$

where $u = t/d$. The graph of them is the whole line.

  Exercise A. (*a*) Plot the line whose parametric equations are $x = 1 + 3t$, $y = 2 - 2t$. (*b*) Eliminate t, and find the cartesian equation.

Illustration 2. Find parametric equations for the ellipse

$$b^2x^2 + a^2y^2 = a^2b^2$$

  Solution: We choose the parameter t as the angle shown in Fig. 14.32. In terms of the angle t we can write down the equations immediately since $x/a = \cos t$ and $y/b = \sin t$. They are therefore

(35) $$x = a \cos t \qquad y = b \sin t$$

and the graph is the complete ellipse.

  Exercise B. Eliminate t from Eqs. (35).
  Exercise C. Write down parametric equations for the circle $x^2 + y^2 = a^2$.

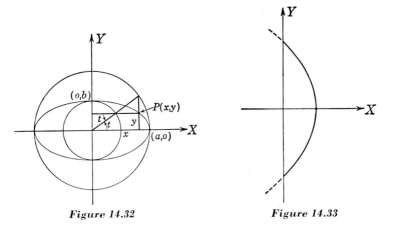

Figure 14.32   Figure 14.33

Illustration 3.   Show that $x = \sin^2 t$, $y = 2 \cos t$ represents only a portion of the parabola whose cartesian equation is $y^2 = 4(1 - x)$ (Fig. 14.33).

    Solution: The given parametric equations permit x to vary from 0 to 1 only and y to vary from -2 to $+2$. We eliminate t as follows:

$$x = \sin^2 t$$
$$\tfrac{1}{4}y^2 = \cos^2 t$$

Adding, we get

$$x + \tfrac{1}{4}y^2 = 1$$
or
$$y^2 = 4(1 - x)$$

Illustration 4.   A circle of radius a rolls along a line. Find the locus described by a point on the circumference.

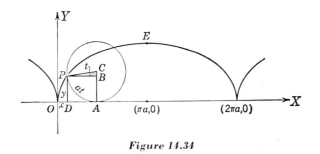

Figure 14.34

    Solution: Take the X-axis as coincident with the line and the initial position of the tracing point as the origin (Fig. 14.34). The positive angle

$$PCA = t \text{ radians}$$

will be chosen as the parameter. The arc $PA = at$ (Sec. 13.1).

Clearly $OA = PA = at$

Hence $x = OA - DA$

                                 $= OA - PB$

                                 $= at - a \sin t$

Further $y = PD = CA - CB$

                                 $= a - a \cos t$

Parametric equations of the locus, called a *cycloid*, are therefore

$$x = a(t - \sin t)$$
$$y = a(1 - \cos t)$$

This curve is very important in physics, where it is called the *bra-chistochrone*, or the *curve of quickest descent*. This means that, if we think of the curve as turned upside down, then, out of all possible curves connecting O and E, the brachistochrone is the one down which a frictionless particle will slide in least time. As a matter of fact this time is independent of the point on the curve from which the particle is released; the particle will slide from O to E in the same time that it will slide from any other point (such as P) to E. The cartesian equation obtained by eliminating t is troublesome; therefore we do not consider it.

PROBLEMS 14.17

In Probs. 1 to 26 eliminate the parameter t, and identify the curve if possible.

1. $x = 1 + 2t,\ y = 2 - t$.

2. $x = 3 - 4t,\ y = 1 + 7t$.

3. $x = 3t^2,\ y = t$.

4. $x = 2t^2,\ y = 1 - t$.

5. $x = t,\ y = t^2 + 2t$.

6. $x = t - t^2,\ y = t$.

7. $x = t^2 + t,\ y = t^2 - t$.

8. $x = 2t + t^2,\ y = 2t - t^2$.

9. $x = \sin t,\ y = \cos^2 t$.

10. $x = \sin^2 t,\ y = \cos t$.

11. $x = t - \sin t,\ y = 1 - \cos t$.

12. $x = 1 + \sin t,\ y = t + \cos t$.

13. $x = \cos t - \sin t,\ y = \cos t + \sin t$.

14. $x = a \cos t + b \sin t,\ y = a \sin t - b \cos t$.

15. $x = t,\ y = 1/t$.

16. $x = 1 + t,\ y = 1/2t$.

17. $x = \dfrac{1}{1 + t},\ y = \dfrac{t}{1 + t}$.

18. $x = \dfrac{3}{\sqrt{1 + t^2}},\ y = \dfrac{3t}{\sqrt{1 + t^2}}$.

19. $x = 1 + t,\ y = 2t + t^2$.

20. $x = t^2 - 3t,\ y = 2t - 3$.

21. $x = 2 \cos t,\ y = \sin t$.

22. $x = 1 - \sin 2t,\ y = 2 + \cos 2t$.

23. $x = t,\ y = 2t^2$.

24. $x = t,\ y = -2/t^2$.

25. $x = \sqrt{-t},\ y = -\tfrac{1}{4}t + 1$.

26. $x = \dfrac{t}{1 + t^3},\ y = \dfrac{t^2}{1 + t^3}$ [folium of Descartes].

27. A circle of radius $a/4$ rolls inside a circle of radius a. Show that parametric equations of the locus described by a point on the circumference of the rolling circle are $x = a \cos^3 t,\ y = a \sin^3 t$. [The parameter t is the angle through which the line of centers turns, the center of the stationary circle being placed at the origin. The initial position of the line of centers coincides with the

X-axis, and $(a,10)$ is the initial position of the tracing point.]　The curve is called the *hypocycloid*.

28. Find the parametric equations of the parabola whose equation is $y^2 = 4px$, in terms of the parameter t, which is the slope of the line $y = tx$.

REFERENCES

In addition to the many standard textbooks on analytic geometry, the reader should consult the following articles in the *American Mathematical Monthly:*

Boyer, C. B.: The Equation of an Ellipse, vol. 54, p. 410 (1947).

Boyer, C. B.: Newton as an Originator of Polar Coordinates, vol. 56, p. 73 (1949).

Hammer, D. C.: Plotting Curves in Polar Coordinates, vol. 48, p. 397 (1941).

Hawthorne, Frank: Derivation of the Equations of Conics, vol. 54, p. 219 (1947).

Johns, A. E.: The Reduced Equation of the General Conic, vol. 54, p. 100 (1947).

Wagner, R. W.: Equations and Loci in Polar Coordinates, vol. 55, p. 360 (1948).

CHAPTER FIFTEEN

Intuitive Integration

15.1. *Introduction*

In this chapter and in the next we shall be concerned with a branch of mathematics known as the "calculus." The treatment is in two parts: integral calculus (integration) and differential calculus (differentiation). This body of material was developed by Newton, Leibniz, and others in the seventeenth century; before their time only Archimedes seems to have had any clear notion of what was involved. That which is involved is the *theory of limits*. Our approach will be an intuitive one inasmuch as a detailed study of limits is beyond the scope of this book.

To begin with we recall that the early Greeks defined the (measure of the) area of a rectangle as the product of length times width. That is, $A = L \times W$ (Fig. 15.1). From this it follows that the area of a right triangle of legs L and W is $\frac{1}{2}LW$, which can be read "one-half the base times the altitude." The notion is readily extended by trigonometry to cover the case of any triangle (A = one-half the product of two sides times the sine of the angle included by those two sides). Since any polygon can be broken up into triangles, the above definition has led to a method of determining the area of a polygon (Fig. 15.2).

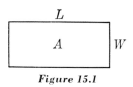

Figure 15.1

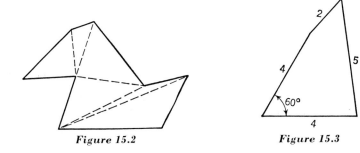

Figure 15.2   *Figure 15.3*

Exercise A. Find the area of Fig. 15.3.

This procedure is obviously applicable only to polygons—plane figures bounded by straight-line segments—and not to figures bounded by curves. Yet, intuitively, we feel that a rope stretched out on the floor in a simple closed curve without kinks, crossings, or knots (Fig. 15.4) encloses something we should like to call "area." This means two things: first, we must give a definition of "area bounded by a closed curve," and second, if area is to be a fruitful idea, we must develop a way of computing it. That is, we should like to be

Figure 15.4

able to find, at least theoretically, a real number which will be called, indifferently, the "measure of the area," or, simply, the "area."

As a matter of fact, Euclid gave such a definition for the area of a circle, and, using it and a circle of radius one unit, Archimedes (287–212 B.C.) was able to approximate π to within the inequality $3\frac{10}{71} < \pi < 3\frac{10}{70}$.

15.2. *Area of a Circle*

Euclid defined the area of a circle as follows:

Definition: The *area of a circle* is the limiting value of the area of an inscribed (or circumscribed) regular polygon of n sides as the number of sides n is increased indefinitely.

Let us try to find the area of a circle of radius r by using this definition. We begin by determining the area of an inscribed regular polygon of n sides. Radii are drawn from the center of the circle to the vertices of the polygon, dividing the polygon into n isosceles triangles. A typical triangle OPQ, with central angle $\theta = 2\pi/n$, is indicated in Fig. 15.5. The inscribed polygon has n times the area of this triangle since there are n such triangles. Now the area of OPQ is $\frac{1}{2}r^2 \sin (2\pi/n)$, and the area of the polygon is $(n/2)r^2 \sin (2\pi/n)$, which, in turn, is less than the area of the circle.   By Euclid's definition

(1)   Area of circle $=$ limiting value of $\dfrac{n}{2} r^2 \sin \dfrac{2\pi}{n}$

as n increases indefinitely

If we had used a circumscribed regular polygon of n sides (Fig. 15.6), we would find that the area of a typical triangle (with central angle

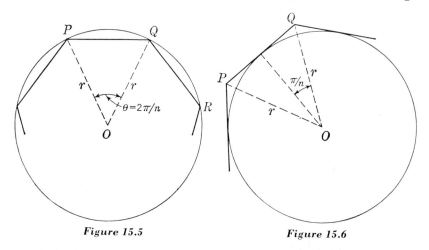

| Figure 15.5 | Figure 15.6 |

$\theta = 2\pi/n$) is $r^2 \tan (\pi/n)$, and so the area of the polygon is $nr^2 \tan (\pi/n)$. This is greater than the area of the circle, but by Euclid's definition

(2)   Area of circle $=$ limiting value of $nr^2 \tan \dfrac{\pi}{n}$

as n increases indefinitely

Archimedes used (1) and (2) and actually carried out the computations for the cases $n = 6, 12, 24, 48, 96$.   It was inscribed and circumscribed regular polygons of 96 sides which produced the famous inequality referred to in Sec. 15.1.

Exercise A.   Set $r = 1$, and compute from (1) $\frac{96}{2} \sin (360°/96) = 3.1392$ and from (2) $96 \tan (180°/96) = 3.1420$.

Exercise B.   From Example A above show that the area πr^2 of a circle of radius r satisfies the inequality

$$3.1392r^2 < \pi r^2 < 3.1420r^2$$

Now the idea of the "limit" expressed in the definition is intuitively clear: we feel that we can "see" what happens geometrically as the number n increases. For very large n an inscribed side AB (which is the chord AB) becomes indistinguishable from the arc AB (Fig. 15.7), and the area of the inscribed polygon differs from the area of the circle by a very, very small amount. On the other hand, when we try to compute the limits in (1) and (2), which we write in the notation

(3)
$$\lim_{n \to \infty} \frac{n}{2} r^2 \sin \frac{2\pi}{n}$$

(4)
$$\lim_{n \to \infty} nr^2 \tan \frac{\pi}{n}$$

we meet some technical difficulties.

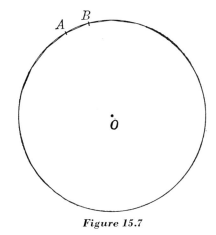

Figure 15.7

It is not the purpose of this book to study in great detail the theory of limits, but in the next section we make a few remarks which should help you see that

$$\lim_{n \to \infty} \frac{n}{2} r^2 \sin \frac{2\pi}{n} = \pi r^2$$

PROBLEMS 15.2

In Probs. 1 to 9 compute the values indicated.

n	6	12	24	48
1. $n \tan \dfrac{180°}{n}$				
2. $\dfrac{n}{2} \sin \dfrac{360°}{n}$				

	x	1.00	0.50	0.05	0.01
3.	$\sin x$				
4.	$\cos x$				
5.	$\tan x$				
6.	$\dfrac{1}{\cos x}$				
7.	$1 - \cos x$				
8.	$\dfrac{\tan x}{x}$				
9.	$\dfrac{\sin x}{x}$				

10. Paraphrase the language of the definition of the *area* of a circle, and give a precise definition of the *circumference* of a circle.
11. Define "length" of the parabolic arc $y = + \sqrt{x}$, from $x = 0$ to $x = 1$.
12. Define the area of the ellipse whose equation is $x^2 + 4y^2 = 4$.

15.3. *Some Limits*

By consulting a table of natural functions in radian measure we find

x	1.00	0.50	0.05	0.01	0.00
$\sin x$	0.84147	0.47943	0.04998	0.01000	0.00000
$\dfrac{\sin x}{x}$	0.84147	0.95886	0.9996	1.00000	?

We are able to write $\sin 0 = 0.00000$, but we are unable to write a number in place of the question mark (we never divide by zero). However, the entries for $(\sin x)/x$ seem to indicate that $(\sin x)/x$ approaches 1 as x approaches 0. This is a correct guess, and we shall prove it later in Theorem 6.

First, we should know what a limit is. The statement

$$\text{``}\lim_{x \to 0} \frac{\sin x}{x} = 1\text{''}$$

means geometrically that, as x gets close to 0, $\dfrac{\sin x}{x}$ gets close to 1.

Or, more generally, the statement "$\lim_{x \to a} f(x) = L$" means that, as x gets close to a, $f(x)$ gets close to L.   This is said more precisely and elegantly in the following definition:

Definition: The value $f(x)$ of the function f is said to *approach* the constant L as a limit as x approaches a if, for every positive number ϵ, there exists a number δ such that, if $0 < |x - a| < \delta$, then $|f(x) - L| < \epsilon$.[1]

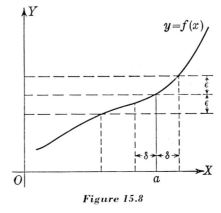

You should examine Fig. 15.8 until you think you understand the wording of the definition even though the process of obtaining limits from it is very complicated.   The following theorems, which we state without proof, will seem quite reasonable to you, and we shall make use

Figure 15.8

of them.   Let $\lim_{x \to a} f(x) = F$ and $\lim_{x \to a} g(x) = G$.

Theorem 1.   For the special function f, where $f(x) = C$, it is true that $\lim_{x \to a} f(x) = C$, for all a.

Theorem 2. $\lim_{x \to a} (f(x) \pm g(x)) = \lim_{x \to a} f(x) \pm \lim_{x \to a} g(x) = F \pm G.$

Theorem 3. $\lim_{x \to a} f(x) \cdot g(x) = \lim_{x \to a} f(x) \cdot \lim_{x \to a} g(x)$
$$= F \cdot G.$$

Corollary. $\lim_{x \to a} k \cdot f(x) = k \cdot \lim_{x \to a} f(x) = kF, \ k$ constant.

Theorem 4. $\lim_{x \to a} \dfrac{f(x)}{g(x)} = \dfrac{\lim_{x \to a} f(x)}{\lim_{x \to a} g(x)} = \dfrac{F}{G},$ if $G \neq 0.$

Illustration 1.   Let $f(x) = x, \ -\infty < x < \infty$.   Find $\lim_{x \to 2} f(x)$.

[1] Similarly we have the definition: The value of the function f is said to approach the limit $+\infty$ as x approaches a if for every positive number A there exists a number δ such that, if $0 < |x - a| < \delta$, then $f(x) > A$.

Solution: From an inspection of $f(x)$ for x near 2, we guess that $f(x) \to 2$ as $x \to 2$. Note that we must not set $x = 2$, for this is not the idea of a limit. Now we prove that our guess is correct.

Using the definition, we choose an ϵ (>0) and try to find a δ such that

$$|f(x) - 2| < \epsilon$$

when $0 < |x - 2| < \delta$. Since $f(x) = x$, this is an easy matter: just choose $\delta = \epsilon$.

Similarly
$$\lim_{x \to a} f(x) = a$$

Illustration 2. Find $\lim_{x \to a} x^2$. From Illustration 1 we know that $\lim_{x \to a} x = a$. Now $x^2 = x \cdot x$. Therefore Theorem 3 tells us that

$$\lim_{x \to a} x^2 = a^2$$

Exercise A. Find $\lim_{x \to a} x^n$.

Exercise B. Find $\lim_{x \to a} Cx^n$, where C is a constant.

Illustration 3. Find $\lim_{x \to 2} (3x^3 - 2x^2 + 4)$. From Theorem 2,

$$\lim_{x \to 2} (3x^3 - 2x^2 + 4) = \lim_{x \to 2} 3x^3 - \lim_{x \to 2} (2x^2) + \lim_{x \to 2} 4$$

Finally, from Exercise B,

$$\lim_{x \to 2} (3x^3 - 2x^2 + 4) = 24 - 8 + 4 = 20$$

Illustration 4. Find $\lim_{x \to 1} \dfrac{x^2 + 3}{x + 2}$. From Theorem 4,

$$\lim_{x \to 1} \frac{x^2 + 3}{x + 2} = \frac{\lim_{x \to 1} (x^2 + 3)}{\lim_{x \to 1} (x + 2)} = \frac{4}{3}$$

An important aid in some proofs is the "domination principle," which, in this case, has the following statement:

Theorem 5. If $F(x) \leq f(x) \leq G(x)$ for all x in an interval containing $x = a$, except possibly at $x = a$, and if $\lim_{x \to a} F(x) = L$ and $\lim_{x \to a} G(x) = L$, then $\lim_{x \to a} f(x) = L$.

We use this principle in the next two illustrations.

Illustration 5. Show that $\lim_{x \to 0} \sin x = 0$.

Solution: We recall the definition of sin x and note that, for small x, $|\sin x| \leq |x|$. This follows from the fact that in Fig. 15.9

$$2|\sin x| = PP'$$
$$2|x| = \text{arc } PP'$$

But a chord has a length less than the corresponding arc; thus $PP' < \text{arc } PP'$ or $|\sin x| \leq |x|$. The equality occurs at $x = 0$. Therefore

$$-|x| \leq \sin x \leq |x|$$

in a small interval about $x = 0$. We apply the domination principle with $F(x) = -|x|$ and $G(x) = |x|$. Since $\lim\limits_{x \to 0} |x| = 0$, we conclude that

$$\lim_{x \to 0} \sin x = 0$$

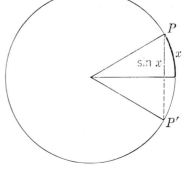

Figure 15.9

Illustration 6. Show that $\lim\limits_{x \to 0} \cos x = 1$.

Solution: Consider $1 - \cos x$

Then $1 - \cos x = \dfrac{1 - \cos^2 x}{1 + \cos x} < 1 - \cos^2 x$

for x near zero. Hence, for x near zero,

$$0 \leq 1 - \cos x \leq 1 - \cos^2 x = \sin^2 x$$

Therefore $\lim\limits_{x \to 0} (1 - \cos x) = 0$ [Theorem 5 and Illustration 5]

and $\lim\limits_{x \to 0} \cos x = 1$

We shall now prove Theorem 6 and, by means of it, find the area of a circle.

Theorem 6. $\lim\limits_{x \to 0} \dfrac{\sin x}{x} = 1$.

Look at Fig. 15.10, which is drawn with x positive. We might have drawn a similar figure with x negative. It is evident that when $|x|$ is not too large and is not equal to zero:

$$\text{Area } OAD > \text{area } OAC > \text{area } OBC$$

From the figure,

$$\text{Area } OAD = \tfrac{1}{2}OA \cdot AD = \tfrac{1}{2}|\tan x|$$

We must use $|\tan x|$ and not $\tan x$ since x may be negative. Also, since x is in radian measure,

$$\text{Area } OAC = \tfrac{1}{2}r|x| = \tfrac{1}{2}|x|$$

Finally, $\text{Area } OBC = \tfrac{1}{2}OB \cdot BC = \tfrac{1}{2}(\cos x) \cdot |\sin x|$

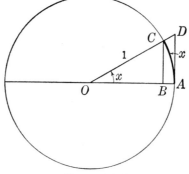

Figure 15.10

Since cos x is positive, we need not write its absolute value.   Therefore

$$|\tan x| > |x| > (\cos x) \cdot |\sin x|$$

Dividing this inequality through by $|\sin x|$, we obtain

$$\frac{1}{\cos x} > \left|\frac{x}{\sin x}\right| > \cos x$$

We already know that $\lim_{x\to 0} \cos x = 1$.   Therefore, from the domination principle,

$$\lim_{x\to 0} \left|\frac{x}{\sin x}\right| = 1$$

or, from Theorem 4,

$$\lim_{x\to 0} \left|\frac{\sin x}{x}\right| = 1$$

Now x and sin x have the same signs for small x, and hence $(\sin x)/x$ is positive.   Therefore for small x $(x \neq 0)$,

$$\frac{\sin x}{x} = \left|\frac{\sin x}{x}\right|$$

and thus

$$\lim_{x\to 0} \frac{\sin x}{x} = 1$$

We are finally in a position to find the area of a circle of radius r by Euclid's definition.   This area is given by

$$\text{Area} = \lim_{n\to\infty} \frac{n}{2}\, r^2 \sin \frac{2\pi}{n}$$

$$= r^2 \lim_{n\to\infty} \pi\, \frac{\sin\,(2\pi/n)}{2\pi/n}$$

Now set $n = 1/t$, and we get (note that, as $n \to \infty$, $t \to 0$)

$$\text{Area} = \pi r^2 \lim_{t=0} \frac{\sin 2\pi t}{2\pi t}$$

$$= \pi r^2$$

since $2\pi t$ plays the same role as x in Theorem 6.

Exercise C. Prove $\lim_{x \to 0} \dfrac{\tan x}{x} = 1$, and hence find the area of a circle by applying Euclid's definition with circumscribed regular polygons.

PROBLEMS 15.3

In Probs. 1 to 23 find the limit indicated.

1. $\lim_{x \to 2} (5x + 4x^2)$.

2. $\lim_{x \to -2} (5x + 4x^2)$.

3. $\lim_{x \to 2} \dfrac{x^2 + 4x}{x - 1}$.

4. $\lim_{x \to 3} \dfrac{x^2 - 4x}{x - 2}$.

5. $\lim_{x \to 2} \dfrac{x}{x^2}$.

6. $\lim_{x \to 0} \left(\dfrac{x}{x^2} \right)$.

7. $\lim_{x \to 0} |x|$.

8. $\lim_{x \to 1} |x - 1|$.

9. $\lim_{x \to 0} (x + \sin x)$.

10. $\lim_{x \to 0} (x - \cos x)$.

11. $\lim_{x \to 0} (x \sin x)$.

12. $\lim_{x \to 0} (x \cos x)$.

13. $\lim_{x \to 0} \dfrac{x}{\sin x}$.

14. $\lim_{x \to 1} \dfrac{\sin (x - 1)}{x - 1}$.

15. $\lim_{x \to 0} 2 \sin x$.

16. $\lim_{x \to 0} 2 \cos x$.

17. $\lim_{x \to 0} \sin 2x$.

18. $\lim_{x \to 0} \cos 2x$.

19. $\lim_{x \to 0} \dfrac{\sin 2x}{x}$.

20. $\lim_{x \to 0} \dfrac{\sin x}{3x}$.

21. $\lim_{x \to 0} \tan x$.

22. $\lim_{x \to 0} \sec x$.

23. $\lim_{x \to 0} \dfrac{x}{|x|}$.

24. Sketch: $y = \sin \dfrac{1}{x}$, $x \neq 0$.

25. Sketch: $y = x \sin (1/x)$, $x \neq 0$.
26. Find (when they exist):

    (a) $\lim_{x \to \infty} \sin x$.

    (b) $\lim_{x \to \infty} \dfrac{1}{x} \sin x$.

    (c) $\lim_{x \to 0} \sin \dfrac{1}{x}$.

    (d) $\lim_{x \to 0} x \sin \dfrac{1}{x}$.

15.4. *Area under* $y = x^2$

Euclid's definition of area works quite well for the circle, but we need a different definition for other types of areas. For example, if the area were that enclosed by the two curves $y = x^2$ and $y^2 = x$, it would not be possible to make sensible use of inscribed (or circumscribed) *regular* polygons (Fig. 15.11).

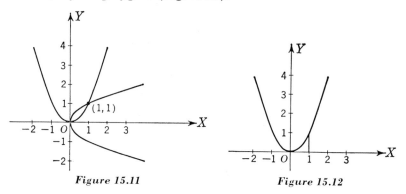

Figure 15.11   Figure 15.12

Exercise A. Give a definition of this area, using inscribed polygons.

Again, consider the area enclosed by the *curves* $y = x^2, y = 0, x = 1$ (Fig. 15.12). To find this area, we use the method which is due, essentially, to Archimedes, who reasoned as follows. The area sought, call it A, is larger than the combined areas of the rectangles formed as in Fig. 15.13, where ordinates have been erected at the quarter marks. That is,

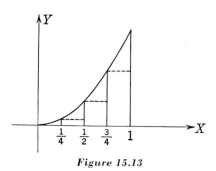

Figure 15.13

$$\tfrac{1}{4}(\tfrac{1}{4})^2 + \tfrac{1}{4}(\tfrac{2}{4})^2 + \tfrac{1}{4}(\tfrac{3}{4})^2 < A$$

or
$$\frac{1}{4^3}[1^2 + 2^2 + 3^2] < A$$

This reduces, numerically, to

$$\tfrac{14}{64} < A$$

Similarly, from Fig. 15.14, A is smaller than the sum of the rectangles which have been drawn. That is,

$$\tfrac{1}{4}(\tfrac{1}{4})^2 + \tfrac{1}{4}(\tfrac{2}{4})^2 + \tfrac{1}{4}(\tfrac{3}{4})^2 + \tfrac{1}{4}(\tfrac{4}{4})^2 > A$$

or
$$\frac{1}{4^3}[1^2 + 2^2 + 3^2 + 4^2] > A$$

that is,
$$\tfrac{30}{64} > A$$

Hence
$$\tfrac{14}{64} < A < \tfrac{30}{64}$$

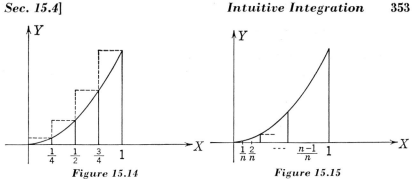

Figure 15.14   **Figure 15.15**

If ordinates had been erected at the eighth marks, the corresponding inequalities would have been (you should draw a figure for each case)

$$\tfrac{1}{8}(\tfrac{1}{8})^2 + \tfrac{1}{8}(\tfrac{2}{8})^2 + \cdots + \tfrac{1}{8}(\tfrac{7}{8})^2 < A$$

$$\frac{1}{8^3}[1^2 + 2^2 + \cdots + 7^2] \quad < A$$

$$\tfrac{140}{512} < A$$

and $$\tfrac{1}{8}(\tfrac{1}{8})^2 + \tfrac{1}{8}(\tfrac{2}{8})^2 + \cdots + \tfrac{1}{8}(\tfrac{8}{8})^2 > A$$

$$\frac{1}{8^3}[1^2 + 2^2 + \cdots + 8^2] \quad > A$$

$$\tfrac{204}{512} > A$$

or $$\tfrac{140}{512} < A < \tfrac{204}{512}$$

Observe that the bounding interval in the second case lies wholly within that of the first case; i.e.,

$$\tfrac{14}{64} < \tfrac{140}{512} < A < \tfrac{204}{512} < \tfrac{30}{64}$$

Now let us *imagine* that ordinates are erected at abscissa marks which are multiples of $1/n$ (Fig. 15.15). Then we would have A "boxed in" by

(5) $$\frac{1}{n^3}[1^2 + 2^2 + \cdots + (n-1)^2] < A$$

$$< \frac{1}{n^3}[1^2 + 2^2 + \cdots + (n-1)^2 + n^2]$$

Let us write L_n for the left term of (5) and R_n for its right term. Hence (5) is rewritten

$$L_n < A < R_n$$

From Prob. 7, Sec. 2.5, we learn by mathematical induction that

$$1^2 + 2^2 + \cdots + n^2 = \tfrac{1}{6}n(n+1)(2n+1)$$

Hence
$$L_n = \frac{(n-1)n(2n-1)}{6n^3} = \frac{(n-1)(2n-1)}{6n^2}$$

$$R_n = \frac{(n+1)(2n+1)}{6n^2}$$

Also
$$L_{n+1} = \frac{n(2n+1)}{6(n+1)^2}$$

$$R_{n+1} = \frac{(n+2)(2n+3)}{6(n+1)^2}$$

From these it follows that

$$
\begin{aligned}
L_{n+1} - L_n &= \frac{n(2n+1)}{6(n+1)^2} - \frac{(n-1)(2n-1)}{6n^2} \\
&= \frac{n^3(2n+1) - (n+1)^2(n-1)(2n-1)}{6(n+1)^2 n^2} \\
&= \frac{3n^2 + n - 1}{6(n+1)^2 n^2} > 0
\end{aligned}
$$

or
$$L_n < L_{n+1}$$

and similarly $R_{n+1} < R_n$. Hence we have

$$L_n < L_{n+1} < A < R_{n+1} < R_n$$

Further, $R_n - L_n = 1/n$, which tends to zero as n tends to ∞. Hence it appears that we can approach the true value of A by taking larger and larger values of n, and A should equal the limiting value of L_n or R_n as n gets larger and larger. [Archimedes did not quite say it this way, but he must have had some such notion in his mind; it was Cavalieri (1598–1647) who first carried out the details in the year 1630.] Pictorially also, this seems reasonable, although you are cautioned against relying too heavily on your geometric intuition. The question now is to find this limiting value.

We have seen that

$$
\begin{aligned}
R_n &= \frac{(n+1)(2n+1)}{6n^2} \\
&= \frac{1}{6}\left(1 + \frac{1}{n}\right)\left(2 + \frac{1}{n}\right)
\end{aligned}
$$

It is reasonable to say that $1/n$ tends to zero as n tends to ∞.[1]

---

[1] More specifically $\displaystyle\lim_{x \to \infty} f(x) = L$ means: The value $f(x)$ of the function f is said to approach the constant L as a limit as x tends to $+\infty$ if, for every positive ϵ, there exists a positive number A such that, if $x > A$, then $|f(x) - L| < \epsilon$.

From this and from Theorem 2 we conclude that $(1 + 1/n)$ tends to 1 as n tends to ∞ and that $(2 + 1/n)$ tends to 2 as n tends to ∞. Consequently, R_n tends to $\frac{1}{6}(1)(2) = \frac{1}{3}$.

Similarly, we have seen that

$$L_n = \frac{(n-1)(2n-1)}{6n^2}$$

$$= \frac{1}{6}\left(1 - \frac{1}{n}\right)\left(2 - \frac{1}{n}\right)$$

By the same argument it follows that L_n tends to $\frac{1}{3}$ as n tends to ∞. Since A is between L_n and R_n, we note that $A = \frac{1}{3}$.

We conclude, therefore, that we did not need to work with both R_n and L_n. From either one the answer follows.

PROBLEMS 15.4

In Probs. 1 to 8 make use of the above results to find the enclosed area. Sketch.

1. $y = +\sqrt{x}$, $y = 0$, $x = 1$. **2.** $y^2 = x$, $x = 1$.

3. $y = x^2$, $y^2 = x$. **4.** $y = 3x^2$, $y = 0$, $x = 1$.

5. $y = kx^2$, $y = 0$, $x = 1$. **6** $y = x^2$, $y = x$.

7. $(y + 1)^2 = x - 2$, $x = 3$. **8.** $(y - k)^2 = x - h$, $x = h + 1$.

9. Consider a unit square, its diagonal AB, and a zigzag path from A to B made up of segments parallel to the sides, as in Fig. 15.16. Now the sum of the lengths of the zigzag is surely just two units. Making the zigs and the zags smaller and smaller indefinitely, we approach the diagonal closer and closer; thus we see that the length of the diagonal of the square is two units. Point out the flaw in the reasoning.

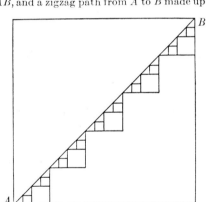

Figure 15.16

10. The following "argument" is ascribed to Zeno[1] (495–435 B.C.). See if you can detect a flaw in the reasoning, and write it down in a few words. Achilles cannot catch the tortoise in a race if the tortoise has a head start; for, before he catches the tortoise, he must get up to the place from which the tortoise started. But in the meantime, the tortoise has gone ahead and so has another headstart. Repeating this argument indefinitely, we see that the tortoise will never be caught.

[1] Look up a fine account of the history of Zeno's Paradoxes by Florian Cajori in the *American Mathematical Monthly*, vol. 22, pp. 1, 39, 77, 109, 143, 179, 215, 253, 292 (1915).

15.5. *Area under* $y = x^n$

The area bounded by $y = x^3$, $y = 0$, $x = 0$, $x = 1$ is set up in the same way in which it was set up for $y = x^2$. Divide the interval $[0,1]$ up into n equal intervals by the points $x_0 = 0$, $x_1 = 1/n$, $x_2 = 2/n, \ldots , x_n = n/n = 1$ (Fig. 15.17). On each interval as base form a rectangle using the ordinate at the right-hand point of that interval as altitude. The areas of the first few rectangles

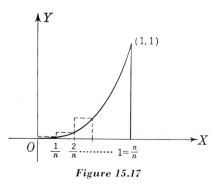

Figure 15.17

are $\left(\dfrac{1}{n}\right)^3 \cdot \dfrac{1}{n}, \left(\dfrac{2}{n}\right)^3 \cdot \dfrac{1}{n}, \left(\dfrac{3}{n}\right)^3 \cdot \dfrac{1}{n},$

and the area A under the curve is approximately

$$A \approx \left[\left(\frac{1}{n}\right)^3 + \left(\frac{2}{n}\right)^3 + \cdots + \left(\frac{n}{n}\right)^3 \right] \cdot \frac{1}{n}$$
$$\approx \frac{1}{n^4}[1^3 + 2^3 + \cdots + n^3]$$

The area is exactly

$$A = \lim_{n \to \infty} \frac{1}{n^4}[1^3 + 2^3 + \cdots + n^3]$$

We are unable to proceed until we have found out how to reduce $1^3 + 2^3 + \cdots + n^3$ to some other form because we cannot take the limit as it stands. To discover this "on our own" would be quite difficult, and here we shall assume the answer,[1] which is:

$$1^3 + 2^3 + \cdots + n^3 = \frac{n^2(n + 1)^2}{4}$$

Therefore

$$A = \lim_{n \to \infty} \frac{n^2(n + 1)^2}{4n^4} = \lim_{n \to \infty} \frac{1}{4} \cdot \frac{n^2 + 2n + 1}{n^2}$$
$$= \lim_{n \to \infty} \frac{1}{4}\left(1 + \frac{2}{n} + \frac{1}{n^2}\right)$$
$$= \tfrac{1}{4}$$

Exercise A. By these methods find the area of the triangle defined by $y = x$, $y = 0$, $x = 1$.

[1] See mathematical induction in Sec 2.5 and Prob. 8, Sec. 2.5.

In a similar way we could set up the area bounded by $y = x^4$, $y = 0$, $x = 1$. It would be

$$A = \lim_{n \to \infty} \left[\left(\frac{1}{n}\right)^4 + \left(\frac{2}{n}\right)^4 + \cdots + \left(\frac{n}{n}\right)^4 \right] \cdot \frac{1}{n}$$

$$= \lim_{n \to \infty} \frac{1}{n^5} [1^4 + 2^4 + \cdots + n^4]$$

and again we are faced with the difficult problem of reducing the sum of the fourth powers of the integers 1, 2, . . . , n to some simpler form. It is

$$1^4 + 2^4 + \cdots + n^4 = \frac{6n^5 + 15n^4 + 10n^3 - n}{30}$$

Now A becomes

$$A = \lim_{n \to \infty} \frac{1}{30} \left[6 + \frac{15}{n} + \frac{10}{n^2} - \frac{1}{n^4} \right]$$

$$= \tfrac{1}{5}$$

You should see that there is a pattern developing:

Table 1

Enclosing Curves	*Area Enclosed*
$y = x,\ x = 0,\ x = 1$	$\frac{1}{2}$
$y = x^2,\ x = 0,\ x = 1$	$\frac{1}{3}$
$y = x^3,\ x = 0,\ x = 1$	$\frac{1}{4}$
$y = x^4,\ x = 0,\ x = 1$	$\frac{1}{5}$

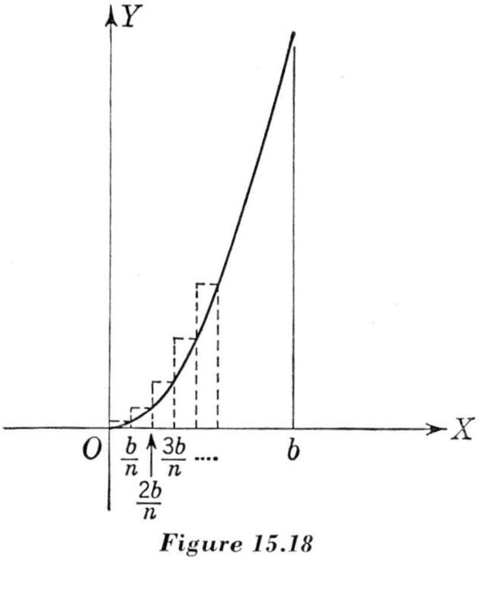

Figure 15.18

It is true that the area enclosed by $y = x^n$, $x = 0$, $x = 1$ is $1/(n + 1)$, for $n = 0, 1, 2, \ldots$, but we defer further study of this until we have met with some of the ideas of the next chapter.

In order to find the area enclosed by $y = x^2$, $y = 0$, $x = b$, we divide the interval $[0,b]$ into n equal intervals by the points $x_0 = 0$, $x_1 = \dfrac{1}{n}\,(b)$, $x_2 = \dfrac{2}{n}\,(b)$, $\ldots$, $x_n = \dfrac{n}{n}\,(b)$ (Fig. 15.18). For $y = x^2$ the area A is therefore

$$
\begin{aligned}
A &= \lim_{n \to \infty} \left\{ \left[\frac{1}{n}\,(b)\right]^2 \cdot \frac{1}{n}\,(b) + \left[\frac{2}{n}\,(b)\right]^2 \cdot \frac{1}{n}\,(b) + \cdots \right. \\
&\qquad\qquad\qquad\qquad\qquad \left. + \left[\frac{n}{n}\,(b)\right]^2 \cdot \frac{1}{n}\,(b) \right\} \\
&= \lim_{n \to \infty} \frac{b^3}{n^3}\,[1^2 + 2^2 + \cdots + n^2] \\
&= \lim_{n \to \infty} \frac{b^3}{n^3}\left[\frac{n(n+1)(2n+1)}{6}\right] \\
&= \frac{b^3}{3}
\end{aligned}
$$

Exercise B. Show that the area bounded by $y = x^3$, $x = 0$, $x = b$ is $b^4/4$.

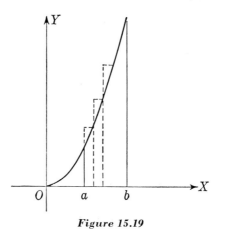

Figure 15.19

By the addition of areas we can readily find the area enclosed by $y = x^2$, $x = a$, $x = b$ (Fig. 15.19). Since the area (under $y = x^2$) from 0 to b is $b^3/3$, the area from 0 to a is $a^3/3$ and the area from a to b is $b^3/3 - a^3/3$.

Again there is a pattern $(b > a)$:

Table 2

Enclosing Curves	Area Enclosed
$y = x,\ y = 0,\ x = a,\ x = b$	$\frac{1}{2}(b^2 - a^2)$
$y = x^2,\ y = 0,\ x = a,\ x = b$	$\frac{1}{3}(b^3 - a^3)$
$y = x^3,\ y = 0,\ x = a,\ x = b$	$\frac{1}{4}(b^4 - a^4)$
$y = x^4,\ y = 0,\ x = a,\ x = b$	$\frac{1}{5}(b^5 - a^5)$
$\cdots\cdots\cdots\cdots\cdots\cdots\cdots$	$\cdots\cdots$
$y = x^n,\ y = 0,\ x = a,\ x = b$	$\dfrac{1}{n+1}(b^{n+1} - a^{n+1})$

Exercise C. Argue that, if $b < a$, then the answers above should be written $\frac{1}{2}(a^2 - b^2)$, etc.

PROBLEMS 15.5

In Probs. 1 to 8 sketch and find the enclosed area by summing and taking the limit.

1. $y = x - x^2,\ y = 0.$ **2.** $y = -x - x^2,\ y = 0.$

3. $y = 1 - x^2,\ y = 0.$ **4.** $y = 4 - x^2,\ y = 0.$

5. $y = x^2,\ y = 0,\ x = 2,\ x = 3.$

6. $y = x^2,\ y = 0,\ x = -2,\ x = -1.$

7. $y = x^3,\ y = 0,\ x = 2.$ **8.** $y = x^3,\ y = 0,\ x = -1.$

In Probs. 9 to 18 sketch and find the enclosed area by using the general results of this section as formulas.

9. $y = x^5,\ y = 0,\ x = 2.$ **10.** $y = -x^5,\ y = 0,\ x = -1.$

11. $y = 2x^7,\ y = 0,\ x = 1.$ **12.** $y = x^7,\ y = 0,\ x = -1.$

13. $y = x^4,\ y = 1.$ **14.** $y = x^6,\ y = 1.$

15. $y = x^{2k},\ y = 0,\ x = 1,\ x = 2.$

16. $y = x^{2k+1},\ y = 0,\ x = 2.$

17. $y = x^{n+1},\ y = 0,\ x = a,\ x = b.$

18. $y = 3x^{n-4},\ y = 0,\ x = 2,\ x = b.$

15.6. *Area under Graph of a Polynomial Function*

With a few exceptions the problems of Sec. 15.5 are such that the enclosed area is above the X-axis. Such areas are positive. The physical area enclosed by $y = -x^2,\ y = 0,\ x = 1$ lies *below* the X-axis. Such an area is negative when computed as above. It is obvious that it should be since the ordinates (heights) of the small rectangles are themselves negative. Regardless of whether the area lies above or below the X-axis, we still speak of the area "under" a curve.

It is our usual convention to read from left to right on the horizontal axis and thus to choose $b > a$ when we develop formulas like those in

Table 2, Sec. 15.5. There are occasions, however, when we wish to read in the opposite direction and thus choose $b < a$. When we do this we will, by convention, maintain the formulas of Table 2 without change. In certain cases this introduces negative area. With these two situations in mind we point out that the area under $y = x^n$, $y = 0$, from $x = a$ to $x = b$ may be positive, negative, or zero. A similar situation arises in the case of polynomials.

The graph of a typical polynomial equation $y = P(x)$ is much like that in Fig. 15.20. In computing the area A under this from $x = a$ to $x = b$, we would arrive at $A = B + C$, where B is the vertically

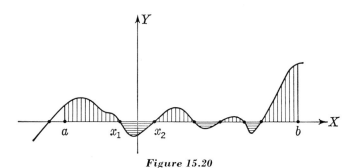

Figure 15.20

shaded areas (positive) and where C is the horizontally shaded areas (negative). Therefore what we get is the *algebraic* sum, and this number A may be positive, negative, or zero.

Remark. If we wish to compute the total shaded area—as if it were land along the banks of a river—then it is necessary first of all to find $\{x \mid P(x) = 0\}$, that is, the roots $x_1, x_2, \ldots$ of the polynomial equation. We would then write for the numerical area A:

$$A = |A_a^{x_1}| + |A_{x_1}^{x_2}| + \cdots$$

We have used "$A_a^{x_1}$" to represent the area from a to x_1, etc.

To compute the area under a polynomial we need the facts that

$$A_a^b \text{ under } kf(x) = k[A_a^b \text{ under } f(x)]$$
$$A_a^b \text{ under } f(x) + g(x) = [A_a^b \text{ under } f(x)] + [A_a^b \text{ under } g(x)]$$

Since A_a^b is given as a limit, these facts are consequences of the corresponding theorems on limits, namely Theorem 2 and the Corollary to Theorem 3, Sec. 15.3. Proceed as in the illustration below.

Illustration 1. Find the algebraic area under $y = \frac{1}{6}x(x^2 - 9)$ from $x = -1$ to $x = 4$.

Solutions: We first sketch the graph (Fig. 15.21). We write $y = \frac{1}{6}x^3 - \frac{3}{2}x$, consider the terms separately, and make use of Table 2, Sec. 15.5.

$$A^0_{-1} = \frac{1}{6}[\frac{1}{4}(0^4 - (-1)^4)] - \frac{3}{2}[\frac{1}{2}(0^2 - (-1)^2)]$$
$$A^3_0 = \frac{1}{6}[\frac{1}{4}(3^4 - 0^4)] - \frac{3}{2}[\frac{1}{2}(3^2 - 0^2)]$$
$$A^4_3 = \frac{1}{6}[\frac{1}{4}(4^4 - 3^4)] - \frac{3}{2}[\frac{1}{2}(4^2 - 3^2)]$$

Reducing, we have $A^0_{-1} = \frac{17}{24}$, $A^3_0 = -\frac{81}{24}$, $A^4_3 = \frac{49}{24}$ so that we can find the algebraic area by adding the separate areas as they stand. Thus the algebraic area $A^4_{-1} = -\frac{15}{24}$, and this is exactly what we get by evaluating A^4_{-1} directly.

$$A^4_{-1} = \frac{1}{6}[\frac{1}{4}(4^4 - (-1)^4)] - \frac{3}{2}[\frac{1}{2}(4^2 - (-1)^2)]$$
$$= \frac{255}{24} - \frac{3(15)}{4}$$
$$= -\frac{15}{24}$$

If, on the other hand, we want the physical area, whether it is above or below the X-axis, then we need to write $|A^0_{-1}| + |A^3_0| + |A^4_3| = \frac{147}{24}$.

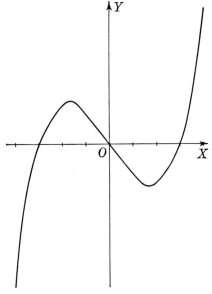

Figure 15.21

Unless explicitly stated to the contrary, algebraic area is implied when "area" is used by itself. In general the context will be clear.

PROBLEMS 15.6

In Probs. 1 to 16 sketch and find the enclosed physical area by using the formulas of Table 2, Sec. 15.5 and the ideas of Sec. 15.6.

1. $y = -(x + 1)(x - 2)$, $y = 0$.   **2.** $y = (x + 1)(x - 2)$, $y = 0$.
3. $y = -2x^2 + 3x - 1$, $y = 0$.   **4.** $y = -x^2 + 7x - 10$, $y = 0$.

5. $y = x^2 + 3x + 2$, $y = 0$, $x = 1$, $x = 2$.
6. $y = x^2 + x - 2$, $y = 0$, $x = 2$, $x = 3$.
7. $y = x^3 - x$, $y = 0$, $x = -1$, $x = 0$.
8. $y = x^3 - x$, $y = 0$, $x = 2$, $x = 3$.
9. $y = 3x^4$, $y = 0$, $x = 2$.   **10.** $y = 3x^4$, $y = 1$.
11. $y = x^4 - 1$, $y = 0$, $x = 2$, $x = 3$.
12. $y = 1 - x^4$, $y = 0$.
13. $y = (x - 1)^2(x + 1)^2$, $y = 0$.
14. $y = (x - 1)^2(x + 1)^2$, $y = 0$, $x = 1$, $x = 2$.
15. $y = x^5$, $y = 0$, $x = 2$.
16. $y = 2x^5 - x$, $y = 0$, $x = -2$, $x = -1$.

In Probs. 17 to 22 sketch and find the algebraic area enclosed; i.e., find A_a^b as indicated.

17. For $y = x$, find A_{-1}^1.   **18.** For $y = x^2$, find A_{-2}^{-1}.
19. For $y = x^3 + 6x$, find A_{-1}^0.   **20.** $y = -x^4 - x + 3$, find A_{-1}^2.
21. For $y = 2x^3 - x^2 + 3x - 5$, find A_1^2.
22. For $y = \frac{1}{4}x^2 - \frac{1}{8}x + 3$, find A_{-2}^2.
23. For $y = a + bx^2 + cx^4 + dx^6$, argue that $A_{-\infty}^0 = A_0^\infty$.
24. For $y = ax + bx^3 + cx^5 + dx^7$, argue that $A_{-\infty}^\infty = 0$.

15.7. *Area under* $y = f(x)$

We are now in a position to define "area enclosed by $y = f(x)$, $y = 0$, $x = a$, $x = b$," at least for some simple functions f (Fig. 15.22).

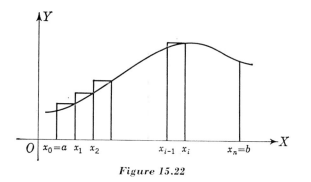

Figure 15.22

First, divide the interval $[a,b]$ up into n *equal* intervals by the points $x_0 = a, x_1, x_2, \ldots, x_{i-1}, x_i, \ldots, x_n = b$. Let us call the common interval width Δx, read "delta x." As we have been doing, use x_1 to determine the height $f(x)$ of a rectangle, use x_2 to determine the height $f(x_2)$ of the next rectangle, etc. Form the rectangles whose areas are $f(x_1) \, \Delta x, f(x_2) \, \Delta x, \ldots, f(x_n) \, \Delta x$. The enclosed area A_a^b—often referred to simply as the "area under the curve from a to b"—is approximately

$$A_a^b \approx f(x_1)\,\Delta x + f(x_2)\,\Delta x + \cdots + f(x_n)\,\Delta x$$

or

(6) $$A_a^b \approx [f(x_1) + f(x_2) + \cdots + f(x_n)]\,\Delta x$$

At this point we should like to introduce a useful shorthand notation, called the Σ notation, for the sum $f(x_1) + f(x_2) + \cdots + f(x_n)$, but we shall first explain the notation with simpler examples. The Greek Σ (sigma, corresponding to S) is used to indicate the "sum of." A dummy letter, such as i or j, is used with Σ. Thus $\sum_{i=1}^{3} x^i$ is read "the sum of x to the ith power, i running from 1 to 3." When written out, this becomes

$$\sum_{i=1}^{3} x^i = x + x^2 + x^3$$

Similarly:

$$\sum_{j=0}^{2} 7x_j = 7x_0 + 7x_1 + 7x_2$$

$$\sum_{i=1}^{n} i = 1 + 2 + 3 + \cdots + n$$

$$\sum_{j=1}^{n} i^2 = 1^2 + 2^2 + \cdots + n^2$$

$$\sum_{i=1}^{k} (2 + 3i) = (2 + 3) + (2 + 3 \cdot 2) + \cdots + (2 + 3k)$$

In this notation we can therefore write (6) in the form

$$A_a^b \approx \sum_{i=1}^{n} f(x_i)\,\Delta x$$

Definition: The *area* A_a^b *under* $y = f(x)$, from $x = a$ to $x = b$, is given by

$$A_a^b = \lim_{n \to \infty}\ [f(x_1) + f(x_2) + \cdots + f(x_n)]\,\Delta x$$

$$= \lim_{n \to \infty} \sum_{i=1}^{n} f(x_i)\,\Delta x$$

if this limit exists.

Although we shall find better ways of computing A_a^b than by working directly with the limit, yet it is important that you understand the definition.

15.8. *Integration*

The limit in the definition above appears so often in mathematical literature (where it has many, many other interpretations) that a very special notation and name have been assigned to it. It is:

$$\lim_{n \to \infty} \sum_{i=1}^{n} f(x_i) \, \Delta x = \int_a^b f(x) \, dx$$

which is read "the integral of f, with respect to x, from a to b." (Some authors refer to this as the *definite integral*.) The function f is called the *integrand;* a and b are called the lower and upper limits[1] of integration, respectively. The dx says that, regardless of the other variables or parameters that might appear in f, the operations of summing and limit taking are to be performed with respect to the variable x, the *variable of integration*. The elongated S, that is, the symbol "$\int$," is to remind us of the sum and limit operations involved. Remember: the integral is *not* a sum; it is the *limit*. The integral is a real number, which depends upon f, a, and b but not upon what we call the independent variable x. The letter x could be called t or z, etc.; for this reason the variable of integration is often referred to as a *dummy variable*. Hence we have

Theorem 7. $\int_a^b f(x) \, dx = \int_a^b f(t) \, dt = \cdots = \int_a^b f(z) \, dz = \cdots .$

To include the case where $a = b$, we give the following intuitively reasonable definition.

Definition: $\int_a^a f(x) \, dx = 0.$

The following theorems (which we actually used, for polynomials, in Sec. 15.6) are readily proved directly from the definition of integral.

Theorem 8. $\int_a^b k \cdot f(x) \, dx = k \cdot \int_a^b f(x) \, dx, \; k \text{ constant.}$

---

[1] The word "limit" here is used in the sense of "bound" and has no connection with the limit of the sequence or of a function. This regrettable confusion is so well established in mathematics that the student will just have to keep alert to be sure of the sense in which "limit" is used.

Theorem 9. $\displaystyle\int_a^b [f(x) \pm g(x)]\, dx = \int_a^b f(x)\, dx \pm \int_a^b g(x)\, dx.$

Theorem 10. $\displaystyle\int_a^b f(x)\, dx = -\int_b^a f(x)\, dx.$

Theorem 11. $\displaystyle\int_a^c f(x)\, dx = \int_a^b f(x)\, dx + \int_b^c f(x)\, dx.$

Exercise A.   Prove Theorem 8.
Exercise B.   Prove Theorem 9.
Exercise C.   Prove Theorem 10.
Exercise D.   Prove Theorem 11.
Exercise E.   Show that

$$\int_a^b (px^2 + qx + r)\, dx = p \int_a^b x^2\, dx + q \int_a^b x\, dx + r \int_a^b 1\, dx$$

The integral $\int_a^b f(x)\, dx$ depends on f, a, and b. In order to study this dependence more fully, let us think of f as a given function, a as being fixed, and b as a variable. We should perhaps change the notation; therefore consider $y = f(u)$, a fixed and x, a variable, as the upper limit.

Definition: The function F whose values are given by

$$F(x,a) = \int_a^x f(u)\, du$$

is called the *integral of f*, with respect to u, from a to x. For fixed a and f it is a function of x.

By changing a to some other number b we get $F(x,b) = \int_b^x f(u)\, du$, another integral. How do $F(x,a)$ and $F(x,b)$ differ? To answer this, we consider the difference $F(x,a) - F(x,b)$. We have

$$
\begin{aligned}
F(x,a) - F(x,b) &= \int_a^x f(u)\, du - \int_b^x f(u)\, du \\
&= \int_a^x f(u)\, du + \int_x^b f(u)\, du \\
&= \int_a^b f(u)\, du = k \qquad \text{a constant}
\end{aligned}
$$

Hence any two integrals of one and the same function differ only by an additive constant; that is, $F(x,a) = F(x,b) + k$.

Exercise F.   Give a geometric interpretation of $\int_a^x f(u)\, du$.

Look now at Table 2, Sec. 15.5, above. In terms of an integral the last line would read $\int_a^b x^n \, dx = \frac{1}{n+1}[b^{n+1} - a^{n+1}]$, but there we were thinking of n as a positive integer. As a matter of fact, the equality holds for every real number $n \neq -1$ according to the following theorem, which we merely state. (It is quite difficult to prove.)

Theorem 12. $\int_a^x u^n \, du = \frac{x^{n+1}}{n+1} - \frac{a^{n+1}}{n+1}$, for any real number $n \neq -1$.

PROBLEMS 15.8

Compute the value of the integral where possible.

1. $\int_0^1 (4x - 1) \, dx.$

2. $\int_0^1 (4t - 1) \, dt.$

3. $\int_1^2 z^2 \, dz.$

4. $\int_1^2 v^2 \, dv.$

5. $\int_0^c 4x^3 \, dx.$

6. $\int_c^0 4y^3 \, dy.$

7. $\int_1^2 u^{\frac{1}{2}} \, du.$

8. $\int_1^2 \sqrt{u} \, du.$

9. $\int_{-1}^1 u^{\frac{1}{3}} \, du.$

10. $\int_1^2 \left(x^2 - x - \frac{1}{x^2} \right) dx.$

11. $\int_1^2 \left(2x - \frac{3}{x^2} \right) dx.$

12. $\int_{-2}^{-1} \frac{1}{x^3} \, dx.$

13. $\int_0^1 (ax + b) \, dx.$

14. $\int_0^1 (ax^2 + bx + c) \, dx.$

15. $\int_0^1 yx^2 \, dx.$

16. $\int_0^1 yx^2 \, dy.$

HINTS: In Prob. 15 treat y as a constant; in Prob. 16 treat x as a constant.

17. $\int_0^1 3x^2 y^3 z^4 \, dx.$

18. $\int_0^1 3x^2 y^3 z^4 \, dy.$

19. $\int_0^1 3x^2 y^3 z^4 \, dz.$

20. $\int_0^1 (\alpha z^2 - 5) \, d\alpha.$

21. $\int_0^x 4 \, dy.$

22. $\int_0^x 4y \, dy.$

23. $\int_1^x dz.$

24. $\int_1^x z \, dz.$

25. $\int_0^{1/a} x^{\frac{1}{2}} \, dx.$

26. $\int_0^a \frac{dx}{\sqrt{x}}.$

27. $\int_1^{1+a} 3x^2 \, dx.$

28. $\int_1^1 \sqrt{x + 1} \, dx.$

29. $\int_1^2 \frac{dx}{x}.$ BT

30. $\int_{-1}^1 \frac{dx}{x^2}.$

31. $\int_0^{2\pi} \sin x \, dx.$

32. $\int_{-0.1}^{0.1} \tan x \, dx.$

15.9. *Setting Up Problems; Applications*

Let us emphasize that in this chapter we have tried to give you some ideas of integration without going into complicated proofs. The subject of integral calculus is large and difficult and will occupy the serious student for many years. We have seen how to find areas under polynomial curves by integration, i.e., by setting up an *approximating sum* and then taking the *limit of the sum*. Actually we made use of the simple formula $\int_a^b x^n \, dx = \dfrac{1}{n+1} [b^{n+1} - a^{n+1}]$ in working with polynomials. In this text we shall not discuss the integration of other functions, but there are obviously a host of others to study.

In discussing a few other applications of the integral calculus it will be our object also to show how the basic definition furnishes us with a powerful method of formulating a given problem. To this end, we consider once more the problem of the area under a curve.

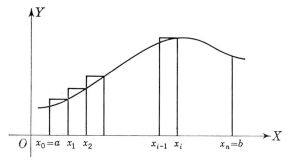

Figure 15.23

Illustration 1. Find the area bounded by the curves $y = f(x)$, $y = 0$, $x = a$, $x = b$.

Solution: We *think* (Fig. 15.23): Divide the interval $[a,b]$ into n equal subintervals by the points whose x-coordinates are $a = x_0, x_1, x_2, \ldots, x_i, \ldots,$ $x_n = b$, and set $\Delta x = x_i - x_{i-1}$. Form the sum $\sum\limits_{i=1}^{n} f(x_i) \, \Delta x$. The area will then be given by

$$\lim_{n \to \infty} \sum_{i=1}^{n} f(x_i) \, \Delta x = \int_a^b f(x) \, dx$$

At this point we would pay no further attention to the left-hand side of the equation *if* we could calculate $\int_a^b f(x) \, dx$.

To shorten the work, we *write* as follows (Fig. 15.24): One small rectangle used in the definition has the area $f(x_i) \, \Delta x$. Because of the end result we are seeking,

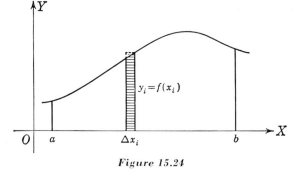

Figure 15.24

we actually write this as $f(x)\,dx$. Then the total area will be the limiting value of the sum of all such small rectangles, or, simply, $\int_a^b f(x)\,dx$. Indeed this is where the symbol $\int$ came from: it is something of an elongated S which is to remind us of both *sum* and *limit.*

You will do well to study the wording of this illustration carefully.

Illustration 2. A bag of sand is raised 10 ft but steadily loses sand at the rate of 3 lb/ft of elevation. Find the work done if at the beginning the full bag weighed 400 lb.

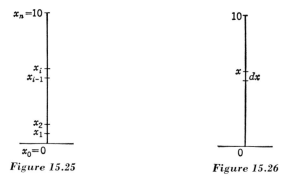

Figure 15.25   *Figure 15.26*

Solution: We *think:* Divide the interval (10 ft) into equal subintervals of width Δx (Fig. 15.25). From the definition of *work = force × distance* we compute, approximately, the work done in lifting the bag through the ith interval $[x_{i-1},x_i]$. It is $(400 - 3x_i)\,\Delta x$. The total work would be, exactly,

$$\lim_{n \to \infty} \sum_{i=1}^{n} (400 - 3x_i)\,\Delta x$$

But we *write* (Fig. 15.26): At height x the bag weighs $400 - 3x$ lb. In lifting this through a distance dx the work done is $(400 - 3x)\,dx$, and the total work is $\int_0^{10} (400 - 3x)\,dx.$

At this point we compute:

$$\text{Work} = \int_0^{10} (400 - 3x)\, dx = 400(10) - \tfrac{3}{2}(10)^2$$
$$= 4{,}000 - 150 = 3{,}850 \text{ ft-lb}$$

Illustration 3. A rectangular fish tank is 3 ft long, 2 ft wide, and 1 ft deep. It is filled with water weighing 62.4 lb/cu ft. Find the total force on one end of the tank.

Solution: We *think* (Fig. 15.27): Divide the interval corresponding to the depth of the tank into equal subintervals of width Δx. From the definition of *total force* $= 62.4 \times A \times h$, where $A =$ area at depth h, we compute, approximately, the total force on the strip between the depths x_{i-1} and x_i. It is $62.4(2)x_i\,\Delta x$.

Hence the total force on the end is exactly $\displaystyle \lim_{n\to\infty} \sum_{i=1}^{n} 62.4(2)x_i\,\Delta x$.

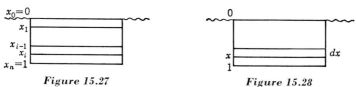

Figure 15.27   Figure 15.28

But we *write* (Fig. 15.28): The force on the small strip at depth x is $62.4(2)x\,dx$, and the total force is $2(62.4) \displaystyle\int_0^1 x\,dx$. This yields total force $= 2(62.4)\tfrac{1}{2} = 62.4$ lb.

Illustration 4. A vertical cylindrical tank of radius 5 ft and height 20 ft is filled with a liquid weighing w lb/cu ft. Find the work done in pumping the water out over the rim of the top (Fig. 15.29).

Solution: We *think:* Divide the interval corresponding to height into equal subintervals of width Δx. The weight contained between x_{i-1} and x_i is $25\pi w\,\Delta x$. This must be lifted x_i ft; so the work done is $25\pi w x_i\,\Delta x$. The total work would be

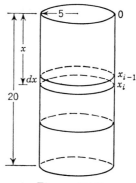

Figure 15.29

$$\lim_{n\to\infty} \sum_{i=1}^{n} 25\pi w x_i\,\Delta x.$$

But we *write:* The typical small weight is $25\pi w\,dx$, and this must be lifted x ft. The work, therefore, is

$$W = 25\pi w \int_0^{20} x\,dx = 25\pi w \frac{20^2}{2} = 5{,}000\pi w \text{ ft-lb}$$

Illustration 5. Find the volume enclosed by a surface of revolution.

Solution: Consider the curve $y = f(x)$, between a and b; revolve it around the X-axis, thus generating a surface of revolution (Fig. 15.30). This surface, together with the planes $x = a$, $x = b$, enclose something we would like to call "volume." This, once again, is an intuitive notion. We shall give a definition of this intuitive notion in a moment. First form n intervals on the X-axis from a to b by the points $x_0 = a$, x_1, x_2, . . . , $x_n = b$ such that $x_i - x_{i-1} = \Delta x$. Cut the surface by the planes $x = x_i$, $i = 0, 1, . . . , n$. Construct the cylinders as indicated in the figure; the general one will have a base of radius $f(x_i)$ and a height of $\Delta x_i = x_i - x_{i-1}$.

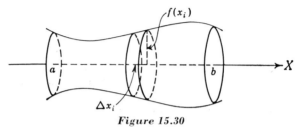

Figure 15.30

We assume that the volume of a cylinder is known from elementary geometry to be area of base times height. Hence the general elementary cylinder will have a volume of $\pi[f(x_i)]^2 \cdot \Delta x$ and the sum of all such

$$\sum_{i=1}^{n} \pi[f(x_i)]^2 \cdot \Delta x$$

will be an approximation to the "volume" being considered. If we take the limit of this sum as $n \to \infty$, we shall have the volume by definition.

Definition: The *volume* contained between the planes $x = a$ and $x = b$ and the surface generated by revolving $y = f(x)$ about the X-axis is

(7)
$$V_a^b = \lim_{n \to \infty} \sum_{i=1}^{n} \pi[f(x_i)]^2 \cdot \Delta x$$

if this limit exists.

By now you should be able to translate this definition directly into the integral

(8)
$$V_a^b = \pi \int_a^b [f(x)]^2 \, dx$$

Recall the mental process we go through in writing down such an expression. We *write* (8) but we *think* and *talk* (7) because (7) is the basic one. We say to ourselves something like this: "A typical little cylinder in a given subinterval will have the volume approximately equal to $\pi[f(x)]^2 \cdot \Delta x$." Then we continue: "If we sum up all such little cylinders, we will get, in the limit, the total volume." And we write $\int$ for limit of sum; so we have

$$\pi \int_a^b [f(x)]^2 \, dx$$

Illustration 6. As a special example we now find the volume generated by revolving $y = x^2$ about the X-axis between $x = 0$ and $x = 2$.

　　Solution:

$$V_0^2 = \pi \int_0^2 [x^2]^2 \, dx$$

$$= \pi \, \frac{2^5}{5}$$

$$= \tfrac{32}{5} \pi \text{ cu units}$$

PROBLEMS 15.9

1. A small boat anchor chain weighs 2 lb/lin ft. What is the work done in pulling up anchor if the anchor itself weighs 100 lb and 30 ft of chain is out? Assume the lift is vertical.

2. The force required to stretch a certain spring x in. is $4x$. Find the work done in stretching the spring 2 in. beyond its natural length.

3. The natural length of a spring is 2 in., and the force required to compress it x in. is $10x$. Find the work done in compressing it to half its natural length.

4. A 10- by 12-ft rectangular floodgate is placed vertically in water with the 10-ft side in the surface of the water. Find the force on one side.

5. A plate in the form of an equilateral triangle, of side 4, is submerged vertically in water until one edge is just in the surface of the water. Find the total force on one side of such a plate.

6. A plate in the form of the parabola $y = x^2$ is lowered vertically into water to a depth of 1 ft, vertex down. Find the force on one side.

7. A conical tank is full of water, is 10 ft deep (vertex down), and the top has a radius of 4 ft. Find the work required to empty the tank by pumping the water to a point 3 ft above the top of the tank. Assume that water weighs w lb/cu ft.

In Probs. 8 to 13 find the volume generated as indicated. Sketch.

8. $y^2 = 4px$ about the X-axis from $x = 0$ to $x = p$.

9. $y = \sqrt{r^2 - x^2}$ about the X-axis from $x = -r$ to $x = +r$.

10. $y = \dfrac{b}{a} \sqrt{a^2 - x^2}$ about the X-axis from $x = -a$ to $x = +a$.

11. $y = x^2 - x$ about the X-axis from $x = 0$ to $x = 1$.

12. $y = x^{\frac{3}{2}}$ about the Y-axis from $y = 0$ to $y = 1$.

13. $y = x^{\frac{2}{3}}$ about the Y-axis from $y = 0$ to $y = 1$.

In Probs. 14 to 17 *set up* the problem as the limit of a sum and as an integral, but *do not* attempt to evaluate.

14. Calculate the work done in pumping out the water from a filled hemispherical reservoir 5 ft deep.

15. A circular water main 8 ft in diameter is full of water. Find the pressure on the gate valve when closed.

16. The natural length of a spring is 10 in., and the force required to stretch it x in. is $100x$. Find the work done extending the length of the spring from 11 in. to 12 in.

17. Find the volume generated by revolving $y = \sin x$ about the X-axis from $x = 0$ to $x = \pi$.

CHAPTER SIXTEEN

Intuitive Differentiation

16.1. *Introduction*

In Chap. 15 we were concerned with the problem of area. There we indicated that Euclid gave a definition of the area of a circle and that Archimedes, using this definition, arrived at the approximation $\pi \approx 3\frac{1}{7}$—a value that is in current use. Archimedes also found, in effect, by methods of sums and limits, the area enclosed by the parabola $y^2 = x$ and $x = 1$. It is reasonable to say that the early Greeks had some insight in that branch of mathematics now called *integral calculus*. They seem to have had no notion of *differential calculus*, the subject of this chapter.

16.2. *Notion of a Tangent*

While the concept of *integral* grew out of the problem of the area under a curve, the concept of *derivative* arose in connection with the *geometric tangent* to a plane curve and also in connection with the physical quantity *velocity*. We shall treat these in turn but begin with Euclid's definition of a tangent to a circle, an idea you met in plane geometry. Euclid said:

> The tangent to a circle at point D, one endpoint of a diameter DD', is the line passing through D and perpendicular to DD'.

You can readily see that such a definition will be of no use to us if we try to apply it to curves other than circles.

Intuitively we feel that a curve, though bending and turning, should have some sort of "nearly con-

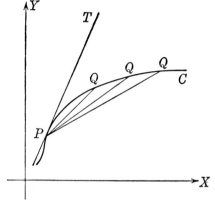

Figure 16.1

stant direction" in a very small interval, and our intuition furnishes us with a clue as to how to define a tangent line.

Consider a curve C, such as is pictured in Fig. 16.1, and draw the line PQ, called a secant line. If Q were made to trace the curve until it approached the point P, the secant PQ would take different positions therewith.

Definition: The line whose position is the unique limiting position PT of the secant line PQ, as $Q \to P$ along the curve, if one exists, is called the *tangent line* to the curve at the point P.

For some curves there is no unique limiting position (for some points P), in which cases there is no tangent at P. But for graphs of polynomials, the tangent line is well defined for each and every point P on the graph. In this chapter we deal mainly with polynomials, but we shall develop our basic concepts for a more general function f.

The definition and the discussion of a tangent so far have been geometric in nature. Now let us translate the geometric wording into an equation for this line. This is indeed quite essential. For our definition of the tangent to a curve we used the phrase "limiting position of a secant." Although this makes intuitive sense, we have not defined the meaning of such a limit and hence cannot proceed deductively here. Instead, we must use our knowledge of analytic geometry to translate this intuitive idea into a sharp, clear one.

We know that a line is completely determined by a point and a slope; and in this case the point is given. Therefore we must seek the slope of the tangent. From our early discussion we might well infer that the slope of the tangent should equal the limit of the slopes of the secants. The slope of a secant which cuts the curve $y = f(x)$ in the points $(x_1, f(x_1))$, $(x_1 + h, f(x_1 + h))$ is

$$\text{Slope of secant} = \frac{f(x_1 + h) - f(x_1)}{h}$$

Hence we state the following definition (Fig. 16.2):

Definition.   The tangent to the curve $y = f(x)$ at the point $(x_1, f(x_1))$ is the line passing through this point whose *slope* $m(x_1)$ is given by

$$(1) \qquad m(x_1) = \lim_{h \to 0} \frac{f(x_1 + h) - f(x_1)}{h}$$

provided this limit exists.

We recall that the equation of such a line is

$$(2) \qquad y - y_1 = m(x_1)(x - x_1)$$

Finally, therefore, we write down the equation of this tangent line by computing $m(x_1)$ and substituting in (2) above.

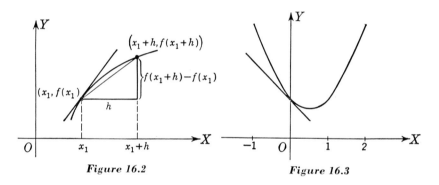

Figure 16.2   Figure 16.3

Illustration 1.   Find the equation of the line tangent to the curve

$$y = x^2 - x + 1$$

at the point $(0,1)$ (Fig. 16.3).

Solution: We have

$$f(x_1) = f(0) = 1$$
$$f(x_1 + h) = (x_1 + h)^2 - (x_1 + h) + 1$$
$$= (0 + h)^2 - (0 + h) + 1$$
$$= h^2 - h + 1$$

$$m(x_1) = \lim_{h \to 0} \frac{f(x_1 + h) - f(x_1)}{h}$$
$$= \lim_{h \to 0} \frac{h^2 - h}{h}$$
$$= \lim_{h \to 0} (h - 1) \qquad h \neq 0$$
$$= -1$$

The equation of the tangent is, therefore,

$$y - 1 = -1(x)$$

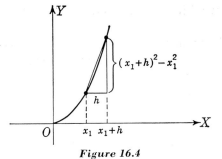

Figure 16.4

Illustration 2. Find the equation of the tangent to $y = x^2$ at the point (x_1, y_1).
    Solution:

$$f(x_1) = x_1{}^2$$
$$f(x_1 + h) = (x_1 + h)^2 = x_1{}^2 + 2x_1 h + h^2$$
$$m(x_1) = \lim_{h \to 0} \frac{f(x_1 + h) - f(x_1)}{h}$$
$$= \lim_{h \to 0} \frac{x_1{}^2 + 2x_1 h + h^2 - x_1{}^2}{h}$$
$$= 2x_1$$

The equation of the tangent is, therefore,

$$y - y_1 = 2x_1(x - x_1)$$

PROBLEMS 16.2

Find the equation of the tangent line as indicated, and sketch.

1. $y = 3x - 6$, at $(1, -3)$.   2. $y = 1 - 2x$, at $(1, -1)$.
3. $y = 5x^2 + 4$, at $(2, 24)$.   4. $y = 2x^2 - 5$, at $(2, 3)$.
5. $y = 3x^2 - 2x$, at $(-1, 5)$.   6. $y = x - 4x^2$, at $(0, 0)$.
7. $y = x^2 + 3x - 5$, at $(-2, -7)$.   8. $y = 1 - x + x^2$, at $(1, 1)$.
9. $y = x^3 + 2$, at $(1, 3)$.   10. $y = 3 - 2x^3$, at $(1, 1)$.
11. $y = x^4 + 2$, at $(1, 3)$.   12. $y = x^5 + 1$, at $(2, 33)$.
13. $y = ax + b$, at $(x_1, ax_1 + b)$.   14. $y = x^3$, at the point where $x = x_1$.
15. $y = ax^2 + bx + c$, at the point where $x = x_1$.

16.3. *Velocity and Acceleration*

When a particle moves, there are associated with the motion certain quantities such as time, distance, velocity, and acceleration. We shall restrict ourselves to the case where the motion takes place on a straight line, since we are unprepared at this time to consider general curvilinear motion.

Let $y = f(t)$ give the position of the particle on the Y-axis at any time t. The time variable is measured continuously by a clock and is usually thought of as positive or zero, although on occasion we may

want to assign a negative value in order to describe a past event.   The
y-coordinate is a linear distance positive, negative, or zero from some
fixed point on the line called the origin (Fig. 16.5).   Suppose the
particle to be at $y = f(t_1)$ and $y = f(t_1 + h)$, when t is t_1
and $t_1 + h$, respectively.   Then the particle has moved
$f(t_1 + h) - f(t_1)$ units of distance in $h > 0$ units of time.

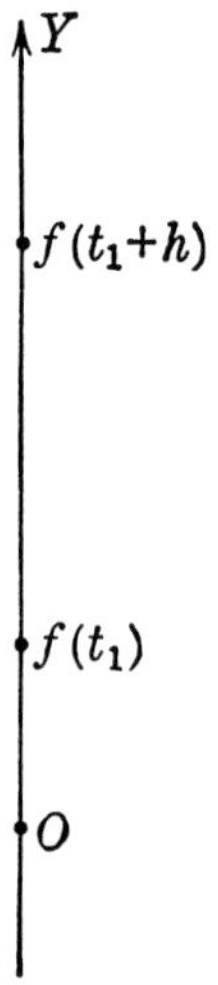

Definition: If a particle moves a distance of

$$f(t_1 + h) - f(t_1)$$

in time h, then the ratio (Fig. 16.6a)

$$(3) \qquad \bar{v} = \frac{f(t_1 + h) - f(t_1)}{h}$$

is called the *average velocity during the time interval h.*

Average velocity is thus the change in distance per
unit change in time.   Units often encountered are miles
per hour, centimeters per second, etc.   These are abbreviated mi/hr, cm/sec, etc.   Since distance may be negative, so also velocity may be negative.   If only the
absolute values of the distances are used, then average
velocity is called average speed.

Figure 16.5

Now average velocity (and also average speed) is an interval property since it describes what happens in an interval of time.   Hence
it cannot directly explain such a statement as "exactly at that instant
the plane was traveling at 500 miles per hour," because there is no
interval of time involved in this observation.   And yet, intuitively
the statement does have some sense.   It seems to say that, if the
plane had continued at the same (constant) speed as it was traveling
at that instant, then it would have covered 500 miles every hour
thereafter.   But this does not supply an answer to the inherent difficulty in the notion of traveling at 500 mi/hr *at* a certain (clock) value,
say t_1, of the time variable.   But let us think of a small interval of
time $[t_1, t_1 + h]$, where $h > 0$, and the average velocity $\bar{v}$ during this
interval.   Then consider the average velocity $\bar{v}$ for smaller and smaller
intervals of time h.   Intuitively we feel that there should be something,
$v(t_1)$, called *instantaneous velocity at $t = t_1$* which the average velocity $\bar{v}$
would approach as h approaches zero.   We lay down the following
definition:

Definition: Given distance y as a function f of t, then the *instantaneous
velocity*, or, simply, *velocity for a particular value of t, say t_1*, is defined

to be

(4)
$$v(t_1) = \lim_{h \to 0} \frac{f(t_1 + h) - f(t_1)}{h}$$

provided this limit exists.

Remark. If we substitute $h = 0$ in the expression $\dfrac{f(t_1 + h) - f(t_1)}{h}$, it takes the meaningless form $0/0$. However, the limit of this expression may still have meaning and be of great value. We shall discuss this further in Sec. 16.4.

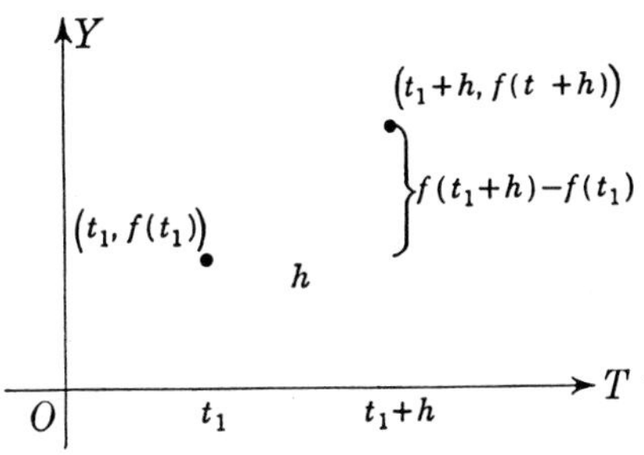

Figure 16.6a

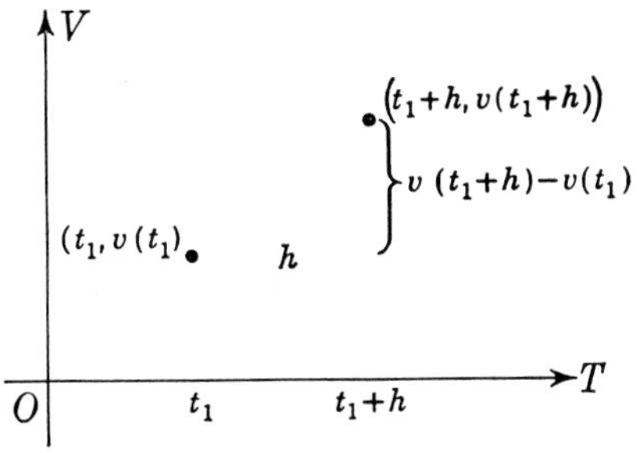

Figure 16.6b

The concept of acceleration is no more difficult to grasp mathematically than that of velocity. It is known to be the rate at which velocity is changing. To describe this precisely, let us compute the two values of instantaneous velocity $v(t_1)$ and $v(t_1 + h)$ corresponding to the two values of t, namely, t_1 and $t_1 + h$.

Definition: The ratio

(5)
$$\bar{a} = \frac{v(t_1 + h) - v(t_1)}{h}$$

is called the *average acceleration during the interval h*. It may be positive, negative, or zero (Fig. 16.6b).

Definition: The *instantaneous acceleration*, or, simply, *acceleration at t_1*, is defined by

(6)
$$a(t_1) = \lim_{h \to 0} \frac{v(t_1 + h) - v(t_1)}{h}$$

provided this limit exists.

Average acceleration is an interval property. Instantaneous acceleration is a point property; it is a limit. The unit of acceleration is "units of velocity per unit of time," such as feet per second, per second;

miles per hour, per minute; etc.   These are abbreviated ft/sec/sec, or ft/sec², mi/hr/min, etc.

To summarize, velocity is rate of change of distance with respect to time.   Acceleration is rate of change of velocity with respect to time.

Illustration 1.   A particle moves vertically (up and down) in a straight line under the following law of motion: $y = 8t - t^2$, where t is in seconds and y is in feet.   Find (a) the velocity at any time t_1; (b) the acceleration at any time t_1; (c) the domain of values of $t > 0$ for which velocity is positive; (d) maximum value of y.

Solution:

(a) $v = \lim\limits_{h \to 0} \dfrac{f(t_1 + h) - f(t_1)}{h} = \lim\limits_{h \to 0} \dfrac{[8(t_1 + h) - (t_1 + h)^2] - [8t_1 - t_1{}^2]}{h}$

$= \lim\limits_{h \to 0} \dfrac{8t_1 + 8h - t_1{}^2 - 2t_1 h - h^2 - 8t_1 - t_1{}^2}{h}$

$= \lim\limits_{h \to 0} \dfrac{8h - 2t_1 h - h^2}{h}$

$= \lim\limits_{h \to 0} (8 - 2t_1 - h) \qquad h \neq 0$

$= 8 - 2t_1 \text{ ft/sec}$

(b) $a = \lim\limits_{h \to 0} \dfrac{v(t_1 + h) - v(t_1)}{h} = \lim\limits_{h \to 0} \dfrac{[8 - 2(t_1 + h)] - [8 - 2t_1]}{h}$

$a = \lim\limits_{h \to 0} \dfrac{8 - 2t_1 - 2h - 8 + 2t_1}{h}$

$= \lim\limits_{h \to 0} \dfrac{-2h}{h} = \lim\limits_{h \to 0} (-2)$

$= -2 \text{ ft/sec/sec}$

(c) $v = 8 - 2t > 0$, or $t < 4$ sec.   Since also $t > 0$, the answer is: $0 < t < 4$.

(d) The particle is at the origin when $t = 0$ and again when $t = 8$.   Since it helps to sketch the graph of $y = 8t - t^2$, we do so in Fig. 16.7; however,

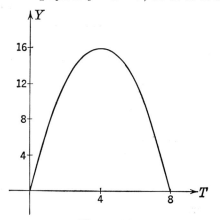

Figure 16.7

this graph does not represent the curve traversed by the particle—it simply shows more clearly how high the particle is at time t. The particle evidently rises to some maximum height, then falls back down again, reaching the "ground" in 8 sec. The velocity is positive $(0 < t < 4)$ going up, negative $(4 < t < 8)$ coming down. It therefore reached its maximum height at $t = 4$, when the velocity was zero. Its maximum height was $8 \cdot 4 - 4^2 = 16$ ft.

PROBLEMS 16.3

Given: The height y, ft, of a particle at time t, sec	Find:		
	(a) Average velocity $\bar{v}$ during interval from	(b) Average velocity $\bar{v}$ during interval from	(c) Velocity v at
1. $y = 16t^2$	$t = 0$, to $t = 1$	$t = 1$, to $t = 2$	$t = 3$
2. $y = 16t - t^2$	$t = 0$, to $t = 1$	$t = 0$, to $t = 2$	$t = 3$
3. $y = 6t - 3t^2$	$t = 0$, to $t = \frac{1}{2}$	$t = \frac{1}{2}$, to $t = 1$	$t = 1$
4. $y = 3t - 2t^2$	$t = 1$, to $t = 2$	$t = 1$, to $t = \frac{3}{2}$	$t = \frac{1}{3}$
5. $y = 4 + 2t - 2t^2$	$t = 0$, to $t = 2$	$t = 0$, to $t = t_1$	$t = t_1$
6. $y = 100 + 30t - 16t^2$	$t = 0$, to $t = t_1$	$t = t_1$, to $t = t_2$	$t = t_2$
7. $y = t(t - 1)$	$t = 0$, to $t = 0.1$	$t = 0.1$, to $t = 0.2$	$t = 0.5$
8. $y = 3t + 4$	$t = 0$, to $t = 1$	$t = 1$, to $t = 2$	$t = 10$

Given: The velocity v, ft/sec, at time t, sec	Find:	
	(a) Average acceleration $\bar{a}$ during interval from	(b) Acceleration a at
9. $v = 6 - 2t$	$t = 0$, to $t = 1$	$t = 2$
10. $v = 8 - 2t$	$t = 0$, to $t = 1$	$t = 3$
11. $v = t - 2t^2$	$t = 0$, to $t = 2$	$t = 10$
12. $v = t^2 - t$	$t = 1$, to $t = 2$	$t = 20$

Given: The height y, ft at time t, sec	Find:	
	(a) Velocity v at	(b) Acceleration a at
13. $y = 8t^2 - 3t$	$t = 2$	$t = 2$
14. $y = 4t - 5t^2$	$t = 3$	$t = 4$
15. $y = 10 - 3t + 3t^2$	$t = t_1$	$t = t_1$
16. $y = 20 - 4t - 2t^2$	$t = t_1$	$t = t_1$
17. $y = t^2 - t^3$	$t = t_1$	$t = t_1$
18. $y = t^4$	$t = t_1$	$t = t_1$
19. $y = t^5$	$t = t_1$	$t = t_1$
20. $y = t^n$, n a positive integer	$t = t_1$	$t = t_1$

16.4. Derivative

In determining the slope $m(x_1)$ of the tangent to the curve $y = f(x)$ at a point $x = x_1$, we were led to formula (1), Sec. 16.2,

$$(1) \qquad m(x_1) = \lim_{h \to 0} \frac{f(x_1 + h) - f(x_1)}{h}$$

Formula (4), Sec. 16.3, for velocity at $t = t_1$ [where $y = f(t)$ relates distance and time] was

$$(4) \qquad v(t_1) = \lim_{h \to 0} \frac{f(t_1 + h) - f(t_1)}{h}$$

and formula (6), Sec. 16.3, for acceleration at $t = t_1$ [where $y = v(t)$ relates velocity and time] was

$$(6) \qquad a(t_1) = \lim_{h \to 0} \frac{v(t_1 + h) - v(t_1)}{h}$$

It is a phenomenon worth recording that these three processes are abstractly identical: each is the same limit operation on a function. A name has been given to this operation.

Definition: The limit

$$(7) \qquad \lim_{h \to 0} \frac{f(x_1 + h) - f(x_1)}{h}$$

if it exists, is called the *derivative of f with respect to x at the point* $x = x_1$.

The derivative is therefore a new function which is the result of an operation on a function at a point. The process is called *differentiation*.

Exercise A. Are the domains of definition of a function and its derivative necessarily the same? Explain.

Other notations are often used. Instead of h let us write Δx (read "delta x"), which stands for a change in x. Also let us write Δf for the quantity

$$f(x_1 + \Delta x) - f(x_1)$$

(Fig. 16.8). Then the derivative is

$$(8) \qquad \lim_{\Delta x \to 0} \frac{\Delta f}{\Delta x}$$

if we make the appropriate substitutions in (7).

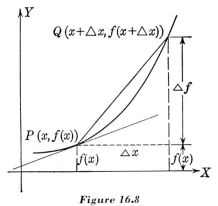

Figure 16.8

The notion of a derivative is more subtle than might appear at first sight. Be sure that you understand the following remarks:

Remarks

(1) The derivative is *not* the value of $\Delta f / \Delta x$ when $\Delta x = 0$; for when $\Delta x = 0$, $\Delta f / \Delta x = 0/0$, which is indeterminate.

(2) The derivative is the *limit* of $\Delta f / \Delta x$ as $\Delta x \to 0$ if this limit exists. However, the limit may fail to exist, and in this case the derivative is not defined. For polynomials, however, the derivative exists for every value of x. An example of a curve which has a point at which there is no derivative is given in the following illustration:

Illustration 1. Find the derivative at the point (0,0), if it exists, of the function f whose values are $f(x) = \sqrt{x}$.

$$\Delta f = \sqrt{x + \Delta x} - \sqrt{x}$$
$$= \sqrt{\Delta x} \qquad \text{when } x = 0$$
$$\frac{\Delta f}{\Delta x} = \frac{\sqrt{\Delta x}}{\Delta x}$$
$$= \frac{1}{\sqrt{\Delta x}} \qquad \text{provided } \Delta x \neq 0$$

But $\lim\limits_{\Delta x \to 0} \Delta f / \Delta x$ does not exist, for $1/\sqrt{\Delta x}$ can be made as large as we please by choosing Δx sufficiently small; i.e., it "tends to infinity."

(3) Where f is a polynomial, we shall evaluate $\lim_{\Delta x \to 0} \Delta f/\Delta x$ by a process which may seem to contradict our first two remarks. Let us examine it closely.

Illustration 2. Find the derivative at the point where $x = 0$ of the function f whose values are $f(x) = x^2 - x + 1$. (See Illustration 1, Sec. 16.2.)

Solution:

$$f(0) = 1$$
$$f(0 + \Delta x) = (0 + \Delta x)^2 - (0 + \Delta x) + 1$$
$$= \overline{\Delta x}^2 - \Delta x + 1$$

So
$$\Delta f = f(0 + \Delta x) - f(0)$$
$$= \overline{\Delta x}^2 - \Delta x$$

Then
$$\frac{\Delta f}{\Delta x} = \frac{\overline{\Delta x}^2 - \Delta x}{\Delta x}$$
$$= \Delta x - 1 \qquad \text{provided } \Delta x \neq 0$$

Finally
$$\lim_{\Delta x \to 0} \frac{\Delta f}{\Delta x} = \lim_{\Delta x \to 0} (\Delta x - 1)$$
$$= -1$$

In the above illustration we first computed Δf at the required point and then found $\Delta f/\Delta x$. In its original form

$$\frac{\Delta f}{\Delta x} = \frac{\overline{\Delta x}^2 - \Delta x}{\Delta x}$$

and we cannot find its limit without another step. We simplify this fraction by dividing numerator and denominator by Δx, a permissible process as long as $\Delta x \neq 0$. This gives

$$\frac{\Delta f}{\Delta x} = \Delta x - 1 \qquad \text{provided } \Delta x \neq 0$$

Now we take the limit of $\Delta x - 1$ as $\Delta x \to 0$ and assert that the answer is -1.

In evaluating $\lim_{\Delta x \to 0} (\Delta x - 1)$ we *do not put* $\Delta x = 0$; we let Δx *approach* zero. As Δx approaches zero, $\Delta x - 1$ approaches -1, the answer. The point of confusion is that we also get the right answer if we put $\Delta x = 0$ in $\Delta x - 1$. Thus we get the right answer by a process which is apparently illegitimate. Actually this process can be justified whenever $\Delta f/\Delta x$ can be reduced (by division) to a polynomial in Δx. The justification follows from the following theorem on polynomials, which we give without proof:

Theorem 1. If $f(x)$ is a polynomial in x, then for any a

$$\lim_{x \to a} f(x) = f(a)$$

In other words, we may find the limit of a polynomial by the simple device of substitution. This is *not* true of functions in general. Since, in Illustration 2, $\Delta x - 1$ is a polynomial in Δx, we can find $\lim_{\Delta x \to 0} (\Delta x - 1)$ by putting $\Delta x = 0$, and hence the apparent confusion is resolved.

The symbols in (7) and (8), while standard, are still long to write down, and thus we devise other symbols which are also quite standard. Let f be the function whose values are given by $y = f(x)$. Then the derivative of f with respect to x is written:

(a) $\lim\limits_{\Delta x \to 0} \dfrac{f(x + \Delta x) - f(x)}{\Delta x}$ [Definition]

(b) $D_x y = D_x f(x) = D_x f$ [After Cauchy, 1789–1857]

(c) $f'(x)$ [After Lagrange, 1736–1813]

(d) $\dfrac{dy}{dx} = \dfrac{df(x)}{dx}$ [After Leibniz, 1646–1716]

In this book we shall use the notations (b) and (c) but shall avoid (d). You will often run across (d) in books on science and engineering, but it is basically misleading. It gives every appearance of being a fraction, but it is *not* a fraction—it is the limit of a fraction. The various terms dy, dx, $df(x)$ have no separate meanings, but students (and others who should know better) sometimes are misled and ascribe meaning to them.

The following statements are easy to prove.

Theorem 2. $D_x cf = c \cdot D_x f$, c constant.

Theorem 3. $D_x(f \pm g) = D_x f \pm D_x g$.

Exercise B.   Prove Theorems 2 and 3.
Exercise C.   Show that

$$D(px^2 + qx + r) = p\, Dx^2 + q\, Dx + Dr$$

We now turn to the problem of differentiating systematically the various nonnegative integral powers of x, namely, $1 = x^0, x, x^2, \ldots ,$ $x^n, \ldots .$ Draw the associated figure, and remember that we are calling

$$\Delta f = f(x + \Delta x) - f(x)$$

Theorem 4. $D_x1 = 0$.
   Proof:

$$f(x) = 1$$
$$f(x + \Delta x) = 1$$
$$\Delta f = 0$$
$$\frac{\Delta f}{\Delta x} = 0 \qquad \Delta x \neq 0$$
$$D_x f = \lim_{\Delta x \to 0} \frac{\Delta f}{\Delta x} = 0$$

Exercise C.   Prove that for a constant C

$$D_x C = 0$$

Theorem 5. $D_x x = 1$.
   Proof:

$$f(x) = x$$
$$f(x + \Delta x) = x + \Delta x$$
$$\Delta f = \Delta x$$
$$\frac{\Delta f}{\Delta x} = \frac{\Delta x}{\Delta x} = 1 \qquad \Delta x \neq 0$$
$$D_x f = \lim_{\Delta x \to 0} \frac{\Delta f}{\Delta x} = 1$$

Theorem 6. $D_x x^2 = 2x$.
   Proof:

$$f(x) = x^2$$
$$f(x + \Delta x) = (x + \Delta x)^2 = x^2 + 2x\,\overline{\Delta x} + \overline{\Delta x}^2$$
$$\Delta f = 2x\,\overline{\Delta x} + \overline{\Delta x}^2$$
$$\frac{\Delta f}{\Delta x} = 2x + \Delta x \qquad \Delta x \neq 0$$
$$D_x f = \lim_{\Delta x \to 0} \frac{\Delta f}{\Delta x} = 2x$$

Theorem 7. $D_x x^3 = 3x^2$.
   Proof:

$$f(x) = x^3$$
$$f(x + \Delta x) = (x + \Delta x)^3 = x^3 + 3x^2\,\overline{\Delta x} + 3x\,\overline{\Delta x}^2 + \overline{\Delta x}^3$$
$$\Delta f = 3x^2\,\overline{\Delta x} + 3x\,\overline{\Delta x}^2 + \overline{\Delta x}^3$$
$$\frac{\Delta f}{\Delta x} = 3x^2 + 3x\,\overline{\Delta x} + \overline{\Delta x}^2 \qquad \Delta x \neq 0$$
$$D_x f = \lim_{\Delta x \to 0} \frac{\Delta f}{\Delta x} = 3x^2$$

Theorem 8. $D_x x^4 = 4x^3$.

  Proof:

$$f(x) = x^4$$
$$f(x + \Delta x) = (x + \Delta x)^4 = x^4 + 4x^3 \overline{\Delta x} + 6x^2 \overline{\Delta x}^2 + 4x \overline{\Delta x}^3 + \overline{\Delta x}^4$$
$$\Delta f = 4x^3 \overline{\Delta x} + 6x^2 \overline{\Delta x}^2 + 4x \overline{\Delta x}^3 + \overline{\Delta x}^4$$
$$\frac{\Delta f}{\Delta x} = 4x^3 + 6x^2 \overline{\Delta x} + 4x \overline{\Delta x}^2 + \overline{\Delta x}^3 \qquad \Delta x \neq 0$$
$$D_x f = \lim_{\Delta x \to 0} \frac{\Delta f}{\Delta x} = 4x^3$$

We have passed over such questions as the $\lim\limits_{\Delta x \to 0} 6x^2 \overline{\Delta x},\ 4x \overline{\Delta x}^2$, etc.
By now it must be clear that these go to zero with Δx for any given fixed x.

You might want to guess what the derivatives of the higher powers would be. A reasonable guess is that $D_x x^n = nx^{n-1}$ for n a positive integer. We shall prove this below.

Theorem 9. $D_x x^n = nx^{n-1}$, when n is a positive integer.
  Proof: We proceed by induction. We know that, for $n = 1$,

$$D_x x^1 = D_x x = 1$$

Thus the formula is verified. Assume it true for $n = k$; that is,

$$D_x x^k = kx^{k-1}$$

Now $x^{k+1} = x^k \cdot x$. To find its derivative, we consider

$$\lim_{\Delta x \to 0} \frac{(x + \Delta x)^{k+1} - x^{k+1}}{\Delta x} = \lim_{\Delta x \to 0} \frac{(x + \Delta x)^k (x + \Delta x) - x^k x}{\Delta x}$$
$$= \lim_{\Delta x \to 0} \frac{[(x + \Delta x)^k - x^k] x}{\Delta x} + \lim_{\Delta x \to 0} \frac{(x + \Delta x)^k \cdot \Delta x}{\Delta x}$$
$$= (D_x x^k) x + x^k$$
$$= kx^{k-1} \cdot x + x^k$$
$$= (k + 1) x^k$$

This verifies the theorem for $n = k + 1$. From the induction axiom it then follows that the theorem is true for all positive integers n. As a matter of fact, we state without proof that Theorem 9 holds for any real value of the exponent n. Memorize:

(9) $$D_x x^n = nx^{n-1} \qquad n \text{ a real number}$$

Exercise D. Prove Theorem 9 by the Δ-process, using the Binomial Theorem (Sec. 3.4). Model your proof on that of Theorem 8.

PROBLEMS 16.4

In Probs. 1 to 12, find $D_x y$.

1. $y = 6x^4 + 5x^{\frac{2}{3}} + x^{\sqrt{2}}$.

2. $y = 7x^3 + \sqrt{x} + 4x^\pi$.

3. $y = 7/x^6 + 7x^6$.

4. $y = 5/x^4 + 5x^5$.

5. $y = (3x + x^3)/x$.

6. $y = (2x^3 - 5x^2)/x^2$.

7. $y = (1 - x^3)(1 - x)$.

8. $y = (1 + x^3)(1 + x)$.

9. $y = (1 - x^3)/(1 - x)$.

10. $y = (1 + x^3)/(1 + x)$.

11. $y = (3x^2 + x - 1)/x$.

12. $y = (2x^3 + 2x - 1)/x$.

In Probs 13 to 20, find the slope of the tangent to each curve at the point indicated and the equation of the tangent at that point.

13. $y = x - x^3$, $(0,0)$.

14. $y = x^4 - x^2$, $(0,0)$.

15. $y = 3\sqrt{x}$, $(1,3)$.

16. $y = -4x^{\frac{1}{2}}$, $(1,-4)$.

17. $y = 2x - x^2 + 3$, $(1,4)$.

18. $y = 1 - 3x + 4x^3$, $(\frac{1}{2},0)$.

19. $y = 1 + 2x - x^2$, $(2,1)$.

20. $y = 2 - 3x + x^2$, $(3,2)$.

21. Find the equation of the tangent to $y = x^4 - x^2 + 1$ at the point where $x = 1$.

22. Find the equation of the tangent to $y = x^3 + x^2 - x - 1$ at the point where $x = 2$.

23. Find (a) the equation of the tangent and (b) the equation of the line perpendicular to the tangent at $(-1,10)$ on the curve $y = 2x^2 - 3x + 5$.

24. Find (a) the equation of the tangent and (b) the equation of the line perpendicular to the tangent at $(1,2)$ on the curve $y = 4 - x - x^2$.

In Probs. 25 to 30, given distance y (feet) as a function of time t (seconds), find the velocity at the time indicated.

25. $y = 2t - t^2$, $t = 1$.

26. $y = 16t^2 - 3t$, $t = 2$.

27. $y = 10t^2 + 2t - 3$, $t = 1$.

28. $y = t^3 - t + 4$, $t = 3$.

29. $y = t - t^2$, $t = t_1$.

30. $y = 2t - 3t^2 + 7$, $t = t_1$.

In Probs. 31 to 36 given velocity v (feet per second) as a function of time t (seconds), find the acceleration at the time indicated.

31. $v = 2 - 2t$, $t = 1$.

32. $v = 32t - 3$, $t = 2$.

33. $v = 20t + 2$, $t = 1$.

34. $v = 3t^3 - 1$, $t = 3$.

35. $v = 1 - 2t$, $t = t_1$.

36. $v = 2 - 6t$, $t = t_1$.

37. From the definition of derivative find $D_x y$ for $y = x^{-2}$. Hence show that the general rule applies.

38. From the definition of derivative find $D_x y$ for $y = x^{-n}$, where n is a positive integer. Hence show that the same rule applies for either positive or negative powers of x. HINT: Use mathematical induction.

39. Illustrate with an example to show that in general $D(f \cdot g) \neq Df \cdot Dg$. (The derivative of a product is not the product of the derivatives.)

40.* From first principles derive the formula for the derivative of a product: $D(f \cdot g) = f\, Dg + g\, Df$.

41. Illustrate with an example to show that, in general, $D(f/g) \neq Df/Dg$. (The derivative of a quotient is not the quotient of the derivatives.)

42.* From first principles derive the formula for the derivative of a quotient: $D(f/g) = (g\, Df - f\, Dg)/g^2$.

16.5. *Second Derivative*

Since $D_x f(x) = f'(x)$ is itself a function f' of x it has a derivative, namely,

$$D_x(D_x f(x)) = \lim_{\Delta x \to 0} \frac{f'(x + \Delta x) - f'(x)}{\Delta x}$$

(provided this limit exists). We write

$$D_x^2 f(x) = \lim_{\Delta x \to 0} \frac{f'(x + \Delta x) - f'(x)}{\Delta x}$$
$$= f''(x)$$

and call this the second derivative of f with respect to x at the point x. The superscript 2 on D is not a square; it stands for the *second* derivative. Where $y = f(x)$, we may write $\dfrac{d^2 y}{dx^2}$ for $f''(x)$. Still higher derivatives could be written,

$$D_x^3 f, \ldots, D_x^n f \quad \text{or} \quad \frac{d^3 f}{dx^3}, \ldots, \frac{d^n f}{dx^n} \quad \text{or} \quad f'''(x), \ldots, f^{(n)}(x)$$

We have already seen that for motion in a straight line, velocity is the derivative of distance with respect to time and that acceleration is the derivative of velocity with respect to time. Therefore acceleration is the second derivative of distance with respect to time. Thus if $y = f(t)$ is the distance from the origin at any time t,

       Distance: $y = f(t)$
       Velocity: $v(t) = D_t y = f'(t)$
       Acceleration: $a(t) = D_t^2 y = f''(t)$

Illustration. If the distance y from the origin at time t is given by $y = -16t^2 + 3{,}000t + 50{,}000$ find:

     (a) The initial distance, i.e., the value of y when $t = 0$.
     (b) The velocity at any time t and the initial velocity.
     (c) The acceleration at any time t and the initial acceleration.

     Solution:
     (a) $y(0) = 50{,}000$.
     (b) $v(t) = -32t + 3{,}000$.
          $v(0) = 3{,}000$.
     (c) $a(t) = -32$.
          $a(0) = -32$.

16.6. *The Chain Rule*

We now know how to differentiate a monomial term of the form x^n, where n is any real number, and a polynomial function provided it is given, in form, by $y = a_0x^n + a_1x^{n-1} + \cdots + a_n$. If, however, it were given in some other form, we might not know, at this stage, how to differentiate it—at least without a lot of work. For example, $y = (x^2 + 3)^{37}$ defines a polynomial function (expand by the binomial theorem), but we should like to find the derivative directly without carrying out this expansion. We can do so by using the following theorem which is a special case of a more general theorem known as the *Chain Rule*.

Theorem 10. Let u be a function of x and n any real number. Let $y = [u(x)]^n$. Then

(10) $$D_xy = D_x[u(x)]^n = n[u(x)]^{n-1} \cdot D_xu(x)$$

Proof: We give the proof only for the case where n is a positive integer, and proceed by induction. The theorem is trivially true for $n = 1$; so we assume it true for $n = k$; that is,

$$D_x[u(x)]^k = k[u(x)]^{k-1} \cdot D_xu(x)$$

To prove it true for $n = k + 1$, write

$$\begin{aligned}
D_x[u(x)]^{k+1} &= D_x[[u(x)]^k \cdot u(x)] \\
&= D_x[u(x)]^k \cdot u(x) + [u(x)]^k \cdot D_xu(x) \quad \text{[Prob. 40, Sec. 16.4]} \\
&= [k[u(x)]^{k-1} \cdot D_xu(x)] \cdot u(x) + [u(x)]^k \cdot D_xu(x) \\
&= k[u(x)]^k \cdot D_xu(x) + [u(x)]^k \cdot D_xu(x) \\
&= (k + 1)[u(x)]^k \cdot D_xu(x)
\end{aligned}$$

This completes the proof. Memorize (10).

Illustration 1. Find the derivative of $(x^3 + 6x - 1)^{17}$ with respect to x.
  Solution: Think of $x^3 + 6x - 1$ as u; then

$$D_x(x^3 + 6x - 1)^{17} = 17(x^3 + 6x - 1)^{16}(3x^2 + 6)$$

Illustration 2. Find the derivative D_xy of $y = u^3 + u - 5$, where $u = x^2 + 6x$.
  Solution: We are asked to find:

$$\begin{aligned}
D_x[(x^2 + 6x)^3 + (x^2 + 6x) - 5] &= D_x(x^2 + 6x)^3 + D_x(x^2 + 6x) - D_x(5) \\
&= 3(x^2 + 6x)^2(2x + 6) + (2x + 6) - 0 \\
&= [3(x^2 + 6x)^2 + 1](2x + 6)
\end{aligned}$$

Illustration 3. Find the derivative of $\sqrt{4 - x^2}$ with respect to x.
  Solution: Since $\sqrt{4 - x^2} = (4 - x^2)^{\frac{1}{2}}$, we have from Theorem 10, where $u(x) = 4 - x^2$, that:

$$\begin{aligned}
D_x \sqrt{4 - x^2} &= \tfrac{1}{2}(4 - x^2)^{-\frac{1}{2}} \cdot (-2x) \\
&= \frac{-x}{\sqrt{4 - x^2}}
\end{aligned}$$

Illustration 4. Find the equation of the tangent to $(x^2/a^2) - (y^2/b^2) = 1$ (an hyperbola) at the point (x_1, y_1). Note that this implies that $|x_1| \geq a$.

Solution: This equation defines a relation, and not a function. In order to differentiate, we must consider one of the functions which can be derived from this relation. We may choose either

$$y = +\frac{b}{a}\sqrt{x^2 - a^2} \quad \text{or} \quad y = -\frac{b}{a}\sqrt{x^2 - a^2}$$

The domain of definition of each function is $|x| \geq a$. The given point on the hyperbola (x_1, y_1) will satisfy exactly one of these equations, and we then select this one as the definition of a function:

$$y = f(x)$$

With this definition of $f(x)$, the function given by

$$F(x) = \frac{x^2}{a^2} - \frac{[f(x)]^2}{b^2} - 1$$

has the value zero for all x such that $|x| \geq a$. Its derivative, $F'(x)$, must also be zero. Hence

$$F'(x) = \frac{2x}{a^2} - \frac{2f(x)f'(x)}{b^2} = 0$$

Solving, we find

$$f'(x) = \frac{b^2}{a^2}\frac{x}{f(x)} = \frac{b^2}{a^2}\frac{x}{y}$$

Hence the slope of the tangent to the hyperbola at (x_1, y_1) is

$$m = \frac{b^2}{a^2}\frac{x_1}{y_1}$$

Hence the equation of the tangent is

$$y - y_1 = \frac{b^2}{a^2}\frac{x_1}{y_1}(x - x_1)$$

or, simplifying,

$$a^2yy_1 - a^2y_1^2 = b^2xx_1 - b^2x_1^2$$

or

$$b^2xx_1 - a^2yy_1 = b^2x_1^2 - a^2y_1^2$$

Since the right-hand member is a^2b^2 [the point (x_1, y_1) is on the hyperbola, and therefore the coordinates satisfy its equation], we have

$$b^2xx_1 - a^2yy_1 = a^2b^2$$

or, finally,

$$\frac{xx_1}{a^2} - \frac{yy_1}{b^2} = 1$$

PROBLEMS 16.6

In Probs. 1 to 8, given distance y (feet) as a function of time t (seconds), find the velocity and acceleration at any time t.

1. $y = 1 - 2t + 3t^2 - 4t^3$.   2. $y = 4 + t - t^2 - 7t^3$.
3. $y = 2t^4 - t + 6$.   4. $y = 3t^5 - 3t^2 + t$.
5. $y = t^5 - t^7$.   6. $y = t^6 - 4t^4$.
7. $y = \sqrt{2t + 1}$.   8. $\sqrt{4t - 1}$.

In Probs. 9 to 18 find the first, second, and third derivatives with respect to t.

9. $y = t^3 + t^2 + t + 1$.   10. $y = t^3 - t^2 + t - 1$.
11. $y = t^2 + t + 1$.   12. $y = t^2 - t + 1$.
13. $y = t + 1$.   14. $y = t - 1$.
15. $y = t^5 - t^2 + 10$.   16. $y = t^4 + t^3 - 15$.
17. $y = (3t - 8)^{\frac{3}{2}}$.   18. $y = (6 - 5t)^{\frac{7}{4}}$.

In Probs. 19 to 26 find $D_x y$ by the chain rule.

19. $y = (x^3 + 6x + 3)^7$.   20. $y = (x^{-2} + x)^5$.
21. $y = w^3 - 2w^2$, $w = x^4 - 5x + 6$.   22. $y = z^3 - 2z^2 + 1$, $z = x + 2/x$.
23. $y = (x + x^2 - 3x^4)^{\frac{3}{2}}$.   24. $y = (x + 1/x^2)^{\frac{1}{4}}$.

25. $y = \dfrac{1}{\sqrt{a^2 - x^2}}$.   26. $y = \dfrac{1}{\sqrt{x^2 - a^2}}$.

27. Interpret y as distance, t as time, and find (a) the acceleration and (b) the *rate of change* of acceleration at time t, where $y = 5t^4 - 2t^3$.

28. Interpret y as distance, t as time, and find (a) the acceleration and (b) the *rate of change* of acceleration at time t, where $y = 3t^3 + 6t^2 - 5t + 1$.

29. For the curve $y = x^3 - 2x + 1$ and point $(1,0)$, find (a) the slope of the tangent and (b) the *rate of change* of slope of the tangent.

30. For the curve $y = 6x^2 - x - 5$ and point (x_1,y_1), find (a) the slope of the tangent and (b) the *rate of change* of slope of the tangent.

31. Find the equation of the tangent to the parabola $y^2 = 4px$ at (x_1,y_1).

32. Find the equation of the tangent to the ellipse $\dfrac{x^2}{a^2} + \dfrac{y^2}{b^2} = 1$ at (x_1,y_1).

16.7. Maxima and Minima

In this section we apply the ideas of the calculus to help us draw the graphs of certain functions.

Definition: A function f is said to be *increasing* at the point x_0 if, for all $|\Delta x|$ sufficiently small,

(11)
$$f(x_0 + \Delta x) < f(x_0) \qquad \text{when } \Delta x < 0$$
$$f(x_0 + \Delta x) > f(x_0) \qquad \text{when } \Delta x > 0$$

A function is increasing in an interval if it is increasing at each point of the interval. As x traces such an interval in the positive direction, the graph of $y = f(x)$ rises.

Theorem 11.   If $f'(x_0) > 0$, then f is increasing at x_0.
    Proof: Given

$$f'(x_0) = \lim_{\Delta x \to 0} \frac{f(x_0 + \Delta x) - f(x_0)}{\Delta x} > 0$$

If in the limit the ratio $\dfrac{f(x_0 + \Delta x) - f(x_0)}{\Delta x}$ is positive, then, for sufficiently small $\Delta x < 0$, it must be true that $f(x_0 + \Delta x) - f(x_0) < 0$. That is, $f(x_0 + \Delta x) < f(x_0)$, which is the first part of condition (11). Again if $\Delta x > 0$ and is small, it must be true that

$$f(x_0 + \Delta x) - f(x_0) > 0$$

and the second condition of (11), $f(x_0 + \Delta x) > f(x_0)$, is satisfied. Hence the theorem is proved.

Exercise A. State and prove the converse of Theorem 11 for a differentiable function f.

Exercise B. Write out a definition of decreasing function and a theorem (and its converse) corresponding to Theorem 11.

Consider the curve $y = f(x)$, where f is a differentiable function (Fig. 16.9). The value $f(x_1)$ is the largest that the function f assumes

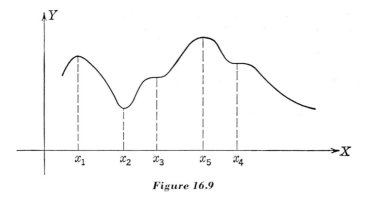

Figure 16.9

in a small interval containing x_1. Such a value of the function f is called a relative maximum of f. Similarly $f(x_2)$ is called a relative minimum of f. We often omit the adjective "relative," but it will still be understood. At each point of a suitably small interval to the left of x_1, the derivative $f'(x) > 0$ (Exercise A). At x_1, the derivative $f'(x_1) = 0$. At each point of a small interval to the right of x_1, the derivative $f'(x) < 0$ (Exercise B).

Exercise C. What are the corresponding facts for small intervals to the left and to the right of x_2?

Definitions: The point where $x = x_0$ is called a (relative) *maximum* of the function f if and only if $f(x_0 \pm \Delta x) < f(x_0)$ for all sufficiently small values of $\Delta x \neq 0$. The point where $x = x_0$ is called a (relative) *minimum* of the function f if and only if $f(x_0 \pm \Delta x) > f(x_0)$ for all sufficiently small values of $\Delta x \neq 0$.

As an aid to finding (relative) maxima and minima we prove the next theorem.

Theorem 12. If f is differentiable for all values of x, then $f'(x) = 0$ at the (relative) maxima and minima of f.

Proof: At any point, $f'(x) > 0$, $= 0$, or < 0. If $f'(x) > 0$ at $x = x_0$, Theorem 11 tells us that $f(x)$ is increasing at this point. Hence x_0 is neither a maximum nor a minimum. Similarly by Exercise B $f'(x)$ cannot be < 0 at a maximum or minimum. Therefore it must be zero.

The converse of Theorem 12 is false, for $f'(x)$ can be zero at points which are neither maxima nor minima. Such points are called stationary points. In Fig. 16.9, x_3 and x_4 are such points.

Definitions: The point $x = x_0$ is called a *stationary point* of f if $f'(x_0) = 0$ and either $f'(x_0 \pm \Delta x) > 0$ or $f'(x_0 \pm \Delta x) < 0$ for all small Δx. Any point $x = x_0$ for which $f'(x_0) = 0$ is called a *critical point* of f.

In Fig. 16.9, x_3 and x_4 are stationary points, while x_1, x_2, x_3, x_4, and x_5 are critical points.

Exercise D. For the differentiable function f to have a maximum at $x = x_0$, it is necessary and sufficient that . . . . Complete so as to form a meaningful theorem.

Exercise E. In order for the differentiable function f to have a minimum at $x = x_0$, it is necessary and sufficient that . . . . Complete so as to form a meaningful theorem.

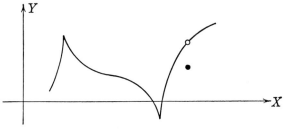

Figure 16.10

Exercise F. On what basis have we ruled out relative maxima and minima as exhibited in the graph in Fig. 16.10?

We summarize with a rule as follows:

Rule for Finding the Maximum (Minimum) Value of a Function. First, find the function to be maximized! This function may be given. Again the statement of the original problem may be in words, and you will then have to translate these into the appropriate mathematical expressions. You may have to differentiate some given function several times, or you may have to perform other operations on given quantities, but, regardless of what the operations are, you must first find the function whose maximum (minimum) is sought. Call this function f.

Second, find $f'(x)$. The solutions of $f'(x) = 0$ are the critical values, and they must be tested in order to determine whether a certain one yields a maximum value of f, a minimum value of f, or a stationary value of f.

In Table 1 the test may be made by using $f(x)$ or by using $f'(x)$ as indicated. In this table α and β are used to designate certain positive constants; each plays the role of a Δx to be chosen so as to simplify the test.

Table 1. Testing for Maxima and Minima

x	$f(x)$	$f'(x)$	Comments
x_0	$f(x_0)$	Given $f'(x_0) = 0$	Testing $f(x_0)$ for a maximum;
$x_0 - \alpha$ $x_0 + \beta$	$f(x_0 - \alpha) < f(x_0)$ $f(x_0 + \beta) < f(x_0)$	$f'(x_0 - \alpha) > 0$ $f'(x_0 + \beta) < 0$	$\therefore f(x_0)$ is a relative maximum [because of the inequalities in either the $f(x)$ or the $f'(x)$ column]
x_0	$f(x_0)$	Given $f'(x_0) = 0$	Testing $f(x_0)$ for a minimum;
$x_0 - \alpha$ $x_0 + \beta$	$f(x_0 - \alpha) > f(x_0)$ $f(x_0 + \beta) > f(x_0)$	$f'(x_0 - \alpha) < 0$ $f'(x_0 + \beta) > 0$	$\therefore f(x_0)$ is a relative minimum [because of the inequalities in either the $f(x)$ or the $f'(x)$ column]

CAUTION: The interval $[x_0 - \alpha, x_0 + \beta]$ must not be so large as to include other critical values of f or of f'.

Exercise G. Make out a similar table for a stationary point.

Let us now apply the above reasoning to the function f', whose values give the slopes of the various tangents to $y = f(x)$. When $f'(x)$ is increasing, $f''(x) > 0$; and geometrically the tangents are rotating counterclockwise as x increases. When $f'(x)$ is decreasing, $f''(x) < 0$; and geometrically the tangents are rotating clockwise as x increases. When $f'(x)$ has a (relative) maximum or minimum, there is a change in the direction of rotation of the tangents. Such a point is called a point of inflection.

Definition: A point at which f' has a (relative) maximum or minimum is called a *point of inflection*.

Theorem 13. If f is differentiable for all values of x, then $f''(x) = 0$ at its points of inflection.

The proof is an immediate consequence of the definition and Theorem 12. The converse of Theorem 13 is false, for $f''(x)$ may be zero at points of other types as well.

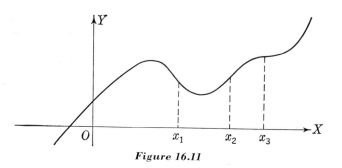

Figure 16.11

In Fig. 16.11, x_1, x_2, x_3 are points of inflection. At x_1 the slope $f'(x_1)$ is a minimum, while at x_2 the slope $f'(x_2)$ is a maximum. At x_3 the slope $f'(x_3)$ has a minimum value of 0, and hence x_3 is also a stationary point.

When we have gained information about the points where f is stationary, about the maximum and minimum values of f, and about the points of inflection, we are in a better position to plot the curve. Hence the calculus is a powerful tool indeed in curve tracing.

Illustration 1. Sketch the graph of $y = 2x^3 + 3x^2 - 12x$.
  Solution: The zeros of the polynomial $2x^3 + 3x^2 - 12x$ are

$$x = 0 \qquad x = -\tfrac{3}{4} \pm \frac{\sqrt{105}}{4}$$

The domain of definition is $-\infty < x < \infty$. There is no symmetry, and the function is everywhere continuous. We find $f'(x)$ and set $f'(x) = 0$.

$$f'(x) = 6x^2 + 6x - 12 = 0$$
that is, $\qquad x^2 + x - 2 = (x - 1)(x + 2) = 0$
$$x = 1, -2$$

These are the critical points which must be tested.

Table 2

x	$f(x)$	$f'(x)$	Comments
1 Set $x_0 - \alpha = 1 - 1 = 0$ Set $x_0 + \beta = 1 + 1 = 2$	$f(1) = -7$ $f(0) = 0 > -7$ $f(2) = 4 > -7$	$f'(1) = 0$ $f'(0) = -12 < 0$ $f'(2) = 24 > 0$	Testing $f(1)$; $\therefore f(1) = -7$ is a relative mini- mum
-2 Set $x_0 - \alpha = -2 - 1$ $= -3$ Set $x_0 + \beta = -2 + 2$ $= 0$	$f(-2) = 20$ $f(-3) = 9 < 20$ $f(0) = 0 < 20$	$f'(-2) = 0$ $f'(-3) = 24 > 0$ $f'(0) = -12 < 0$	Testing $f(-2)$; $\therefore f(-2) = 20$ is a relative maximum

Further, $f''(x) = 12x + 6 = 0$ when solved for $x = -\frac{1}{2}$ gives the point of inflection which is $(-\frac{1}{2}, 6\frac{1}{2})$. We compute a few more values of the function and sketch in Fig. 16.12.

Illustration 2. Prove that among all rectangles with fixed perimeter P the square is the one with maximum area.

Solution: Call the sides of the general rectangle x and y. Then

$$(12) \qquad P = 2x + 2y$$

The quantity to be maximized is the area A, where

$$A = xy$$

We cannot yet proceed to differentiate A, however, because there are two variables momentarily present, namely, x and y. But, using relation (12), we may eliminate either x or y. From (12),

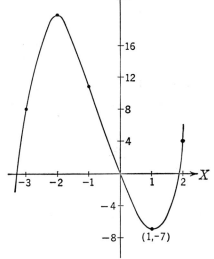

Figure 16.12

$$y = \frac{P}{2} - x$$

so that $A = xy$ becomes

$$A = x\left(\frac{P}{2} - x\right)$$

Now we may proceed.

$$A'(x) = \frac{P}{2} - 2x$$

The critical value is obtained by setting

$$A'(x) = \frac{P}{2} - 2x = 0$$

and solving; hence $x = P/4$. Using this, we find, from (12), that $y = P/4$; also that the rectangle has equal sides, i.e., is a square.

We still do not know (except intuitively) that these values correspond to a maximum; we must test.

Table 3

x	$A(x)$	$A'(x)$	Comments
$\dfrac{P}{4}$	This test will not be used in this problem	$A'\left(\dfrac{P}{4}\right) = 0$	Testing $A\left(\dfrac{P}{4}\right)$;
$\dfrac{P}{4} - \alpha = 0$		$A'(0) = \dfrac{P}{2} > 0$	$A\left(\dfrac{P}{4}\right) = \dfrac{P^2}{16}$ is a relative maximum given by $x = y = \dfrac{P}{4}$;
$\dfrac{P}{4} + \beta = \dfrac{P}{2}$		$A'\left(\dfrac{P}{2}\right) = -\dfrac{P}{2} < 0$	$\therefore$ rectangle of maximum area is a square

PROBLEMS 16.7

In Probs. 1 to 20 find all maxima, minima, and points of inflection, and plot the curve.

1. $y = 3x^2 - 6x + 1$.
2. $y = x^2 - 3x - 10$.
3. $y = 2 - 3x - x^2$.
4. $y = 6x^2 - 5x + 1$.
5. $y = 1 - x - x^2$.
6. $y = x^2 - 1$.
7. $y = x^3$.
8. $y = x^4$.
9. $y = x^3 - 6x^2$.
10. $y = x^2 - x^3$.
11. $y = x^3 - x$.
12. $y = 4x - x^3$.
13. $y = x^4 - x^2$.
14. $y = 9x^2 - x^4$.
15. $y = \sqrt{4 - x^2}$.
16. $y = \sqrt{x^2 - 4}$.
17. $y = (1 - x)^{\frac{1}{3}}$.
18. $y = (1 - x)^{\frac{2}{3}}$.
19. $y = \frac{2}{3}\sqrt{9 - x^2}$.
20. $y = \frac{2}{3}\sqrt{x^2 - 9}$.

In Probs. 21 to 30 find the coordinates of all critical points of $f'(x)$.

21. $f(x) = x^3 - 3x^2 + 2$.
22. $f(x) = x^3 + 6x^2 + x$.
23. $f(x) = 2x^3 - x^2 - x$.
24. $f(x) = 3x^3 - 12x^2 + x - 5$.
25. $f(x) = 1 - x + x^2 - 3x^3$.
26. $f(x) = 2 + 3x - 4x^3$.
27. $f(x) = x^4 - 4x^2 + 4$.
28. $f(x) = x^4 - 8x^3 + 6x$.
29. $f(x) = x^4 - 4x^3 + 6x^2 + 1$.
30. $f(x) = 3x^4 + 8x^3 + 8x^2 + 3$.

In Probs. 31 to 34 find the coordinates of the minimum points on the graph.

31. $y = \dfrac{x^4}{4} - \dfrac{x^3}{3} + 2x^2 - 4x - 1.$ **32.** $y = \dfrac{x^4}{4} + \dfrac{x^3}{3} + \dfrac{x^2}{2} + x + 1.$

33. $y = x^4 - 2x^2.$ **34.** $y = x^4 + 4x^3 + 4x^2 + 4.$

35. If the velocity of a particle at any time is given by $v = t(t - 2)$, find the minimum velocity.

36. If the acceleration of a particle at any time t is given by $a = t^2 + 2t - 1$, find the minimum acceleration.

37. If the height of a particle at any time is given by $y = 2t^5 + 5t^4 - 40t^3 + 100t^2 + 2$, find the maximum acceleration.

38. A particle starts at the origin and moves out along the positive X-axis for a while, then stops and moves back toward the origin, and then stops again and moves away from the origin. The distance of the particle from the origin is given by $x = 2t^3 - 9t^2 + 12t$. Find:
(a) The time t_1 when the particle stopped for the first time.
(b) The time t_2 when the particle stopped for the second time.
(c) The velocity at t_1 and t_2.
(d) The acceleration at t_1 and t_2.
(e) The time when the velocity was a minimum.

39. A man has P running feet of chicken wire and with it wishes to form a rectangular pen, making use of an existing stone wall as one side. Find the dimensions so that the pen will have maximum area.

40. Prove that among all rectangles with fixed area A the square is the one with minimum perimeter.

41. (a) Find the relative dimensions of a closed tin can (cylindrical), to be made from a given amount of metal (without losses in cutting, etc.), that will have maximum volume.
(b) The same for an open tin cup.

42. A watermelon grower wishes to ship as early as possible in the season to catch the higher prices. He can ship now 6 tons at a profit of $2 per ton. By waiting he estimates he can add 3 tons per week to his shipment but that the profit will be reduced $\frac{1}{3}$ dollar per ton per week. How long should he wait for maximum profit?

43. A man in a boat offshore 3 miles from the nearest point P wishes to reach a point Q on down the shore 6 miles from P. On water he can travel 4 mi/hr, on land 5 mi/hr. Where should he land in order to minimize his total travel time?

44. What is the absolute maximum value assumed by the function given by $y = 3x^4 - 4x^3 - 2x + 1$ in the interval $-1 \leq x \leq 1$?

45. What is the absolute minimum value assumed by the function given by $y = x^3/3 - x$ in the interval $-2 \leq x < 1$? For what value of x does this occur?

46. "The volume of insured unemployment continues to rise to record levels, but the rate of increase has slowed with the declining volume of new claims." Explain by means of a graph.

16.8. *Related Rates*

Theorem 10 gave the formula for $D_x y$, where $y = u(x)^n$. Since this has many applications in rate problems involving time as independent variable, we shall replace x by the letter t and write

(13) $$D_t y = n[u(t)]^{n-1} D_t u$$

Usually the variable t does not enter explicitly: we are given either
$D_t y$ or $D_t u$ and are asked to solve for the other by using formula (13).

Illustration 1.   The radius of a circle is increasing at the rate of 2 ft/min.   How
fast is the area increasing when $r = r$ ft? when $r = 3$ ft?
    Solution: Evidently we have

$$A = \pi r^2$$

where r is such a function of t that $D_t r$ (given) $= 2$ ft/min.   We are asked to find
$D_t A$; we therefore differentiate A with respect to t, getting

(14) $$D_t A = 2\pi r \, D_t r$$
                             $$= 4\pi r \text{ sq ft/min}$$

which is the first part of the answer.   For the second part we substitute $r = 3$ in
(14), getting

$$D_t A = 12\pi \text{ sq ft/min}$$

when $r = 3$ ft.

Illustration 2.   A man, 100 ft away from the base of a flagpole, starts walking

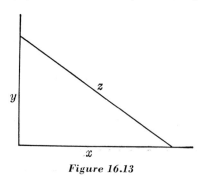

Figure 16.13

toward the base at 10 ft/sec just as a
flag at the top of the pole is lowered at
the rate of 5 ft/sec.   If the pole is 70 ft
tall, find how the distance between the
man and the flag is changing per unit of
time at the end of 2 sec.
    Solution: Call x the distance the
man is from the base, y the height of
flag, and z the distance between man
and flag at any time t (Fig. 16.13).
Then we are given

$$D_t x = -10 \text{ ft/sec}$$
$$D_t y = -5 \text{ ft/sec}$$

(The minus sign is present because x and y are decreasing.)   Moreover,

(15) $$x = -10t + 100 \qquad y = -5t + 70$$

Now, always we have

(16) $$z^2 = x^2 + y^2$$

and differentiating with respect to time gives

(17) $$2z \, D_t z = 2x \, D_t x + 2y \, D_t y$$

[z^2, x^2, and y^2, each is a u^n problem, Sec. 16.6, formula (10)].   From (15) we compute $x = 80$ ft, $y = 60$ ft, when $t = 2$; and then, from (16),

$$z = \sqrt{x^2 + y^2} = \sqrt{(80)^2 + (60)^2} = 100 \text{ ft}$$

Illustration 2. Find a primitive of $6x^2 - 2$.
   Solution:

$$G(x) = \int (6x^2 - 2)\, dx$$
$$= 2x^3 - 2x + C$$

We can apply this method of integration to solve problems involving distance and velocity.

Illustration 3. The velocity of a particle moving on the X-axis is given by $v = 2t - 3t^2 + 1$. At $t = 0$, the particle is at the origin. Where is it when $t = 1$?
   Solution: We know that $D_t x = v = 2t - 3t^2 + 1$. Thus x is some primitive of $2t - 3t^2 + 1$, or

$$x = t^2 - t^3 + t + C$$

The value of C is obtained by putting $x = 0$, $t = 0$ in this equation and solving for C. We find that $C = 0$; thus

$$x = t^2 - t^3 + t$$

At $t = 1$, $x = 1 - 1 + 1 = 1$ unit from the origin.

Illustration 4. Find the area under the curve $y = 3x - x^2$ from $x = 1$ to $x = 2$.
   Solution:

$$A_1^2 = \int_1^2 (3x - x^2)\, dx$$
$$= \frac{3x^2}{2} - \frac{x^3}{3}\Bigg]_1^2$$
$$= \frac{3 \cdot 4}{2} - \frac{8}{3} - \left(\frac{3}{2} - \frac{1}{3}\right)$$
$$= \tfrac{11}{6} \text{ sq units}$$

PROBLEMS 16.9

In Probs. 1 to 12 a primitive of a certain function is given. Find the function.

1. $4x^3 - 6x + 2$.
2. $x^3 - x^2 + 2x$.
3. $x^4 - x^2 + 2$.
4. $3x^4 + x^3 - x$.
5. $x^2 - x^{-2}$.
6. $x^3 + x^{-3} + 1$.
7. $x^4 + 3/x^2 - 1$.
8. $x^5 - 4/x^3 + 6x + 20$.
9. $ax^2 + bx + c$.
10. $ax^3 + bx^2 + cx + d$.
11. $Ax^\alpha + Bx^{-\beta}$.
12. $Ax^\alpha + Bx^{2\alpha} + Cx^{3\alpha}$.

In Probs. 13 to 26 a function is given. Find a primitive of the function.

13. $2x^3 - x^2 + 5$.
14. $4x^3 + x - 8$.
15. $9x^4 + x^2 - 1$.
16. $x^5 + x^3 - x + 14$.
17. $x^{-4} - x^{-2}$.
18. $x^{-5} + x^{-3} + 1$.
19. $x^{-3} - x^{-2} + x$.
20. $x^{-2} + x^2 + x + 1$.
21. $ax^2 + bx + c$.
22. $ax^3 + bx^2 + cx + d$.
23. $ax^{-2} + bx^{-3}$.
24. $ax^{-3} + bx^{-4}$.
25. $Ax^{-n} + Bx^{-m}$, $n, m \neq -1$.
26. $Ax^{\alpha^2} + Bx^{\beta^2 + 1}$.

In Probs. 27 to 41 evaluate

27. $\int_0^1 (x^2 - x^3)\, dx.$

28. $\int_{-2}^2 (7x - 4)\, dx.$

29. $\int_{-1}^1 7x\, dx.$

30. $\int_{-2}^0 (1 - x + x^2)\, dx.$

31. $\int_{-1}^0 (2 + 3x - x^2)\, dx.$

32. $\int_{-1}^1 (ax + b)\, dx.$

33. $\int_0^a (x^2 + 5)\, dx.$

34. $\int_0^b (u^3 - u)\, du.$

35. $\int_0^a (t^2 + 3t)\, dt.$

36. $\int_1^2 (y^2 - 3y)\, dy.$

37. $\int_1^3 \alpha\, d\alpha.$

38. $\int_2^3 (\beta + 1)\, d\beta.$

39. $\int_1^2 z^{-4}\, dz.$

40. $\int_1^2 z^{-5}\, dz.$

41. $\int_1^3 (z^{-2} - 2z^{-3})\, dz.$

In Probs. 42 to 49 find the area bounded by

42. $y = x^3,\ n = 1,\ x = 2,\ y = 0.$ **43.** $y = x^2,\ x = -3,\ x = 2,\ y = 0.$
44. $y = 2x + 6,\ x = 0,\ x = 1,\ y = 0.$ **45.** $y = 1/x^2,\ x = 1,\ x = 2,\ y = 0.$
46. $y = 2/x^4,\ x = -2,\ x = -1,\ y = 0.$ **47.** $y = x(x - 1),\ y = -x(x - 1).$
48. $y = x,\ y = x(x - 1).$ **49.** $y = \frac{1}{2}x,\ y = -x(x - 1).$
50. The distance from the origin at time t of a particle is $y = t^4 + t^2 - t + 1.$ (a) Find the velocity at any time t. (b) Find the velocity when $t = 0$.
51. The velocity at any time t is given by $v = t^3 + 2t - 5$. (a) Find the acceleration at any time t. (b) Find the acceleration when $t = 0$.
52. The distance from the origin at time t is given by $y = t^3 + 2t^2 - t + 1$. Find: (a) the velocity at any time t; (b) the acceleration at any time t.
53. The velocity at any time t is given by $v = t^2 + t + 3$. If the particle was at the origin when $t = 0$, find the distance traveled between $t = 0$ and $t = 1$.
54. Prove: The rate of change of area [enclosed by $y = f(x),\ x = a,\ x = x_0,\ y = 0$)] per unit change in x, at $x = x_0$, is $f(x_0)$.
55. If the graph of $y = f(x)$ is a curve passing through the point $(1,0)$ and if $D_x f = x + 1$, what is the exact expression for $f(x)$?
56. The area A bounded by the curve $y = f(x)$, the X-axis, and the lines $x = 0$ and $x = x_1$ is given by $A = x_1^2$. Find $f(x)$.

16.10. *Falling Bodies*

As a first approximation to the theory of falling bodies it is customary to disregard the retarding forces due to air friction, etc., and to assume that the only force acting is that of gravity. Under these circumstances, the acceleration will be -32 ft/sec/sec. This figure has been determined empirically by physicists, and the minus sign is supplied so that to a falling body is assigned a negative velocity. Now if we call y the height (feet) of a particle at time t (seconds), then we may write acceleration $= D_t^2 y = -32$. One integration yields (the primitive)

$$(21) \qquad\qquad \text{Velocity} = D_t y = -32t + C$$

If now we know that the particle was fired from a **height of y_0 ft** with *initial velocity v_0*, then we may write

$$(\text{Velocity}, t = 0) = D_t y|_{t=0} = -32(0) + C_1 = v_0$$

Hence $\qquad\qquad\qquad\qquad C_1 = v_0$

and (21) becomes

$$(22) \qquad\qquad\qquad D_t y = -32t + v_0$$

which gives the velocity at any time t. The integration of (22) yields

$$y = -16t^2 + v_0 t + C_2$$

Since we were told that the particle was fired from a height of y_0 ft (from the ground), we can write

$$y(0) = -16(0) + v_0(0) + C_2 = y_0$$

Therefore $C_2 = y_0$, and, for this problem, the height at any time t is given by

$$(23) \qquad\qquad\qquad y = -16t^2 + v_0 t + y_0$$

This is the general equation which applies to falling bodies under our assumptions.

Illustration 1. A bomb was dropped from an airplane 16,000 ft high. When did it strike the ground?

Solution: We are given $v_0 = 0$, $y_0 = 16,000$. From (23), the height at any time t is given by

$$y = -16t^2 + 16,000$$

The bomb struck the ground at the time when $y = 0$. Thus

$$0 = -16t^2 + 16,000$$
$$\text{and} \qquad\qquad t = \pm 10 \sqrt{10}$$

The minus sign is of no interest here, and so the answer is: The bomb struck the ground $10 \sqrt{10}$ sec later.

Illustration 2. At 12 noon the motors of a certain rocket burned out at 6,400 ft elevation when the rocket was still traveling straight up and at 8.0×10^4 ft/sec. When was it highest? What was its maximum height? When did it strike the ground, and with what velocity?

Solution:

$$D_t{}^2y = -32$$
$$D_ty = -32t + 8.0 \times 10^4$$
$$y = -16t^2 + 8.0 \times 10^4t + 6.4 \times 10^3$$

It was highest when $D_ty = -32t + 8.0 \times 10^4 = 0$, that is, when $t = 2,500$ sec (past noon, or at 12:42). The maximum height was

$$y_{max} = -16(625 \times 10^4) + 20,000 \times 10^4 + 0.64 \times 10^4$$
$$= 10^4(10^4 + 0.64)$$
$$= 100,006,400 \text{ ft}$$

Since $Dy\Big|_{t<2,500} > 0$ and $Dy\Big|_{t>2,500} < 0$, the test for maximum is satisfied.

It struck the ground when $y = 0$, that is, when:

$$-16t^2 + 8.0 \times 10^4t + 6.4 \times 10^3 = 0$$
$$t = \frac{-8.0 \times 10^4 \pm \sqrt{64 \times 10^8 + (64)^210^2}}{-32}$$
$$= 0.25 \times 10^4 \pm 2.5 \sqrt{10^6 + 64}$$
$$\approx 2,500 \pm 2502$$
$$= 5,002 \text{ sec (past noon, or 1:23)}$$

It struck the ground with velocity

$$Dy\Big|_{t=5,002} = -32(5002) + 8.0 \times 10^4$$
$$= -80,064 \text{ ft/sec}$$

PROBLEMS 16.10

In Probs. 1 to 8 you are given the height y ft after t sec of a body moving straight up and down. Find: (a) the velocity and acceleration at any time t; (b) the initial velocity; (c) the maximum height; (d) the time when it struck the ground.

1. $y = 96t - 16t^2$.
2. $y = 320t - 16t^2$.
3. $y = 32,000 - 16t^2$.
4. $y = 3,200 - 16t^2$.
5. $y = 16,000 + 160t - 16t^2$.
6. $y = 16,000 + 320t - 16t^2$.
7. $y = 32,000 + 640t - 16t^2$.
8. (BT) $y = 32,000 - 640t - 16t^2$.

In Probs. 9 to 12 vertical motion is assumed. Find the height y ft at time t sec from the conditions given.

9. Particle dropped from 1,000 ft elevation.
10. Particle projected upward from ground with 100 ft/sec initial velocity.
11. Particle projected upward from space platform 100 miles up with initial velocity of 3,000 ft/sec.
12. Particle fired downward from a stationary flying saucer 10,000 ft high and with initial velocity of 3,000 mi/hr.

REFERENCE

Courant, Richard, and Herbert Robbins: "What Is Mathematics?" Chap. 8, Oxford, New York (1941).

Further details are given in the many standard texts on calculus.

CHAPTER SEVENTEEN

Hyperbolic Functions

17.1. *Hyperbolic Functions*

In many areas of pure and applied mathematics and engineering there are functions, closely related to sine and cosine, that are of very great importance. These are $f:\left(\theta,\dfrac{e^\theta - e^{-\theta}}{2}\right)$ and $g:\left(\theta,\dfrac{e^\theta + e^{-\theta}}{2}\right)$; the domain of each is the set of real numbers.

Although these are just simple combinations of the exponential functions given by $y = e^\theta$ and $y = e^{-\theta}$, they are used so extensively that tables have been prepared for them and names given to them. For reasons that will be made clear in the next section, they are called the "hyperbolic sine of the number θ" and the "hyperbolic cosine of the number θ," respectively. These are written "sinh θ" and "cosh θ." Thus we write

$$(1) \qquad \sinh \theta = \frac{e^\theta - e^{-\theta}}{2}$$

$$(2) \qquad \cosh \theta = \frac{e^\theta + e^{-\theta}}{2}$$

17.2. *Hyperbolic and Circular Trigometric Functions*

In order to make clear the connection between the hyperbolic and the circular functions, we first reconsider the latter. These (sin θ, cos θ, etc.) were defined with respect to the circle $x^2 + y^2 = 1$. This is the reason for our referring to them as the "circular trigonometric functions" (Fig. 17.1).

Let $P(x,y)$ be a point on the circle in the first quadrant, and set $\theta = $ arc AP. The area of the sector OAP is equal to $\theta/2$ sq units.[1] Since the area of triangle OAB is $\frac{1}{2}$ sq unit, the number θ may be

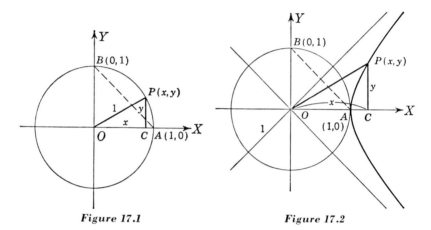

Figure 17.1   Figure 17.2

thought of as the ratio of the area of the sector to the area of the triangle. That is,

(3) $$\theta = \frac{\text{area of sector } OAP}{\text{area of } \triangle OAB} = \frac{\text{sector } OAP}{\triangle OAB} \left(= \frac{\theta/2}{\frac{1}{2}} \right)$$

As in Chap. 13

(4) $$\sin \theta = PC = y \qquad \cos \theta = OC = x$$

Exercise A. Extend these ideas to the case of the circle $x^2 + y^2 = a^2$.

It is this new way of looking at θ that shows us how to develop a trigonometry based upon the hyperbola $x^2 - y^2 = 1$. Let $P(x,y)$ be a point on this hyperbola in the first quadrant, and set (Fig. 17.2)

$$\theta = \frac{\text{area of sector } OAP}{\text{area of } \triangle OAB} = \frac{\text{sector } OAP}{\frac{1}{2}}$$

Now

Sector OAP = area OCP − area under hyperbola from A to C

---

[1] In your study of plane geometry you should have met with the more general result that, in a circle of radius a, the area of a sector of central angle θ radians is $a^2\theta/2$.

The area under the hyperbola can be found by calculus as follows: The equation of the curve is $y = + \sqrt{x^2 - 1}$, and the area is given by

$$\text{Area } ACP = \int_1^x \sqrt{z^2 - 1} \, dz$$

(We changed to the dummy variable of integration z because we have already used x as the abscissa of P.)   The evaluation of this integral involves more calculus than we have studied in this text, and so we can only write down the results without derivation.   We write $\log_e \alpha$ simply as $\ln \alpha$.

$$\int_1^x \sqrt{z^2 - 1} \, dz = \left[\frac{z}{2} \sqrt{z^2 - 1} - \frac{1}{2} \ln (z + \sqrt{z^2 - 1}) \right]_1^x$$

$$= \frac{x}{2} \sqrt{x^2 - 1} - \frac{1}{2} \ln (x + \sqrt{x^2 - 1})$$

From this we get

$$\text{Sector } OAP = \tfrac{1}{2}xy - \frac{x}{2} \sqrt{x^2 - 1} + \frac{1}{2} \ln (x + \sqrt{x^2 - 1})$$

$$= \tfrac{1}{2}xy - \tfrac{1}{2}xy + \frac{1}{2} \ln (x + y) = \frac{1}{2} \ln (x + y)$$

since $y = \sqrt{x^2 - 1}$.   Therefore

(5) $$\theta = \ln (x + y)$$

We now define

(6) $$\sinh \theta = PC = y \qquad \cosh \theta = OC = x$$

to correspond to $\sin \theta$ and $\cos \theta$ in (4).   In order to obtain (1) and (2) from (6), we solve (5) for x and for y by the following device: From (5) it follows at once that

(7) $$e^\theta = x + y \qquad e^{-\theta} = \frac{1}{x + y}$$

From (6) and (7) we have

$$\frac{e^\theta - e^{-\theta}}{2} = \frac{x + y - 1/(x + y)}{2}$$

$$= \frac{x^2 + 2xy + y^2 - 1}{2(x + y)}$$

$$= \frac{2xy + 2y^2}{2(x + y)} \qquad \text{since } x^2 = 1 + y^2$$

$$= y$$

Hence $$\sinh \theta = y = \frac{e^\theta - e^{-\theta}}{2}$$

Similarly from (6) and (7) we have

$$\frac{e^\theta + e^{-\theta}}{2} = \frac{x + y + 1/(x + y)}{2}$$

$$= \frac{x^2 + 2xy + y^2 + 1}{2(x + y)}$$

$$= x$$

Hence $$\cosh \theta = x = \frac{e^\theta + e^{-\theta}}{2}$$

Exercise B.   Extend these ideas to the case of the hyperbola $x^2 - y^2 = a^2$.

Although these geometric derivations assume that $P(x,y)$ lies in the first quadrant, the analytic definitions of sinh θ and cosh θ in (1) and (2) are subject to no such restrictions.   These hyperbolic functions are hence defined for all real values of θ.   Note that θ is *not* the angle AOP as it is in the case of the circular functions.

17.3. *Hyperbolic Trigonometry*

Other hyperbolic functions are defined by the following rules:

$$\tanh \theta = \frac{\sinh \theta}{\cosh \theta} = \frac{e^\theta - e^{-\theta}}{e^\theta + e^{-\theta}}$$

$$\coth \theta = \frac{e^\theta + e^{-\theta}}{e^\theta - e^{-\theta}} \qquad \theta \neq 0$$

$$\operatorname{sech} \theta = \frac{1}{\cosh \theta}$$

$$\operatorname{csch} \theta = \frac{1}{\sinh \theta} \qquad \theta \neq 0$$

A trigonometry of hyperbolic functions can be developed comparable with that of the circular functions.

Illustration 1.   Show that $\cosh^2 \theta - \sinh^2 \theta = 1$.
   Solution:

$$\cosh^2 \theta = \frac{(e^\theta + e^{-\theta})^2}{4}$$

$$= \frac{e^{2\theta} + 2 + e^{-2\theta}}{4}$$

$$\sinh^2 \theta = \frac{(e^\theta - e^{-\theta})^2}{4}$$

$$= \frac{e^{2\theta} - 2 + e^{-2\theta}}{4}$$

By subtraction the result follows.

ANSWERS TO PROBLEMS 1.3

3. An isosceles triangle is a 3-sided polygon at least 2 of whose sides are equal.

5. A rectangle is a 4-sided polygon, all of whose angles are equal.

7. Two lines are said to intersect if and only if they have exactly one point in common.

9. Two fractions a/b and c/d are equal if and only if $ad = bc$.

11. Two triangles are congruent if and only if the angles and sides of one are equal respectively to the corresponding angles and sides of the other.

13. For all x.   **15.** For some x.

17. For all x.   **19.** For no x.

21. The base angles of a given triangle are not equal.

23. 241 is not an even number.

25. For some x, $3x + 7x \neq 10x$.   **27.** For all x, $2x + 3 \neq 7$.

29. For some pair of similar triangles, x_1 and x_2, x_1 is not congruent to x_2.

31. Complete statement: For some x, $\dfrac{x}{2} + \dfrac{x}{3} = \dfrac{x}{5}$.

Negation: For all x, $\dfrac{x}{2} + \dfrac{x}{3} \neq \dfrac{x}{5}$.

33. Complete statement: For all x, $(4x + 9)(x - 1) = 5x + 4x^2 - 9$.

Negation: For some x, $(4x + 9)(x - 1) \neq 5x + 4x^2 - 9$.

35. Complete statement: For some x, $\dfrac{16x^2 - 9}{4x - 3} = 4x + 3$.

We cannot use "For all x" here since the statement is false for $x = \frac{3}{4}$.

Negation: For all x, $\dfrac{16x^2 - 9}{4x - 3} \neq 4x + 3$.

ANSWERS TO PROBLEMS 1.5

1. Converse: If $2a$ is divisible by 6, then a is divisible by 3.
Contrapositive: If $2a$ is not divisible by 6, then a is not divisible by 3.

3. Converse: If the diagonals of a quadrilateral bisect each other, then the quadrilateral is a parallelogram.   Contrapositive: If the diagonals of a quadrilateral do not bisect each other, then the quadrilateral is not a parallelogram.

5. Converse: If $a + c$ is greater than $b + c$, then a is greater than b.

Contrapositive: If $a + c$ is not greater than $b + c$, then a is not greater than b.

7. If *not-p*, then *not-q*.

11. A sufficient condition that a triangle be isosceles is that its base angles be equal.

13. A sufficient condition that two lines be parallel is that they be perpendicular to the same line.

15. A sufficient condition that $x = 1$ is that $3x + 2 = x + 4$.

17. A necessary condition that a triangle be inscribed in a semicircle is that it be a right triangle.

19. A necessary condition that a body be in static equilibrium is that the vector sum of all forces acting on it is zero.

21. A necessary condition that two forces be in equilibrium is that they be equal, opposite, and collinear.

23. A triangle is inscribed in a semicircle only if it is a right triangle.

25. A body is in static equilibrium only if the vector sum of all forces acting on it is zero.

27. Two forces are in equilibrium only if they are equal, opposite, and collinear.

29. A necessary condition that a triangle be isosceles is that its base angles be equal.

or

A sufficient condition that the base angles of a triangle be equal is that the triangle be isosceles.

31. A necessary condition that two lines be parallel is that they be perpendicular to the same line.

or

A sufficient condition that two lines be perpendicular to the same line is that they be parallel.

33. A necessary condition that $x = 1$ is that $3x + 2 = x + 4$.

or

A sufficient condition that $3x + 2 = x + 4$ is that $x = 1$.

35. A triangle is a right triangle only if it is inscribed in a semicircle.

37. The vector sum of all forces acting on a body is zero only if it is in static equilibrium.

39. Two forces are equal, opposite, and collinear only if they are in equilibrium.

41. A necessary and sufficient condition that two lines be parallel is that they be equidistant.

43. A necessary and sufficient condition that three concurrent forces be in equilibrium is that their vector sum be zero.

45. No. Promise is converse of that required for her to win.

ANSWERS TO PROBLEMS 1.8

1. False. Counterexample: $2 + 4 = 6$.

3. True. Expand the right-hand side.

5. True. $x = 3$ is a suitable x.

7. True. The roots are -3 and -4.

9. False. Counterexample: $x = 1$.

11. False. This is the "ambiguous case" for triangles. If a, b, and B are given and if b is neither too long nor too short (see figure), there are two noncongruent triangles each of which has these three given parts.

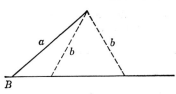

13. **False.** Counterexample: In the figure the sum of the forces is zero, but there is a moment of 50 ft-lb about point A.

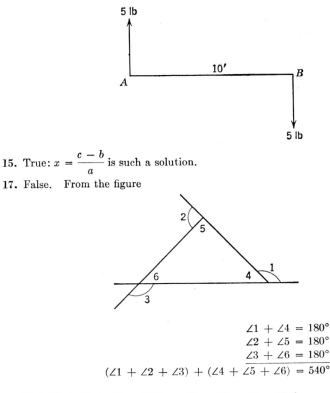

15. **True:** $x = \dfrac{c - b}{a}$ is such a solution.

17. **False.** From the figure

$$\angle 1 + \angle 4 = 180°$$
$$\angle 2 + \angle 5 = 180°$$
$$\angle 3 + \angle 6 = 180°$$
$$(\angle 1 + \angle 2 + \angle 3) + (\angle 4 + \angle 5 + \angle 6) = 540°$$

But $\angle 4 + \angle 5 + \angle 6 = 180°$; so $\angle 1 + \angle 2 + \angle 3 = 360°$.

19. Assume the negation of the conclusion, namely: Some two distinct lines meet in more than one point. Choose any two such points A and B. Then there are two distinct lines through A and B. This contradicts the axiom.

21. Assume the negation of the conclusion: Some equation of the form $a + x = b$ has more than one solution. Let x_1 and x_2 be two such solutions with $x_1 \neq x_2$. Then

$$a + x_1 = b$$
$$a + x_2 = b$$

Subtracting, we have: $x_1 - x_2 = 0$, which is a contradiction.

ANSWERS TO PROBLEMS 2.4.

5. $a + b + c + d = (a + b + c) + d$.

7. $-2, -\frac{1}{4}, 3, 0, \sqrt{3}$.   **9.** $5, 1, 0, \frac{1}{2}, \frac{3}{4}$.

11. -1.   **13.** -1.   **15.** -35.

17. $a \times b \times c = (a \times b) \times c$.   **23.** $2, -\frac{1}{3}, -\frac{5}{2}, 1$, none.

25. -69.   **27.** -76.   **29.** 179.

31. No.   **33.** No.   **35.** No.

37. True.   Use distributive and commutative laws.

39. False.   Find counterexample.

41. True.   Imitate the illustrations.

43. True.   There are two parts to be proved: (1) existence, (2) uniqueness. Refer back to Chap. 1.

ANSWERS TO PROBLEMS 2.8

1. 0, meaningless, 1, 0, indeterminate.

3. $-1, 0, 1$, none, 2 and 4.   **5.** $0, 1$, none, $0, \frac{1}{2}$.

7. $-3, -4$.   **9.** $\pm \sqrt{10}$.   **15.** No.

19. Let a be a natural number and $b = 1$.

ANSWERS TO PROBLEMS 2.10

1. $0.\overline{428571}$.   **3.** $0.\overline{2}$.   **5.** $2.\overline{8}$.

7. $\frac{7}{9}$.   **9.** $\frac{189}{11}$.   **11.** $2,116/555$. .

ANSWERS TO PROBLEMS 2.13

1. $4 > 1, 6 > -2, 3 > -5, -3 > -7, 0 > -4$.

3. $a < c, c < b$.   **5.** 13, 11, 5, 5, 38.

7. 4, 2, 9, 9, 6.   **9.** I $(+, +)$; III $(-, -)$.

11. IV, I, III, II, II.   **15.** $K = 273° + C$.

19. $F = \frac{1}{12}I$.   **23.** $F = 32 + \frac{9}{5}C; -40°$.

25. $x' = 2x + 3$.   **27.** $x' = \frac{3}{4}x + 25; 100$.

ANSWERS TO PROBLEMS 2.14

1. $11 + i$.   **3.** $5 - 15i$.   **5.** $-2 - 13i$.

7. $3 + 3i$.   **9.** $2 - 5i$.   **11.** $2 + 4i$.

13. $4 + 3i$.   **15.** $-36 - 3i$.   **17.** $58 - 30i$.

19. 3.   **21.** 89.   **23.** $30 - 15i$.

25. $-18 + 6i$.   **27.** -16.   **29.** $-i$.

31. $\dfrac{23 - 14i}{29}$.   **33.** $\dfrac{-3 + 46i}{25}$.   **35.** $\dfrac{12 + 9i}{5}$.

37. $\dfrac{21 + 12i}{65}$.   **39.** $\dfrac{3 - i}{2}$.

41. $x = -\frac{23}{29}; y = \frac{15}{29}$.   **43.** $x = \frac{43}{17}; y = -\frac{19}{17}$.

45. $x = 0, y = -2$.

ANSWERS TO PROBLEMS 3.2

1. $-a^2 + 3c$.   **3.** $-6pq + 2q^3 - p^2$.

5. $15x^2y + 5xy^2 + 2xy + x^2 - y^2 + 2$.

7. $x^3 - 5y^3 - xy - 4y$.

9. $2x^2 - 3y^2 + x + 5a^2 + 2b^2 + y$.

11. $11x^2y - 4xy^2 + 12xy + 4x^3 + 3$.

13. $7x^2 - 8y^2 - 3r^2 + 5s^2$. **15.** $8x^4 - 7a^2 + 11xy$.

17. $-5xy + 2x^2 - 3y^4 + 2y^2 - x^3$. **19.** $-3a^2 - 15b^2 - 11ab$.

ANSWERS TO PROBLEMS 3.3

1. $-12a^6b^7$. **3.** $64x^3y^5z^3w$.

5. $6a^2 - 8ab - 30b^2$. **7.** $64x^2 + 48xy + 9y^2$.

9. $8p^3 - 12p^2q + 6pq^2 - q^3$. **11.** $16x^2 - 9y^2$.

13. $10x^6 + 9x^5 + 13x^4 - 11x^3 + 3x^2 - x + 4$.

15. $-63x^6 + 2x^5 + 28x^4 + 3x^3 + 45x^2 + 5x$.

17. $28a^7 - 67a^4b^2 + 7a^3b^3 + 9ab^4 - b^5 + 12a^4 - 27ab^2 + 3b^3$.

19. $16x^6 - 18x^5y + 31x^4y^2 - 8x^3y^3 + 4x^2y^4 + 4xy^5 - y^6$.

ANSWERS TO PROBLEMS 3.4

1. $10, 35, 20, 1, 3$. **3.** $15 + 20 = 35$.

5. $1 + 4 + 6 + 4 + 1 = 16$.

7. $x^5 + 10x^4y + 40x^3y^2 + 80x^2y^3 + 80xy^4 + 32y^5$.

9. $64r^6 - 192r^5s + 240r^4s^2 - 160r^3s^3 + 60r^2s^4 - 12rs^5 + s^6$.

11. $\frac{1}{64}x^6 + \frac{3}{16}x^5y + \frac{15}{16}x^4y^2 + \frac{5}{2}x^3y^3 + \frac{15}{4}x^2y^4 + 3xy^5 + y^6$.

13. $\frac{27}{x^3} + 27 + 9x^3 + x^6$. **15.** 1.0510100501.

17. 715. **19.** $-\binom{7}{5} \cdot 2^2 \cdot 3^5$. **21.** 4.

23. $x^3 + y^3 + z^3 + 3(x^2y + x^2z + xy^2 + xz^2 + y^2z + yz^2) + 6xyz$.

ANSWERS TO PROBLEMS 3.5

	Quotient	Remainder
1.	$2x^2 - x + 1$	0
3.	$4x^2 - 3x + 5$	6
5.	$5x^2 + x - 6$	$2x + 1$
7.	$3x^3 - x + 4$	$x + 3$
9.	$2x^2 - x$	$2x^2 - x + 3$
11.	$7x^3 - 5x^2 + x - 2$	3
13.	$x^2 + 1$	0
15.	$x^4 - x^2 + 1$	-2
17.	$x^5 + x^4y + x^3y^2 + x^2y^3 + xy^4 + y^5$	0
19.	$\frac{1}{3}x^2 - 2x + \frac{1}{2}$	$-\frac{1}{2}$

ANSWERS TO PROBLEMS 3.6

1. $(x + 3)(y + 2)$.

3. $(x^2 + 1)(x + 1) = (x + i)(x - i)(x + 1)$.

5. $(s + v)(x + y)$. **7.** $(x + 4)(x - 2)$.

9. $(x - 10)(x - 4)$. **11.** $(x - 12)(x - 3)$.

13. $(y - 21x)(y - 2x)$. **15.** Does not factor.

17. $(3x + 2)(x + 1)$. **19.** $(3x - 1)(x + 2)$.

21. $(2x - 3)(x - 1)$. **23.** $(5x - y)(x - 2y)$.

25. $(5x + 12)(2x - 3)$.

29. $(3x + 8)(2x - 15)$.

33. $(5x + 4)(5x - 4)$.

37. $(2x + 3i)(2x - 3i)$.

41. $(x + iy)(x - iy)(x + y)(x - y)$.

43. $(x - y + 1)(x + y - 5)$.

47. $(x + 5)(x^2 - 5x + 25)$.

51. $(x^2 + 2x + 3)(x^2 - 2x + 3)$.

53. $x(9x^2 + 2xy + 4y^2)$.

27. $2(4x - 3)(4x + 9)$.

31. $(3x + 8)(x + 2)$.

35. $(x + \sqrt{5})(x - \sqrt{5})$.

39. $12(x + 2)$.

45. $(2x - y)(4x^2 + 2xy + y^2)$.

49. $[(a + 2b)x + 1][(a - 2b)x + 1]$.

55. $2(x^2 + x + 21)$.

ANSWERS TO PROBLEMS 4.2

1. $\dfrac{x - 2}{x + 2}$.

3. Does not simplify.

5. Does not simplify.

7. $\dfrac{3x - 1}{2x + 3}$.

9. $\dfrac{2x + 3}{x + 7}$.

11. $\dfrac{c + d}{3 - y}$.

13. $\dfrac{x^2 + xy + y^2}{x + y}$.

15. Does not simplify.

17. $\dfrac{x^2(a + 3)}{a - 3}$.

19. Does not simplify.

ANSWERS TO PROBLEMS 4.3

1. $\dfrac{7x - 3}{x^2 - 1}$.

3. $\dfrac{4}{2r - s}$.

5. $\dfrac{a - 4b}{a(a - b)}$.

7. $\dfrac{2x + 3y}{xy(x + y)}$.

9. $\dfrac{x^2 - 4x}{(x - 1)(x + 1)(x + 2)}$.

11. $\dfrac{-x(x^3 + x^2 - 2x - 3)}{(x + 2)^2(x + 1)^2}$.

13. $\dfrac{2x^3 + 4x^2 + 5x + 4}{(x^2 + x + 1)(x^2 + x + 2)}$.

15. $\dfrac{x^3 - 2x^2 - 5x + 2}{x(x + 2)(x + 1)}$.

17. $\dfrac{6x - 49}{(x + 4)(x - 3)(x - 5)}$.

19. $\dfrac{-y^2}{x(x - y)^2}$.

ANSWERS TO PROBLEMS 4.4

1. $\dfrac{(x - 1)^2}{2(x + 1)}$.

3. $\dfrac{x - 1}{x - 2}$.

5. $\dfrac{(x + 2)^3(x - 2)}{(x + 3)(x + 1)^3}$.

7. $\dfrac{(x + 4)(x + 5)}{x + 1}$.

9. $\frac{14}{9}$.

11. $\dfrac{(2x + 3)(x + 1)}{x(x + 2)}$.

13. $\dfrac{(2x - 3)(2x + 1)}{(x - 2)(2x + 3)}$.

15. 1.

17. $\dfrac{x^2(x+y)^2}{y^2(x-y)}.$

19. $\dfrac{(x+3)(x+6)(x-3)(x+4)}{(x-1)(x+5)(x+2)(x+1)}.$

21. $p/r.$

ANSWERS TO PROBLEMS 4.5

1. $\dfrac{-2x}{(x-3)(x-4)}.$

3. $\dfrac{7(3x+5)}{2(x+3)(-2x+1)}.$

5. $\dfrac{x^2+y^2}{x^2+2xy-y^2}.$

7. $\dfrac{125x^3-30x}{25x^2-3}=\dfrac{5x(25x^2-6)}{25x^2-3}.$

9. $\dfrac{2(x^2-2x-2)}{x(x+1)}.$

11. $\dfrac{7x+8}{(x+1)(x+3)(x-2)}.$

13. $\dfrac{(x+2)(x+3)}{(2x-1)(4x+3)}.$

15. $\dfrac{(3x+1)(x+1)(26x^2-10x+1)}{x^2(2x+1)(5x-1)}.$

17. $\dfrac{(x^3+3x^2+2x-3)(x-2)(x+4)}{(-x^3+2x^2+2x+8)(x+3)(x+2)}.$

19. $\dfrac{-3x^2+x(-5+6i)+1}{x^2+4x+8}.$

ANSWERS TO PROBLEMS 5.2

1. $5^{11}.$

3. $3^2.$

5. $(\tfrac{5}{2})^4.$

7. $(-22)^7.$

9. $79.$

11. $x^2+3xy+y^2.$

13. $a^2b^3-bc^2.$

15. $3y+7+\dfrac{2}{y}.$

17. $1-3x.$

19. $x^2+3.$

ANSWERS TO PROBLEMS 5.6

1. $2x-3.$

3. $x+2x^{\frac{1}{2}}y^{\frac{1}{2}}+y.$

5. $p-q^{\frac{2}{3}}.$

7. $x^{\frac{1}{2}}-x^{-1}.$

9. $x^{-\frac{1}{2}}-x^{-\frac{5}{2}}+x^{\frac{5}{2}}.$

11. $|x+2|.$

13. $|x+1|+|x-1|.$

15. $\dfrac{|2x+1|}{2x+1}.$

17. $-3\sqrt{7}.$

19. $8i.$

21. $-8.$

23. $-20.$

25. $3\sqrt{2}.$

27. $\sqrt{5}-2\sqrt{7}$ (no simplification is possible).

29. $(4+i)\sqrt{3}.$

ANSWERS TO PROBLEMS 5.7

1. $\dfrac{2\sqrt{5}}{5}.$

3. $4(\sqrt{3}+\sqrt{2}).$

5. $\dfrac{3\sqrt{x+1}}{x+1}.$

7. $\dfrac{2x(\sqrt{x+2}-\sqrt{x-1})}{3}.$

9. $\dfrac{3\sqrt{2}-\sqrt{3}}{3}.$

11. $\tfrac{1}{4}.$

13. $\dfrac{5\sqrt{2} + 2\sqrt{5}}{10}.$

15. $\dfrac{2x - x\sqrt{x} - 1}{x(1 - x)}.$

17. $\dfrac{3x}{1 - x}$

19. 1.342.

21. 0.252.

23. 0.04 (exact).

ANSWERS TO PROBLEMS 6.3

1. (b) and (d); (a) and (c).
3. $n \leftrightarrow -n.$
5. Not possible because of bigamy.
7. Not possible.
9. State fielding position of each batter.
11. 0   1   −1   2   −2   3   −3   · · · .
    1   2   3   4   5   6   7   · · · .
17. {2,6}, {2}, {6}, ∅; all but {2,6}.
19. {3,5,7}, {3,5}, {3,7}, {5,7}, {3}, {5}, {7}, ∅; all but {3,5,7}.
21. {a,b,c,d}, {a,b,c}, {a,b,d}, {a,c,d}, {b,c,d}, {a,b}, {a,c}, {a,d}, {b,c}, {b,d}, {c,d}, {a}, {b}, {c}, {d}, ∅.   All but {a,b,c,d}.
23. If the set has n elements, the number of subsets is 2^n.
25. [3,7].
27. [5,8].
29. [1,6].
31.]1,3[.
33. Set of positive integers.
35. Set of all reals.
37. ∅.
39. Set of all ordered pairs.

ANSWERS TO PROBLEMS 6.6

1. $A = B.$
3. $A \supset B.$
5. $A = B.$
7. $A = B.$
9. $A \subset B.$
11. $A \supset B.$

13. $1 \pm \dfrac{i\sqrt{10}}{2}.$

15. $-\frac{1}{2}, -\frac{1}{2}.$

17. $1, -5.$
19. $\frac{7}{9}, -\frac{5}{4}.$
21. $2 + i, 2 + i.$
23. $x^2 + 3x + \frac{9}{4} = \frac{5}{4}.$
25. $x^2 + 12x + 36 = 0.$
27. $4x^2 - 8x + 4 = 2.$
29. Sum $= -8$, product $= 9.$
31. Sum $= -\frac{8}{3}$, product $= -\frac{5}{3}.$
33. Sum $= -1 + 2i$; product $= 3 + i.$
35. $\frac{25}{4}.$
37. $-\frac{9}{8}.$
39. $k = \pm 2.$
41. $x^2 - 6x + 8 = 0.$
43. $x^2 - 7x + 5 = 0.$
45. $5x^2 - 3x + 2 = 0.$

47. $2\left(x - \dfrac{3 + i\sqrt{23}}{4}\right)\left(x - \dfrac{3 - i\sqrt{23}}{4}\right).$

49. $(x + 1 + i)(x + 1 - i).$
51. $(8x + 7)(4x + 9).$
55. $k = 2.$
57. $x^2 + x + 25 = 0.$

ANSWERS TO PROBLEMS 6.8

1. $4, -1.$
3. 3, 4.
5. 2, 3.
7. $-3, -4.$
9. 5.
11. 4.
13. No solutions.
15. $-2.$
17. $-1.$
19. 1.

ANSWERS TO PROBLEMS 7.5

1.

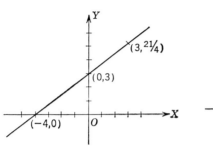

3.

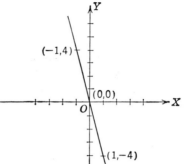

5.

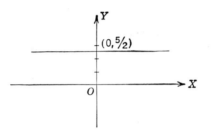

7. (1,1).   **9.** (1,4).   **11.** (4,2).

13. None, parallel lines.   **15.** All points on common line.

17. (1,1,2).   **19.** $(2,1,-1)$.   **21.** None.

23. Line of solutions.   **25.** Plane of solutions.

27. $4x - 3y + 2 = 0$.   **29.** $4x - 3y + 3 = 0$.

31. $x - 2 = 0$.   **33.** $x - 2y + 4 = 0$.

35. $(y_2 - y_1)(x - x_1) - (x_2 - x_1)(y - y_1) = 0$.

ANSWERS TO PROBLEMS 7.7

1. $(-1,7)$.   **3.** $(-2,3)$.   **5.** $(-1,3)$.

7. $(-4,-4,3)$.   **9.** $(17,1,-19)$.   **11.** $2\mathbf{i} - 17\mathbf{j} - 9\mathbf{k}$.

17. 13.   **19.** -1.   **21.** 0.

23. 3.   **25.** $\sqrt{10}$.   **27.** 1.

29. $\sqrt{17}$.

ANSWERS TO PROBLEMS 7.9

1. (5).   **3.** $\begin{pmatrix} 4 \\ 13 \end{pmatrix}$.   **5.** $\begin{pmatrix} 24 & -14 \\ 29 & 6 \end{pmatrix}$.

7. $\begin{pmatrix} 11 & -14 \\ 11 & 26 \end{pmatrix}$.   **9.** $\begin{pmatrix} 8 & -13 \\ 16 & 29 \end{pmatrix}$.   **11.** $\begin{pmatrix} -13 & -7 \\ 4 & -2 \\ 3 & 3 \end{pmatrix}$.

13. $\begin{pmatrix} 3 & -18 & 9 \\ 9 & -54 & 27 \\ 2 & -12 & 6 \end{pmatrix}$.

15. $\begin{pmatrix} -1 & 1 & 9 \\ 6 & 2 & -6 \\ 14 & 0 & -18 \end{pmatrix}$.

17. $\begin{pmatrix} 1 & 0 & 0 \\ 0 & 1 & 0 \\ 0 & 0 & 1 \end{pmatrix}$.

19. $\begin{pmatrix} 0 & 0 \\ 0 & 0 \end{pmatrix}$.

21. $\begin{pmatrix} 6 & 4 \\ 2 & 1 \end{pmatrix}, \begin{pmatrix} 1 & 4 & -1 \\ 2 & 5 & -2 \\ -1 & -2 & 1 \end{pmatrix}$.

23. MN is 2×2, NM is 3×3.

ANSWERS TO PROBLEMS 7.10

1. $\frac{1}{7}\begin{pmatrix} 3 & 1 \\ -1 & 2 \end{pmatrix}$.

3. $\begin{pmatrix} 3 & -5 \\ -1 & 2 \end{pmatrix}$.

5. No inverse.

7. $\begin{pmatrix} 1 & 0 \\ 0 & 1 \end{pmatrix}$.

9. $\begin{pmatrix} \dfrac{1}{\sqrt{2}} & -\dfrac{1}{\sqrt{2}} \\ \dfrac{1}{\sqrt{2}} & \dfrac{1}{\sqrt{2}} \end{pmatrix}$.

11. $x_2' - x_1' = (x_2 + a) - (x_1 + a) = (x_2 - x_1)$; similarly $y_2' - y_1' = y_2 - y_1$. Then $(s')^2 = s^2$.

13. The transformation gives a unique (x',y') for each (x,y). Solve for (x,y) in terms of (x',y'), and show that each (x',y') thus determines a unique (x,y).

15. Show that $x_2' - x_1' = a(x_2 - x_1)$, etc.

17. Solve $x = ax$, $y = ay$ for a, assuming $(x,y) \neq (0,0)$.

19. $x_2' - x_1' = -(x_2 - x_1)$; $y_2' - y_1' = y_2 - y_1$. Hence $(s')^2 = s^2$.

21. Same method as for Prob. 13.

23. $x_2' - x_1' = a(x_2 - x_1) + b(y_2 - y_1)$.
$y_2' - y_1' = -b(x_2 - x_1) + a(y_2 - y_1)$.
$(x_2' - x_1')^2 + (y_2' - y_1')^2 = (a^2 + b^2)[(x_2 - x_1)^2 + (y_2 - y_1)^2]$
$= (x_2 - x_1)^2 + (y_2 - y_1)^2$.

25. Solve:

$$\left. \begin{array}{l} ax + by = x \\ ay - bx = y \end{array} \right\} \quad \text{for } a \text{ and } b$$

The result is: $a(x^2 + y^2) = x^2 + y^2$, or $a = 1$. Hence $b = 0$.

27. The equations

$$x + y = 0$$
$$x + y = 0$$

have a line of solutions.

29. The equations

$$(a_1 - 1)x + b_1 y = 0$$
$$a_2 x + (b_2 - 1)y = 0$$

have the unique solution $(0,0)$ unless $(a_1 - 1)(b_2 - 1) - a_2 b_2 = 0$.

31. Same method as for Prob. 13. Use the computation of Prob. 30.

33. $X = \begin{pmatrix} x \\ y \end{pmatrix}$; $X' = \begin{pmatrix} x' \\ y' \end{pmatrix}$; $X'' = \begin{pmatrix} x'' \\ y'' \end{pmatrix}$;

$A = \begin{pmatrix} a & b \\ c & d \end{pmatrix}$; $B = \begin{pmatrix} p & q \\ r & s \end{pmatrix}$.

Then $X'' = BX' = B(AX) = (BA)X$.

ANSWERS TO PROBLEMS 7.11

1. 22. **3.** 38. **5.** 0.

7. 12. **9.** 37. **11.** 1.

13. 1. **15.** 0. **17.** $\begin{pmatrix} -2 & -3 & 4 \\ 2 & 2 & -3 \\ 1 & 2 & -2 \end{pmatrix}.$

19. $\dfrac{1}{8}\begin{pmatrix} -7 & 5 & -6 \\ -3 & 1 & 2 \\ 6 & -2 & 4 \end{pmatrix}.$ **21.** $\dfrac{1}{11}\begin{pmatrix} -2 & 8 & -1 \\ 1 & -4 & 6 \\ 4 & -5 & 2 \end{pmatrix}.$

ANSWERS TO PROBLEMS 7.12

1. $\dfrac{1}{7}\begin{pmatrix} 3 & 1 \\ -1 & 2 \end{pmatrix}\begin{pmatrix} -3 \\ 1 \end{pmatrix} = \dfrac{1}{7}\begin{pmatrix} -8 \\ 5 \end{pmatrix}.$ $x = -\dfrac{8}{7}, y = \dfrac{5}{7}.$

3. $\begin{pmatrix} 3 & -5 \\ -1 & 2 \end{pmatrix}\begin{pmatrix} 7 \\ -3 \end{pmatrix} = \begin{pmatrix} 36 \\ -13 \end{pmatrix}.$ $x = 36, y = -13.$

5. $-\dfrac{1}{8}\begin{pmatrix} -2 & -4 \\ -1 & 2 \end{pmatrix}\begin{pmatrix} -3 \\ -7 \end{pmatrix} = -\dfrac{1}{8}\begin{pmatrix} 34 \\ -11 \end{pmatrix}.$ $x = -\dfrac{34}{8}, y = \dfrac{11}{8}.$

7. $(23, -16, -13).$ **9.** $(\tfrac{41}{8}, -\tfrac{3}{8}, -\tfrac{26}{8}).$

11. $x = 31k, y = -11k, z = -15k.$

13. $x = 3k, y = 5k, z = 11k.$ **15.** $k(8, -3, -5).$

17. $k(-24, -18, 12),$ or, better, $k'(-4, -3, 2).$

19. Equations represent same plane, hence plane of solutions.

21. $(27, -12, -7).$ **23.** $(-5, -2, 6).$ **25.** k.

27. j. **29.** $(0, 0, 0).$

ANSWERS TO PROBLEMS 7.13

1. 0, 2. **3.** 9,281.

5. Wind = 50 mi/hr; airplane = 300 mi/hr.

7. 9 and 6 bricks/min. **9.** $C = 20$ g, $D = 9$ g.

11. $I = 5$ amp, $R = 3$ ohms. **13.** $P = 8$ lb/sq in., $V = 3$ cu in.

15. $v_0 = 8,000$ ft/sec, $a = 300$ ft/sec^2.

17. One.

19. Munitions: utilities: department stores = 16:15:55.

ANSWERS TO PROBLEMS 8.4

1. $x < -2$ or $]-\infty, -2[.$ **3.** $x < \tfrac{3}{2},$ or $]\infty, \tfrac{3}{2}[.$

5. $x \le -5$ or $]-\infty, -5].$ **7.** $x > \tfrac{1}{5}$ or $]\tfrac{1}{5}, \infty[.$

9. $x \ge \tfrac{8}{5}$ or $[\tfrac{8}{5}, \infty[.$

11. $x > -1$ or $x < -2$; that is, $]-1, \infty[\cup]-\infty, -2[.$

13. $1 \le x \le 3$; that is, $[1, 3].$

15. $x > 3$ or $x < 3$; that is, $]-\infty, 3[\cup]3, \infty[.$

17. All x. **19.** No x.

ANSWERS TO PROBLEMS 8.7

1.

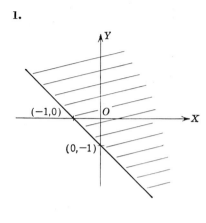

3.

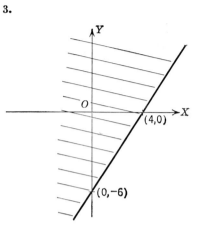

5.

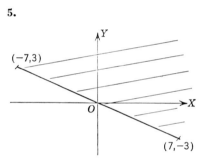

7.

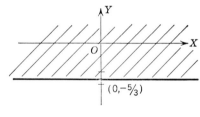

9.

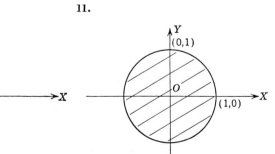

11.

13. No graph.

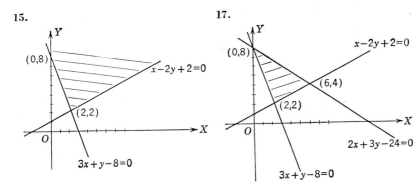

15.   17.

19.   21.

ANSWERS TO PROBLEMS 9.1

1. $X; Y.$
3. $X; \{y \mid y \geq 0\}.$
5. $\{x \mid -1 \leq x \leq 1\}; \{y \mid -1 \leq y \leq 1\}.$
7. $X; \{y \mid y \geq 0\}.$
9. $\{x \mid -2 \leq x \leq 2\}; \{y \mid -2 \leq y \leq 2\}.$
11. $X; Y.$
13. $\{x \mid x > 0\}; \{y \mid y < 1\}.$
15. $\{x \mid x < -\frac{1}{3}\}; \{y \mid y < -3\}.$
17. $\{1, 3\}; \{7, 14\}.$
19. $\{2\}; \{2, 3\}.$

ANSWERS TO PROBLEMS 9.2

1. $X; Y.$
3. $X; \{y \mid y \geq 0\}.$
5. $-4; 64; 1.$
7. $(1,1), (2,2), (3,2); \{1, 2, 3\}; \{1, 2\}.$
9. Function.
11. Function.
13. Function.
15. Not a function.
17. $X; \{-1, 0, 1\}.$
19. $X; Y.$
21. $0; 0; \dfrac{\sqrt{2} - 2}{3}; \dfrac{\sqrt{3} - 3}{3}$; not real; not real.
23. $2a + h.$
25. 1.

27.

D	S	M	T	W	Th.	F	Sat.
N	200	90	85	60	75	90	150

$f:(D,N).$

29. $f:(x,y)$, where $\{x\}$ is the set of the five days of the sale (domain) and $\{y\}$ is the set of five numbers 5,000, 3,000, 1,000, 500, 500 (range).

31. (a) Assume domain $\{x \mid 0 \leq x \leq 20\}$; range, $\{y \mid 1 \leq y \leq 5\}$. The function is $f:(x,y)$, where we know only five ordered pairs. We might assume $y = \frac{1}{5}x + 1$.

(b) Assume wheel is mired when it has settled 10 in. $3\frac{1}{3}$ min, $9\frac{291}{301}$ min.

33. X, except $\{0, 1, 2\}$.   **35.** X, except $\{-1, 1\}$.

37. (a) $\{y \mid -\frac{1}{4} \leq y \leq 0\}$.

(b) $\{y \mid 0 \leq y\}$.

ANSWERS TO PROBLEMS 9.4

1. $\dfrac{1}{x} + \dfrac{1}{x-1} + x$, X except $\{0, 1\}$.

$\dfrac{1}{x} + \dfrac{1}{x-1} - x$, X except $\{0, 1\}$.

$\left(\dfrac{1}{x} + \dfrac{1}{x-1}\right) x$, X except $\{0, 1\}$.

$\left(\dfrac{1}{x} + \dfrac{1}{x-1}\right)\dfrac{1}{x}$, X except $\{0, 1\}$.

3. $\dfrac{1}{x-1} + x + 1$, X except $\{1\}$.

$\dfrac{1}{x-1} - x - 1$, X except $\{1\}$.

$\dfrac{x+1}{x-1}$, X except $\{1\}$.

$\dfrac{1}{(x-1)(x+1)}$, X except $\{-1, 1\}$.

5. $x - 1 + \dfrac{1}{(x-1)^2}$, X except $\{1\}$.

$x - 1 - \dfrac{1}{(x-1)^2}$, X except $\{1\}$.

$\dfrac{x-1}{(x-1)^2}$, X except $\{1\}$.

$(x-1)^3$, X except $\{1\}$.

7. $(f \pm g)(x) = \begin{cases} \dfrac{1}{x-1} \pm \dfrac{2}{(x-1)(x+1)}, & X \text{ except } \{-1, 1\}. \\ 16 \pm \sqrt{15}, & \{x \mid x = 1\}. \\ \text{undefined}, & \{x \mid x = -1\}. \end{cases}$

$(fg)(x) = \begin{cases} \dfrac{2}{(x-1)^2(x+1)}, & X \text{ except } \{-1, 1\}. \\ 16\sqrt{15}, & \{x \mid x = 1\}. \\ \text{undefined}, & \{x \mid x = -1\}. \end{cases}$

$$\left(\frac{f}{g}\right)(x) = \begin{cases} \frac{1}{2}(x+1), \ X \text{ except } \{-1, 1\}. \\ \frac{16}{\sqrt{15}}, \ \{x \mid x = 1\}. \\ \text{undefined}, \ \{x \mid x = -1\}. \end{cases}$$

9. $(g \circ f)(x) = \dfrac{1}{1 - 1/(1 - x)}$, X except $\{0, 1\}$.

11. $(g \circ f)(x) = \left(2 - \dfrac{1}{x} + |x|\right)^2 - 4$, X except $\{0\}$.

$(f \circ g)(x) = 2 - \dfrac{1}{x^2 - 4} + |x^2 - 4|$, X except $\{-2, 2\}$.

13. $(g \circ f)(x) = |x| - 1$, X.
$(f \circ g)(x) = |x - 1|$, X.

15. $(g \circ f)(x) = x$, X.   **17.** 1, 5, 5.
$(f \circ g)(x) = x$, X.

ANSWERS TO PROBLEMS 9.5

1.   **3.**

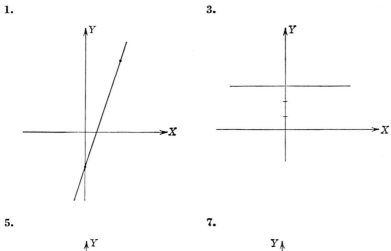

5.   **7.**

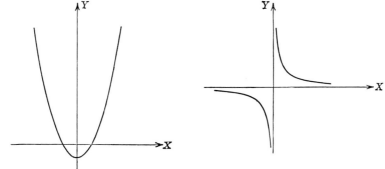

9.

11.

13.

15.

17.

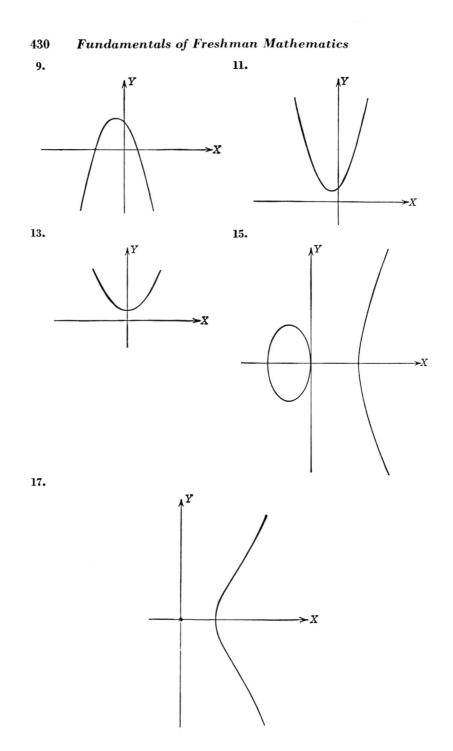

19.

21.

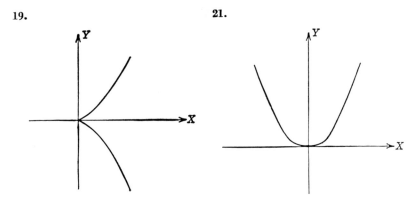

23.

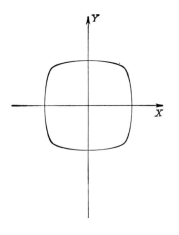

25.

27.

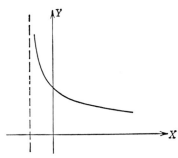

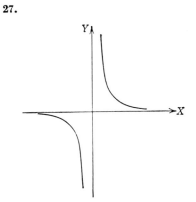

29.

31.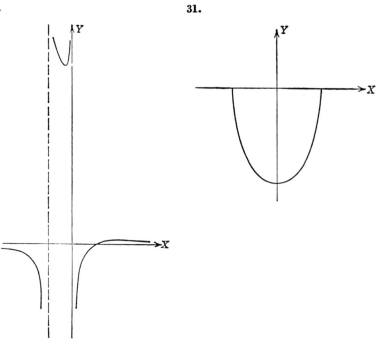

33. No.
35. Straight line.

37. Circle.

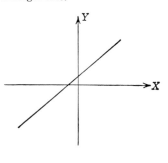

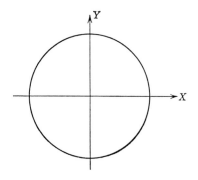

39. Two lines.

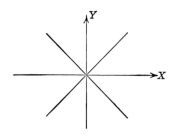

41. Intercepts $-\frac{1}{2}$, $\frac{1}{2}$; domain $\{x \mid |x| \geq \frac{1}{2}\}$; range Y; symmetric with respect to X-axis, Y-axis, origin.

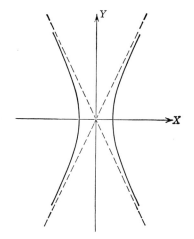

43. Intercept 0; domain $\{x \mid x \geq 0\}$; range Y; symmetric with respect to X-axis.

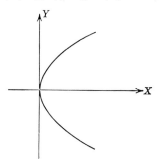

45. Intercepts -3, -2, 1; domain X; range Y.

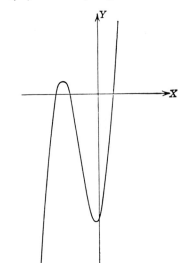

47. Intercepts 0, 2; domain X except $\{-3\}$; vertical asymptote $x = -3$.

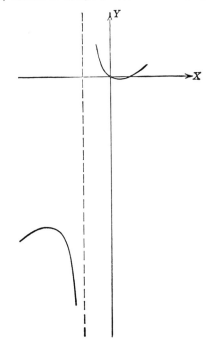

ANSWERS TO PROBLEMS 9.6

1.

3.

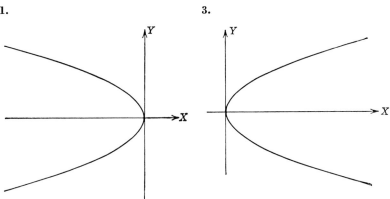

5.

7.

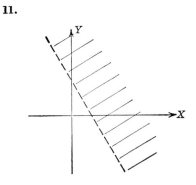

9.

11.

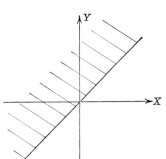

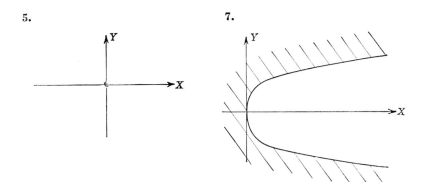

13.

15.

17.

19.

21.

23.

25.

27.

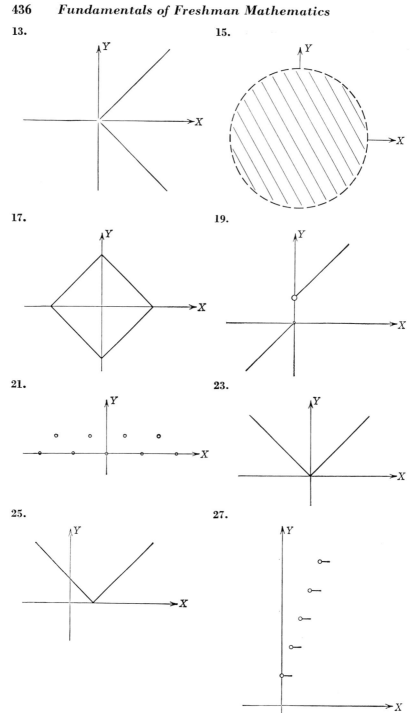

ANSWERS TO PROBLEMS 9.7

1, 3, 5, 7. d_f, reals; r_f, reals; $d_{f^{-1}}$, reals; $r_{f^{-1}}$ reals.

1.   **3.**

5.   **7.**

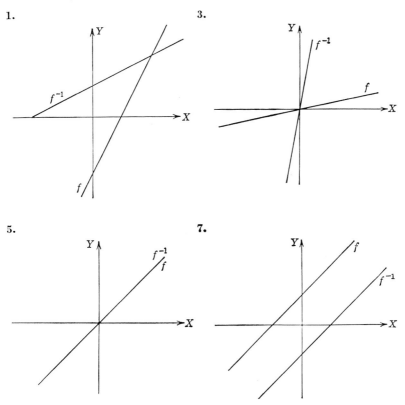

9. r_f, nonnegative reals; $d_{f^{-1}} = r_f$; $r_{f^{-1}} = d_f$.

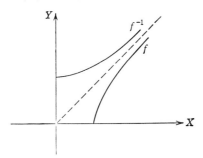

11. r_f is the set of real numbers $[-0,2]$; $d_{f^{-1}} = r_f$; $r_{f^{-1}} = d_f$.

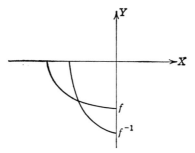

13. Let f be the set of ordered pairs $\{(a,b)\}$. Then f^{-1} is $\{(b,a)\}$. The mid-point of any line segment joining (a,b) and (b,a) is $\left(\dfrac{a+b}{2}, \dfrac{a+b}{2}\right)$, which lies on $y = x$.

ANSWERS TO PROBLEMS 9.8

1. $\left\{\left(x, \dfrac{3x-3}{4}\right)\right\}$; domain X; range Y.

3. $\{(x, -\sqrt{1-2x^2})\}$; domain $\{x \mid x^2 \le \frac{1}{2}\}$: range $\{y \mid -1 \le y \le 0\}$.

5. $\left\{\left(x, \dfrac{2}{x^2+1}\right)\right\}$; domain X; range $0 < y \le 2$.

7. $\{(x, 1 - |x|)\}$; domain $\{x \mid -1 \le x \le 1\}$; range $\{y \mid 0 \le y \le 1\}$.

9. $\{(s, \sqrt{2gs})\}$; domain $\{s \mid s \ge 0\}$; range $\{v \mid v \ge 0\}$.

11. $\{(x,x)\}$; domain X; range Y.

ANSWERS TO PROBLEMS 10.4

1. None.   3. (a), (b), (c).   5. (a).
7. (a), (c).   9. (a), (b), (c).   11. (b) since $|x|^4 = x^4$.
13. (a) Polynomial; domain X.
   (b) Explicit algebraic; domain $\{x \mid x \ge 0\}$.
   (c) Rational; domain $\{x \mid |x| > 0\}$.
15. (a) Explicit algebraic; domain $\{x \mid |x| \ge 1\}$.
   (b) No function defined since no domain.
   (c) Rational; domain X except $\{0, -1\}$.
17. (a) Constant; domain reals.
   (b) Rational; domain $\{y \mid |y| > 0\}$.
   (c) Explicit algebraic; domain $\{\theta \mid \theta \le 0\}$.

ANSWERS TO PROBLEMS 10.5

1. Polynomial; domain X; range Y; zeros $\{-1, 0, 1\}$.

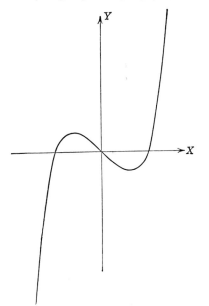

3. Explicit algebraic; domain $\{x \mid (-1 \leq x \leq 0) \cup (x \geq 1)\}$; range $\{y(y \geq 0)\}$; zeros $\{-1, 0, 1\}$; points of discontinuity $\{-1, 0, 1\}$.

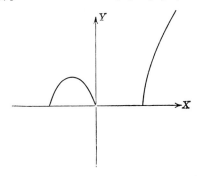

5. Polynomial; domain X; range (complete square) $\{y \mid y \leq \frac{1}{4}\}$; zeros $\{-1, 0$ (double), $1\}$.

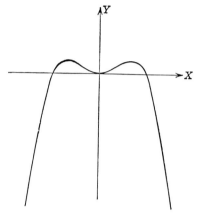

7. Explicit algebraic; domain $\{x \mid |x| \leq 1\}$; zeros $\{-1, 0, 1\}$; points of discontinuity $\{-1, 1\}$.

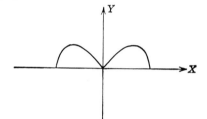

9. Polynomial; domain X; range Y; zero $\{-1\}$.

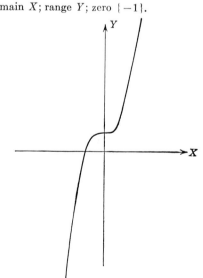

11. Explicit algebraic; domain $\{x \mid x \geq -1\}$; range $\{y \mid y \geq 0\}$; zero $\{-1\}$; point of discontinuity $\{-1\}$.

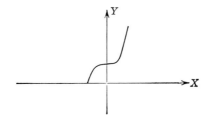

13. Explicit algebraic; domain X; range Y; zero $\{-1\}$.

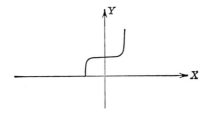

15. Explicit algebraic; domain $\{x \mid 0 \leq x\}$; range $\{y \mid 0 \leq y\}$; zero $\{1\}$; point of discontinuity $\{0\}$.

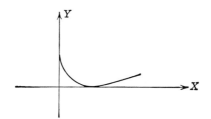

17. Rational; domain X; range $\{y \mid 0 < y \leq 2\}$.

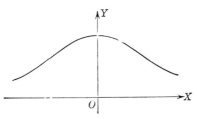

19. Explicit algebraic; domain $\{x \mid 0 \le x < 2\}$; range $\{y \mid y \ge 0\}$; zero $\{0\}$; points of discontinuity $\{0, 2\}$.

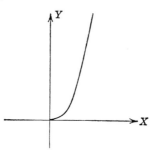

21. Explicit algebraic; domain $\{x \mid (-3 \le x \le 0) \cup (x \ge 1)\}$; range $\{y \mid y \le 0\}$; zeros $\{-3, 0, 1\}$; points of discontinuity $\{-3, 0, 1\}$.

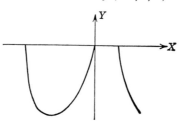

23. Algebraic; domain $\{x \mid -1 \le x \le 1\}$; range $\{y \mid -1 \le y \le 1\}$; zeros $\{-1, 1\}$. Hypocycloid.
25. Algebraic; domain X; range Y; zero $\{0\}$.

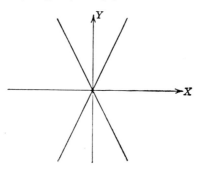

27. The line $y = -x$ *and* the hyperbola $xy + 1 = 0$.

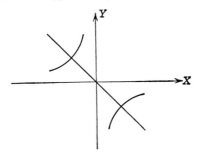

ANSWERS TO PROBLEMS 10.6

1. $a(x - 1)(x + 1) = 0$. **3.** $a(x - 2 - i) = 0$.
5. $2(x - 1)(x - 2)(x - 3)(x - 4) = 0$.
7. $ax(x - i)(x + 1) = 0$. **9.** $a(x - 1)^3 = 0$.
11. $ax(x^2 - 1)$. **13.** $a(x^3 + 2x^2 - 2x - 4)$.
15. $k(x^3 - 2ax^2 + (a^2 + b^2)x)$. **17.** $(ax + b)(x - 2)^2$.
19. 3. **21.** -5. **23.** 59.
25. $\{1, -1, i, -i\}$.

27. $\left\{0, -\sqrt{-\dfrac{1}{2} - i\dfrac{\sqrt{3}}{2}}, \sqrt{-\dfrac{1}{2} - i\dfrac{\sqrt{3}}{2}}, -\sqrt{-\dfrac{1}{2} + i\dfrac{\sqrt{3}}{2}}, \right.$

$\left. \sqrt{-\dfrac{1}{2} + i\dfrac{\sqrt{3}}{2}} \right\}$.

29. Four. **31.** Three.
33. A double root r_1 leads to the quadratic factor $(x - r_1)^2$, and conversely. Hence $n/2$ double roots lead to $(x - r_1)^2(x - r_2)^2 \cdots (x - r_{n/2})^2$, which is of degree n.
35. If $(x - r_1)(x_1 - r_2) \cdots (x - r_n) = c(x - r_1)(x - r_2) \cdots (x - r_n) = 0$, then $P(x) - cQ(x) = 0$. If $P(x) - cQ(x) = 0$, then $(x - r_1)(x - r_2) \cdots (x - r_n) = c(x - r_1)(x - r_2) \cdots (x - r_n)$ and roots are equal.

ANSWERS TO PROBLEMS 10.7

1. 19, -9. **3.** 3, 45. **5.** $\frac{17}{4}$, $\frac{63}{16}$.
7. $3x^2 + 11x + 34$, 101. **9.** $x^3 - 3x^2 + 6x - 14$, 31.
11. $x^4 + x^3 + 4x^2 + 4x + 4$, 3. **13.** $x^2 - \frac{3}{2}x + \frac{1}{4}$, $\frac{9}{8}$.
15. $x - \frac{8}{3}$, $\frac{55}{9}$. **17.** $Q = 2x^2 - 3x + 5$, $R = 0$.
19. $Q = x^3 + 3x^2 - x - 1$, $R = 0$.
21. $Q = 2x^2 + 4x - 6$, $R = 0$.
23. $x - r \overline{)ax^2 + bx + c}\ ax$ a b $c\ \overline{)r}$
       $\underline{ax^2 - arx}$ ar
          $(ar + b)x \cdots$ a $ar + b \cdots$
25. $k = 0$. **27.** $P(-2) = 2$. **29.** $r = 1, -2$.
31. $f(x) = x^n - a^n$, $R = f(a) = a^n - a^n = 0$.

ANSWERS TO PROBLEMS 10.8

1. HINT: $(2x - 5)(x - 1) = 0$.   **3.** HINT: $x(2x + 1)(x + 6) = 0$.

5. HINT: $[(3x + 1) - 3][(3x + 1) - 4] = 0$.

7. HINT: $(x - 1)(x + 1)(x^2 + 1) = 0$.

9. HINT: $\left(\dfrac{1}{x} - 1\right)\left(\dfrac{1}{x} + 1\right) = 0$.

11. HINT: $(x - 1)(x^2 - x - 6) = 0$.

13. $\{0, i, -i\}$.   **15.** $\{1, -1, i, -i\}$.

17. $\{0 \text{ (double)}, 1, 2\}$.   **19.** $\{0 \text{ (triple)}, 1, -1\}$.

21. $\{-1, 0, 2, 3\}$.

ANSWERS TO PROBLEMS 10.9

1. $\left\{1, \dfrac{1}{2} - \dfrac{\sqrt{13}}{2}, \dfrac{1}{2} + \dfrac{\sqrt{13}}{2}\right\}$.   **3.** $\{-3, -\frac{1}{2}, 1\}$.

5. HINT: $(x^2 + x + 1)(x^2 + x + 2) = 0$.

7. $\{-5, -1, 2, 5\}$.

9. $\left\{0, \dfrac{1}{3}, -\frac{1}{2} - i\dfrac{\sqrt{3}}{2}, -\frac{1}{2} + i\dfrac{\sqrt{3}}{2}\right\}$.

11. $\{-1, -i, i\}$.

13. By rational-root theorem equation has no rational root.

ANSWERS TO PROBLEMS 10.10

1. $-0.78, -0.8$.   **3.** $-0.43, -0.4$.   **5.** $0.61, 0.6$.

7. $-1.41, -1.4; 1.41, 1.4$.   **9.** $1.63, 1.6$.

11. -2.57 (exact).   **13.** $1.32, 1.3$.

15. $-0.35, -0.4$.   (Drop 5, and change preceding odd digit to next larger digit.)

ANSWERS TO PROBLEMS 11.1

1. $a^x \cdot a^y = a^{x+y}$.   **3.** $\frac{5}{2}$.

5. 0.729.   **7.** $\frac{1}{4}\sqrt{2}$.   **9.** $1/3^9$.

11. 20.   **13.** $1{,}000\sqrt{1.23}$.   **15.** 1.

17. $a^{2x/3}b^{7x/2}$.   **19.** $10^{-\frac{2}{6}^3+\frac{3}{4}x}$.

21.   **23.**

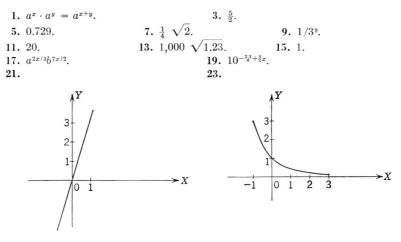

25.

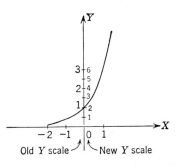

27. Since $f(a) < f(b)$ for $a < b$, it follows that $f(a) = f(b)$ when and only when $a = b$. Therefore $(a,f(a))$, $(b,f(a))$ implies $a = b$, and f has an inverse.

ANSWERS TO PROBLEMS 11.2

1. 3.3201.

3. 407.57.

5. 0.049787.

7. 0.270670.

9. 4.1124.

11.

13.

15.   **17.**

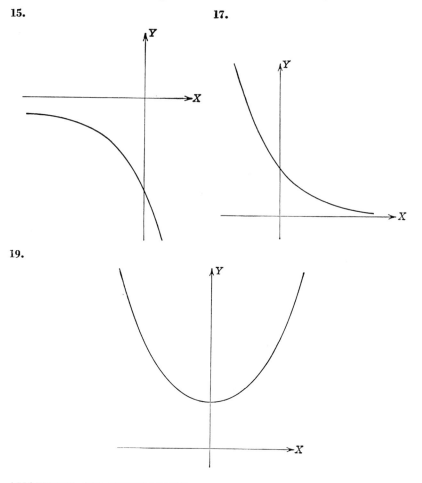

19.

ANSWERS TO PROBLEMS 11.3

1. Let $x = 5^{3.2}$. Then $\log_{10} x = 3.2 \log_{10} 5 = 2.23670$. Therefore $x = 172.46$.

3. 1.4918.   **5.** 1,258,900.

7. Let $x = 5^{3.2}$. Then $\log x = 3.2 \log 5 = (3.2)(1.60944) = 5.150208$.
Therefore $x = 172.5$.

9. 1.492.   **11.** 1,259,000.   **13.** 2.

15. 3.   **17.** 4.   **19.** $y = x^x$.

$$\log_a y = x \log_a x.$$
$$y = a^{x \log_a x}.$$
$$x^x = a^{x \log_a x}.$$

21. $(x, a^{x(1+\log_a b)})$.

23. $(1.1)^{10} = 2.593$.
$(1.01)^{100} = 2.704$.
$(1.001)^{1,000} = 2.717$.
$e = 2.71828$.

ANSWERS TO PROBLEMS 11.4

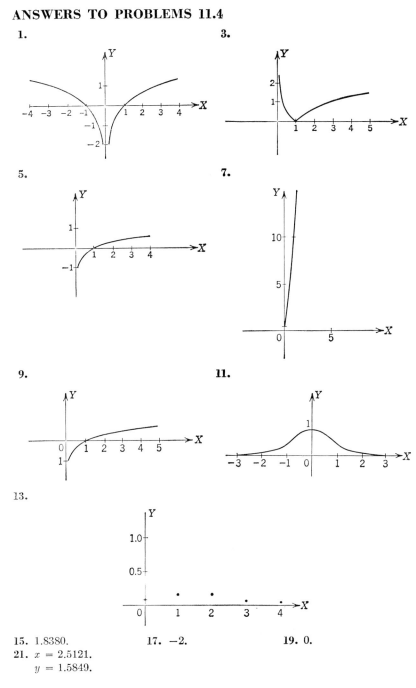

1.

3.

5.

7.

9.

11.

13.

15. 1.8380.   **17.** −2.   **19.** 0.

21. $x = 2.5121.$

$y = 1.5849.$

5. $B = 62°25.4'$.
$b = 19.147$.
$c = 21.601$.

7. $A = 50°$.
$b = 64.279$.
$a = 76.604$.

9. $A = 45°6'$.
$B = 44°54'$.
$b = 22.023$.

11. 60 in.

13. 61.229 in.

15. 61.804 in.

17. 99.967 ft.

19. (*a*) 59.441 sq in.
(*b*) 90.818 sq in.

21. $8 + \sqrt{19} = 12.358$ ft.

23. 4,574.7 sq ft.

25. Area $= \frac{1}{2}ab = \frac{1}{2}(c \sin A)(c \cos A)$.

ANSWERS TO PROBLEMS 12.11

1. $L = 12.806$.
$\theta = 51°20.4'$.

3. $L = 10.170$.
$\theta = 24°39.4'$.

5. Downstream at $17°8.4'$ with bank and with speed of 4.7989 mi/hr.

7. 776.46 lb.

9. 18.807.

11. $a = 44.974$.
$b = 75.249$.

13. $L = 19.103$.
$\theta = 30°18.18'$.

15. $t = \dfrac{W \sin \beta}{\sin \alpha \cos \beta + \cos \alpha \sin \beta}$.

$c = \dfrac{W \sin \alpha}{\sin \alpha \cos \beta + \cos \alpha \sin \beta}$.

17. $a = 241.06$.
$\theta = 98°31.8'$.

ANSWERS TO PROBLEMS 12.12

1. $A = 110°$, $b = 5.3209$, $c = 6.8404$.
3. $B = 75°$, $a = 2.9575$, $c = 3.6222$.
5. $C = 44°53.0'$, $a = 7.6805$, $b = 2.3128$.
7. $B = 63°03.3'$, $A = 60°56.7'$, $a = 9.8062$.
$B = 116°56.7'$, $A = 7°03.3'$, $a = 1.3778$.
9. No solution.

15. $L = 10.336$; $139°48.6'$.

ANSWERS TO PROBLEMS 12.13

1. $43°31.8'$.
3. $30°45.2'$.
5. $90°26.2'$.
7. 1.3327.
9. 18.739.
11. 15.658.
13. 4.2837, 12.006.
15. Area $= \frac{1}{4}na^2 \cot (180°/n)$.
17. $14°21.7'$, $41°24.6'$, $R = 124°13.8'$.
19. $16°46.0'$, $35°14.0'$, $r = 13.659$.

ANSWERS TO PROBLEMS 13.2

1. $0°$, $30°$, $45°$, $60°$.
3. $180°$, $210°$, $225°$, $240°$.
5. $36°$, $72°$, $25.714°$, $57.296°$.
7. $450°$, $990°$, $1260°$, $171.89°$.
9. 0, $\pi/6$, $\pi/4$, $\pi/3$, $\pi/2$.
11. 3.4907, 3.8397, 5.3582, 6.1959, 0.00000485.
13. $\sin 0 = \tan 0 = 0$, $\cos 0 = \sec 0 = 1$.
15. $\sin \pi = \tan \pi = 0$, $\cos \pi = \sec \pi = -1$.
17. $\sin 2\pi = \tan 2\pi = 0$, $\cos 2\pi = \sec 2\pi = 1$.
19. $\sin (-8\pi) = \tan (-8\pi) = 0$, $\cos (-8\pi) = \sec (-8\pi) = 1$.

21.

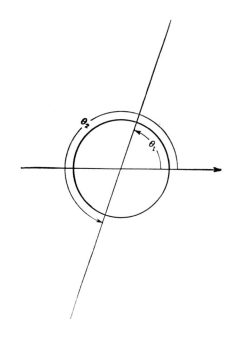

23. HINT: If $\sin \theta = y$, then $\sin (-\theta) = -y$.

27. HINT: If $\sin (\theta + 2\pi) = y$, then $\sin \theta = y$ and if $\sin (\theta + \pi) = y$, then $\sin \theta = -y$.

29. HINT: $\sec^2 \theta - \tan^2 \theta = 1$ and $\csc^2 \theta - \cot^2 \theta = 1$.

31. $\sin 0.1 \approx 0.1 - \dfrac{(0.1)^3}{3!} + \dfrac{(0.1)^5}{5!} \approx 0.09983$.

33. 0.98215.   **35.** 0.75784.   **37.** 0.81965.
39. −0.27559.   **41.** 14.101.   **43.** 14.101.

ANSWERS TO PROBLEMS 13.3

3.   **5.**

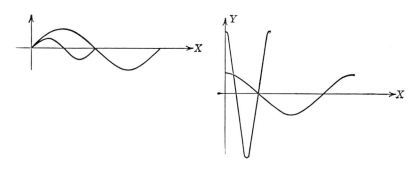

7.

9.

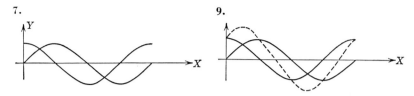

13. sec, $\{y \mid y \geq 1\}$, $\{y \mid y \leq -1\}$, $\{y \mid y \leq -1\}$, $\{y \mid y \geq 1\}$. csc, $\{y \mid y \geq 1\}$,
$\{y \mid y \geq 1\}$, $\{y \mid y \leq -1\}$, $\{y \mid y \leq -1\}$.
cot, $\{y \mid y \geq 0\}$, $\{y \mid y \leq 0\}$, $\{y \mid y \geq 0\}$, $\{y \mid y \leq 0\}$.

ANSWERS TO PROBLEMS 13.4

1. $2, 2\pi, -\pi/4$.   **3.** $3, 2\pi, \pi/4$.   **5.** $\frac{1}{2}, \pi, -\pi/6$.
7. $2, 4\pi, \pi$.   **9.** $\frac{1}{3}, 2\pi/3, 0$.

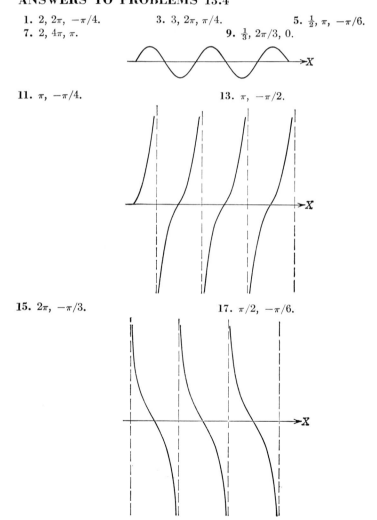

11. $\pi, -\pi/4$.   **13.** $\pi, -\pi/2$.

15. $2\pi, -\pi/3$.   **17.** $\pi/2, -\pi/6$.

19. π, **0.**   **21.** π, **0.**

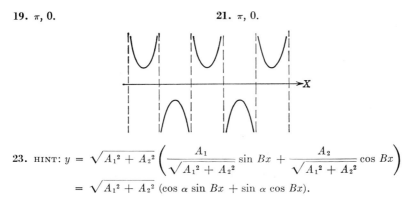

23. HINT: $y = \sqrt{A_1{}^2 + A_2{}^2} \left(\dfrac{A_1}{\sqrt{A_1{}^2 + A_2{}^2}} \sin Bx + \dfrac{A_2}{\sqrt{A_1{}^2 + A_2{}^2}} \cos Bx \right)$

$= \sqrt{A_1{}^2 + A_2{}^2} \, (\cos \alpha \sin Bx + \sin \alpha \cos Bx).$

ANSWERS TO PROBLEMS 13.5

1. $\dfrac{\sqrt{2} \, (\sqrt{3} + 1)}{4}.$ **3.** $\dfrac{\sqrt{2} \, (\sqrt{3} + 1)}{4}.$

5. $\dfrac{\sqrt{2} \, (\sqrt{3} - 1)}{4}.$ **7.** $\dfrac{\sqrt{2} \, (1 - \sqrt{3})}{4}.$

9. $\dfrac{3 + \sqrt{3}}{3 - \sqrt{3}}.$ **11.** $\dfrac{1 + \sqrt{3}}{1 - \sqrt{3}}.$

13. $\dfrac{4}{\sqrt{2} \, (\sqrt{3} - 1)}.$ **15.** $\dfrac{4}{\sqrt{2} \, (\sqrt{3} + 1)}.$

17. $\mp \cos \theta.$ **19.** $\mp \sin \theta.$ **21.** $\mp \cot \theta.$

23. $\mp \cos \theta.$ **25.** HINT: $\dfrac{13\pi}{12} = \dfrac{3\pi}{4} + \dfrac{\pi}{3}.$

29. $\sin 3.$ **31.** $\cos 1.$ **33.** $\tan 0.3.$

ANSWERS TO PROBLEMS 13.6

11. $\frac{171}{221}.$ **13.** $-21/221.$ **15.** $-21/220.$

21. $\frac{1}{2} \sqrt{2 + \sqrt{3}}.$ **23.** $\frac{1}{2}.$

ANSWERS TO PROBLEMS 13.8

1. $\left\{ (2n + 1) \dfrac{\pi}{2} \right\}, \ \left\{ \pm \dfrac{\pi}{3} + 2n\pi \right\}.$

3. $\left\{ \dfrac{\pi}{2} + 2n\pi \right\}, \left\{ \dfrac{3}{2} \pi \pm \dfrac{\pi}{3} + 2n\pi \right\}.$

5. $\left\{ \dfrac{\pi}{4} \pm \dfrac{\pi}{6} + n\pi \right\}.$ **7.** $\left\{ \dfrac{\pi}{6} \pm \dfrac{\pi}{9} + \dfrac{2n\pi}{3} \right\}.$

9. $\left\{ \dfrac{\pi}{4} \pm \dfrac{\pi}{8} + n\pi \right\}.$ **11.** $\left\{ \pm \dfrac{\pi}{8} + n\pi \right\}.$

13. $\left\{\dfrac{\pi}{4} + \dfrac{n\pi}{2}\right\}.$ **15.** $\left\{\pm\dfrac{\pi}{3} + n\pi\right\}.$

17. $\left\{\pi \pm \dfrac{\pi}{6} + 2n\pi\right\}, \left\{\pm\dfrac{\pi}{3} + 2n\pi\right\}.$

19. $\left\{\dfrac{2n\pi}{3}\right\}.$ **21.** $\{\pm 1.19 + 2n\pi\}.$

23. $\{0.525 + n\pi\}, \{-0.944 + n\pi\}.$

ANSWERS TO PROBLEMS 13.9

1. $\pi/4.$ **3.** $\pi/6.$ **5.** $\pi/3.$
7. $-\pi/4.$ **9.** $-\pi/6.$ **11.** $-\pi/4.$
13. $\frac{4}{5}.$ **15.** $2.$ **17.** $0.3.$
19. $36°40.6'.$ **21.** $48°23'.$ **23.** $51°45.4'.$
25. HINT: $\mathrm{Sin}^{-1}\frac{1}{2} = \pi/6.$
27. HINT:

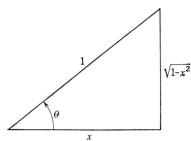

ANSWERS TO PROBLEMS 13.10

1. $2\,\mathrm{cis}\,60°.$ **3.** $\sqrt{2}\,\mathrm{cis}\,225°.$
5. $\mathrm{cis}\,270°.$ **7.** $\mathrm{cis}\,180°.$
9. $\frac{1}{2}\sqrt{3}\,\mathrm{cis}\,54°44.1'.$ **11.** $1.$
13. $\sqrt{2} + \sqrt{2}\,i.$ **15.** $-\sqrt{3} + i.$
17. $-4i.$ **19.** $2 - 2\sqrt{3}\,i.$
21. $6\,\mathrm{cis}\,165°.$ **23.** $12\,\mathrm{cis}\,(\pi/2) = 12i.$
25. $\frac{2}{3}\,\mathrm{cis}\,(-75°).$ **27.** $5\,\mathrm{cis}\,\pi = -5.$
29. $16\,\mathrm{cis}\,880° = 16\,\mathrm{cis}\,160°.$ **31.** $16\,\mathrm{cis}\,7\pi = -16.$
33. $2i, 2\,\mathrm{cis}\,210°, 2\,\mathrm{cis}\,330°.$ **35.** $\pm 1, \pm i.$
37. $3\,\mathrm{cis}\,(\pi/3), -3, 3\,\mathrm{cis}\,\frac{5}{3}\pi.$
39. $1, 2\,\mathrm{cis}\,72°, 2\,\mathrm{cis}\,144°, 2\,\mathrm{cis}\,216°, 2\,\mathrm{cis}\,288°.$
41. $1.1006, 1.1006\,\mathrm{cis}\,120°, 1.1006\,\mathrm{cis}\,240°.$

ANSWERS TO PROBLEMS 14.4

1. $(3.3).$ **3.** $(6.9).$ **5.** $(2,2).$

7. $(\frac{3}{2},2k).$ **9.** $\left(\dfrac{a+c}{2}, \dfrac{b+d}{2}\right).$

11. $(a)\ 3; (b)\ 2; (c)\ \frac{3}{2}.$ **13.** $(a)\ 0; (b)\ 2; (c)\ 0.$

15. (*a*) -15; (*b*) 25; (*c*) $-\frac{3}{5}$. **17.** (*a*) 33; (*b*) 87; (*c*) $\frac{11}{29}$.

19. (*a*) 0; (*b*) $0°$. **21.** (*a*) 1; (*b*) $45°$.

23. (*a*) $\sqrt{3}$; (*b*) $60°$. **25.** (*a*) $-\sqrt{3}$; (*b*) $120°$.

27. (*a*) $\sqrt{3}/3$; (*b*) $30°$. **29.** (*a*) 2; (*b*) $\text{Tan}^{-1} 2$.

31. $\sqrt{61}$. **33.** $\sqrt{17}$. **35.** 10.

37. $(0,0)$. **39.** $(-6,-6)$.

41. $\overline{AB} = \frac{9}{2}$, $\overline{AC} = \sqrt{34}$, $\overline{BC} = \frac{1}{2}\sqrt{37}$.

43. $m_{AB} = \frac{3}{2} = m_{AC}$.

45. Slopes of medians: not defined; $-\frac{1}{3}$; $-\frac{8}{3}$.

47. $x^2 + y^2 + 4x - 2y - 11 = 0$.

49. $(2,-1)$. **51.** $x = \dfrac{x_1 r_2 + x_2 r_1}{r_1 + r_2}$, $y = \dfrac{y_1 r_2 + y_2 r_1}{r_1 + r_2}$.

ANSWERS TO PROBLEMS 14.6

1. $\lambda = \frac{1}{5}\sqrt{5}$, $\mu = \frac{2}{5}\sqrt{5}$. **3.** $\lambda = 1$, $\mu = 0$.

5. $\lambda = -\frac{1}{257}\sqrt{257}$, $\mu = \frac{16}{257}\sqrt{257}$.

7. $\lambda = \frac{5}{701}\sqrt{701}$, $\mu = \frac{26}{701}\sqrt{701}$.

9. $\lambda = 0$, $\mu = 1$.

11. (*a*) $AB \perp AC$; $(5)(4) + (10)(-2) = 0$.
(*b*) $m_{AB} = 2$, $m_{AC} = -\frac{1}{2}$.

13. (*a*) $BA \perp BC$; $(3)(-3) + (9)(1) = 0$.
(*b*) $m_{BA} = 3$, $m_{BC} = -\frac{1}{3}$.

15. (*a*) $BA \perp BC$; $(2)(4) + (-8)(1) = 0$.
(*b*) $m_{BA} = -4$, $m_{BC} = \frac{1}{4}$.

17. $m_{AB} = -2 = m_{CD}$, $m_{BC} = 1 = m_{DA}$.

19. AB and CD are parallel to the Y-axis, and $m_{AC} = \frac{1}{4} = m_{BD}$.

21. $m_{AB} = 1 = m_{CD}$, $m_{BC} = -2 = m_{DA}$.

23. $\frac{24}{485}\sqrt{97}$. **25.** $\frac{4}{65}\sqrt{65}$. **27.** $\dfrac{116}{\sqrt{16,820}}$.

29. $\dfrac{245}{\sqrt{71,050}}$. **31.** $7/\sqrt{85}$. **33.** $-3/\sqrt{130}$.

35. (*a*) $\frac{7}{5}$; (*b*) $-\frac{5}{7}$. **37.** (*a*) -2; (*b*) $\frac{1}{2}$.

39. (*a*) 2; (*b*) $-\frac{1}{2}$. **41.** $\dfrac{3\sqrt{5} + 20\sqrt{2}}{35}$.

43. 0. **45.** $\frac{3}{5}$. **47.** $\frac{1}{170}\sqrt{170}$.

51. $a = 3b + 4$.

ANSWERS TO PROBLEMS 14.8

15. $x + y - 1 = 0$. **17.** $2x - 3y = 0$.

19. $y = 2x$. **21.** $2x - y + 5 = 0$.

23. $2x + y = 3$. **25.** A straight line.

27. $y + 2 = \dfrac{\sqrt{3}}{3}(x - 3)$.

29. HINT: Substitute for (x_1, y_1) and (x_2, y_2).

31. Yes. In solving these simultaneous equations only the elementary processes authorized by the axioms of a field are used.

33. HINT: If $P(x_1,y_1)$ lies on $L_1 \equiv A_1x + B_1y + C_1 = 0$ and on $L_2 \equiv A_2x + B_2y + C_2 = 0$, it lies on $L_1 + kL_2 = 0$. If no point of intersection, then $L_1 = 0$, $L_2 = 0$, and $L_1 + kL_2 = 0$ are parallel.

35. The three points lie on $2x - y + 7 = 0$.

37. $\dfrac{x - y + 5}{-\sqrt{2}} = 0.$

39. $\dfrac{x + 3y + 6}{-\sqrt{10}} = 0.$

41. $\dfrac{2x - y - 3}{\sqrt{5}} = 0.$

43. $-0.6x - 0.8y - 1 = 0.$

45. $d = \frac{22}{5}\sqrt{5}.$

47. $\dfrac{x - y + 6}{-\sqrt{2}} = \pm \dfrac{2x + y - 2}{\sqrt{5}}.$

49. $5x - 3y + 6 = 0.$

ANSWERS TO PROBLEMS 14.10

1. $x^2 + y^2 - 4x - 14y - 11 = 0.$
3. $x^2 + y^2 + 10x - 6y + 25 = 0.$
5. $x^2 + y^2 - 10x + y + 18 = 0.$
7. $x^2 + y^2 - 6x - 14y + 9 = 0.$
9. $x^2 + y^2 - 8x - 2y = 0.$
11. $(x - 5)^2 + y^2 = 16.$
13. $C(-\frac{1}{2}, -\frac{1}{2}), r = \frac{1}{2}\sqrt{2}.$
15. $C(4,0), r = 3.$
17. $C(\frac{5}{4}, -\frac{3}{4}), r = \sqrt{\frac{21}{8}}.$
19. $C\left(-\dfrac{a}{2}, 0\right), r = \dfrac{a}{2}.$
21. $x^2 + y^2 - x + 2y - 1 = 0.$
23. $x^2 + y^2 + ax + by = 0.$
25. $(x - h)^2 + (y - h)^2 = 1.$

ANSWERS TO PROBLEMS 14.11

1. $F(\frac{1}{4},0); DD', x = -\frac{1}{4}.$
3. $F(\frac{17}{4},0); DD', x = -\frac{17}{4}.$
5. $F(-1,0); DD', x = 1.$
7. $F(0,\frac{1}{2}); DD', y = -\frac{1}{2}.$
9. $F(-3 + \frac{8}{4}, 1); DD', x = -3 - \frac{8}{4}.$
11. $y^2 = 40x.$
13. $y^2 = 20x.$
15. $y^2 = -16x.$
17. $x^2 = 20y.$
19. $x^2 = -12y.$
21. $(0,0), (4\frac{1}{3}, 4\frac{2}{3}).$
23. $y^2 = 6(x + \frac{1}{2}).$

ANSWERS TO PROBLEMS 14.12

1. $F(\pm 2\sqrt{3},0), V(\pm 4,0).$
3. $F(\pm\sqrt{19},0), V(\pm 10,0).$
5. $F(\pm 1,0), V(\pm\sqrt{3},0).$
7. $F(0, \pm 2\sqrt{6}), V(0, \pm 7).$
9. $F(-2 \pm \sqrt{3}, 1), V(-2 \pm 2, 1).$
11. $F(\pm\frac{1}{2}\sqrt{2},0), V(\pm\sqrt{2},0).$
13. $\dfrac{x^2}{9} + \dfrac{y^2}{5} = 1.$
15. $\dfrac{x^2}{13} + \dfrac{y^2}{9} = 1.$
17. $\dfrac{x^2}{25} + \dfrac{y^2}{16} = 1.$
19. $\dfrac{x^2}{16} + \dfrac{y^2}{7} = 1.$
21. $\dfrac{x^2}{7} + \dfrac{y^2}{16} = 1.$
23. $\dfrac{x^2}{4} - \dfrac{(y - 2)^2}{21} = 1.$

ANSWERS TO PROBLEMS 14.13

1. $(x - \frac{1}{2})^2 + (y + 1)^2 = \frac{17}{4}$, circle.

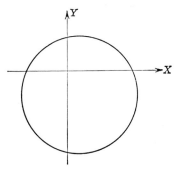

3. $F(-1, -\frac{1}{4})$; DD', $y = \frac{1}{4}$, parabola.

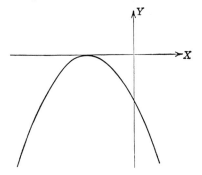

5. $F(-\frac{1}{16}, 0)$; DD', $x = \frac{1}{16}$, parabola.

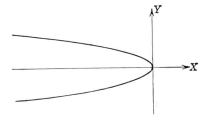

7. $y = \pm\frac{3}{2}x$, hyperbola.

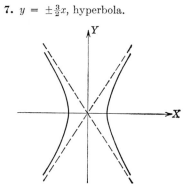

9. $C(0,0)$, $r = 3$, circle.

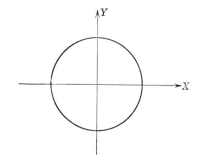

11. $y = \pm x$, hyperbola.

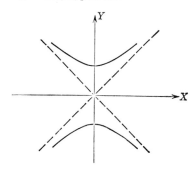

13. Two lines.

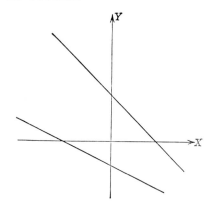

15. $(x + 2)^2 + (y - 3)^2 = 25$, circle.

17. $\dfrac{x^2}{25} + \dfrac{y^2}{9} = 1$.

19. $b^2 + c^2 = a^2$.

21. $V(h,k)$, $F(h + p, k)$; DD', $x = h - p$, parabola.

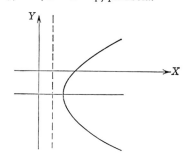

23. $C(h,k)$, $V(h \pm a, k)$, $F(h \pm \sqrt{a^2 + b^2}, k)$, asymptotes, $(y - k) = \pm \dfrac{b}{a}(x - h)$,

hyperbola.

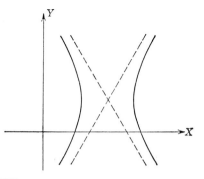

25. $x = m \pm \sqrt{m^2 - 1}$; $m^2 - 1 = 0$; each line is tangent to the parabola.
27. $(x - y)(x + 2y + 6) = 0$.

ANSWERS TO PROBLEMS 14.15

1. $r = 3 \sin \theta$.   **3.** $r \cos \theta - r \sin \theta = 0$ or $\theta = \dfrac{\pi}{4}$.

5. $r = 4 \cot \theta \csc \theta$.   **7.** $4r^2 \cos^2 \theta + 9r^2 \sin^2 \theta = 36$.

9. $4r^2 \cos^2 \theta - 9r^2 \sin^2 \theta = 36$.

11. $(r + \sin \theta + 1)(r + \sin \theta - 1) = 0$.

13. $x^2 + y^2 - 2x = 0$.   **15.** $x^2 + y^2 - 5y = 0$.

17. $(x^2 + y^2 - x)^2 = x^2 + y^2$.   **19.** $(x^2 + y^2 + 2y)^2 = x^2 + y^2$.

21. $y^2 = 2(x + \frac{1}{2})$.   **23.** $x^2 + y^2 = 25$.

25. $y + \sqrt{3}\, x = 0$.   **27.** $\dfrac{y}{x} = -\tan \dfrac{1}{\sqrt{x^2 + y^2}}$.

ANSWERS TO PROBLEMS 14.16

1. $\dfrac{(x - 1)^2}{9} + \dfrac{y^2}{8} = 1$.   **3.** $\dfrac{(x - \frac{8}{3})^2}{\frac{16}{9}} - \dfrac{y^2}{\frac{16}{3}} = 1$.

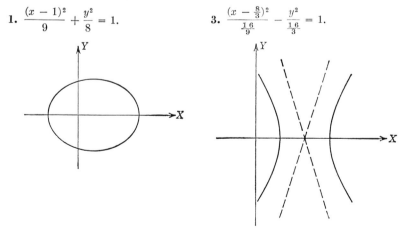

5. $\dfrac{x^2}{\frac{25}{6}} + \dfrac{(y - \frac{5}{12})^2}{\frac{625}{144}} = 1.$

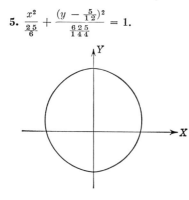

7. $x^2 + y^2 - 2\sqrt{3}\,x - 2y = 0.$

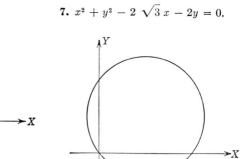

9. $x^2 + y^2 - y = 0.$

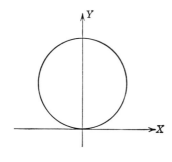

11. $(x^2 + y^2)^2 = y(3x^2 - y^2).$

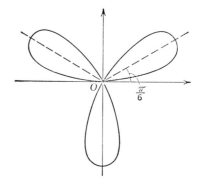

13. $x^2 + y^2 - x = 0.$

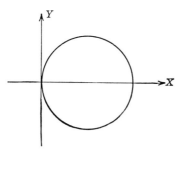

15. $(x^2 + y^2)^2 = x(x^2 - 3y^2).$

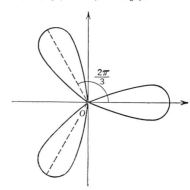

17. $(x^2 + y^2 + 2x)^2 = x^2 + y^2.$ **19.** $(x^2 + y^2 + x)^2 = x^2 + y^2.$

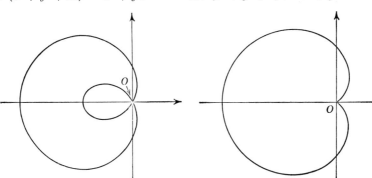

21. $(x^2 + y^2 + x)^2 = 4(x^2 + y^2).$

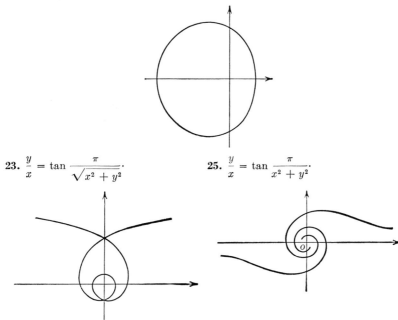

23. $\dfrac{y}{x} = \tan \dfrac{\pi}{\sqrt{x^2 + y^2}}.$ **25.** $\dfrac{y}{x} = \tan \dfrac{\pi}{x^2 + y^2}.$

27. $(x^2 + y^2)^2 = x^2 - y^2.$

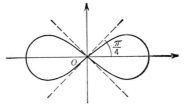

29. $(\frac{1}{2}\sqrt{2}, 45°)$ and, geometrically, the origin.

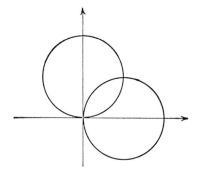

31. $d^2 = r_1{}^2 + r_2{}^2 - 2r_1r_2 \cos (\theta_2 - \theta_1)$.

33. Let the circle be $r = a \cos \theta$, and let the fixed point O be the origin. $r = \frac{1}{2}a \cos \theta$.

ANSWERS TO PROBLEMS 14.17

1. $x + 2y - 5 = 0$; straight line.

3. $y^2 = x/3$; parabola.   **5.** $(x + 1)^2 = y + 1$; parabola.

7. $x^2 - 2xy + y^2 - 2x - 2y = 0$.

9. $x^2 = -(y - 1)$; parabola.   **11.** $(1 - y)^2 + [\text{Cos}^{-1}(1 - y) - x]^2 = 1$.

13. $x^2 + y^2 = 2$; circle.   **15.** $y = 1/x$; hyperbola.

17. $x + y = 1$; straight line.   **19.** $x^2 = y + 1$; parabola.

21. $\dfrac{x^2}{4} + \dfrac{y^2}{1} = 1$; ellipse.   **23.** $x^2 = \frac{1}{2}y$; parabola.

25. $x = 2\sqrt{y - 1}$; portion of a parabola.

ANSWERS TO PROBLEMS 15.2

1. 3.46410, 3.21540, 3.15960, 3.14592.

3. 0.84147, 0.47943, 0.04998, 0.01000.

5. 1.5574, 0.54630, 0.05004, 0.01000.

7. 0.45970, 0.12242, 0.00125, 0.00005.

9. 0.84147, 0.95886, 0.9996, 1.000.

11. Join with straight-line segments the points $(i/n, \sqrt{i/n})$, $i = 0, 1, 2, \ldots, n$. The length of the parabolic arc is the limiting value of the sum of these line segments as n is increased indefinitely.

ANSWERS TO PROBLEMS 15.3

1. 26.   **3.** 12.   **5.** $\frac{1}{2}$.

7. 0.   **9.** 0.   **11.** 0.

13. 1.   **15.** 0.   **17.** 0.

19. 2.   **21.** 0.   **23.** No limit.

25.

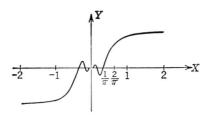

ANSWERS TO PROBLEMS 15.4

1. $\frac{2}{3}$.   **3.** $\frac{1}{3}$.   **5.** $k/3$.
7. $\frac{4}{3}$.
9. Sum of zigzag lengths is *always* 2. Hence the limit is 2. But each individual zig-zag sum is $\sqrt{2}$ times its diagonal. Hence limit is not length of diagonal.

ANSWERS TO PROBLEMS 15.5

1. $\frac{1}{6}$.   **3.** $\frac{4}{3}$.   **5.** $\frac{19}{3}$.
7. 4.   **9.** $\frac{32}{3}$.   **11.** $\frac{1}{4}$.
13. $\frac{8}{5}$.   **15.** $\dfrac{2^{2k+1} - 1}{2k + 1}$.   **17.** $\dfrac{b^{n+2} - a^{n+2}}{n + 2}$.

ANSWERS TO PROBLEMS 15.6

1. $\frac{11}{2}$.   **3.** $\frac{1}{24}$.   **5.** $\frac{53}{6}$.
7. $\frac{1}{4}$.   **9.** $\frac{96}{5}$.   **11.** $\frac{206}{5}$.
13. $\frac{16}{15}$.   **15.** $\frac{32}{3}$.   **17.** 0.
19. $-\frac{13}{4}$.   **21.** $\frac{14}{3}$.
23. Symmetry with respect to Y-axis.

ANSWERS TO PROBLEMS 15.8

1. 1.   **3.** $\frac{7}{3}$.   **5.** c^4.
7. $\frac{2}{3}(2^{\frac{3}{2}} - 1)$.   **9.** 0.   **11.** $\frac{3}{2}$.
13. $\dfrac{a}{2} + b$.   **15.** $y/3$.   **17.** y^3z^4.
19. $\frac{3}{5}x^2y^3$.   **21.** $4x$.   **23.** $x - 1$.
25. $2/3a^{\frac{3}{2}}$.   **27.** $a(3 + 3a + a^2)$.
29. —. $(n = -1.)$ **31.** 0.

ANSWERS TO PROBLEMS 15.9

1. 3,900 ft-lb.   **3.** 5 in.-lb.   **5.** 499.2 lb.
7. $(800\pi w)/3$ ft-lb.   **9.** $\frac{4}{3}\pi r^3$ cu units.
11. $\pi/30$ cu units.   **13.** $\pi/4$ cu units.
15. $2w \displaystyle\int_0^{-8} y \sqrt{16 - (y + 4)^2}\, dy$.
17. $\pi \displaystyle\int_0^{\pi} \sin^2 x\, dx$.

ANSWERS TO PROBLEMS 16.2

1. $y = 3x - 6$.

3. $y - 24 = 20(x - 2)$.

5. $y - 5 = -8(x + 1)$.

7. $y + 7 = -(x + 2)$.

9. $y - 3 = 3(x - 1)$.

11. $y - 3 = 4(x - 1)$.

13. $y = ax + b$.

15. $y - (2ax_1 + b)x + ax_1^2 - c = 0$.

ANSWERS TO PROBLEMS 16.3

1. (a) 16; (b) 48; (c) 96.

3. (a) $\frac{9}{2}$; (b) $\frac{3}{2}$; (c) 0.

5. (a) 1; (b) $2 - 2t_1$; (c) $2 - 4t_1$.

7. (a) $-\frac{9}{10}$; (b) $-\frac{7}{10}$; (c) 0.

9. (a) -2; (b) -2.

11. (a) -3; (b) -39.

13. (a) 29; (b) 16.

15. (a) $-3 + 6t_1$; (b) 6.

17. (a) $2t_1 - 3t_1^2$; (b) $2 - 6t_1$.

19. (a) $5t_1^4$; (b) $20t_1^3$.

ANSWERS TO PROBLEMS 16.4

1. $D_x y = 24x^3 + \frac{10}{3}x^{-\frac{4}{3}} + \sqrt{2}x^{\sqrt{2}-1}$.

3. $D_x y = -\dfrac{42}{x^7} + 42x^5$.

5. $D_x y = 2x$.

7. $D_x y = 4x^3 - 3x^2 - 1$.

9. $D_x y = 1 + 2x$.

11. $D_x y = 3 + \dfrac{1}{x^2}$.

13. $1;\ y = x$.

15. $\frac{3}{2};\ y - 3 = \frac{3}{2}(x - 1)$.

17. $0;\ y = 4$.

19. $-2;\ y - 1 = -2(x - 2)$.

21. $y - 1 = 2(x - 1)$.

23. (a) $y - 10 = -7(x + 1)$; (b) $y - 10 = \frac{1}{7}(x + 1)$.

25. 0.

27. 22.

29. $1 - 2t_1$.

31. -2.

33. 20.

35. -2.

37. $Dy = -2x^{-2-1}$.

39. $D(1 \cdot x) \neq D1 \cdot Dx$.

41. $D\left(\dfrac{x}{x}\right) \neq \dfrac{Dx}{Dx}$.

ANSWERS TO PROBLEMS 16.6

1. $v = -2 + 6t - 12t^2,\ a = 6 - 24t$.

3. $v = 8t^3 - 1,\ a = 24t^2$.

5. $v = 5t^4 - 7t^6,\ a = 20t^3 - 42t^5$.

7. $v = \dfrac{1}{\sqrt{2t + 1}},\ a = \dfrac{-1}{\sqrt{(2t + 1)^3}}$.

9. $Dy = 3t^2 + 2t + 1,\ D^2y = 6t + 2,\ D^3y = 6$.

11. $Dy = 2t + 1,\ D^2y = 2,\ D^3y = 0$.

13. $Dy = 1,\ D^2y = 0,\ D^3y = 0$.

15. $Dy = 5t^4 - 2t,\ D^2y = 20t^3 - 2,\ D^3y = 60t^2$.

17. $Dy = \frac{15}{2}(3t - 8)^{\frac{3}{2}},\ D^2y = \frac{135}{4}(3t - 8)^{\frac{1}{2}},\ D^3y = \frac{405}{8}(3t - 8)^{-\frac{1}{2}}$.

19. $D_x y = 7(x^3 + 6x + 3)^6(3x^2 + 6)$.

21. $D_x y = (3w^2 - 4w)(4x^3 - 5)$.

23. $D_x y = \frac{3}{2}(x + x^2 - 3x^4)^{\frac{1}{2}}(1 + 2x - 12x^3)$.

25. $D_x y = -\frac{1}{2}(a^2 - x^2)^{-\frac{3}{2}}(-2x)$.

27. $a = 60t^2 - 12t$, $D_t a = 120t - 12$.

29. $m = 1$, $D_x m = 6$.   **31.** $yy_1 = 2p(x + x_1)$.

ANSWERS TO PROBLEMS 16.7

1. $x = 1$.   **3.** $x = -\frac{3}{2}$.   **5.** $x = -\frac{1}{2}$.

7. $x = 0$.   **9.** $x = 0, 4$.   **11.** $x = \pm \dfrac{\sqrt{3}}{3}$.

13. $x = 0, \pm\frac{1}{2}\sqrt{2}$.   **15.** $x = 0$.

17. None.   **19.** $x = 0$.   **21.** $(1,0)$.

23. $(\frac{1}{6}, -\frac{5}{27})$.   **25.** $(\frac{1}{9}, \frac{218}{243})$.

27. $((\frac{2}{3})^{\frac{1}{2}}, \frac{16}{9})$, $(-(\frac{2}{3})^{\frac{1}{2}}, \frac{16}{9})$.   **29.** $(1,4)$.

31. $(1, -\frac{37}{12})$.   **33.** $(-1,-1)$, $(1,-1)$.

35. -1.   **37.** 460.

39. Side parallel to wall $= P/2$; other side $= P/4$.

41. (a) $h = 2r$; (b) $h = r$.   **43.** Four miles from P toward Q.

45. $-\frac{2}{3}$ (at $x = -2$).

ANSWERS TO PROBLEMS 16.8

1. (a) $\frac{1}{30}$ in./sec.   (b) $\frac{4}{5}$ sq in./sec.

3. $2\sqrt{3}$ ft/sec.

5. (a) $5/2\pi$ ft/min.   (b) 200 sq ft/min.

7. (a) 3 mi/hr.   (b) 9 mi/hr.

9. $D_t V = 2\pi r^2 - 6\pi h r$.

ANSWERS TO PROBLEMS 16.9

1. $12x^2 - 6$.   **3.** $4x^3 - 2x$.   **5.** $2x + 2x^{-3}$.

7. $4x^3 - \dfrac{6}{x^3}$.   **9.** $2ax + b$.   **11.** $\alpha A x^{\alpha-1} - \beta B x^{-\beta-1}$.

13. $\frac{1}{2}x^4 - \frac{1}{3}x^3 + 5x + C$.   **15.** $\frac{9}{5}x^5 + \frac{1}{3}x^3 - x + C$.

17. $-\frac{1}{3}x^{-3} + x^{-1} + C$.   **19.** $-\frac{1}{2}x^{-2} + x^{-1} + \frac{1}{2}x^2 + C$.

21. $\dfrac{a}{3}x^3 + \dfrac{b}{2}x^2 + cx + C$.   **23.** $-ax^{-1} - \dfrac{b}{2}x^{-2} + C$.

25. $\dfrac{A}{1-n}x^{1-n} + \dfrac{B}{1-m}x^{1-m} + C$.

27. $\frac{1}{12}$.   **29.** 0.   **31.** $\frac{1}{6}$.

33. $\dfrac{a^3}{3} + 5a$.   **35.** $\dfrac{a^3}{3} + \frac{3}{2}a^2$.   **37.** 4.

39. $\frac{7}{24}$.   **41.** $-\frac{2}{9}$.   **43.** $\frac{35}{3}$.

45. $\frac{1}{2}$.   **47.** $\frac{1}{3}$.   **49.** $\frac{1}{48}$.

51. (a) $3t^2 + 2$; (b) 2.   **53.** $\frac{23}{6}$.

55. $f(x) = \dfrac{x^2}{2} + x - \dfrac{3}{2}$.

ANSWERS TO PROBLEMS 16.10

1. (a) $v = 96 - 32t$, $a = -32$; (b) 96; (c) 144; (d) $0, 6$.

3. (a) $v = -32t$, $a = -32$; (b) 0; (c) $32{,}000$; (d) $20\sqrt{5}$.

5. (a) $v = 160 - 32t$, $a = -32$; (b) 160; (c) $16,400$; $5 + 5\sqrt{41}$.

7. (a) $v = 640 - 32t$, $a = -32$; (b) 640; (c) $38,400$; $20 + 20\sqrt{6}$.

9. $y = 1,000 - 16t^2$.   **11.** $y = 528,000 + 3000t - 16t^2$.

ANSWERS TO PROBLEMS 17.3

19. $\left\{\left(x, \dfrac{1}{2}\ln\dfrac{x+1}{x-1}\right)\right\}$; $\{x \mid -1 < x < 1\}$.

21. $\{(x, \ln(x + \sqrt{x^2 - 1}))\}$; $\{x \mid x \geq 1\}$.

Index

Index

The Symbols Used in this Book ～